ENGINEERING METALLURGY

Bell X-1 rocket plane. This was the first airplane to fly faster than the speed of sound. It contained 90 per cent by weight of metals and alloys, as follows: 53 per cent aluminum, 34 per cent steel, 2 per cent magnesium, and a total of 1 per cent copper, beryllium copper, brass, lead, zinc, and tin; and 10 per cent by weight of nonmetals, such as fabrics, rubber, and plastics (*Courtesy of Bell Aircraft Corporation.*)

ENGINEERING
METALLURGY

A TEXTBOOK FOR USERS OF METALS

BRADLEY STOUGHTON, Ph.B., B.S., D.Eng.

Formerly Dean of Engineering and Professor of Metallurgy, Lehigh University; Author of "The Metallurgy of Iron and Steel"

ALLISON BUTTS, A.B., S.B.

Head, Department of Metallurgical Engineering, Lehigh University; Author of "Metallurgical Problems"

AND

ARDREY M. BOUNDS, B.S., M.S.

Chief Metallurgist, Superior Tube Company

FOURTH EDITION

McGRAW-HILL BOOK COMPANY, Inc.
New York   Toronto   London
1953

ENGINEERING METALLURGY

Copyright, 1926, 1930, 1938, 1953, by the McGraw-Hill Book Company, Inc. Printed in the United States of America. All rights reserved. This book, or parts thereof, may not be reproduced in any form without permission of the publishers.

Library of Congress Catalog Card Number: 53-5559

THE MAPLE PRESS COMPANY, YORK, PA.

PREFACE

When the first edition of "Engineering Metallurgy" was prepared, it was the purpose of the authors to supply the need for an introductory textbook in the field of metallurgy, and especially to make available a book adapted to the needs of students in the engineering branches representing users of metals. Broadly, these would include all engineering students. Metals are essential engineering materials, and the value of metallurgy as an accessory subject in the study of other branches of engineering has become more and more recognized during the past quarter of a century. Hand in hand with the expansion in use of metals during this period, and with increase in knowledge of the science and technology of metals, has gone a greater appreciation of the advantage of study of metallurgy in all the diverse fields of engineering. Popular acquaintance with metals has grown much during this time, too, as is strikingly evident in the advertising pages of newspapers and magazines.

The literature of metallurgy has likewise increased enormously. The bibliographies of metallurgy appended to the various chapters of this book are very large compared with those in the first edition. It is notable how many of the books listed are of recent date. Many of those listed in the first edition have been superseded by later works on the same subject, and most of those remaining have appeared in new editions.

When "Engineering Metallurgy" was first published, it stood almost alone in its special field as a text for users of metals. Today, because of the wider study and greater interest in metallurgy, there are numerous books in this field. The authors are glad that so many have found this a useful book and hope that the fourth edition may serve requirements both in and outside the colleges. So rapid is the development of metallurgical knowledge and so great are the changes in metallurgical practice that a textbook in this field soon loses much of its value unless revised at intervals.

The purpose of the book is still the original one, but it has become increasingly difficult to encompass a comprehensive survey in one book of a length suitable for a college textbook, at the same time including sufficient detail as a basis for knowledge of the essentials of the subject. The desirability of supplementary lectures or supplementary reading is even greater than it was. It has seemed best to abridge further the material on production and refining of metals in order to give more space to physical metallurgy, properties, and utilization. This is in accord with the trend in metallurgical education and particularly so for students in the nonmetallurgical curricula, in which it is often felt that time is not available for study of the principles and processes of metal production. Most of this latter material has been placed after the physical and adaptive metallurgy in this edition, so that those who believe that production metallurgy is of minor importance for their needs may omit these chapters without interrupting the sequence of those more essential to them. These chapters have been retained, in abridged form, because the production process often has a direct bearing on the quality, properties, and utilization of the metal; because so few books are available that include both branches of metallurgy; and in order that the book may, as in the past, be useful as an introductory book for those having a broad interest in the whole field of metallurgy as well as a text for students in the non-metallurgical branches of engineering.

The many new developments in metallurgy that have become important since the third edition of this book will be evident in the pages that follow. It may be of interest to list some of them here. They include time-temperature-transformation curves, hardenability and hardenability tests, new methods of testing such as the acoustic and supersonic, new welding methods, new casting methods, induction hardening, shot peening, powder metallurgy development, metals and alloys for high-temperature service, metals in atomic-energy development, new types of steel and cast iron, and new nonferrous alloys. The treatment of some subjects has been expanded, including stress-strain relations and mechanical properties, impact strength and impact testing, creep, hardness testing, cold working, machining, annealing, carburizing, corrosion and corrosion prevention, stainless steel and other alloy steels, and nonferrous alloys, especially those of copper, aluminum, magnesium, and nickel. A short section on plastics has been added because of their association with metals as materials of construction and the need of metallurgists for knowledge of them.

In response to suggestions, the authors have included a section listing available motion pictures of metallurgical plants and operations. The use of visual aids for instruction at the college level has apparently been developed further in Europe than in the United States. Such use is obviously limited in its adaptability to teaching of principles, but it has large possibilities for presenting illustrative material. We hope that this section may help to further progress in this direction and facilitate obtaining films that may be used in lieu of visits to metallurgical plants and for showing at group meetings.

In addition to the acknowledgments that appear in the text, the authors wish to record their appreciation of the cooperation and assistance of a number of companies and individuals. Certain sections have been reviewed by members of the technical staffs of the Aluminum Company of America, Dow Chemical Company, Leeds and Northrup, Lukens Steel Company, New Jersey Zinc Company, International Nickel Company, and others. New illustrations or other material were received from the above companies and also from American Metal Company, American Steel & Wire Company, Bethlehem Steel Company, Bridgeport Brass Company, Brown Instrument Company, Carpenter Steel Company, Chambersburg Engineering Company, General Refractories Company, Kaiser Aluminum and Chemical Corporation, Superior Tube Company, Tinius Olsen Testing Machine Company, United States Steel Corporation, Westinghouse Electric Corporation, Wilson Mechanical Instrument Company, Wyman-Gordon Company, and others mentioned in the text. Many new photomicrographs were made in the laboratory of the Superior Tube Company. Individuals to whom we are indebted, in addition to various members of the companies named above, include the late Carter S. Cole, Joseph F. Libsch, M. G. Fontana, H. W. Poole, W. G. Theisinger, and L. W. Williams.

BRADLEY STOUGHTON
ALLISON BUTTS
ARDREY M. BOUNDS

CONTENTS

Preface v
1. Introduction 1
2. Metals as Materials of Construction 8
3. The Sources of Metals 40
4. Sizing and Shaping Metallic Bodies 64
5. Welding and Joining Metallic Bodies 97
6. Metallurgical Inspection and Testing 119
7. The Theory of Alloys 150
8. Heat-treatment of Metals and Alloys 170
9. Properties and Uses of Iron and Steel 195
10. Properties and Uses of Nonferrous Metals 243
11. Examples of Application of Metals in Engineering Service . . . 328
12. Corrosion and Its Prevention 340
13. Producing and Refining Iron and Steel: Effects on Properties . . 357
14. Producing and Refining Nonferrous Metals 382
15. Furnaces, Refractories, and Fuels 418
16. Measurement of Temperature in Industrial Operations . . . 443
    Some Available Motion Pictures 457
    Index 465

CHAPTER 1

INTRODUCTION

Metallurgy is the art and science of extracting metals from their ores, refining them, and adapting them to use. Adapting includes such diverse, processes as rolling, forging, casting, welding, drawing, and stamping; also heat-treatment for improvement of properties and plating, pickling, and numerous other operations. Today there are at least twice as many metallurgists engaged in the field of adaptation and adjustment of properties as there are in extracting and refining. With the development of metallography, heat-treatment, and other phases of the science of metals, the field of metallurgy has broadened, and it is now generally held that metallurgy properly embraces all phases of working with metals as raw materials.

Metallurgy in this broader sense falls into three divisions: chemical or extractive, physical, and mechanical. *Chemical metallurgy* includes the metallurgical processes involving chemical change and, accordingly, embraces chiefly the methods of production and refining.

Physical metallurgy deals with the nature, structure, and physical properties of metals and alloys. The physical metallurgist uses the most appropriate tools at his command, for example, the optical and electron microscopes for the study of metal and alloy structures and X rays for the study of basic crystal structure. He studies such things as electrical and magnetic properties, hardness patterns, damping capacity, coefficients of expansion, resistance, and even nuclear properties. In short, he applies the techniques of the physicist to metals in the solid state. Research in the area of physical metallurgy has resulted in remarkable improvement in metal products.

Mechanical metallurgy includes the processes of working and shaping metals—processes which do not involve chemical changes but which adapt metals as to size and form.

Metallurgy as a Manufacturing Industry. Few persons realize the magnitude of the metallurgical industry, because it is so intimately bound up in the other great industries. The total value of metals produced in the United States in 1949 in unmanufactured ingots or equivalent form was over six billion dollars, and to this value the manufacturing operations involved in making semifinished metal products such as sheets, plates, pipes and tubes, wire, etc., added about eleven billion dollars. Only one industry, namely, food and kindred products, exceeds this value. Nearly four-fifths of the metal value is represented by iron and steel products and one-fifth by nonferrous metal products. The value added by manufacture in the two leading industries making finished products from these metals was about twelve billion for machinery and seven billion for transportation equipment; of the latter, 4.7 billion was for motor cars and trucks and 1.3 billion for aircraft. These figures, from publications of the U.S. Department of Commerce, are for 1949, the last year before our economy was affected by the war in Korea.

Metallurgy does not include the construction and assembly of finished products. Great variation in properties, however, must be produced in order to meet the demands of all the different articles made of metals. Often the metallurgist must take the same metal or alloy and confer upon it different properties for different purposes in the service of industry. The ever-increasing demand for materials of greater strength, lightness, safety, reliability, electric conductivity, electromagnetism and permanent magnetism, hardness, hardenability, cutting power, softness, cheapness, etc., offers almost unlimited opportunities for men of intelligence and training. It is evident that the metallurgist has a most important function in materials engineering. The selection of material, its treatment, testing, and inspection are vital to his work.

History of Metallurgy. The beginnings of metallurgy are shrouded in the mystery of the distant past. Reliable documentary evidence indicates that the Chinese had a knowledge of the properties and even the heat-treatment of several metals, including the knowledge that careful heat-treatment was necessary to make a permanent magnet from a piece of high-carbon steel.

The Far East is apparently the original source of metallurgical knowledge. It is said that the Phoenicians came from a country on the Indian Ocean and settled on the shores of the Mediterranean more than 2,000 years before the Christian era. They were miners and workers of ores and metals of no mean ability. It also appears that the Egyptians, Syrians, and Babylonians had a knowledge of metallurgy at a very early time. The quest of the Phoenicians for metallic wealth, coupled with their skill as navigators, resulted in the spread of Eastern civilization along the shores of the Mediterranean. It is said that before 1000 B.C. they sailed through what is now the Straits of Gibraltar and founded a city in Spain now known as Cadiz. They discovered great stores of gold, silver, copper, and lead in Spain, and it is known that the Spanish mines were worked by them and by their successors as late as the days of Hannibal.

It is probable that the metals which occur most commonly in the native state, especially gold, were the first used by men. Many metals are mentioned in the Bible, including gold, silver, lead, mercury, copper, and iron, and the alloys brass and bronze. Something about control of composition and properties was apparently also known in early times. It is evident that some of the metals must have been extracted from their ores by crude smelting processes long before the Christian era, because there is every reason to believe that iron did not exist in unoxidized form, except for occasional meteorites which fell from the sky. Iron, copper, tin, and lead are easily extracted from some of their ores. It is only necessary to mix the oxide ores with charcoal and, by the application of sufficient heat, cause the metal to separate. If the ores are pure, the metal itself will be relatively pure and require little, if any, refining. Lead and tin may be produced in this way in liquid form. Copper is not so easily fused, but when the ores of copper and tin occur together, a more fusible alloy, bronze, may be produced in liquid form. It is probable that such mixed ores were found by primitive man, or else were mixed together and smelted, for bronze was an alloy well known to the ancients.

The reduction of ores of iron by the process mentioned results in a pasty and unfused mass of iron. But this is very easily worked under the hammer and welded into masses of large size, so that its production and use did not offer insuperable difficulties. If this primitive wrought iron is heated in contact with charcoal at a red heat, it absorbs carbon rapidly and becomes converted into steel. By this crude process the famous swords of Damascus were made. These swords received their name from the city in which they were purchased by Western Europeans, but they were manufactured and tempered in countries some distance east of ancient Damascus. The extent to which knowledge of the manufacture and hardening of steel by heat-treatment was possessed in early times is indicated not only by the skill of the Chinese, as mentioned above, but also by the fact that steel articles requiring considerable expertness and skill in fabrication were known at the time of Alexander the Great, some three hundred to four hundred years before the Christian era. All sorts of armor and weapons, as well as agricultural implements and even razors, were in use at that time.

The date at which primitive man began to use gold, silver, lead, tin, iron (steel), copper, bronze, and mercury is previous to history or legend. The same is not true, however, of four metals in common usage at the present time, *viz.*, zinc, aluminum, nickel, and magnesium; nor of the large number of minor metals which now supply the complex demands of the modern world. The existence of these metals was unknown to the ancients because they are found only in the form of chemical compounds which early man either could not or did not try to decompose.

The Relation between the Search for Metals and the Spread of Civilization. Possession of the precious metals has always led bold men into adventure and wars of conquest. As civilization advanced in the countries bordering on the Mediterranean, the demand for precious metal increased and there grew also a great demand for metals of industrial value, such as iron, steel, bronze, lead, etc. A knowledge of primitive arts and sciences and the beginnings of culture and civilization were spread by the Phoenicians in their search for new sources of metals, first to Greece and other countries on the eastern end of the Mediterranean and then to most of the countries bordering that great inland sea. From all civilized countries, throughout the ages, pioneers have pushed from the centers of culture into new fields in quest of sources of wealth. A guess may be hazarded that the early metallurgists were frequently in need of ores of tin to mix with copper ores, which were relatively abundant in the Mediterranean countries, for the purpose of producing bronze. It is recorded, in fact, that reports of the tin ores in Cornwall led to Julius Caesar's first expedition to Britain, which resulted in the introduction of civilization, such as it then was, to that semibarbarous land. The same motive was responsible for the majority of the early expeditions made from Europe to Central and South America. The conquests and methods of the Spaniards in getting gold and silver from Mexico and Peru form interesting chapters of history.

The Relation between the Production of Metals and the Wealth of a Country. Next to farming, the production of metals is the greatest wealth producer that exists. This has always been so to some extent, but is more particularly the case at the present time when civilization and industry demand a very large supply of metals and alloys. The discovery of America by Columbus put the Spanish nation in possession of fabulous wealth, wrested first from the natives and then from the mineral resources of the country. For nearly a hundred years the greatness of Spain, outrivaling every other country of her time, was based on the riches which flowed to her, chiefly in the form of metals, from her new possessions. England's supremacy in capital resources and manufacturing productivity depended chiefly upon her exploitation of her great supplies of iron ore and coal. In her steel industry she was first surpassed in point of magnitude by the United States, then by Germany, and now by Russia. She decreased in manufacturing wealth accordingly. Mineral resources are recognized as great potential sources of power.

Since prehistoric times, wars have been fought for the possession of mines and metallic deposits. In the settlement of two great European wars, the possession of large iron-ore deposits played a prominent part. During the First World War, the first rush of Germany through Belgium deprived her rivals of their chief source of zinc, from which to make brass for munitions. All countries which are rivals, or expect to be rivals in future wars, cope with each other both to possess, and at the same time to deprive others of, sources of iron ore and fuel from which to make munitions. During the Second World War, Germany drove to the Donetz Basin, and also encircled Sweden, for iron ore, while Japan drove into Malaya for her supply of tin, and to cut off tin from her enemies.

During the past four decades the United States has been the world's greatest producer of copper, lead, zinc, aluminum, and iron (steel). The present financial supremacy of the United States has been largely built from the foundation of her mineral resources and her metallurgical industry, combined with her resources of field and forest.

The Use of Metallurgical Problems. The authors have endeavored to give in the following pages information of interest and value for the users of metals. But information is only food for thought, whereas the act of constructive thinking must be practiced by anyone desiring to apply engineering knowledge to an engineering problem.

While it has been thought best not to interrupt the sequence nor extend the length of this book by the introduction of metallurgical problems, the value of such work in connection with the study of metallurgy should be emphasized. The making of practical calculations is one of the best ways of getting training in bridging the gap between theory and practice, which is one of the most essential and at the same time one of the most difficult requirements for success in engineering. It is suggested that the study of this book be accompanied by suitable related problems, which may include both quantitative problems of calculation dealing with metallurgical processes and qualitative problems of selection, treatment, and application of metals as materials of engineering.

Literature. Lists of books for reference and further study are appended to each chapter for the convenience of teachers and students. The lists prepared by Sybil E. Warren of the Lindgren Library of the Massachusetts Institute of Technology, published in *Metals Review*, have been useful in preparing these. In using the appended lists, the reader is advised to refer to different chapters, for it is obvious that some books may be classified under more than one chapter.

Books

American Society for Metals: "Metals Handbook," Cleveland, Ohio, 1948. A comprehensive treatise by many experts covering ferrous and nonferrous physical and mechanical metallurgy. It is the most exhaustive treatise existing on this subject.

Butts, Allison: "Metallurgical Problems," 2d ed., McGraw-Hill Book Company, Inc., New York, 1943.

Eshbach, O. W. (editor): "Handbook of Engineering Fundamentals," 2d ed., John Wiley & Sons, Inc., New York, 1952.

Evans, U. R.: "Metals and Metallic Compounds," 4 vols., Edward Arnold & Co., London; Longmans, Green & Co., Inc., New York, 1923.

Friend, J. Newton: "Iron in Antiquity," Charles Griffin & Co., Ltd., London, 1926.

GARLAND, H., and C. O. BANNISTER: "Ancient Egyptian Metallurgy," Charles Griffin & Co., Ltd., London, 1927.
HADFIELD, ROBERT A.: "Metallurgy and Its Influence on Modern Progress," Chapman & Hall, Ltd., London, 1925.
HODGMAN, CHARLES D. (editor): "Handbook of Chemistry and Physics," 33d ed., Chemical Rubber Publishing Company, Cleveland, Ohio, 1951–1952.
HOYT, S. L.: "Metals and Alloys Data Book," 2d ed., Reinhold Publishing Corporation, New York, 1952.
KENT, R. T. (editor): "Mechanical Engineers' Handbook," 12th ed., John Wiley & Sons, Inc., New York, 1938.
LIDDELL, DONALD M. (editor): "Handbook of Non-ferrous Metallurgy," 2d ed., Vol. I, "Principles and Processes," Vol. II, "Recovery of the Metals," McGraw-Hill Book Company, Inc., New York, 1945.
NEWTON, J.: "An Introduction to Metallurgy," 2d ed., John Wiley & Sons, Inc., New York, 1947.
PARSONS, W. B.: "Engineers and Engineering in the Renaissance." The Williams & Wilkins Company, Baltimore, 1939.
PULSIFER, WILLIAM B.: "Notes for a History of Lead," D. Van Nostrand Company, Inc., New York, 1888. Discusses also history of other metals.
SACHS, GEORGE, and K. R. VAN HORN: "Practical Metallurgy," American Society for Metals, Cleveland, Ohio, 1940.
SAMANS, CARL H.: "Engineering Metals and Their Alloys," The Macmillan Company, New York, 1949.
SMITHELLS, C. J.: "Metal Reference Book," Interscience Publishers, Inc., New York, 1949.
WOLDMAN, N. E., and R. J. METZLER: "Engineering Alloys." American Society for Metals, Cleveland, Ohio, 1945.

PERIODICALS

Acta Metallurgica. Bimonthly, University of Toronto Press. Toronto. Sponsored by American Society for Metals.
Aluminum and the Non-Ferrous Review. Monthly, London.
American Society for Testing Materials: *Bulletin.* Bimonthly. Philadelphia.
———: *ASTM Standards.* Annual, Philadelphia.
Blast Furnace and Steel Plant. Monthly, Steel Publications, Inc., Pittsburgh.
Canadian Mining and Metallurgical Bulletin. Monthly, Canadian Institute of Mining and Metallurgy, Montreal.
Chemical Abstracts. Semimonthly, American Chemical Society, Columbus, Ohio.
Chemical Engineering (with *Chemical and Metallurgical Engineering*). Monthly, New York.
Corrosion and Material Protection. Bimonthly, Corrosion Publishing Company, Pittsburgh.
Engineering and Mining Journal. Monthly, McGraw-Hill Publishing Company, Inc., New York.
Foundry. Monthly, Penton Publishing Company, Cleveland, Ohio.
Foundry Trade Journal. Weekly, London.
Guidebook and Directory for the Metal Finishing Industries (formerly *Plating and Finishing Guidebook*). Annual (21st ed., 1952), Finishing Publications, Inc., New York.
Iron Age. Weekly, Chilton Company, Inc., New York.
Iron and Steel Engineer. Monthly, Pittsburgh.

Journal of Metals (succeeding *Metals Technology* and *Mining and Metallurgy*). Monthly, American Institute of Mining and Metallurgical Engineers, New York.
Light Metal Age. Bimonthly, Roy Fellom, Jr., Chicago.
Materials and Methods (formerly *Metals and Alloys*). Monthly, Reinhold Publishing Corporation, New York.
Metal Finishing (formerly *Metal Industry*). Monthly, Finishing Publications, Inc., New York.
Metal Industry. Weekly, London.
Metallurgia. Monthly, Manchester, England.
Metal Progress. Monthly, American Society for Metals, Cleveland, Ohio.
Metals Review (including A.S.M. Review of Metal Literature). Monthly, American Society for Metals, Cleveland.
Mineral Industry. Annual from 1892 to 1941, McGraw-Hill Publishing Company, Inc., New York.
Minerals Yearbook. Annual, U.S. Bureau of Mines, Department of the Interior, Washington, D.C.
Modern Metals. Monthly, Chicago.
Non-Destructive Testing. Quarterly, Society for Non-Destructive Testing, Inc., Skokie, Ill.
Plating. Monthly, American Electroplaters Society, Jenkintown, Pa.
Powder Metallurgy Bulletin. Bimonthly, Paul Schwarzkopf, Yonkers, N.Y.
Review of Metal Literature. Annual, American Society for Metals, Cleveland, Ohio.
Revue de métallurgie. Monthly, Paris.
Stahl und Eisen. Weekly, Düsseldorf.
Steel. Weekly, Penton Publishing Company, Cleveland, Ohio.
Steelways. Bimonthly, American Iron and Steel Institute, New York.
Welding Engineer. Monthly, McGraw-Hill Publishing Company, Inc., New York.
Welding Journal. Monthly, American Welding Society, New York.
Year Book of the American Bureau of Metal Statistics. Annual, New York.
Zeitschrift für Metallkunde. Monthly, Gesellschaft für Metallkunde im Verein Deutscher Ingenieure, Berlin.

Transactions

Archiv für das Eisenhüttenwesen. Annual, Verein Deutscher Eisenhüttenleute und Kaiser-Wilhelm Institute für Eisenforshung, Düsseldorf.
Journal of Metals. Monthly, American Institute of Mining and Metallurgical Engineers, New York.
Journal of the Electrochemical Society. Monthly, New York.
Journal of the Institute of Metals (of Great Britain). Monthly (with metallurgical abstracts), London.
Journal of the Iron and Steel Institute (with abstracts). Monthly, London.
Proceedings of the American Society for Testing Materials. Annual, Philadelphia.
Proceedings of the Metal Powder Association. Annual, New York.
Transactions of the American Foundrymen's Association. Bimonthly, Chicago.
Transactions of the American Institute of Mining and Metallurgical Engineers. 3 vols. annually, New York.
Transactions of the American Society for Metals. Quarterly and annual, Cleveland.
Transactions of the Electrochemical Society. 2 vols. annually through 1949; now combined with the *Journal.* New York.
Yearbook of the American Iron and Steel Institute. Annual, New York.

CHAPTER 2

METALS AS MATERIALS OF CONSTRUCTION

The mechanics of all the materials of construction is a vital subject for civil engineers and, to only a slightly less extent, for mechanical, metallurgical, electrical, mining, chemical, and industrial engineers. Metals are the most important of the structural materials, but wood, stone and masonry, plastics, glass, cement, mortar and concrete, brick and clay products, rubber, fabrics, and hempen rope all have their place.

Definition of a Metal. The chemical elements are divided into metals and nonmetals, but there is no sharp dividing line between the two groups. Elements whose properties are such as to cause them to fall on the border between metals and nonmetals are sometimes called *metalloids*, but here we shall include as metals all the elements having characteristically the important metallic properties. A *metal* may be defined as a chemical element that possesses metallic luster and which in electrolysis carries a positive charge and is liberated at the cathode. Most nonmetallic elements do not possess metallic luster; in electrolysis the nonmetals carry negative charges and are liberated at the anode. In general, metals are also characterized by high conductivity, and most metals possess higher density, strength, malleability, and ductility than most nonmetals. They are also characterized by being monatomic in the gaseous state.

Of the 92 natural chemical elements about 70 are metals, and of these about 39 are used commercially. These 39 metals may be grouped as in Table 1. Four of these, *viz.*, selenium, tellurium, arsenic, and silicon, are sometimes classed by chemists as nonmetals, but they exhibit marked metallic physical properties, including metallic luster.

Alloys. An alloy is a metallic substance, but it is not a single chemical element. It is formed by the union or mixture of two or more metals, or it may consist of one or more metals and a nonmetal. For example, iron and carbon basically form the alloy called *steel*, and copper and zinc form *brass*. The subject of alloys is discussed at length in Chap. 7.

Physical and Mechanical Properties of Metals and Alloys. The study of the properties of metals can be conveniently divided into two main categories: (1) the *physical* properties, which are inherent and basic characteristics of the material, such as electrical conductivity, heat conductivity, crystal structure, and magnetic properties; and (2) the mechanical properties, such as hardness, strength, toughness, and ductility, which are of special importance in constructional engineering design. The mechanical properties are of chief consideration in the larger industrial applications of metals and will be discussed first in this section. The attributes of metals having the widest importance in industry are cost, strength, toughness, resistance to corrosion, machinability, specific gravity, resistance to fatigue, resistance to creep, and also strength combined with resistance to oxidation at high temperatures; but for certain industries, even more importance may be attached to electrical conductivity, magnetic permeability or retentivity, hardness, or some other property.

TABLE 1. METALLIC ELEMENTS COMMERCIALLY USED AS METALS OR ALLOYS

Used as either metals or alloys or both		Used in metallic form almost entirely as alloys
Aluminum	Palladium	Antimony
Barium	Platinum	Arsenic
Beryllium	Rhodium	Bismuth
Cadmium	Selenium	Cerium
Calcium	Silicon	Cobalt
Copper	Silver	Columbium (niobium)
Gold	Sodium	Manganese
Iridium	Tantalum	Tellurium
Iron	Thorium	Vanadium
Lead	Tin	
Lithium	Titanium	
Magnesium	Tungsten (wolfram)	
Mercury	Uranium	
Molybdenum	Zinc	
Nickel	Zirconium	

Since the advent of the atomic bomb, it is becoming increasingly important to know the nuclear characteristics of metals and alloys and to study their behavior as structural materials in nuclear reactor construction.

MECHANICAL PROPERTIES OF METALS AND ALLOYS

Strength. The strength of a material is the property of resistance to external loads or stresses without incurring structural damage. The term *ultimate strength* refers to the unit stress (pounds per square inch) developed in the material by the maximum slowly applied load that the material can resist without rupturing in a tensile test (refer to Fig. 1). The tensile test is the one most often applied to metals because it tells so much more about their properties than any other single test. The mechanical properties of several common metals and alloys given in Tables 2 and 3 all are derived from tensile tests. In metallurgy, break-

Table 2. Some Mechanical Properties of Common Metals and Alloys[1]

Material	Designation	Composition, per cent	Tensile strength, psi Ultimate	Tensile strength, psi Yield	Elongation, per cent in 2 in.	Reduction of area, per cent	Endurance limit, psi	Elastic modulus, tension
Aluminum alloy, cast	ASTM-JJ	5 Si	19,000	9,000	6	..	6,500	10,300,000
Aluminum alloy, wrought	24S	4.5 Cu, 0.6 Mn, 1.5 Mg	68,000	45,000	22	..	18,000	10,300,000
Antimony	......	Commercially pure	1,500	......	..	..	......	11,300,000
Bismuth	......	Commercially pure	3,000	......	..	..	......	4,600,000
Brass, soft	Cartridge brass	70 Cu, 30 Zn	47,000	20,000	50	75	22,500	14,900,000
Bronze, soft	......	90 Cu, 10 Sn	63,500	18,500	76	72	20,500	14,100,000
Bronze, manganese (cast)	Manganese bronze	58 Cu, 1 Al and Fe, 0.2 Mn	72,000	26,000	30	30	......	15,000,000
Cobalt, cast	......	99.3 Co	34,000	......	..	..	......	30,000,000
Copper, soft	Tough pitch	99.95 Cu	31,500	5,500	53	71	10,000	15,000,000
Iron, soft	Armco	99.8 Fe	42,500	19,000	48	76	26,000	28,000,000
Lead	Refined	Commercially pure	2,100	Negligible	119	..	380	2,500,000
Magnesium, extruded	......	Commercially pure	32,500	16,000	6	4	7,800	6,700,000
Magnesium alloy, extruded	ASTM-A-10	10 Al, 0.1 Mn	51,000	38,000	9	..	18,000	6,500,000
Molybdenum, soft	......	Commercially pure	75,000	55,000	41	36	......	46,000,000
Monel, soft	"A" nickel	67 Ni, 30 Cu	75,000	35,000	45	67	33,000	26,000,000
Nickel, soft	......	Commercially pure	65,000	28,000	42	67	24,000	30,000,000
Steel:								
Low-carbon, soft	AISI-1010	0.12 C	50,000	30,000	40	65	25,000	29,500,000
High-carbon, soft	AISI-1095	0.95 C	84,000	34,000	25	37	30,500	29,500,000
Alloy steel, hardened and tempered	AISI-6150	0.50 C, 0.95 Cr, 0.20 V	230,000	224,000	10	43	......	29,500,000
Stainless, annealed	AISI-304	18 Cr, 9 Ni, 0.08 C	85,000	32,000	55	60	35,000	28,000,000
Tin	......	Commercially pure	2,200	1,300	45	..	......	5,900,000
Titanium, soft	......	Commercially pure	72,000	55,000	32	..	42,000	12,000,000
Tungsten, hard (wire, 0.01 in. diam.)	......	Commercially pure	250,000	......	3	65	......	50,000,000
Zinc	......	Commercially pure	22,000	Very low	40	..	......	12,000,000
Zirconium, soft	......	Very pure	39,600	14,400	35	33	......	10,800,000

[1] Except as noted, the values for each metal are shown in the soft condition so that they may be fairly compared. Most of the metals or alloys shown can be considerably strengthened to varying degrees by cold work and some by heat-treatment.

METALS AS MATERIALS OF CONSTRUCTION 11

TABLE 3. SOME AVERAGE MECHANICAL PROPERTIES OF IRON AND STEEL PRODUCTS

Material	Designation, ASTM or AISI	Composition, per cent	Tensile strength, psi Ultimate	Tensile strength, psi Yield	Elongation in 2 in., per cent	Reduction of area, per cent	Endurance limit, psi	Brinell hardness	Impact strength, ft-lb (Izod)
Gray cast iron[1]	ASTM Class 30	3.6 C	30,000	[a]	Negligible	..	14,000	170	1
Ductile (nodular) cast iron, as cast	ASTM-A-60	3.6 C low Mn and P	70,000	50,000	12	..	28,000[4]	125	16
Ductile (nodular) cast iron, heat-treated	ASTM-A-80	3.6 C low Mn and P	90,000	70,000	6	..	36,000[4]	105	45
Malleable cast iron	ASTM 35018	2 C, 1.2 Si, 0.4 Mn	55,000	36,500	20	..	27,000	125	16
Wrought iron[2,5]		2.0 slag, 0.08 C	47,000	30,000	35	40	23,000	105	45
Steel:									
0.10 carbon, hot-rolled	C 1010	0.10 C, 0.45 Mn	51,000	29,000	38	70	26,000	101	
0.10 carbon, cast		0.10 C, 0.60 Mn, 0.40 Si	60,000	35,000	29	59	30,000	116	50
0.20 carbon, hot-rolled	C 1020	0.20 C, 0.45 Mn	67,000	45,000	32	62	32,000	137	39
0.20 carbon, cast		0.20 C, 0.60 Mn, 0.30 Si	68,000	37,000	30	52	32,000	135	
0.40 carbon, hot-rolled	C 1040	0.40 C, 0.75 Mn	93,000	58,000	27	52	46,000	190	20
0.40 carbon, cast		0.40 C, 0.60 Mn, 0.30 Si	88,000	52,000	18	20	43,000	182	
0.60 carbon, hot-rolled, annealed	C 1060	0.60 C, 0.75 Mn	95,000	59,000	25	52	47,000	197	
0.80 carbon, hot-rolled, annealed		0.80 C, 0.75 Mn	119,000	70,000	11	21	56,000	248	
0.40 carbon, heat-treated	C 1040	0.40 C, 0.75 Mn	110,000	84,000	21	58	55,000	235	
Alloy steel (examples) heat-treated:									
Chromium-molybdenum, 0.40 C	4140	0.40 C, 1.0 Cr, 0.2 Mo, 0.9 Mn	170,000	147,000	16	56	80,000	321	42
Chromium-vanadium, 0.40 C	6140	0.40 C, 1.0 Cr, 0.2 V, 0.8 Mn	175,000	170,000	15	52	82,000	363	20
Nickel, 0.40 C	2340	0.40 C, 3.5 Ni, 0.8 Mn	137,000	120,000	21	60	75,000	302	49
Stainless steels:									
Austenitic chromium-nickel, annealed[5]	304	18.0 Cr, 9.0 Ni, 0.07 C	85,000	32,000	60	70	35,000	140	100
Austenitic chromium-nickel, hard-rolled[5]	304	18.0 Cr, 9.0 Ni, 0.07 C	200,000	160,000	10	64	100,000	335	34
Martensitic chromium type, annealed	410	12.0 Cr, 0.10 C	75,000	40,000	35	70	40,000	155	90
Martensitic chromium type, heat-treated	410	12.0 Cr, 0.10 C	180,000	140,000	15	55	90,000	375	35
Ferritic chromium type, annealed	430	18.0 Cr, 0.15 C	75,000	45,000	30	65	40,000	155	40

[1] Compressive strength is the most important attribute of cast iron. For this class it is approximately 100,000 psi.
[2] Compressive strength of wrought iron is less than tensile strength. In compression ultimate strength is 35,000 psi, yield strength 18,000.
[3] Tensile yield strength of cast iron is very indefinite. For design purposes 12,000 psi may be used.
[4] Varies considerably with section thickness.
[5] Elastic modulus of cast iron is approximately 13,000,000, ductile cast iron 25,000,000, wrought iron 27,000,000, and austenitic stainless steel 28,000,000. All the other steels show approximately 29,000,000 in all conditions.

ing is often spoken of as failure, or rupture, or fracture; the fracture of a metal is the name given to the surface across which the break has occurred.

The strength of metals and alloys depends upon two factors, *viz.*, the strength of the crystals of which the metals are constructed and the tenacity of adherence between these crystals. This conception of strength will be discussed under the Constitution of Metals and Alloys. The strongest substance known is the tungsten wire of incandescent electric lights. Molybdenum, titanium, and nickel follow in order of strength of commercially pure metals. Pure iron is much weaker, but when alloyed with carbon to make steel, the steel may be stronger than any of the pure metals except tungsten.

Elasticity. Any material subjected to an external load is distorted or strained. Elastically stressed materials return to their original dimensions when the load is released, if the load is not too great. Such distortion or deformation is in proportion to the amount of the load up to a certain point, but when the load is too great the material is permanently deformed, and when the load is increased further to a certain point the material breaks. The property of regaining the original dimensions upon removal of the external load is known as *elasticity*, and the proportionality between the load and the elastic deformation (*i.e.*, between stress and strain) is expressed by Hooke's law.

Stress and Strain. A stress is the force within a body which resists deformation due to an externally applied load. If this load acts upon a surface of unit area, it is called a unit force and the stress resisting it a *unit stress*. Quantitatively, then, stress is force per unit area; in the United States it is expressed in pounds per square inch, while in England long tons per square inch is commonly used, and on the European continent, kilograms per square millimeter.

When an external force acts upon an elastic material, the material is deformed and the deformation is in proportion to the load. This distortion or deformation is *strain*, and unit strain is measured in the United States and in England in inches per inch, while on the continent it is measured in centimeters per centimeter. Unit strain, then, is a ratio of distances or lengths.

Modulus of Elasticity. Within the limit of elasticity the ratio of stress to strain is known as the *modulus of elasticity* (*i.e.*, measure of elasticity), and when determined by the tensile test it may be expressed thus:

$$E = \frac{S}{\Delta l}$$

where E is the modulus of elasticity, S is the unit stress, and Δl is the unit strain.

The modulus of elasticity is often called Young's modulus. Since unit strain is a pure number (inches per inch), the modulus of elasticity is expressed in the same units as the unit stress S, commonly pounds per square inch.

The modulus of elasticity expresses the stiffness of a material. For steel and most metals this is a constant property very little affected by heat-treatment, hot or cold working, or the actual ultimate strength of the metal. Their moduli of elasticity show that, when equal-size bars of steel and aluminum are subjected to the same load, the resulting elastic deformation in the aluminum will be almost three times as great as in the steel bar.

Proportional Elastic Limit. Metals generally are not elastic over the entire loading range. The limit of proportionality of stress to strain is known as the *proportional limit* (see Fig. 1). It is difficult to determine precisely, and the higher the magnification of the plot and the more sensitive the strain gage, the lower the proportional limit appears. The *elastic limit* is the highest unit stress which the specimen under test will support and still return to its original dimensions when the load is removed. The proportional limit and the elastic limit in metals are very close together, so much so that they are often confused, and it is now common to combine them in the single term *proportional elastic limit*. This is an important property, a stress which must not be exceeded in engineering design.

Yield Point. This is a point on the stress-strain curve at which the stress levels off or actually decreases while strain continues. The term is strictly applicable only to mild steels, since the characteristic which defines it is not found in other metals or in alloy steels or even in cold-worked or normalized low-carbon steels. The point is determined by a drop in the weighing beam of the testing machine, or hesitation or actual regression of the pointer on hydraulic-type machines. The term "yield point" is often misapplied when "yield strength" is meant.

Yield Strength. Most metals show a smooth stress-strain curve in the tensile test. Since the proportional elastic limit is difficult and time-consuming to determine, it is now customary to determine the stress necessary to produce a limiting or defined value of permanent deformation ("set"). This is explained by Fig. 2. For most materials, if the load is released after the proportional limit B is exceeded, as for instance at the point C, the diagram for the decreasing load will follow the line CM parallel to the initial stress-strain plot AB. The offset AM will then give the value of permanent set after release of stress AD.

To determine yield strength by "offset," plot the stress-strain diagram and lay off AM equal to the offset that has been specified. Draw a line parallel to AB and determine its point of intersection with the stress-strain curve. The stress AD, given by the height of this point of intersection, is the yield strength by the offset method.

For steel, nickel-base, aluminum-base, and magnesium-base alloys, the magnitude of the offset represented by AM is usually specified as 0.2 per cent (equal to 0.002 in.).

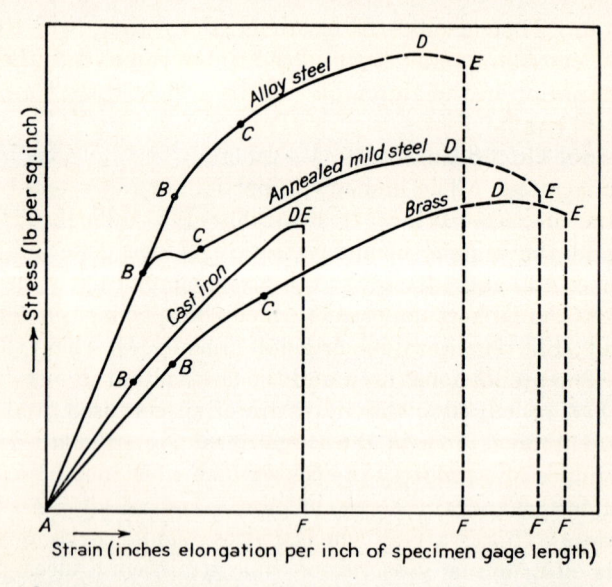

Slope of A-B = Modulus of elasticity (measure of stiffness)
B = Proportional elastic limit
C = Yield strength at arbitrarily fixed permanent elongation or extension under load
D = Ultimate tensile strength
E = Fracture

The area $ABDEFA$ = The total energy absorbed by the metal before it fractures. Toughness is often defined by this area.

Fig. 1. Typical stress-strain diagrams of ductile metals (alloy steel, annealed mild steel, and brass) and a brittle metal (gray cast iron), as determined by tensile tests.

Yield strength is also determined by the "extension-under-load" method. When the stress-strain diagram of a material is well known, the total strain AN corresponding to the stress at which the specified permanent set occurs will be known within satisfactory limits; a specified total strain may then be used to define yield strength. The stress AD (determined by the line CN) that has been applied to the specimen when the total strain AN is reached is the yield strength as determined by the extension-under-load method. For copper-base alloys and many ferrous and nonferrous alloys, a 0.5 per cent extension under load is usually specified as determining the yield strength. This corresponds to approximately 0.35 per cent offset for materials having a modulus of elasticity of 15,000,000, which is the value for copper, and to approximately 0.2 per cent offset for metals having a modulus of 30,000,000, *e.g.*, steels. This definition of yield strength is often used for acceptance testing of metals where the test is made only to determine compliance with specifications.

Ultimate Strength. From the continuance of the tensile test illustrated in Fig. 1, it may be seen that as the load gradually increases the specimen begins to deform plastically (the strain is no longer proportional to the stress) and the specimen continues to stretch until fracture occurs. The greatest load that the specimen has supported divided by the *original* cross-sectional area is called the *ultimate tensile strength* or the *ultimate strength* of the piece. Since at the time of breaking the necking-down effect has changed the area of the specimen, and the cold working which took place during the plastic deformation has changed the strength of the material, this value is not an absolute mechanical property, but simply a useful numerical value which is the result of a particular method of testing.

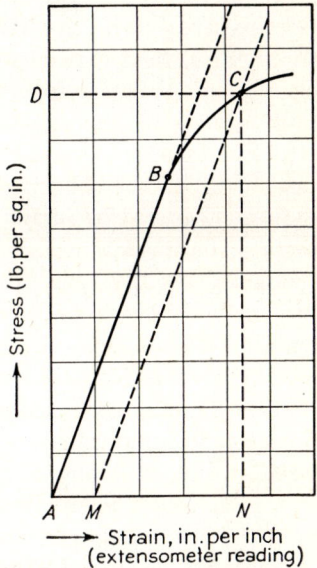

Fig. 2. Determination of yield strength.

Ductility. Ductility is the capacity of a metal to be permanently deformed in tension without breaking. Specifically, the term denotes the capacity to be drawn from a larger to a smaller diameter of wire. Such an operation obviously involves both elongation and reduction of area, and the values for these two characteristics of a metal determined in the tension test are usually taken as a measure of the ductility of the metal. The increase in length between gage marks on the tensile specimen divided by the original length between marks multiplied by 100 gives the percentage elongation; this is used as one measure of ductility. The diameter of the tension specimen at the fracture is smaller than the original diameter because it has necked down in pulling. This quality of reduction of area is obtained from the broken tensile specimen by subtracting the final area from the original area and dividing by the original area. These measures of ductility are not quite satisfactory, because, among other things, a rapid application of the load may increase or decrease the apparent ductility. A more exacting test of ductility is the bend test, in which the outer surface of the bend is elongated and the inner surface compressed. Steel from the top third of an ingot may fail in the bend test although it shows satisfactory values in the tension test.

Toughness. Toughness has been defined by some metallurgists as "the property of absorbing considerable energy before fracture"; it is usually represented by the area under the stress-strain curve (Fig. 1) and therefore involves both ductility and strength. It is a measure of the total energy-absorbing capacity of the material, including the energy of both elastic and plastic deformation under a gradually applied load. However, sometimes metals that pass tension tests satisfactorily fail when struck suddenly. One of the commonest tests for toughness is the impact test, in which the energy absorbed by breaking a specimen by a sudden blow is measured (see next paragraph). But this is not altogether satisfactory, because it measures only resistance to a sudden blow, whereas toughness involves energy of resistance to a blow as well as energy of resistance to slowly applied stresses in excess of the elastic limit of the metal. Webster says that a tough substance is "flexible without brittleness." Generally speaking, toughness implies both strength and plasticity. Thus a very easily deformed substance of low strength would not be considered tough, nor on the other hand would a material of high strength but little plasticity, like hardened tool steel. Another conception of a tough metal is one that will rapidly distribute within itself both the stress and resulting strain caused by a rapidly applied load.

Impact Strength. Impact tests are commonly used to evaluate toughness, even though it is recognized that such tests do not measure all the factors involved in this property. The tests chiefly used today are the Izod and the Charpy, named for the men who developed them. The specimen for the Izod test (see Fig. 60) is a small bar of rectangular or square cross section in which has been cut a V notch of 90 deg included angle and 0.010-in. radius at the bottom. The bar is supported as a cantilever beam and the notch faces a swinging hammer, so that the specimen is broken with the notch in tension. For the Charpy test a specimen containing a keyhole notch is commonly used, although the V notch may also be used, and this specimen is supported as a simple beam with the notch facing away from the swinging hammer. In both tests the foot-pounds of energy absorbed from the swinging hammer in breaking the sample are recorded as the Izod or Charpy values.

Certain highly alloyed steels which are called austenitic and also most of the nonferrous metals such as copper, nickel, or aluminum-base alloys (but not magnesium-base alloys) show a ductile fracture in the impact test at all temperatures. On the other hand notched-bar fractures of plain carbon steel and many of the alloy steels depend upon the temperature at which the test is carried out, showing a brittle fracture and a low impact value below a certain temperature known as the "transition" temperature, while ductile fractures and higher impact values are recorded above this temperature. This characteristic transition temperature depends upon a number of variables such as chemical composition, heat-treatment, grain size, and most particularly the deoxidation practice used in making the steel. The transition temperature may vary from several hundred degrees below to several hundred degrees above 0°F. This fairly well-defined transition temperature is illustrated in the data in the accompanying table, which have been taken from "Ferrous Metallurgy" by E. J. Teichert, and which indicate a transition temperature somewhere between +10 and +20°C (50 and 68°F).

CHARPY NOTCH TOUGHNESS ON ANNEALED 0.25 PER CENT CARBON STEEL

Temperature, °C....	100	50	20	10	0	−20	−30	−40	−50
Results, ft-lb.......	36.1	27.3	19.1	8.8	4.8	3.0	3.7	2.2	2.1

Notch Sensitivity. The ratio of the strength determined on a notched specimen to the strength determined on an unnotched specimen (either by static or by impact test), that is to say, the reduction of strength caused by the concentration of stresses as the result of a notch, is known as the notch sensitivity of that material. To be significant in meaning, the kind of test employed must be indicated.

Resilience. Work must be expended in deforming a metal both elastically and plastically. Work expended in elastic deformation is stored up as potential energy. When the load on an elastic substance is removed and it returns to its original dimensions, the stored energy can do work. This elastic energy is the *resilience* of the material; it is illustrated by the energy recoverable from a clock spring or from a fishing rod when casting. The work expended in deforming a unit volume of a material to its elastic limit is called the modulus of resilience of the material. Resilience of steel is discussed on page 216.

Malleability. Malleability is the property of a metal which permits permanent deformation by compression without rupture. Specifically, it means the capacity to be rolled or hammered into thin sheets. The property of malleability is similar to, but not the same as, that of ductility, and different metals do not possess the two properties in the same degree. While lead and tin are relatively high in order of malleability, they lack the necessary tensile strength to be drawn into fine wire. Most metals have increased malleability and ductility at higher temperatures. For example, iron and nickel are very malleable at a bright red heat (1000°C, 1830°F).

Brittleness. Brittleness implies sudden failure. It is the property of breaking without warning, *i.e.*, without visible permanent deformation. It is the reverse of toughness in the sense that a brittle body has little resistance to rupture after it reaches its elastic limit. Brittleness is the opposite of ductility in the sense that it involves rupture without much deformation. Often the hard metals are brittle, but the terms should not be confused or used synonymously.

Strength at High Temperatures. At elevated temperatures metals gain in ductility but lose strength. Thus a steel which has an ultimate tensile strength of 80,000 psi at room temperature may have a strength as low as 2,200 psi at 1000°C (1830°F). Therefore the rolling and forging of steel at 1000°C requires much less power than cold rolling or forging.

Fatigue Failure. If metal is subjected to frequent repetitions of a stress, it will ultimately rupture and fail, even though the stress may not be sufficient to produce permanent deformation if continuously applied for a relatively brief time. Such a repetition of stress may occur, for example, in the shank of a rock drill. Alternations of stress will produce failure more rapidly than repetition of stress. By "alternations of stress" is meant alternate tension and compression in any fiber. This is exemplified in stresses on the outer fibers of a rotating shaft which is drawn slightly out of alignment by a pulley belt. Failure of metals and alloys under repeated or alternating stresses, too small to produce even a permanent deformation when applied statically, is called *fatigue failure*.

Failure of Metals through Fatigue. For wrought steel or iron at atmospheric temperatures, a unit stress of one third to one half of the ultimate tensile strength of the material will produce failure by fatigue. This failure is produced first by the development of slip within the crystals. With repetition or alternation of the stress, slip continues until cracks are developed and finally rupture. It is especially interesting to note that this development of slip and cracks will result from a unit stress less than the apparent elastic limit of the material. Evidently, microscopic slips will occur at unit stresses which are less than those which will produce a permanent deformation that can be measured in a test specimen. But the occurrence of even microscopic slip will act as a *stress raiser* at the locality in question, which may cause a repetition of the previous stress to produce still further permanent displacement. Any other inhomogeneity in the metal would likewise act as a stress raiser, for example, a microscopic gas bubble or included particle, such as a particle of oxidized metal, an unequalized internal stress pattern, or an almost invisible scratch on the surface.

The behavior of the nonferrous metals and alloys under fatigue is erratic and uncertain. In most of them the unit stress which will produce fatigue failure is below the elastic limit, in some cases 33 per cent below. Its relation to the ultimate tensile strength of the nonferrous alloys is 20 to 50 per cent. In magnesium and magnesium alloys, whose elastic limits are relatively small, the apparent endurance limit (*i.e.*, safe unit stress in fatigue) is very much larger than the elastic limit, although still only about 20 to 40 per cent of the ultimate tensile strength.

Engineering Service Involving Fatigue. The outer fibers of rotating axles and shafts are subjected to alternate tensile and compressive stresses. The same is true of vibrating springs and the reciprocating parts of all engines, especially pistons and connecting rods, and of rock drills, air hammers, machine guns, riveting machines, and the like. The same is true to a less extent of parts of bridges and other structures which are subject to a slight movement or vibration, *e.g.*, suspension cables in bridges, electrical conducting cables, and cable sheathing. Fatigue stresses are especially present in rotating shafts and axles under stress, *e.g.*, locomotive driving-wheel axles, propeller shafts in ships, crankshafts in automobile and airplane engines. Resistance to fatigue is often the most important consideration in design of the structural parts of a moving body.

Intensification of Fatigue Stresses. If one takes for illustration a rotating shaft under stress, it is obvious that any mechanical imperfection on or near the surface will act as a stress raiser and decrease the resistance to fatigue. Examples have been given on page 18. In addition, there may be mentioned sharp corners due to inadequate fillets, rough surfaces or scratches due to imperfect machining, and even invisible cracks caused by excessive heat in grinding or by sudden contraction in quenching. Another example is the presence of unequalized stresses. The importance of stress raisers may be recognized from the fact that fine polishing of machined shafts has increased by one-third the unit stress which these shafts have been able to withstand in fatigue.

Corrosion Fatigue. If a member exposed to fatigue is exposed also to corrosive agencies, such as a damp atmosphere or oil not freed from acid, the stress necessary to cause failure is much lower. The strongest steels will fail under fatigue and corrosion with a unit fiber stress of not more than 24,000 psi, even when their ultimate strengths might indicate that they could withstand a much higher stress. It is interesting to note that the unit stress of an extremely strong heat-treated alloy steel subject to corrosion fatigue will be not greater than that of a relatively weak structural steel. The importance of protecting the surfaces of fatigue members against corrosion by galvanizing, plating, etc., if and when possible, is obvious.

Failure by corrosion fatigue is a fatigue failure in which corrosion has lowered the endurance limit by the formation of pits that act as centers for the development of fatigue cracks. Moreover, any protective film on the metal is repeatedly broken by the fatigue stresses; corrosion spreads through cracks in the film and produces pits which act as stress raisers.

Table 4, based on data obtained by D. J. McAdam, Jr., shows typically the extent to which the strength of metals is lowered by fatigue and further lowered by corrosion fatigue.

TABLE 4. RESULTS OF CORROSION-FATIGUE TESTS

Metal	Tensile strength, psi	Endurance limit,[1] psi	
		In air	In stream of water
Armco iron, as rolled	44,000	24,000	20,000
0.15 carbon steel, annealed	52,000	25,000	16,000
0.26 carbon steel, as-rolled	84,000	36,000	15,000
0.35 carbon steel, heat-treated	104,000	52,000	19,000
0.56 carbon steel, heat-treated	112,000	54,000	16,000
Nickel steel, AISI 2320	124,000	69,000	24,000
Stainless steel, 18–8, ¼ hard	125,000	52,000	49,000
Copper, cold drawn	47,000	18,000	18,000
Brass, 60–40, wrought, hard	84,000	24,000	18,000
Monel metal, wrought, hard	128,000	51,000	26,000
Aluminum, wrought	16,000	7,500	2,500
Duralumin, wrought and aged	69,000	18,000	8,000

[1] Stress causing failure at 20,000,000 cycles in a rotating-beam fatigue machine.

Hardness. The quality of hardness is a complex one which detailed study has shown to be a combination of a number of physical and mechanical properties. It is most often defined in terms of the method used for its measurement and usually means the resistance of a substance to indentation. Hardness may also be defined in terms of resistance to scratching, and thus is related to wear resistance. The term hardness is sometimes used to refer to the stiffness or temper of wrought products because the indentation hardness of a metal is closely related to its tensile strength. The cutting characteristic of a metal when used as a tool is sometimes called its hardness, but reflection will show that these various manifestations of hardness are not the same.

In engineering practice the resistance of a metal to penetration by a hard indenting tool is generally accepted as defining the hardness property. A number of standardized testing machines and penetrators have been devised, the most common of which are the Brinell, Rockwell, and Vickers machines.

TABLE 5. CONVERSION TABLE FOR APPROXIMATE HARDNESS NUMBERS OBTAINED BY DIFFERENT METHODS
(Compiled mainly from manufacturers' tables)

| Brinell, 3,000-kg load, 10-mm ball || Rockwell number || Shore scleroscope number | Vickers pyramid number |
Diameter of indentation, d mm	Hardness number	C scale, 150-kg load, 120-deg diamond cone	B scale, 100-kg load, $\frac{1}{16}$-in. ball		
2.40	653	62	..	86	783
2.60	555	55	..	75	622
2.80	477	49	..	66	513
3.00	415	44	..	58	439
3.10	388	41	..	54	404
3.20	363	39	..	51	374
3.30	341	37	..	48	352
3.40	321	35	..	45	329
3.50	302	32	..	42	303
3.60	285	30	..	40	285
3.70	269	27	..	37	269
3.80	255	25	..	35	255
3.90	241	23	99	33	241
4.00	229	20	98	32	229
4.10	217	..	96	30	217
4.20	207	..	95	29	207
4.30	197	..	93	28	197
4.40	187	..	91	27	187
4.50	179	..	89	25	179
4.60	170	..	87	24	170
4.70	163	..	85	23	163
4.80	156	..	82	23	156
4.90	149	..	80	22	149
5.00	143	..	78	21	143
5.10	137	..	75	20	137
5.20	131	..	73	19	131
5.30	126	..	70	18	126
5.40	121	..	68	17	121
5.50	116	..	65	16	116
5.60	111	..	62	..	111
5.70	107	..	60	..	107
5.80	103	..	57	..	103
5.90	99.2	..	55	..	99.2
6.00	95.5	..	52	..	95.5
6.10	92.0	..	49	..	92.0
6.20	88.7	..	47	..	88.7
6.30	85.5	..	44	..	85.5
6.40	82.5	..	42	..	82.5

In the Brinell test a hardened steel ball 10 mm in diameter is pressed into the surface of the material to be tested under a load of either 500 or 3,000 kg, and the area of the indentation is measured. The Brinell hardness is then expressed as the quotient of applied load divided by area of the impression.

The Rockwell tests employ a number of different testing scales using various penetrators and loads. The most commonly used scales are the "C" scale, which employs a diamond cone penetrator under a major load of 150 kg, and the "B" scale, which employs a $\frac{1}{16}$-in. diameter hardened steel ball under a major load of 100 kg. In this test the differential depth of penetration between that produced by a minor load of 10 kg and the imposed major load is taken as a measure of the hardness.

In the Vickers test a square-based diamond pyramid indenter is used which may be loaded with 1 to 120 kg. As in the Brinell test, the hardness is expressed in terms of applied load divided by the surface area of the pyramidal impression.

The Brinell test is usually used only for fairly thick sections such as bars and forgings, while the Rockwell test is commonly used both on thick and on thin sections such as strip and tubing. The superficial Rockwell may be used on pieces as thin as 0.010 in. The Vickers tester is most commonly used as a laboratory instrument for very precise hardness measurements rather than as a tool of production control.

The Shore scleroscope test measures resilience rather than hardness, although the two are related. The scleroscope measures the rebound of a falling hammer from the test surface, and the hardness number is expressed as the height of a rebound in terms of the maximum rebound from fully hardened high-carbon steel (arbitrarily assigned a scleroscope hardness of 100).

Hardness-testing methods and apparatus are discussed further in Chap. 6. A comparison of figures obtained by the Brinell, the Rockwell, the Vickers, and the Shore methods on differing hard surfaces is given in Table 5 to show the approximate hardness correlation of these tests.

PHYSICAL PROPERTIES OF METALS AND ALLOYS

Melting and Boiling Points. The temperature at which a metal melts, called its *melting point*, is a measure of its *fusibility*. The melting points of the common metals are given in Table 6. While the order of fusibility does not follow closely the sequence as to softness, with a few important exceptions the metals of lower melting points are generally the soft metals and those of high melting points the hard metals.

The boiling point of a substance depends on the surrounding pressure. Unless otherwise stated, the term *boiling point* refers to the temperature at which the metal boils under normal atmospheric pressure (760 mm); it is a measure of *volatility*. The normal boiling points of the common metals are also given in Table 6; many of the high boiling points are known only approximately. The order of fusibility and volatility is not the same among the metals, but with some exceptions high boiling points accompany high melting points.

Electrical Conductivity. The electrical conductivity of a substance is the electrical conducting power of a unit length per unit of cross-sectional area. It is the reciprocal of resistivity, and is discussed at length on page 244. The relative conductivities of the common metals are given in Table 6, based on the conductivity of silver as 100 per cent. Metals are built up of individual crystals, and it is important to note that they conduct electricity better through the crystals than across the crystal boundaries. In other words, the greatest resistance is encountered in the passage from one metallic crystal to another. The electrical resistance of metals or alloys is increased by decreasing the size of the crystals and, therefore, increasing the number of crystal boundaries. In general, all metals increase in resistivity with increase in impurities. This increase of resistivity caused by impurities is due in part to the increase in the specific resistivity of crystal boundaries, in part to the decrease in crystal size which most impurities produce, and in part to other causes. Inpurities in solid solution usually increase resistivity very much more than the same amount of impurity in the form of an insoluble second phase. The resistivity of metals is also increased in most cases by an increase in temperature. In this behavior metals differ from other materials, since the resistivity of most nonmetals and of solutions decreases with rise of temperature. The resistivity of metals is also increased by the existence of strain, such as that induced by cold wire drawing.

Heat Conductivity. *Heat conductivity* is measured as the heat-conducting ability of a unit length or thickness of a substance per unit of cross-sectional area. The relative heat conductivities of some metals and alloys are given in Table 6, based on the conductivity of silver as 100 per cent.

Magnetism. *Magnetism* is measured as the magnetic force exerted by a unit volume of a substance under a standard magnetizing force. The relative order of magnetism under an arbitrary magnetizing force is given in Table 6. Iron, cobalt, and nickel are the only common metals possessing considerable magnetism at room temperature, and they become nonmagnetic when heated to a certain temperature called the *Curie point*. Gadolinium is also a magnetic metal at room temperature, and others become so at lower temperatures. Strong permanent magnets have been made chiefly of one of several compositions of steel, but in recent years a number of magnet alloys of much greater magnetism, able to exert forces many times their own weights, have been developed. The best known of these are the Alnico series of alloys, composed principally of iron, aluminum, nickel, and cobalt, the exact compositions depending on the properties desired.

TABLE 6. SOME PHYSICAL PROPERTIES OF METALS

Metal	Atomic number	Melting point °C	Melting point °F	Boiling point °C	Boiling point °F	Specific gravity	Electric conductivity, per cent[1]	Heat conductivity, per cent[1]	Magnetism (relative)
Mercury......	80	−39	−38	357	674	13.6	1.7	1.8	
Tin..........	50	232	449	2,270	4,120	7.3	11.3	15.2	
Bismuth......	83	271	520	1,420	2,642	9.9	1.1	1.8	
Cadmium.....	48	321	610	765	1,404	8.7	21.2		
Lead.........	82	327	621	1,740	2,948	11.3	7.6	8.2	
Zinc..........	30	419	787	905	1,661	7.1	26.0	28.1	
Antimony.....	51	630	1,167	1,440	2,590	6.7	3.5	4.2	
Magnesium....	12	650	1,202	1,110	2,030	1.7	35.8	37.6	
Aluminum....	13	659	1,218	2,060	3,740	2.7	53.0	48.0	
Silver.........	47	961	1,761	2,210	4,010	10.5	100.0	100.0	
Copper........	29	1,084	1,983	2,595	4,700	8.9	94.0	89.0	
Vanadium.....	23	1,130	2,066	3,000	5,430	5.7			
Manganese....	25	1,244	2,271	2,095	3,800	7.4			
Nickel........	28	1,455	2,651	2,730	4,950	8.9	11.8	14.0	29
Cobalt........	27	1,490	2,714	3,100	5,610	8.9	16.3	....	44
Iron..........	26	1,534	2,793	3,000	5,430	7.9	17.7	18.0	100
Chromium....	24	1,550	2,822	2,480	4,500	7.1			
Titanium.....	22	1,725	3,135	3,000	5,430	4.5	3.4	3.0	
Molybdenum..	42	2,620	4,748	4,800	8,670	10.2	33.2		
Tungsten......	74	3,387	6,129	5,900	10,650	20.2	28.9		

[1] Silver = 100 per cent.

An important magnetic alloy is Permalloy, containing about 80 per cent nickel plus 20 per cent iron. For very low magnetizing forces, amounting to only small fractions of a gauss, such as are used in submarine-cable and telephone construction, its magnetic permeability is exceptionally high. It can be magnetized or demagnetized about two hundred times as readily as pure iron. Another interesting alloy made of the three metals copper, manganese, and aluminum has one-fourth to one-third the magnetism of iron, although none of the constituent metals is magnetic. It is called "Heussler's alloy." Silmanal is a permanent-magnet alloy containing silver (86 per cent), manganese, and aluminum, and it has the largest coercive force of any substance so far discovered. *Coercive force* is the magnetizing force that must be applied in order to remove residual magnetism; it is therefore a measure of the magnetic retentivity of a substance. *Hysteresis* is the lag of magnetization behind the magnetizing field; it therefore results in a loss of energy which appears as heat in the piece being magnetized (see page 217).

Density and Porosity. *Porosity*, the quality of containing pores or voids, is lack of *denseness*. *Density*, on the other hand, denotes weight per unit of volume. The distinction will be manifest from the fact that some heavy metals, like gray cast iron, are porous enough to leak under heavy hydraulic pressures, whereas some lightweight metals, like aluminum, are dense and compact.

Expansion and Contraction with Heat. Most metals expand on heating and contract on cooling. For certain ranges of temperature where changes of physical state occur, there are some important exceptions to this rule, especially in respect to alloys. For example, cast iron expands during the process of freezing, due to the separation from liquid solution of flakes of lightweight and bulky graphite. The metal bismuth and alloys containing over 50 per cent bismuth also expand on freezing. Steel expands when it cools through the range of temperature from 800 to 700°C (1472 to 1292°F), because it is then undergoing changes in constitution, as will be explained in Chap. 7, and pure iron expands when it undergoes a change in its crystal form at about 910°C (1670°F). When these are heated through the same ranges of temperature, they temporarily contract instead of expanding.

Color. Most of the metals are silvery white or gray in color. Copper is the only red metal, and gold the only yellow one, although a number of copper-base alloys are also yellow. All solid metals have metallic luster, although the true color and luster of many metals are often obscured by a coating of oxide—which may be white, gray, red, brown, bluish, or black —formed by oxidation or tarnishing.

THE CONSTITUTION OF METALS AND ALLOYS

The word *constitution* used with reference to metallic substances does not have the same meaning as *composition*. *Constitution* denotes the manner of arrangement of the metal atoms as to geometric form in solid crystals, and the regular or ordered arrangement of different kinds of metal atoms and their relation to each other in such a crystal. In the liquid state the atoms are free to move in all directions. (Note that while atoms may sometimes be bound together into molecules, nevertheless such molecules act the same as do atoms, so that in the following discussion atoms and molecules may be treated synonymously.) Upon solidification the atoms lose their freedom of motion and assume comparatively stationary positions with respect to one another in a regular and repeated geometric pattern known as a space lattice (see Fig. 3). The arrangements characteristic of most metals (there are other types) are of two kinds, *viz.*, an isometric cube similar to Fig. 3a or 3b, or the hexagonal form similar to Fig. 3c. It is important to note that the unit cells which make up metallic crystals, as illustrated in Fig. 3, are actually arrangements of atoms in space, and the lines on the drawing which connect the lattice points are imaginary and only denote the intersection of planes in space. A space lattice, then, is an imaginary representation of the manner in which unit cells, made up of a number of atoms, are related to each other in the gross crystal structure. Such a concept helps a great deal in describing a crystal if it is remembered that the

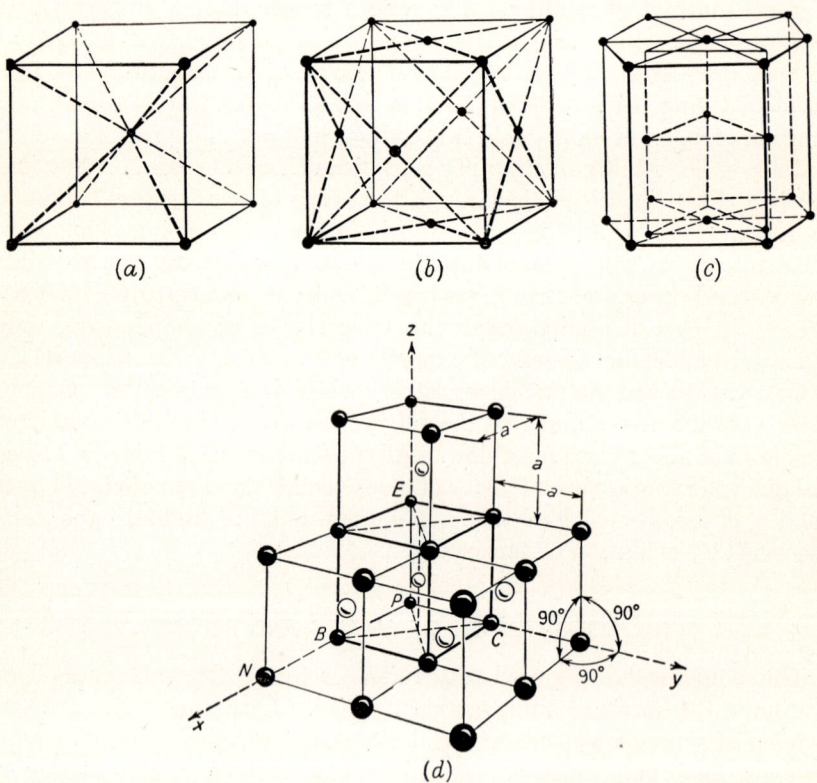

(a)   (b)   (c)

(d)

Fig. 3. (a) Body-centered cubic cell. (b) Face-centered cubic cell. (c) Hexagonal close-packed cell. (d) Relation of cubic cells to each other in forming a metal crystal.

arrangement of atoms about every lattice point is exactly the same. Figure 3d shows the manner in which the simple cubic building blocks called unit cells arrange themselves to form solid metal crystals.

This union of atoms into a geometric array is the physical difference between liquid and solid metal. Figure 4 illustrates further the manner in which the union of many millions of unit cells may be imagined to take place in the solidification of even the tiniest metal crystal.

Actually, this description of the process of solidification is greatly simplified because many million such unit cells must agglomerate in order to form a stable nucleus large enough to initiate the growth of a crystal, since the distances between lattice points are measured in millionths of a centimeter and are of the order of several angstrom units. Such measurements are called lattice parameters (measurements) and may be determined by X-ray methods as well as by other techniques. As with the minerals, each metal and alloy has its own unique set of lattice parameters which is not exactly like that of any other metal or alloy.

The formation of metal crystals within a melt begins at each cooling surface of the liquid mass and extends from the exterior to the interior as heat is lost from the mass. The crystals grow by the process of metal atoms stopping their random motion in the liquid and extending the

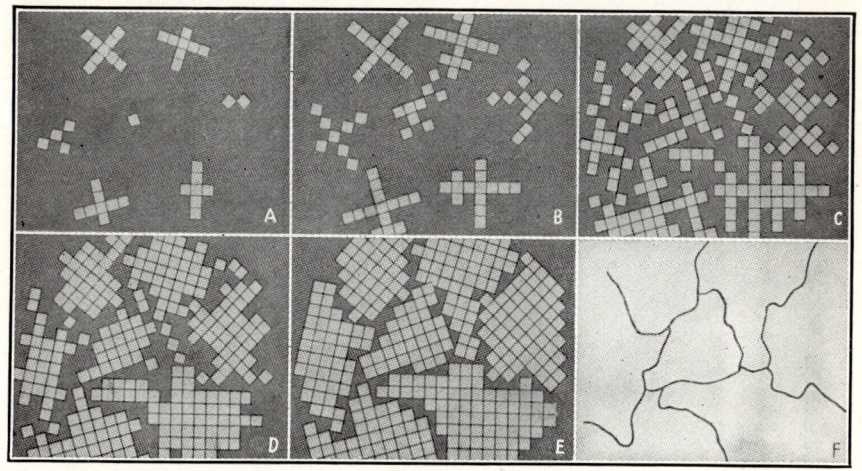

Fig. 4. Stages in the formation of metallic crystals by freezing of a molten mass. (*From Walter Rosenhain, "Physical Metallurgy," D. Van Nostrand Company, Inc.*)

lattice configuration in all directions, but usually at a faster rate in one of these directions coinciding with a crystallographic axis. Obviously, such crystals cannot grow very large before they interfere with each other. Although each metal or alloy tends to follow a crystal form individual to itself, because of such interferences the resulting crystal aggregate forming the solidified metallic mass bears only a rough resemblance to the typical crystalline form, as shown in Fig. 4*f*. When crystal growth is very slow, because of slow cooling, and the crystals originate from only a relatively few nuclei, large *dendritic* (fir-tree) crystals often result. Figure 6, a photograph of the surface of a slowly cooled ingot of antimony, shows the form in which such crystals occur. Every change in the conditions of cooling, such as increasing or decreasing the rate at which heat is conducted away from the freezing mass, will have an influence on the size and shape of the crystals and, therefore, on the constitution and properties of the solidified mass.

Forms of Unit Cells. The body-centered cubic form, shown in Fig. 3a, is assumed at room temperature by the metals chromium, alpha iron (ferrite), molybdenum, tungsten, and others; some common face-centered cubic metals, as illustrated in Fig. 3b, are aluminum, gamma iron (aus-

FIG. 5. Metal crystals built up of rectangular masses. Magnified photograph by Stead. (*From Walter Rosenhain, "Physical Metallurgy," D. Van Nostrand Company, Inc.*)

FIG. 6. Crystal growth on upper surface of antimony casting. Magnification 4.5 ×. (*F. J. G. Duck, author's laboratory.*)

tenite), copper, nickel, and the noble metals. The hexagonal form is characteristic at room temperature of antimony, beryllium, bismuth, cadmium, magnesium, alpha titanium, zinc, and alpha zirconium (see Fig. 3c). Some of the metals have the face-centered cubic form at one temperature and the body-centered cubic form at another. This is true of iron, for example, which is in the face-centered cubic mode at temperatures above 910°C (1670°F) and changes into the body-centered form when cooled below that temperature. Sometimes the metals change their mode completely, being in the cubic form at one temperature and in a hexagonal form at another, as, for instance, titanium and zirconium. This changing from one crystallographic form to another occurs in the solid state and is known as an allotropic change. Since the number of equivalent whole atoms in one type of unit cell is different from the number in another type, if follows that there must be a rearrangement of atoms within the lattice with an attendant change in volume of the metallic crystal when such an allotropic change takes place.

The Nature of Cohesion and Strength. Considering a metallic crystalline mass under tensile stress, it is obvious that the strength of the mass will depend upon both the cohesion within the individual crystals and the adhesion of the crystals to one another at the crystal boundaries. Obviously, the mass will fail by tearing asunder at the weakest point. In most of the common ductile metals, rupture will take place at atmospheric temperature by *transcrystalline failure*. The same metals at temperatures approaching their melting points will fail under tension by the disjunction or tearing apart of the crystals from each other. The latter type is a *brittle failure;* it usually occurs suddenly and without significant prior deformation.

In comparing the moduli of elasticity of the different metals, it is seen that they represent the relative resistances of the atomic array to any change of position of the individual atoms within the crystals. As the modulus of elasticity in tension is practically the same as that in compression, it follows that both the bonds between the atoms in the space lattice and the atomic bonds across the crystal boundaries offer the same resistance to either extension or compression and that the modulus of elasticity of the metal is a measure of the algebraic total strength of the atomic bonds resisting the elastic deformation. In the heterogeneous arrangement of space lattices indicated in Figs. 4 and 5, it is evident that the interatomic bonds will not all be acting directly against the force tending to produce rupture of the metal. Actually, it has been calculated that the *theoretical* strength of a perfect metal lattice would run into millions of pounds per square inch if there were no atom dislocations, lattice distortions by impurities, or other forces acting to reduce the algebraic total which is measured by the modulus of elasticity. This theoretical strength is the absolute cohesion. When metals are worked to extremely small size, and by the process of working attain a pronounced orientation of the crystals, they more nearly approach conditions of absolute cohesion. This is perhaps one reason why all metals have greatly increased tensile strength when drawn into the form of extremely fine wire. This effect is illustrated by the increase in tensile strength of tungsten, which has but a very moderate strength when in the form of sintered rod, but increases with work to almost 600,000 psi in the form of very fine wire.

Flow of Ductile Metals When Strained. By considering the effect of external stress upon the elastic deformation of a metallic mass built up of crystals as indicated diagrammatically in Fig. 4 and by actual photographs of substructure as shown in Fig. 5, it is evident that the first effect of stress will be a distortion of the lattices somewhat as shown in Fig. 7b. Upon removal of the external stress, the lattice resumes its original undistorted shape.

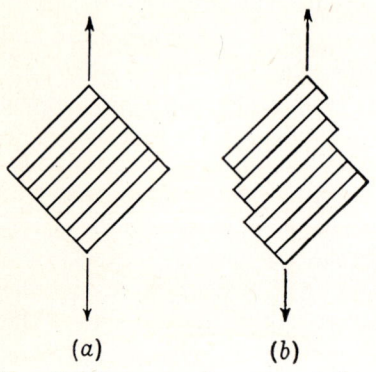

Fig. 7. Diagrammatic representation of crystal deformation in a metal having cubic space lattices.

No permanent deformation has occurred in the mass. If the mass is visualized as being made up of a great many blocks such as shown in Figs. 4 and 5, each block being composed of millions of unit cells,

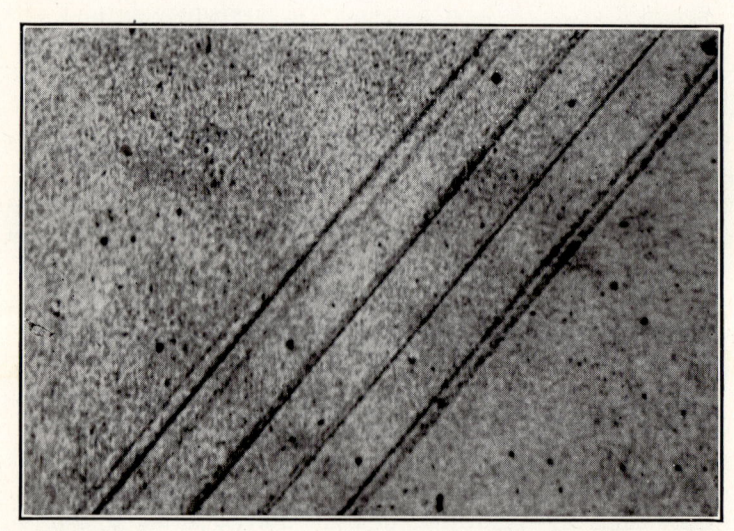

Fig. 8. Slipbands in a single crystal of brass. Magnification 800 ×. (*Courtesy of R. M. Brick.*)

the distortion of the lattice in yielding to stress might reach that degree in which the individual blocks would slide along one another. This action is called slippage along slip planes or glide planes, and is illustrated diagrammatically in Fig. 7b. The result is the formation of slipbands situated within the crystals and readily discernible under a microscope (see Fig. 8). With light overstrain (stressing above the yield strength) these slip planes are faint and small in number, but microscopic examination of a metal strained nearly to the breaking point shows a great increase in the number and width of these slipbands. They often cross one another at definite angles, but each set of slipbands is usually parallel. The yielding along slip planes naturally results in deformation of the crystals and therefore of the mass as a whole.

Creep. If a ductile metal or alloy is subjected to a continuous load, even though well below its apparent elastic limit, it may yield slowly for a period of months or even years. This yielding may continue to the point of fracture, and is most often encountered at elevated temperature. This is called *creep*, and has been studied at many temperatures in steels, alloy steels, heat-resisting alloys, nickel, light structural alloys, and other nonferrous materials. Creep occurs in the weaker metals at room temperature, and is not unknown at room temperature even in steel.

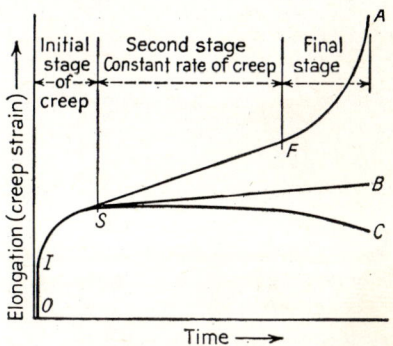

FIG. 9. Illustrating creep in metals.

The vertical part of the curve OI, which indicates elongation without the passage of time, represents the elongation which occurs below the yield point of the metal when the load is first applied. The load and the temperature are continuous and unvarying over a long period of time. During this time there is a slow stretching or permanent elongation of the specimen. Should the deformation result in an increase of the yield point of the metal, linear elongation will decrease and the line SC will result. If not, then the stretching will continue until the specimen becomes so weakened by the deformation that the curve will take the shape indicated from F to A, and fracture occurs at A.

The action of creep is illustrated graphically in Figs. 9 and 10.

For applications requiring strength and stability at high temperatures the designer specifies that the rate of linear expansion at the service temperature shall not exceed, for example, 0.1 per cent in 1,000 hr, or perhaps 1 per cent in 100,000 hr. One point is to be noted in this connection: stressing a metal beyond its yield point at room temperature usually results in *strain hardening*, *i.e.*, an increase in the value of the yield point. (This does not occur at temperatures where the metal is beginning to soften appreciably.) The same action occurs in extremely slow straining (stretching). Thus sometimes after months of creep an alloy will become strengthened by the strain hardening to the point where it will no longer yield, or yield only very slightly, to the stress. This is indicated by the line SB in Fig. 9.

Creep Limit. A creep limit is defined as the maximum stress that will result in creep at a rate lower than some assigned rate. For example, if it is decided that at a given temperature a member must not creep faster than, say, 0.001 in. in 1,000 hr, then the creep limit will be the maximum stress that will result in less than this rate of creep. This is a factor that must often be used in design. Actual tests are made to determine this limit, and it is considered that tests of less than 1,000 hr duration are not satisfactory.

Stress to Rupture. Creep rates at high temperatures are determined for alloys and parts which must maintain their dimensions over long periods of time. "Some applications such as turbo-superchargers, gas

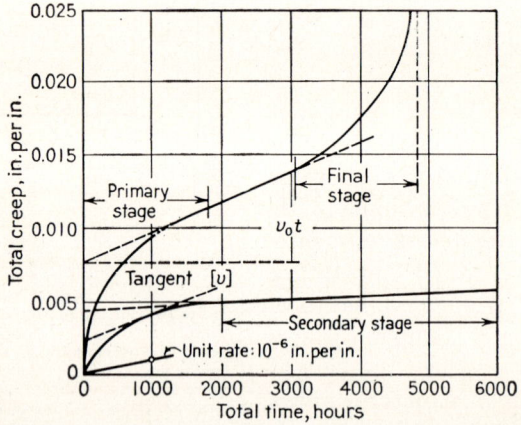

Fig. 10. Typical tensile creep curves obtained under different loadings for two alloy steels, with a constant stress and a constant temperature. (*From J. J. Kanter.*)

The primary stage is rapid, but the creep (strain) decelerates until a constant rate is approximated. This continues during the secondary stage. The third stage is characterized by a rapidly increasing creep, until fracture occurs. The lower curve shows no increase in rate up to 5,000 hr, and tests have been made in which the creep has continued in the second stage for several times this period, for example, 15,000 or 30,000 hr. (One year is 8,760 hr.)

turbines, and jet aircraft engines require materials to operate under rather extreme conditions of temperature and stress. In these applications the useful life may be of the order of only several hundred or a thousand hours. In many of these applications, the permissible deformation is high or may not even be limited, and the only requirement is that rupture must not occur during the life of the part."[1] A test for rupture strength at high temperatures (stress to rupture) indicates the time required for fracture at a given temperature, under various constant loads. The stress-to-rupture test is similar to a creep test except that higher stresses are employed and accurate determinations of rate of strain are not necessary. Creep and stress-to-rupture values for several heat-resisting alloys are shown in the accompanying table.

[1] J. J. Kanter, "Metals Handbook," 1948, p. 117.

Alloy	Composition per cent	Creep limit at 650°C (1200°F), psi (1 per cent in 10,000 hr)	Stress to rupture at 650°C (1200°F), psi (1,000 hr)
Type 304 stainless.	18 Cr, 8 Ni	6,500	15,000
Type 316 stainless.	18 Cr, 8 Ni, 2.5 Mo	10,000	25,000
Type 310 stainless.	25 Cr, 20 Ni	8,000	17,000

Deformation Produced by Cold Working. Any form of cold work produces, in ductile metals, a deformation and a great number and confusion of slipbands. The crystals are actually fragmented and elongated, but the series of slipbands in each crystal fragment is roughly parallel. Such deformation produces not only an increase in ultimate strength, but a still greater increase in the elastic limit or yield strength as well as an increase in hardness. This effect has been explained upon the theory that when slip occurs it is accompanied by fragmentation and the lodging of such fragments between the slip planes, which inhibits further slip from taking place locally at the same imposed stress, as represented schematically in Fig. 7b. As the preferred crystallographic planes of slip become exhausted, the stress necessary to deform the piece further becomes greater and greater, but such slippage can continue on new and more resistant crystallographic planes; thus the piece becomes harder and harder and stronger and stronger as work progresses. Deformation then does not take place easily, and the elastic limit of the metal is materially increased. As the planes of easy slip become "locked" in this fashion, the yield strength of the material is increased. Since such a deformed structure is more resistant to penetration as well as to tensile, shear, and compressive stresses, the hardness of the mass is increased. While this explanation is not accepted by all metallurgists, it is given here as one theory of the hardening and strengthening resulting from cold working.

Nature of Failure at High and Low Temperatures. It has already been noted that, at atmospheric temperature, most metals fail by rupture along intracrystalline cleavage planes, rather than through the grain boundaries. By referring to Fig. 7 it will be evident that a stress can produce gliding along slip planes more easily than it could produce breaking of many atomic bonds. However, when a metal is heated to a high temperature, the loss in grain-boundary strength is more rapid than the decrease in intracrystalline strength, and metals at high temperatures often fail by separation of the crystals from each other instead of by the usual mode of transcrystalline fracture. This failure is of the sudden brittle type, as contrasted with the deformation and slow failure in the slippage type. Most alloys suffer rupture through intercrystalline junctions (grain boundaries) above a characteristic temperature and by crystalline slippage below this temperature, which is different for each individual alloy. This *equicohesive* temperature is not sharply defined since it is somewhat dependent on rate of strain (see Fig. 11).

The Nature of Elasticity. From the foregoing discussion it is evident that the elasticity of metallic substances is a function of the resistance of its atoms to separation or compression or rotation about one another, and thus is a fundamental property of the material. Elasticity is thus demonstrated as a function of atomic forces. This explains why the modulus of elasticity of a strong and brittle heat-treated alloy steel is exactly the same as that of a comparatively weak and ductile annealed

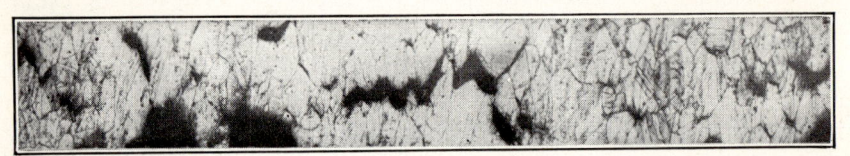

FIG. 11. Stainless steel (18-8) fractured at elevated temperature, showing intercrystalline rupture along with deformation. Magnification 25 ×. (*Courtesy of Francis B. Foley.*)

steel. A hard steel is mechanically prevented from deforming by slipping along its slip planes; its strength is due not alone to the forces which bind its atoms together, but also to the resistance to slip characteristic of hardened steel structures in which the supersaturation of the lattice with carbon effectively introduces "wedges" in all the possible slip planes.

The Nature of Toughness. The toughness of a metal is indicated by the amount of slip which may occur within the crystals without resulting in rupture of the metal. It is perhaps the result of alternate slippings and wedgings, each wedged crystallographic plane holding until a greater stress is applied. A brittle metal or alloy either will not stop slipping after the elastic strain is reached, or else will stop only for a brief period before breaking. Obviously, the successive stopping and slipping will produce deformation; therefore, the tough metals and alloys are often the most malleable and ductile.

Sometimes the crystals of a metal may be tough, but the crystal boundaries may contain impurities so that the least deformation of the crystal mass may cause cracking through the brittle grain boundary material. This is true of steel containing considerable phosphorus and of copper containing bismuth. The impurity forms a eutectic (see page 155) with the metal, which segregates in the crystal boundaries and is brittle whether hot or cold, so that it causes the metal to crack during rolling at red heat, and also to break in a brittle manner when cold.

The Nature of Hardness and Softness. The resistance of a metal to penetration by another body is evidently in part a function of the resisting power of its interatomic bonds. This is indicated by the almost exact parallel of the order of hardness of metals and their moduli of elasticity. The only known exception is the relation of magnesium and aluminum. Magnesium will scratch aluminum, although its modulus of elasticity and its average strength of interatomic bonds are less. They are not much less, however, and apparently the greater toughness of magnesium and its greater ultimate strength account for its ability to scratch aluminum.

THE EFFECT OF TEMPERATURE ON METALS AND ALLOYS

All pure metals and many alloys show higher electrical resistivity with increase of temperature. This is important in making heating elements for electric furnaces, filaments for incandescent lighting, and like objects. All metals are stronger and harder and most metals are more brittle when very cold than at atmospheric temperature, and they become very weak as the temperature approaches their melting points. For some of the nonferrous metals, attention will be called to this behavior in Chap. 10. Metals with high melting points are generally the most capable of retaining their strength at high temperatures.

Scaling, or the formation of oxide coatings by attack of oxygen in the air, occurs more rapidly as the temperature rises. However, the noble metals, such as gold, silver, platinum, and palladium, have surfaces that are permanent in air, while chromium, nickel, and aluminum resist deep scaling. As little as 12 per cent of chromium in steel will protect the latter from scaling at red heat, and an aluminized coating on steel will make scaling very slow. Moreover, one of the outstanding characteristics of the "heat-resisting alloys," which are discussed in Chap. 11, is resistance to scaling at elevated temperatures.

Grain growth and "burning" occur at certain temperatures; these will be discussed with respect to steel in Chap. 9.

Heat-treatment is a combination of heating and cooling operations in order to produce desired properties, such as softness, hardness, and toughness. Because of the great importance and complexity of the heat-treatment of steel, this subject forms Chap. 8 of this book. Further discussion of heat-treatment of nonferrous alloys is given in Chap. 10.

PLASTICS

It is beyond the scope of this book to cover engineering materials other than metals. However, an exception will be made to provide a brief discussion of plastics. The production of new types of plastics, competing with some metals and alloys in certain limited fields of use, is a comparatively new development, and the last few years have witnessed a rapid growth in the competition in industrial design between plastics and metals.

Plastics, as defined today, are substances derived from natural or synthetic organic materials, which are plastically molded, extruded, or cast in a semiliquid state into a desired form which they approximately retain subsequently. For molding or extruding they are heated until plastic, namely, to temperatures usually between 120 and 180°C (250 to 360°F). The work is performed at pressures of 1,000 to 8,000 psi. Sometimes, however, they are in a semiliquid form and are cast at atmospheric temperatures into molds, being subsequently polymerized for several days at elevated temperatures of less than 100°C (212°F) which causes them to acquire hardness and strength. Most plastics, after cooling to atmospheric temperature, are brittle as compared with pure metals, but they vary among themselves in toughness and strength. A few have ductility equal to that of soft steel. They all scratch somewhat easily. They are characterized particularly by low specific gravity (1.07 to 2.00) and, therefore, sometimes have a fair strength-weight factor; by high electrical insulation; and often by attractive texture, finish, and color. Usually they are translucent or transparent. They vary in tensile strength from about 4,000 to 18,000 psi, in compressive strength from about 16,000 to 44,000 psi, and in Izod notched impact strength from about 0.13 to 5.4 ft-lb. Celluloid was the first plastic (1855 to 1865); but the engineering use of plastics dates from the advent of bakelite in 1909, and the thirties and forties saw a great expansion in the development and use of the new plastics. There is now scarcely any large industry which does not use them in some form. Lest this statement lead to a misconception, we may record that the total annual tonnage of all plastics is only about 1 per cent of that of steel, and much of this tonnage is used for purposes for which metals could not be, and never were, applicable.

There are two chief types of plastics, namely, the thermoplastic and the thermosetting types. A third group, known as the protein-plastic type, is based on casein, and it has not replaced metals to any great extent. When thermoplastics are molded under heat and pressure, they do not change chemically, and thus may be reheated and re-formed, so that scrap can be used. But thermosetting plastics, when once they have been shaped, cannot be changed and can be worked only by cutting and grinding. Incidentally, they are the only ones that have replaced metals to any considerable extent. This is especially true of the synthetic resins (phenolics) on account of their strength-weight and impact characteristics. Plastics have specific gravities about one-fifth to one-sixth of those of steel or copper; their tensile strength is about one-quarter to one-tenth, their compressive strength about one-quarter, and their moduli of elasticity about one-tenth to one-twenty-fifth of those of steel or copper. Since the impact strength of phenolics is relatively high, they have excellent properties for gears and bearings, but the enthusiastic talk about their replacing metals for structural parts for automobiles, airplanes, and the like, is still premature. Plastics make attractive materials for instrument panels, furniture, etc., but their low resistance to heat and relatively low hardness make them unsuitable for many purposes. Their translucence, extreme lightness, clarity, splinterproof qualities, and exclusion of certain rays of the sun make them applicable for windows and cockpit covers for airplanes. The synthetic resins (phenolics) are used extensively as bonding agents and impregnations for plywood fuselages, wings, and secondary structural airplane parts. The plywood preserves much of the character of wood and eliminates many of its disadvantages. Plastic parts are also often combined with metal parts, and plastics are sometimes electroplated with metals.

Bibliography

See also the references following Chaps. 9 to 11.

ALCUTT, E. A., and E. MILLER: "Materials and Their Application to Engineering Design," Charles Griffin & Co., Ltd., London, 1923.

AMERICAN SOCIETY FOR METALS: "Surface Treatment of Metals," Cleveland, Ohio, 1941.

AMERICAN SOCIETY FOR TESTING MATERIALS: "Compilation of Available High-Temperature Creep Characteristics of Metals and Alloys," Joint Research Committee Report, Philadelphia, 1938.

AMERICAN SOCIETY FOR TESTING MATERIALS AND AMERICAN INSTITUTE OF MINING AND METALLURGICAL ENGINEERS: "Symposium on Stress-Corrosion Cracking of Metals," 1945.

BALLARD, W. E.: "Metal Spraying and Sprayed Metal," 3d ed., Charles Griffin & Co., Ltd., London, 1948.

BARRETT, C. S.: "Structure of Metals," 2d ed., McGraw-Hill Book Company, Inc., New York, 1952.

BATTELLE MEMORIAL INSTITUTE: "Prevention of the Failure of Metals under Repeated Stress," John Wiley & Sons, Inc., New York, 1941.

BOAS, WALTER: "An Introduction to the Physics of Metals and Alloys," John Wiley & Sons, Inc., New York, 1948.

BRICK, R. M., and ARTHUR PHILLIPS: "Structure and Properties of Alloys," 2d ed., McGraw-Hill Book Company, Inc., New York, 1949.

CAMM, F. J. (editor): "Dictionary of Metals and Alloys," 3d ed., G. Newnes, Ltd., London, 1944.

CARPENTER, H., and J. M. ROBERTSON: "Metals," 2 vols., Oxford University Press, New York, 1939.

CLAPP, W. H., and D. S. CLARK: "Engineering Materials and Processes; Metals and Plastics," International Textbook Company, Scranton, Pa., 1938.

COONAN, F. J.: "Principles of Physical Metallurgy," Harper & Brothers, New York, 1943.

Doan, G. E.: "Principles of Physical Metallurgy," 3d ed., McGraw-Hill Book Company, Inc., New York, 1953.

Eastwood, L. W.: "Gas in Light Alloys," John Wiley & Sons, Inc., New York, 1946.

Eddy, C. T., and R. J. Marcotte: "Fundamental Principles in Physical Metallurgy," Edwards Bros., Inc., Ann Arbor, Mich., 1940.

Elberfield, J.: "Metallurgical Materials and Processes," Prentice-Hall, Inc., New York, 1948.

Everhart, J. L., W. E. Lindlief, J. Kanegis, P. G. Weissler, and F. Siegel: "Mechanical Properties of Metals and Alloys," National Bureau of Standards, Circular C-477, U.S. Government Printing Office, Washington, D.C., 1943.

Frier, W. T.: "Elementary Metallurgy," 2d ed., McGraw-Hill Book Company, Inc., New York, 1952.

Garside, J. E.: "Process and Physical Metallurgy," Charles Griffin & Co., Ltd., London, 1949.

Grosvenor, A. W., and others: "Metal Inside Out," American Society for Metals, Cleveland, Ohio, 1941.

Harrington, R. H.: "The Modern Metallurgy of Alloys," John Wiley & Sons, Inc., New York, 1948.

Heindlhofer, K.: "Evaluation of Residual Stresses," McGraw-Hill Book Company, Inc., New York, 1948.

Hessenbruch, Werner: "Metalle und Legierungen fuer Hohe Temperaturen," TI, 1, Verlag Julius Springer, Berlin, 1940.

Heyer, R. H.: "Engineering Physical Metallurgy," D. Van Nostrand Company, Inc., New York, 1939.

Houghton, E. F., and Company: "Practical Metallurgy for Engineers," 5th ed., Philadelphia, 1953.

Hughes, T. P.: "Metals and Plastics," Irwin-Farnham Publishing Company, Chicago, 1947.

Hume-Rothery, W.: "The Structure of Metals and Alloys," Institute of Metals, London, 1947.

———: "Atomic Theory for Students of Metallurgy," Institute of Metals, London, 1947.

Institute of Metals, "Symposium on Internal Stresses in Metals and Alloys," London, 1948.

Jeffries, Zay, and R. S. Archer: "The Science of Metals," McGraw-Hill Book Company, Inc., New York, 1924.

Johnson, C. G.: "Metallurgy," 3d ed., American Technical Society, Chicago, 1946.

Judge, A. W.: "Engineering Materials," Vols. I and II, 2d ed., Sir Isaac Pitman & Sons, Ltd., London, 1943.

———: "Aircraft Engines," Chapman & Hall, Ltd., London, 1945.

Leighou, R. B.: "Chemistry of Engineering Materials," 4th ed., McGraw-Hill Book Company, Inc., New York, 1942.

Masing, G.: "Handbuch der Metallphysik; unter Mitwirkung zahlreicher Fachgenossen," Akademische Verlagsgeschellschaft, Leipsig, 1935–1944.

Mason, Clyde: "Introductory Physical Metallurgy," American Society for Metals, Cleveland, Ohio, 1948.

McMullan, O. W., and A. M. Talbot: "Metallurgy," International Textbook Company, Scranton, Pa., 1936–1940.

Melbourne University: "The Failure of Metals by Fatigue," with a foreword by H. J. Gouch, Melbourne University Press, Melbourne, Australia, 1947.

Moore, H. F.: "Textbook of the Materials of Engineering," 7th ed., McGraw-Hill Book Company, Inc., New York, 1947.

Murphy, G.: "Properties of Engineering Materials," 2d ed., International Textbook Company, Scranton, Pa., 1947.
Rollason, E. C.: "Metallurgy for Engineers," Longmans, Green & Co., Inc., New York, 1939.
Roys, F. W.: "Materials of Engineering Construction," The Ronald Press Company, New York, 1930.
Sasso, John (editor): "Plastics Handbook for Product Engineers," McGraw-Hill Book Company, Inc., New York, 1946.
Seitz, F.: "The Physics of Metals," McGraw-Hill Book Company, Inc., New York, 1943.
Shrager, A. M.: "Elementary Metallurgy and Metallography," The Macmillan Company, New York, 1949.
Simonds, H. R.: "The New Plastics," D. Van Nostrand Company, Inc., New York, 1945.
Sisco, F. T.: "Modern Metallurgy for Engineers," 2d ed., Pitman Publishing Corp., New York, 1948.
Smith, G. V.: "Properties of Metals at Elevated Temperatures," McGraw-Hill Book Company, Inc., New York, 1950.
Society of Plastics Industry, Inc.: "SPI Handbook," New York, 1947.
Timoshenko, S.: "Strength of Materials," D. Van Nostrand Company, Inc., New York, 1930.
Vivian, A. C.: "Essential Metallurgy for Engineers: The Causes and Control of Metallic Properties," 2d ed., Sir Isaac Pitman & Sons, Ltd., London, 1945.
White, A. H.: "Engineering Materials," 2d ed., McGraw-Hill Book Company, Inc., New York, 1948.
Wilson, A. H.: "Semi-Conductors and Metals: An Introduction to the Electron Theory of Metals," Cambridge University Press, London, 1939.
———: "The Theory of Metals," The Macmillan Company, New York, 1937.
Withey, M. E., and James Aston: "Johnson's Materials of Construction," 6th ed., John Wiley & Sons, Inc., New York, 1939.
Young, J. F. (editor): "Materials and Processes," John Wiley & Sons, Inc., New York, 1944.

CHAPTER 3

THE SOURCES OF METALS

It is logical from one point of view that the study of metallurgy should begin with a consideration of how metals are obtained. Only in a few and relatively unimportant instances do metals occur in nature in metallic form, and even then they are mixed with many times as great an amount of nonmetallic material. For the most part, metals occur chemically combined with nonmetallic elements, such as oxygen or sulfur, and the compound is mixed with a great deal of earthy or rocky substance. The mixture constitutes an ore of the metal in question, and it is the purpose of this chapter to consider briefly the nature of ores and the general principles and kinds of processes involved in extracting the metal from the ore.

It has been pointed out in the Introduction that there are three divisions of metallurgy: chemical, mechanical, and physical. Chemical metallurgy is largely concerned with the processes of treating ores for extraction of the metal and with purifying (refining) the metal after it has been extracted. It may be called *extractive metallurgy* or *production metallurgy*. Mechanical and physical metallurgy deal with shaping and preparing the metal for use and study of the many factors involved therein, such as metallic properties and structures and the relations between them. The user of metals is more directly concerned with these latter two divisions, and accordingly the greater part of this book is devoted to them. Some knowledge of chemical metallurgy, however, is also important to the user. Metals are sold commercially in various grades and under standard specifications, with concomitant variation in quality and price. Intelligent selection and proper use require knowledge of compositional factors, and these depend on the processes used in extraction and refining, and go back ultimately to the nature of the ore itself. The technological relations between the producer and the user of metals are so interwoven that neither can afford to be ignorant of the field of the other.

Until recently it was believed that all matter is made up of combinations of one or more of 92 natural elements, although a few of these have not been found in nature, either free or chemically combined with other elements. The invention of the cyclotron and the investigation of nuclear energy have resulted in the artificial formation of three elements of the series of 92, and in addition four other artificially made elements have been produced by neutron or deuteron bombardment of uranium. Accordingly 96 elements are now known. One of the four elements derived from uranium, which have atomic numbers 93 to 96, is the metal plutonium (element 94). The properties of plutonium are being studied for possible applications other than in the atomic bomb or in utilization of nuclear energy as a source of power.

The elements may be classified as metals, nonmetals, and metalloids. About 39 of the elements are commercial metals, that is, metals that are being continually marketed for some practical use. Seven of the 39 account for more than 99.5 per cent of the total tonnage of metals used, and iron alone comprises about 93 per cent (see Table 8).

F. W. Clarke,[1] after assembling the data from thousands of complete analyses of the various kinds of rocks and estimating the amount of each kind present in the earth's crust, has calculated the average composition of the earth's crust as shown in Table 7.

TABLE 7. AVERAGE COMPOSITION OF KNOWN TERRESTRIAL MATTER

	Per cent		Per cent
Oxygen	46.46	Phosphorus	0.12
Silicon	27.61	Carbon	0.09
Aluminum	8.07	Manganese	0.09
Iron	5.06	Sulfur	0.06
Calcium	3.64	Chlorine	0.05
Sodium	2.75	Barium	0.04
Potassium	2.58	Fluorine	0.03
Magnesium	2.07	Strontium	0.02
Titanium	0.62	All other elements	0.50
Hydrogen	0.14		

An inspection of this table discloses the interesting fact that only 7 of the commercial metals are present in the earth's crust to the extent of 0.02 per cent or more; all the others are included with the 74 other elements which together make up but 0.50 per cent of the total. And of the 7 that do appear only 2—aluminum and iron—are metals used in large amounts.

The earth's crust to a depth of 10 miles would have a total weight of about 1.7×10^{19} tons. Thus even an extremely small fraction of 1 per cent would amount in the aggregate to an enormous quantity of material.

Such common metals as zinc, lead, and copper are not sufficiently abundant to appear in Table 7. However, they occur in the earth concentrated in relatively large amounts in certain places, so that great quantities of material containing fairly large percentages of these metals may be obtained. Thus it is not the total amount of the metal present

[1] F. W. Clarke, "Data of Geochemistry," *U.S. Geol. Survey Bull.* 770, 5th ed., 1924.

in the earth which is of practical importance, but rather the amount of it occurring in concentrated or enriched deposits, and the degree of concentration or enrichment.

Table 8 gives some figures which are instructive as regards occurrence, production, and value of the commoner metals. The interesting fact appears that the total value of iron considerably exceeds the total value of all the nonferrous metals combined. The nonferrous metals, however, taken together exhibit a greater range of properties and uses, and are steadily growing in importance.

TABLE 8. OCCURRENCE, PRODUCTION, AND VALUE OF THE COMMON METALS[1]

Metal	Estimated present average grade of ore as mined, per cent	World production, tons of 2,000 lb	Average price per pound avoirdupois	Total value of production[2]
Iron[3]	50	160,000,000	$ 0.024	$7,680,000,000
Copper	1.5	2,900,000	0.242	1,400,000,000
Zinc	5	2,400,000	0.180	860,000,000
Lead	7	1,800,000	0.175	630,000,000
Aluminum	30	1,800,000	0.190	680,000,000
Tin	2	185,000	1.27	470,000,000
Nickel	2	160,000	0.54	170,000,000
Silver	0.02	6,000	13.03	160,000,000
Gold	0.0002	1,070	510.30	1,090,000,000

[1] The purpose of this table is to indicate the comparative amounts and values of the principal metals in the world. The stated world production is the approximate tonnage in the year 1951. The stated price is the average New York price during that year.

[2] The stated total value is the product of the two preceding columns.

[3] The figures given are for pig iron, just as the figures for the other metals are for unmanufactured ingots. Corresponding figures for steel are world production, 225,000,000 tons; price per pound, $0.028 (for steel in the form of slabs and billets for rerolling); total value on the calculated basis, $12,600,000,000. This value would include the value of scrap used in steelmaking and the cost of rolling the billets.

ORES

Metals in nature are associated with other material in two ways—in chemical combination and in mechanical mixture.

The chemical combination of a metal with another element or elements constitutes a mineral. A *mineral* is defined as a chemical compound occurring in the earth.

Ore is defined as a mixture of minerals that may be mined with commercial profit. At least one of the minerals in the mixture is valuable; the remainder of the mixture—the worthless part of the ore—is called *gangue*. The gangue itself is composed of minerals, and the minerals composing it are metallic compounds, but not of such a kind or condition as to be of economic value. For example, consider a lead ore in which the lead mineral—the valuable part of the ore—is galena (PbS). This may perhaps amount to 5 to 10 per cent of the ore. The balance of 90 to 95 per cent is gangue—the valueless part of the ore. The gangue may be composed of SiO_2, $CaCO_3$, Al_2O_3, FeS_2, ZnS, etc. Some of these minerals are valuable when present in sufficient amounts, or under certain conditions, but in an ordinary lead ore they are present in small amounts or in such a way as simply to constitute part of the gangue. Many galena ores have silver associated with the lead (chiefly as Ag_2S), and if the silver is present in appreciable amount, the ore then contains two valuable minerals and would properly be called a silver-lead ore, or an argentiferous lead ore. The ore might also contain ZnS in an amount large enough to make profitable the separation of this constituent for recovery of zinc. The same ore might also contain Cu_2S in paying quantities. An ore that carries valuable amounts of two or more base metals is termed a *complex* ore.

There is no specific name given to a mixture of minerals that cannot be mined with commercial profit; it would simply be called rock or earth or some such term. To be called an *ore*, the material must be at least potentially a commercial source of metal. There are vast deposits in various parts of the world containing as much as 30 or 40 per cent iron that are not iron-ore deposits, because they could not be profitably mined at present. Many of these will undoubtedly sometime become deposits of ore, not through any change in themselves, but through the exhaustion of the higher-grade iron deposits, accompanied by an increase in the price of iron or some other economic or technological change that will render such deposits valuable as sources of iron.

The relations discussed above may be summarized as follows:

Metal = an element.
Metal + another element or elements = a mineral (chemical combination).
Mineral + gangue = ore (physical mixture).

These are merely relations; they are not to be construed as definitions.

Preliminary to the actual separation of the metal in metallic form—an operation which obviously involves chemical change—it is in the majority of cases profitable to perform a process of concentration, whereby the mineral constituents of the ore are separated into two or more products of which one is a waste product and at least one is to be treated further for recovery of metal. Concentration is essentially a mechanical process, although it is often assisted by a chemical alteration of the surfaces of ore particles.

Ore dressing and *mineral preparation* are terms given to this treatment of the ore prior to the metallurgical treatment which follows. If the ore as it is obtained from the earth contains relatively little gangue, concentration of this sort may not be profitable. It may then be better to proceed directly with the chemical operations. The cases in which concentration may be omitted are growing fewer as the richer ores are being used up and it becomes necessary to treat ores of lower and lower valuable metal content. The ores of most nonferrous metals are concentrated, and iron ores are being dressed more often than formerly.

The question of whether or not the step should be omitted with any particular ore is, of course, entirely one of the greatest ultimate net profit, as is, indeed, the entire selection of procedure in obtaining metallic products. Concentrating ore at the mine means saving of freight charges on the gangue that is separated; concentration prior to furnace treatment means a huge saving of fuel that would otherwise be used in heating and melting worthless material. Much less slag is formed in the furnace, and much less flux is required. Thus this step reduces the cost of subsequent handling and treatment, the question at issue being whether this saving is greater or less than the cost of the concentration plus the loss of some values which always occurs in concentration. Crushing and grinding of ore preparatory to concentration is often an expensive step.

Gravity Separation. One of the chief methods of concentration depends on the difference in specific gravity between the valuable mineral and the gangue. The ore is crushed sufficiently fine to break apart the mineral and gangue particles, and then, mixed with water, is fed to some form of apparatus—as a jig, classifier, table, etc.—which separates the heavier particles or concentrates from the lighter particles or tailings.

Flotation. The most important method of concentration now is the flotation process, in which the particles of valuable mineral, usually a sulfide mineral, are floated in a froth on the surface of water away from the particles of gangue, which do not float. This process constitutes an interesting inversion of the older method, in that the heavier particles rise to the top; in the early days many ore dressers did not believe it to be workable in practice. The floating of the heavy particles, which must first be crushed to $\frac{1}{100}$ in. or finer, is a phenomenon of surface tension, in which the attachment of the particles to bubbles of air causes them to rise in the cell in the form of a froth. Most flotation methods involve use of a certain amount of oil in the ore-water mixture, and other controlling reagents are commonly added. It is possible by the use of certain reagents to separate two or more valuable minerals from one another and from the gangue, thus recovering separately two or more valuable constituents from a complex ore. This process is called *selective* or *differential flotation*, and it affords a solution of some difficult problems in the profitable treatment of ores containing all or some combination of the metals iron, copper, lead, and zinc, usually with small amounts of gold and silver in addition.

Other Processes. A method of concentration applicable to magnetic minerals and particularly applicable to magnetic iron ore is that of magnetic separation—running the crushed ore on belts through the field of electromagnets, which attract the more magnetic mineral particles. There are also a number of minor processes of ore dressing which are based on other physical properties of minerals, and hand sorting of material in lump form is practiced to some extent.

METHODS OF ATTACKING ORES

Having obtained an ore or a concentrate of suitable richness, the metallurgist now takes up the problem of subjecting it to a process, essentially chemical in nature, in which the principal mineral will be decomposed into its elements, setting free the metal and at the same time separating it from the remainder of the gangue. There are three main divisions of chemical metallurgy. In the most important of these the chemical action is carried on by means of heat supplied by the burning of fuel, and the operation usually takes place in a furnace. This division is called *pyrometallurgy*. In the second of the three divisions the chemical action is carried on by means of electrical energy; this division is called *electrometallurgy*. The electrical energy may be used directly, as in electrolysis, or it may be used indirectly for its heating effect, as in electric furnaces.

Often, a chemical method of treatment may be followed which does not involve the use of a high temperature, but, instead, brings the ore in contact with a solution, such as dilute sulfuric acid, for example, which will dissolve the metal from the ore, forming a solution from which the metal may then be obtained in the metallic state. Such a process is sometimes called a "wet process," and constitutes a third division of chemical metallurgy known as *hydrometallurgy*. The operation of dissolving the metal from the ore is usually called *leaching*.

The term *chemical strength* when applied to a metal refers to its relative chemical activity and, specifically, to its position in a series in which the metals are arranged in order with respect to their chemical activities. The principle of so arranging the metals needs to be presented at this point, since it constitutes the key to an understanding of the chief processes of production and refining of metals. It is the most important fundamental precept of chemical metallurgy.

Two series of this kind are found most useful, one having an electrochemical and the other a thermochemical basis. Since both series represent measures of chemical activity, the order of the metals is much the same in each; but, since each is based on a different kind of measurement, there is some variation between the two. This may be seen by a comparison of Tables 9 and 10. Although the tables give actual values in

TABLE 9. ELECTROPOTENTIAL SERIES OF METALS

Metal	Ion[1]	Potential, volts[2]	Metal	Ion[1]	Potential, volts[2]
Potassium	K^+	−2.92	Nickel	Ni^{++}	−0.231
Calcium	Ca^{++}	−2.87	Tin	Sn^{++}	−0.136
Sodium	Na^+	−2.71	Lead	Pb^{++}	−0.122
Magnesium	Mg^{++}	−2.40	Hydrogen	H^+	0.000
Aluminum	Al^{+++}	−1.70	Antimony	Sb^{+++}	+0.100
Beryllium	Be^{++}	−1.13	Bismuth	Bi^{+++}	+0.226
Manganese	Mn^{++}	−1.10	Arsenic	As^{+++}	+0.300
Zinc	Zn^{++}	−0.762	Copper	Cu^{++}	+0.344
Chromium	Cr^{++}	−0.557	Silver	Ag^+	+0.798
Iron	Fe^{++}	−0.441	Mercury	Hg^{++}	+0.799
Cadmium	Cd^{++}	−0.401	Platinum	Pt^{++++}	+0.863
Cobalt	Co^{++}	−0.278	Gold	Au^{+++}	+1.360

[1] The symbol + indicates a positive ion having a valence equal to the number of the symbols.
[2] In normal ionic solution at 25°C.

volts and calories, respectively, it is the order of the metals in the series, rather than the values given, which is of most significance for the present purpose.

The first of these series is known as the *electropotential series* or *electromotive-force series* of metals. If a piece of metal is dipped into a solution of one of its salts, a difference of electric potential is set up between the metal and the solution. This potential difference can be measured and is used as the quantitative basis of the electropotential series. On a scale in which the potential for hydrogen is taken arbitrarily as zero, the chemically active or "strong" metals exhibit large negative potentials and the chemically "weak" metals have large positive potentials. Table 9 lists the metals in order of decreasing chemical strength. If a piece of iron is dipped into a solution of copper sulfate, the piece is seen at once to become coated with bright metallic copper. This action is due to the iron replacing the copper in the solution, iron dissolving and copper precipitating or plating out:

$$Fe + CuSO_4 = Cu + FeSO_4$$

In a similar manner any metal will replace in a solution of one of its salts any other metal below it in the electropotential series; the chemically stronger metal goes into solution, and the chemically weaker metal comes out. Among other things this series is of great importance in the study of corrosion (see Chap. 12).

<small>The actual value of the potential difference varies with several factors, especially the concentration of the solution and, to a lesser extent, the temperature. Consequently the values given in volts hold only for a given set of conditions; the standard concentration on which the table is based is that the solution in each case is a normal solution with respect to the amount of the metal ionized in solution, and the standard temperature is 25°C. At other temperatures the order of the metals may change slightly, and with wide differences in concentration, the values change greatly. As some of the metals ionize in solution with more than one valence, one column of the table shows for which ion the value is given; the common one of lower valence has been chosen as most significant for the purpose.</small>

A negative sign signifies that the metal is anodic with respect to hydrogen, a positive sign that it is cathodic. This convention with respect to the signs is used in the opposite sense in some books.

For the series of metals based on thermochemical data, shown in Table 10, the heat of formation of the oxide from the metal is used as the basis. When a unit weight of an element unites with the combining weight of oxygen to form the oxide, a certain amount of heat is liberated or "generated." Those metals high in the series—the chemically active or strong metals—liberate relatively large amounts of heat, and the chemically weak metals are low in the series and liberate relatively small amounts of heat. In order to make the figures comparable for the different elements, the heat liberated has been expressed in calories[1] per gram of oxygen in the oxide formed. Again the exact value will vary with the temperature at which the oxidation takes place; the figures given are for 18°C. Since in this case the temperature may vary over a range of many hundreds of degrees, the possible variation is considerable, and the position of a given element in the series may be somewhat different at an elevated temperature. Since the amount of heat absorbed when the oxide is reduced to metal is the same as the amount liberated when the oxide is formed, this series indicates the order of reducibility of the oxides (inversely), as well as the ease of oxidation of the metal.

---

[1] A calorie is $\frac{1}{860}$ of a watthour; it is approximately the quantity of heat required to raise the temperature of 1 g of water 1°C.

A more accurate indication of the order of reducibility of the oxides may be obtained from the free energy of the oxide formation instead of the heat of formation. Heats of formation are based on total energy change, whereas free-energy values properly take account of the fact that some of the energy is locked up in the products of the reaction, or is derived from the heat contents of the reacting substances. Free-energy

TABLE 10. HEATS OF FORMATION OF OXIDES
(Calories per gram of oxygen contained in the oxide)

Element	Oxide	Heat of formation[1]	Element	Oxide	Heat of formation[1]
Sodium	Na_2O	12,432	Tungsten	WO_3	4,077
Calcium	CaO	9,475	Cadmium	CdO	4,075
Magnesium	MgO	9,131	Iron	FeO	4,019
Lithium	Li_2O	8,875	Molybdenum	MoO_3	3,677
Beryllium	BeO	8,438	Nickel	NiO	3,613
Barium	BaO_2	8,312	Cobalt	CoO	3,600
Zirconium	ZrO_2	8,066	Antimony	Sb_2O_3	3,454
Aluminum	Al_2O_3	7,917	Lead	PbO	3,281
Cerium	CeO_2	7,294	Arsenic	As_2O_3	3,208
Vanadium	V_2O_3	6,944	Bismuth	Bi_2O_3	2,856
Titanium	TiO_2	6,813	Tellurium	TeO_2	2,423
Tantalum	Ta_2O_5	6,313	Copper	CuO	2,406
Silicon	SiO_2	6,281	Selenium	SeO_2	1,761
Uranium	UO_3	6,075	Mercury	HgO	1,356
Boron	B_2O_3	5,833	Palladium	PdO	1,344
Chromium	Cr_2O_3	5,688	Platinum	PtO	1,063
Manganese	MnO	5,406	Silver	Ag_2O	434
Zinc	ZnO	5,219	Iridium	IrO_2	156
Phosphorus	P_2O_5	4,586	Gold	Au_2O_3	−229
Tin	SnO_2	4,313			

[1] At 18°C.

data are not available for all compounds, and at present they are used mainly in precise calculations where account is taken of the effect of temperature. Further discussion of this principle must be omitted here for lack of space.

Pyrometallurgy

Pyrometallurgy is the oldest and most important of the three divisions of chemical metallurgy. In the broadest sense it includes all operations carried on at high temperature for the purpose of producing or refining metals, except when the necessary heat is obtained by the use of electricity.

The principal operations included in pyrometallurgy are those of drying, calcining, roasting, sintering, smelting, converting, reduction without fusion, refining by oxidation, and liquation. Some of these are concerned with preparing the ore (or concentrates) for extraction of the metal, some with the process of extraction, and some with purification (refining) of the crude metal after extraction.

Drying is simply the removal of moisture from the ore or other material, preparatory to further treatment.

Calcining is the heating of carbonates to expel CO_2 from them by decomposition into metal oxide and CO_2. Its most important application is the manufacture of lime (CaO) from limestone ($CaCO_3$), but it is sometimes applied in metallurgy to remove CO_2 from carbonate ores, for example,

$$FeCO_3 \rightarrow FeO + CO_2$$

It is a simple heating process without other chemical change than decomposition. The term is sometimes loosely applied to the operation of roasting, and it is not uncommon to refer to roasted ore as *calcines*.

Roasting in metallurgy is defined as heating with access of air. Thus it differs from calcining in that air is essential, and it is also basically different in being essentially a process of combination with oxygen, whereas calcining is simply a decomposition. The oxidation in roasting, however, usually does effect decomposition of a sulfide by removing sulfur from it, the sulfur passing off chiefly as sulfur dioxide (SO_2).

Removal of sulfur is usually the primary object of roasting, but the process may also remove other elements that form gaseous oxides, such as arsenic, antimony, and selenium. It may also be used to change the chemical form of one or more constituents of the ore without removing them, for example, changing them to oxides, sulfates, or chlorides (by addition of salt) in preparation for an extractive process to follow.

Sintering is the process of agglomeration of finely divided ore into lumps or caked material by heating. It occurs through a softening—an incipient fusion without actual melting—of the fine ore particles, causing them to stick together. The agglomerated product is called *sinter*. Sinter consists of porous masses of material of varying size and is in excellent condition for smelting. The sintering action may be the only object in view, but if sulfur is present, the sintering will be accompanied by oxidation of the sulfur and the double operation may be called roast-sintering.

Roasting, calcining, and sintering do not effect an actual separation of metal from ore; they are merely steps in preparation for some form of separating process which is to follow. The most important process of this kind is *smelting*, which may be defined as melting accompanied by chemical change. Usually more than one chemical reaction occurs, both the valuable mineral and the gangue of the ore undergoing a change. The valuable mineral is usually reduced to the elemental condition, *i.e.*, to metal. The gangue is caused to combine with another material in order to produce a substance that will melt at a sufficiently low temperature for practicable and economical furnace operation. The resulting combination constitutes the slag. The metal is separated from the ore in a molten state by means of the difference in specific gravity between the molten metal and the slag.

In general, natural gangues have melting points far above the temperatures that can be economically attained in the furnace; one form of pure silica, for example, melts at about 1625°C (2960°F); but by the addition of the proper amount of another substance, a compound of the desired low melting temperature may be obtained. A substance added in smelting to lower the melting point of the gangue is called a *flux*. The addition of flux is not basically a rule-of-thumb procedure; it is governed by well-defined principles. These principles, as well as the nature and functions of slags, are taken up in the section on Metallurgical Slags and Fluxes. For the present it will be sufficient to point out that the slag removes most of the undesired constituents of the ore, separating them from the metal, and that the slag is composed of the unreduced (chiefly oxide) constituents of the charge, while the reduced portions make up the metal. Thus, in an iron blast furnace the slag is composed chiefly of SiO_2 and CaO, while the metal—in this case pig iron—is composed chiefly of Fe, together with some carbon, silicon, and any other reduced elements. Any iron that escapes reduction passes off in the slag as FeO and is lost.

In smelting the ores of some metals, notably those of copper and nickel, the usual practice is to leave some sulfur in the ore when it goes to the smelting furnace. The metal will then combine or remain in combination with the sulfur, and the main product of the smelting operation will be a mixture of sulfides instead of metal. A mixture of sulfides formed in smelting is called *matte*. It requires further treatment to produce metal from it.

Having in mind the principles just stated, we may formulate the following principle of pyrometallurgy, which applies to the operations of smelting, converting, and refining: *All the reduced (metallic or sulfide) constituents enter the metal or matte; all the unreduced (oxidized) constituents enter the slag.* Usually the slag is lighter than the metal and floats on it.

In reducing smelting, which is the commonest type, the carbonaceous material may play a double role of fuel and reducing agent, part of the carbon being consumed by air and part by the oxides of the charge.

The products of the smelting furnace consist principally of four materials, as follows:

1. The metal or matte (in lead smelting, usually both). This is the main product, to obtain which the smelting operation was employed. In general, the "metal" here obtained is not in sufficiently pure form for commercial use, but requires refining. It is not surprising that the chemical reactions which occur during smelting are not confined to the desired metal alone and that a complete separation of one metal from all others cannot be obtained in the operation. When reducing smelting is employed, the metals are reduced in accordance with their position in the thermochemical series, the chemically weak metals first, in order, and the strong metals last. Thus in the iron blast furnace the metals below iron in the series are completely reduced along with the iron; while those just above are reduced in part, and those further above are not reduced at all. In the lead blast furnace the temperature is not so high and the gases are not so strongly reducing, so that no silicon or manganese and but little iron is reduced.

2. The slag. This contains the unreduced metals; it contains the gangue of the ore, made fusible by combination with the flux.

3. The gases. These consist largely of the products of combustion of the fuel, including nitrogen from the air used in burning the fuel and sometimes excess air. They may contain also oxides of sulfur and other elements from the ore, volatile constituents of the ore (including moisture), and CO_2 resulting from decomposition of limestone or other carbonates.

4. Flue dust and fume. Flue dust consists of fine particles of the charge carried out by the gases, and fume is composed of material which passes out of the furnace in the vapor state and condenses in the flue to solid or liquid particles.

In addition to these four, other minor products are sometimes found.

Converting is the name which has been applied in metallurgy to a process of oxidation in which the charge in the molten state is put into a particular type of furnace called a *converter* and air is blown through it under pressure, the necessary heat being generated by the oxidation, and fuel being entirely dispensed with. There are two important applications of converting in metallurgy. One is in converting pig iron into steel by the bessemer process, described in Chap. 13. The other is in converting copper matte into blister copper, described in Chap. 14. In the former the blast of air oxidizes the silicon, manganese, carbon, and sometimes the phosphorus of the pig iron. In the latter the air oxidizes principally the sulfur and iron of the matte. The oxidized elements are eliminated in the form of either slag or gases.

Refining in metallurgy is the removal of impurities from impure metal. The material at the start is crude metal, not ore, matte, or other compound. The product is metal purified for use, but not necessarily chemically pure metal. The degree of purity attained depends primarily on what specifications are demanded of the metal in commerce, and these, in turn, depend on what use is to be made of the metal, and how and to what degree the properties of the metal are affected by the various impurities. The effect, of course, varies enormously for different metals and for different impurities, both in kind of effect and in amount for a given percentage of impurity. The degree of purity aimed for in refining is also a question of cost: whether or not the cost of removing the impurities down to a given percentage is greater than the value added to the metal by such removal. An *impurity* may be defined as a foreign element or substance of undesirable effect. When the foreign substance is either beneficial or harmless, it may be regarded rather as an alloying element or its presence may be practically disregarded. Thus small amounts of silver in refined copper, of manganese in steel, and of cobalt in nickel are not ordinarily regarded as impurities, though larger amounts of these elements might be so regarded.

The chief methods of refining metals, in relative order of importance, are the following:

1. Furnace refining by oxidation.
2. Electrolytic refining.
3. Refining by means of a chemical reagent.
4. Refining by liquation.
5. Refining by distillation.

In furnace refining the impure metal is melted and subjected to oxidation by simply allowing air to pass over the molten bath, or by blowing air into it, or by adding an oxidizing agent. The oxidation is a selective action depending on the order of the elements in the thermochemical series of metals. The chemically stronger metals will oxidize first, followed by the weaker in descending order. The oxidized metals rise to the top of the bath and become components of the slag, being thus effectively separated. It will be noted that the action is just the reverse of what occurs in reducing smelting. There small amounts of elements higher in the series were reduced in amounts decreasing with higher position; here small amounts of elements previously reduced are reoxidized in order, starting with those in the highest position.

Next in importance as a method of refining is refining by electrolysis; as this involves the use of electricity, it falls under the division of electrometallurgy. It is discussed in that section (page 60).

An impure metal may be refined by treating the molten metal with some reagent that will combine with impurities and so remove them, without combining with the metal itself. Such, for example, is the use of Fe_2O_3 to accomplish oxidation of impurities in the open-hearth steel furnace. Other chemical reagents used in refining include fluorspar (CaF_2), soda or soda ash (Na_2CO_3), niter ($NaNO_3$), and lime (CaO). When the impurities removed enter the slag, it is obvious that such use of a chemical reagent is closely related to "fluxing,"[1] and the reagent itself may really be a flux. Examples of refining by a chemical reagent quite different from fluxing are the use of chlorine gas to remove impurities as chlorides and the addition of zinc to alloy with silver and separate it from lead.

Liquation is defined as the process of separating a fusible substance from one less fusible, by means of a temperature sufficient to melt one and not the other. The example just given of the use of zinc as a chemical refining agent involves also an example of liquation, since the alloy formed by the zinc is less fusible than the remaining purified lead; solidifying slowly, it rises to the top of the bath and is skimmed off.

Distillation is changing a substance from the liquid to the vapor state by heating. *Sublimation* is vaporization directly from the solid state. These processes are used both as means of separating metals from their ores and also as methods of refining. In the extractive process the ore is heated to a temperature at which the metal or some compound of the metal will vaporize and thus separate from the gangue. In the case of most metals obtained in this way, the ore must be mixed with coal or some other reducing agent, reduction of the metal oxide occurring at a temperature above that required for vaporization of the metal. Distillation is regularly applied in the production of zinc and mercury, and sometimes for magnesium and other relatively volatile metals. A retort furnace is often used, and a condenser is attached to the retort, since the vapor must be condensed to recover the metal. Sometimes the oxide of the metal is vaporized and condensed to the solid state, as with antimony and arsenic.

In refining by distillation, the metal to be purified is usually vaporized and condensed, leaving the impurities behind. Sometimes the impurity is vaporized, if it is more volatile than the desired metal.

Reduction without Fusion. Metals having very high melting points may be produced in powder form by reduction of the oxide of the metal with hydrogen. The oxide is first extracted from the ore and purified. The metal powder may be consolidated to a dense ingot or rod by combined sintering and pressing.

The oxides of chemically strong metals require high temperatures for reduction. In this case it is sometimes desirable to employ another chemically strong metal as the reducing agent instead of carbon or

[1] See p. 54.

hydrogen. Metals may be obtained in this way either with or without fusion. Manganese and chromium may be reduced from their oxides with silicon, the process being carried on in electric furnaces. Titanium is obtained by reducing its chloride with molten magnesium. The titanium is produced in solid spongy form.

Metallurgical Slags and Fluxes. *Functions of Slag.* Slag is essentially composed of a mixture of metal oxides. In smelting, the main function of the slag is to take up the gangue or worthless part of the ore; in refining, the main function of the slag is to take up the impurities. Another function of the slag, chiefly employed in refining, is to act as a carrier of oxygen to the bath of metal, thus assisting in the refining action.

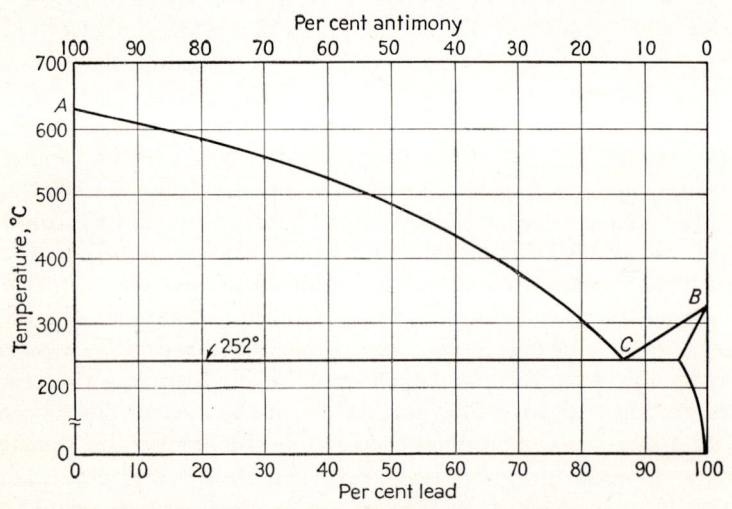

Fig. 12. The antimony-lead constitution diagram.

This the slag can do when it contains a *higher* oxide which easily becomes a *lower* oxide by liberating a portion of its oxygen, as, for example:

$$Fe_2O_3 = 2FeO + O$$

Still another function of slag is to act as a protective covering to the metal, protecting it from becoming either overheated or adversely affected by the furnace gases.

Fluxing. Since slags must be liquid at the temperature of the furnace, their melting points are a matter of great importance. The melting temperature of a single metallic oxide is usually high, and the common earthy oxides which make up the usual gangue, such as SiO_2, CaO, Al_2O_3, or FeO, if taken singly, have melting points far higher than can readily be attained in a furnace. A combination of two such substances, provided no chemical compound is formed between them, has a lower melting

THE SOURCES OF METALS

temperature than that of one of the substances alone; stated in another way, it may be said, in general, that the addition of one substance to another results in a lowering of melting temperature. In alloying, for example, the addition of one metal to another often results in a combination having a lower melting point than that of the original metal. Further additions of the second metal, up to a certain definite point, result in further lowering of the melting point, as illustrated for antimony and lead in Fig. 12. Discussion and examples of this principle are given in Chap. 7. The same principle applies to the addition of oxides to each other, though the situation is complicated through formation of chemical compounds between the oxides. In Fig. 13 is shown the curve

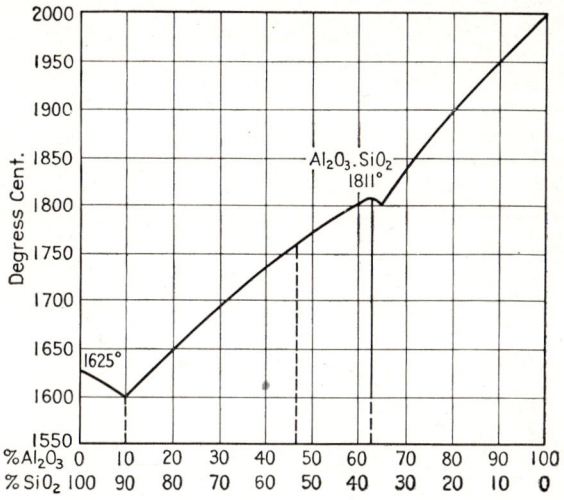

Fig. 13. The silica-alumina (SiO_2-Al_2O_3) constitution diagram.

of freezing temperatures of the series SiO_2-Al_2O_3. The diagram shows that, while SiO_2 requires a temperature of 1625°C (2960°F) to melt it and Al_2O_3 requires 2000°C (3630°F), a mixture of 90 per cent SiO_2 with 10 per cent Al_2O_3 requires only 1600°C (2910°F).

The addition of a third substance to a combination of two others results in a further lowering of the freezing point. Thus if CaO is added to Al_2O_3 and SiO_2, the freezing point may be as low as 1165°C (2130°F). The following list gives the most commonly used fluxes, classified according to their chemical character. Since most gangues are siliceous, the basic fluxes are most used.

Commercial Fluxes

Acid: Silica (SiO_2).
Basic: Lime (CaO) or limestone ($CaCO_3$), iron oxide (Fe_2O_3 or Fe_3O_4), dolomite ($CaCO_3 + MgCO_3$), soda or soda ash (Na_2CO_3), niter ($NaNO_3$).
Neutral: Fluorspar (CaF_2), borax ($Na_2B_4O_7$).

When a flux is used in refining, it may serve the double purpose of producing a fusible slag and supplying oxygen to assist in the refining. It is then a combined flux and oxidizing agent. Examples of materials often used in this way are Fe_2O_3 and $NaNO_3$.

Typical Slag Compositions. Table 11 shows typical compositions of various slags as regards their chief constituents.

TABLE 11. TYPICAL SLAG COMPOSITIONS
(In per cent)

Source of slag	SiO_2	CaO	FeO	Al_2O_3	Balance
Iron blast furnace	45	30	1	10	14
Lead blast furnace	30	15	30	10	15
Reverberatory copper smelting	35	2	48	7	8
Basic open-hearth steel furnace	12	40	18	4	26
Acid open-hearth steel furnace	57	5	25	4	9

These figures are to be taken as illustrative; they are not at all fixed and may vary considerably.

It should be emphasized that slags as a whole are not definite chemical compounds; no single chemical formulas can be assigned to them; they are indefinite solutions of several compounds. When molten, the compounds forming them probably dissociate into ions just as do the compounds in aqueous solutions.

Hydrometallurgy

The methods of treating ores and recovering metals so far outlined in this book are carried out at high temperatures. Wet processes, usually performed at ordinary temperatures, are also very important. These are essentially adaptations of the chemical methods of the analytical laboratory to large-scale work, the performing of such operations as dissolving, washing, filtering, and precipitation with tons of material instead of with fractions of a gram or a few milliliters of solution.

There are many large hydrometallurgical plants, one of which is producing 250,000 tons of copper per year. Most of our gold and nearly half of our zinc are obtained by wet methods, and there are a number of applications to other metals.

Hydrometallurgy is particularly applicable in two cases, namely, for large-scale operations and for ores of low grade, *i.e.*, where the ore contains a relatively small amount of the valuable metal. In this kind of process, fuel and flux—two expensive materials—are not needed. Instead a dissolving liquid is used, usually a cheap acid, most of which is often recovered or regenerated for use over and over again. The ease with which the solvent may be applied to large quantities of ore and the fact that it penetrates all parts of it often renders concentration unnecessary. In order to avoid high transportation costs, hydrometallurgy is usually carried on at the mines. Expensive refractory materials such as are needed for furnace construction are also avoided, but often a considerable variety of apparatus is needed in large units. Large amounts of water, both for the leaching solution and for washing, must be available at low cost. The percentage of the metal in the ore that is actually recovered is usually high, though not always higher than in a smelting process on the same ore. If the metal is precipitated from the leaching solution by electrolysis, no refining is necessary. All these points and others must be considered in relation to the character of the ore, the place where it occurs, the market for the metal, possible recovery of valuable by-products, etc., in selecting the best process of ore treatment.

A hydrometallurgical process may include the following steps:

1. Crushing the ore to suitable size (not always necessary).
2. Roasting to convert the desired mineral to a soluble form or to render undesired constituents inactive (not necessary for most ores).
3. Leaching the ore with a suitable solvent.
4. Washing the leached ore.
5. Clarifying the solution by some form of settling or filtering or both.
6. Precipitating the desired metal from the solution.
7. Melting the metal and converting it to a marketable form.

The two principal methods of leaching are *percolation*, in which the solvent is simply allowed to flow on and through the mass of ore, and *agitation*, involving intimate mixing and stirring of the ore in the solvent.

Precipitation of the metal from the solution may be done either electrolytically or by chemical replacement. The former method is better when the cost is not too great, because it yields a purer product. It is best adapted to large installations. The electrolytic deposition may yield directly a product of the same high quality as electrolytic refining of the metal. Frequently, however, a chemical precipitant is used on account of cheapness and simplicity. A common method is replacement in solution by another metal (called *cementation*), in accordance with the principle that a metal will be replaced in solution by another metal that is above it in the electropotential series. Thus, a copper sulfate solution may be passed over scrap iron, the iron going into solution and the copper precipitating out:

$$CuSO_4 + Fe = FeSO_4 + Cu$$

The copper so obtained is impure and must be refined before it is ready for the market.

Electrometallurgy

Electrometallurgy includes all metallurgical operations carried on by the use of electric current. It has two main divisions: (1) that in which the current is used for its electrolytic effect, and (2) that in which the current is used for its heating effect only. The first of these main divisions has in turn two subdivisions: (*a*) electrolysis of aqueous solutions, carried on at temperatures below the boiling point of water; and (*b*) electrolysis of fused salts, carried on at high temperatures.

Class *a* includes electrolytic refining of impure metals, electrolytic recovery of metals from solutions obtained in leaching processes, and electroplating. The importance of the electrolytic processes in metallurgy is realized when it is noted that nearly all our copper is electrolytically refined or electrolytically precipitated from leaching solutions and all our aluminum is obtained by electrolysis of a molten bath. In the latter type of process, *i.e.*, class *b*, both the electrolytic effect and the heating effect of the current are utilized; the cells in which the process takes place are sometimes called *electrolytic furnaces*, distinguishing them from *electric* or *electrothermic furnaces*, which are those used in division 2 above.

Division 2 embraces all processes carried out in electric furnaces, whether it be smelting or refining or simple melting or heat-treatment—all processes where electric power is substituted for fuel as the direct source of heat.

Electrolytic Processes. When direct current is passed through a conducting liquid, chemical decomposition of the liquid occurs. It is natural that great use of this fact should be made in metallurgy.

Electrolysis is the chemical decomposition accompanying the passage of electric current through a solution or a fused salt. According to convention the terminology of an electrolytic cell is based on flow of positive current, opposite in direction to the flow of electrons. The pole *from* which the positive current flows is given the positive sign, and the pole *to* which the positive current flows is given the negative sign. The positive current enters the electrolytic cell through the pole called the *anode*, and leaves the cell through the other pole called the *cathode*.

The conducting liquid between anode and cathode is called the *electrolyte*. The electrolyte must contain a compound that separates ("dissociates") into charged particles called *ions*. The ions carrying positive charges are called *cations*, because they are attracted to the (negative) cathode. The ions carrying negative charges are called *anions*, because they are attracted to the (positive) anode. Metals are cations; nonmetals are anions. In a typical metallurgical process, the cathode receives the deposit of metal. The anode may or may not dissolve in the electrolyte, depending on its ability to form soluble ions.

Electrolysis therefore results in liberation of metallic ions (including hydrogen) at the cathode and nonmetallic ions at the anode. The ions give up their electric charges at the electrodes and either may be liberated as elements or may react chemically with other substances present. The former case results in deposition of metal on the cathode. The metal is not necessarily pure, as it is possible to deposit more than one kind of ion at a time; mechanical contamination may also occur. Through proper control, however, nearly pure deposits may usually be obtained.

Electrolysis is governed quantitatively by two laws discovered by Faraday in 1833. From the first law of Faraday it follows that the amount of metal liberated in a given time is proportional to the current flowing. The amount is not related to the voltage, except in so far as the voltage affects the current. The second law tells us how the amount of metal liberated may be easily calculated; according to this law the amounts of metals (or other substances) liberated by a given current are proportional to their chemical equivalents. A chemical equivalent of a metal is equal to its atomic weight divided by its valence, and, specifically, 96,500 amp-sec of electricity will liberate one chemical equivalent in grams of any substance. A chemical equivalent of copper in $CuSO_4$ would be 63.6/2, or 31.8 g. Thus, for example, 1,000 amp flowing for 1 hr would liberate

$$\frac{1{,}000 \times 60 \times 60 \times 31.8}{96{,}500} = 1{,}186 \text{ g of copper (about 2.6 lb)}$$

The amount of a given metal actually deposited as such may be much less than the amount liberated because some of the metal may be lost after liberation by entering into a secondary chemical reaction or otherwise, and also part of the current may be liberating the ion of another metal, or hydrogen. The ratio of the amount of a given substance actually deposited and recovered to the amount liberated in accordance with Faraday's laws is the *current efficiency*.

Electrolysis of Molten Salts. This is an important method of metal production, one of the principal metals, aluminum, being produced exclusively by electrolyzing a fused bath (electrolyte) in which aluminum oxide is dissolved. Other metals made by this method include magnesium, sodium, calcium, barium, lithium, cerium and other rare-earth metals, and sometimes beryllium. As a class they comprise the metals so high in their affinities for oxygen that they cannot be reduced practicably from the oxide or other compound form in fuel-fired furnaces and, likewise, cannot be electrodeposited from aqueous solutions because they would be reoxidized by reaction with the water. Aluminum, for example, reacts thus when attempt is made to deposit it from an aqueous electrolyte:

$$Al + 3H_2O = Al(OH)_3 + 3H$$

These metals can be reduced by carbon at very high temperature, such as that obtained in an electric-arc furnace, but will be formed as vapor instead of liquid, and at the high temperature necessary, difficulties are encountered in condensing the vapor, in preventing reoxidation of the metal, and because of combination of the metal with carbon to form a carbide.

In electrolysis it is usual to dissolve the compound of the desired metal in a salt of another metal even higher in the electropotential series, *e.g.*, Al_2O_3 in cryolite (Na_3AlF_6) and $MgCl_2$ in $NaCl$. By this means the melting point of the bath and therefore the operating temperature is made lower, and the solvent compound is not reduced at the cathode. The current has the dual function of electrolysis and supplying the heat necessary to keep the bath molten; usually no external heating is required. The metal in most cases collects in a liquid pool in the cell, either at the bottom if the metal is heavier than the electrolyte or at the top if it is lighter. Very high current densities are employed. The anodes are insoluble, commonly made of carbon, while the steel pot or tank itself, or the carbon with which it is lined, is the cathode.

Electrolytic Refining. In refining by electrolysis the impure metal is used as anode, while the electrolyte is a solution of a salt of the desired metal, and the purified metal deposits out at the cathode. The impure metal is first melted and cast into plates of suitable size and shape to serve as anodes when suspended in the electrolytic tanks. This melting and casting operation is frequently made the occasion of a preliminary (partial) furnace refining. To serve as cathodes and receive the deposit of pure metal there are usually hung in the tanks, alternating with the anodes, thin metallic sheets from which the pure metal deposit may be removed, or else these "starting sheets" may be composed of the desired metal itself, in which case no removal or separation is necessary. When the deposit of pure metal adheres firmly to the cathode sheets of some other metal, the pure deposit is stripped off after it has plated out to a suitable thickness. With some metals, however, the deposit is one of coarse nonadhering crystals, which simply drop off or are scraped off and collected from the bottom of the tank. The action of the electric current consists of entering the electrolyte from the anode, causing the electrolyte to be decomposed, and passing out through the cathode, resulting in the passage of charged particles of metal (*i.e.*, metallic ions) to the cathode, where they give up their (positive) charges and are liberated, forming crystals of metal, and the simultaneous passage of nonmetallic ions to the anode, where they give up their (negative) charges and combine with particles of metal from the anode, thus regenerating the electrolyte. A specific example will make the process clear.

In copper refining the electrolyte is (essentially) of copper sulfate, which ionizes thus:

$$CuSO_4 = Cu^{++} + SO_4^{--}$$

The Cu^{++} ions are liberated at the cathode as pure copper; the SO_4^{--} ions combine with copper from the anode, re-forming $CuSO_4$.

Electrolytic refining is practiced in preference to furnace refining chiefly in two cases: (1) when it results in the recovery of valuable by-products that could not be recovered in the furnace, *e.g.*, gold and silver in copper refining; (2) when there is a demand for metal of greater purity than can ordinarily be obtained in furnace refining. When the additional profit resulting from one or a combination of both of the above circumstances is sufficient to outweigh the (usually) greater cost of electrolytic refining, this method is used. The principal metals sometimes refined electrolytically are copper, gold, silver, nickel, and lead; applications of less importance are made to aluminum, bismuth, cadmium, iron, and other metals.

Electrolytic Precipitation. This process of recovering metals from solutions obtained in leaching is sometimes called *electrowinning*. The two principal metals produced in this way are copper and zinc. Other applications of this method are in the production of manganese, nickel, iron, and lead, and in the recovery of tin from tin-plate scrap.

Electroplating. Electroplating is the deposition by electrolysis of a coating of metal on an object. The purpose of it is usually (1) protection against corrosion or (2) for attractive appearance. The plating is nearly always done with a metal costlier than the metal underneath, so that the plated object may serve as a substitute for an object made solidly of the more expensive material. Such substitution can be made where the conditions of use are determined by the character of the surface rather than of the object as a whole. Sometimes also, as in plating iron or steel for protection against corrosion, it may be necessary to have the main body constructed of a material with a certain strength or other property, but with the surface of a material with a different property. The principal metals used for electroplating, in approximate order of statistical importance, are nickel, silver, chromium, copper, zinc, gold, cadmium, tin, iron, lead, cobalt, platinum, rhodium, indium. The alloy brass is used extensively in electroplating, and other alloys are sometimes used. The hardness of nickel and chromium and their retention of a bright luster make them well suited for both of the purposes mentioned above.

For some purposes a metal may be electrodeposited on a form or mold with the object of making an article of a desired shape or reproducing the shape of another article. This process includes *electrotyping*, and is often called *electroforming*. The negative cast or mold is usually made of wax brushed over with graphite to make it conducting. Master phonograph records are made in this way. The metal most often used for the plating is copper, nickel, chromium, or zinc.

Primary and Storage Cells. Production of electric energy by electrolysis in electrogenetic cells is of particular interest to the metallurgist. In dry cells zinc in sheet form usually serves the dual purpose of anode and container. In storage batteries the active material in the commonest type is lead compounds and the framework of the plates is an antimony-lead alloy. Storage batteries constitute the largest single use both of lead and of antimony.

Electrothermic Processes. Electrothermic processes are those in which electric energy is converted into heat, the current having no other function than to supply the heat required for the process. Important applications are in the production of ferroalloys and calcium carbide by smelting; melting and refining steel; melting iron for iron foundries; melting or making brass, bronze, nickel-base, and other alloys; melting copper cathodes after electrolytic refining; heating metals and alloys in heat-treatment processes for hardening, annealing, tempering, etc. Minor amounts of pig iron and of zinc are produced in electric smelting furnaces.

Electric smelting is practiced where the temperature obtained from fuel combustion is not high enough to accomplish reduction, as is the case with ores of the chemically strong metals; also in localities where fuels are scarce and electric power is relatively cheap, such as in Sweden, Norway, northern Italy, and parts of Japan. Ferrochromium, ferrovanadium, ferrotungsten, and other ferroalloys are made exclusively in electric furnaces, as well as are most of our ferromanganese and ferrosilicon. Two considerations often lead to electric melting of iron and steel for casting: (1) a product can be had which is lower in sulfur, oxygen, and nonmetallic inclusions; and (2) the composition of the product and the temperature can be adjusted within close limits. The possibilities of high temperatures in electric furnaces sometimes lead manufacturers to heat steel for castings to such a high point that its quality suffers. When induction furnaces are used for melting steel and nonferrous alloys, the advantages over melting in combustion furnaces rest chiefly on the lesser oxidation of the metal, uniformity in composition and temperature of the bath due to stirring and circulation through electromagnetic currents, cleanliness, and convenience.

Electric heating of steel and other alloys for heat-treatment is advantageous when it is desired to maintain the metal at a certain temperature for some time and when much surface oxidation is to be avoided. In the annealing, hardening, or tempering of steel, especially high-speed and other alloy steels, the best results are obtainable when the temperature is raised at a predetermined rate and is brought to a definite point with exactness. This may also be true in annealing of brass and other nonferrous alloys.

Refining also is often done in electric furnaces. Since there are no gases resulting from the combustion of fuel in the furnace, and air may be excluded, the atmosphere surrounding the charge may be controlled and the charge held for some time without oxidation or absorption of impurities. Thus the action of some particular refining agent can be made effective and a better product obtained. The production of electric steel is the most important example of a process of this kind.

Electric energy may be converted into heat through the medium of an arc, or by means of resistance. In heating by resistance, the flow of current may be obtained by direct connection to the source or by induction. These methods give rise to three types of electric furnaces: arc, resistance, and induction. These are described and explained in Chap. 15.

Bibliography

ALLMAND, A. J., and H. J. T. ELLINGHAM: "The Principles of Applied Electrochemistry," 2d ed., Edward Arnold & Co., London, 1924.

ANON.: "Modern Electroplating," The Electrochemical Society, Inc., New York, 1942.

BLUM, W., and G. B. HOGABOOM: "Principles of Electroplating and Electroforming," 3d ed., McGraw-Hill Book Company, Inc., New York, 1949.

DOLBEAR, S. H. (editor): "Industrial Minerals and Rocks," 2d ed., American Institute of Mining and Metallurgical Engineers, New York, 1949.

FIELD, S., and A. D. WEILL: "Electroplating," 5th ed., Sir Isaac Pitman & Sons, Ltd., London, 1945.

GAUDIN, A. M.: "Principles of Mineral Dressing," McGraw-Hill Book Company, Inc., New York, 1939.

KOEHLER, W. A.: "Electrochemistry—Applications," 2d ed., Vol. II, John Wiley & Sons, Inc., New York, 1944.

LEWIS, G. N., and M. RANDALL: "Thermodynamics and the Free Energy of Chemical Substances," McGraw-Hill Book Company, Inc., New York, 1923.

LIDDELL, D. M. (editor): "Handbook of Non-ferrous Metallurgy, 2d ed., Vol. I, "Principles and Processes," McGraw-Hill Book Company, Inc., New York, 1945.

MANTELL, C. L.: "Industrial Electrochemistry," 3d ed., McGraw-Hill Book Company, Inc., New York, 1950.

RICHARDS, R. H., and C. E. LOCKE: "Textbook of Ore Dressing," 3d ed., McGraw-Hill Book Company, Inc., New York, 1940.

SCHUHMANN, R., JR.: "Metallurgical Engineering," Addison-Wesley Press, Inc., Cambridge, Mass., 1952.

SILMAN, H.: "Chemical and Electroplated Finishes," Chapman & Hall, Ltd., London; The Sherwood Press, Pacoima, Calif., 1949.

TAGGART, A. F.: "Elements of Ore Dressing," John Wiley & Sons, Inc., New York, 1951.

———: "Handbook of Mineral Dressing," Vol. I, John Wiley & Sons, Inc., New York, 1945.

THOMPSON, M. DEK.: "Theoretical and Applied Electrochemistry," 3d ed., The Macmillan Company, New York, 1939.

WERNICK, S.: "Electrolytic Polishing and Bright Plating of Metals," Alvin Redman, Ltd., London, 1948.

WOLDMAN, N. W.: "Metal Process Engineering," Reinhold Publishing Corporation, New York, 1948.

CHAPTER 4

SIZING AND SHAPING METALLIC BODIES

As pointed out in Chap. 1, the art of extracting metals from their ores and refining is chemical metallurgy; bringing them to the proper size and shape by mechanical processes is mechanical metallurgy; and adapting and adjusting their physical and mechanical properties is physical metallurgy. A good illustration of the threefold nature of the metallurgist's art is the old process of making a permanent magnet, as follows: First, iron was extracted from its ore and brought to a good degree of purity; then it was compounded with carbon, and sometimes also with tungsten, chromium, or cobalt. These operations are classed as chemical metallurgy. Next the steel was brought to the desired size and shape by some mechanical process, such as casting and then forging or rolling. Finally, it was given a high degree of magnetic permanence by heating to a yellow heat and cooling rapidly, as by quenching in water, and then by treatment in a magnetic field. There is some overlapping between these three classes of metallurgical practice, because the carbon, etc., added to iron limits the types of mechanical work which can be performed on it, and also vitally affects its physical properties; also, the mechanical operations knead and work the metallic crystals into different sizes and shapes (or crush them into smaller fragments), thus increasing the strength and altering other characteristics of the body.

Means of Producing or Adjusting Physical and Mechanical Properties. The properties of metals can be adjusted or changed by chemical, mechanical, or physical processes. The chemical processes consist in mixing metals to form alloys, or in adding more or less of various ingredients to the metals or alloys to produce special characteristics. For example, carbon added to pure iron strengthens it and produces what is called steel; the removal of arsenic from copper, in which it is a common impurity, greatly increases the electrical conductivity of the copper. Besides chemical influences the means of changing properties are divided into two classes, *viz.*, those which belong in the domain of general physics, such as rapid or slow cooling, retention of allotropic modifications, etc.; and those which are of a mechanical nature, *viz.*, the treatment of the metal by rolling, forging, etc. This chapter will discuss especially mechanical treatment and its effect on properties; the chemical adjustment of properties and the adjustment of properties by heat-treatment will be considered in detail in later chapters.

In this chapter, and in many other instances throughout this book, where metals are spoken of it is the intention to include alloys, for in general they obey the same laws as regards mechanical treatment.

Types of Mechanical Processes on Metals. Metals can be shaped by the following different methods:

1. Shaping while liquid, as by pouring into a mold, or by forming liquid metal.

2. Shaping while pasty, or semiliquid, such as forcing through a die when just on the point of freezing. The metal enters the die in liquid condition and comes out practically solid.

3. Shaping while hot and plastic, such as rolling, forging, or extrusion at high temperature.

4. Shaping while cold, such as rolling or drawing at atmospheric temperature.

5. Shaping by fastening pieces together, as in welding.

6. Shaping by cutting, as in machining and flame cutting.

7. Shaping from powders by hot or cold pressing and sintering, such as in making tungsten carbide tools.

In addition to the illustrations of methods of shaping given in this chapter, some are shown in Figs. 151 to 154. Welding and flame cutting are discussed in Chap. 5.

SHAPING WHILE LIQUID

Ordinary Casting or Founding. Almost all metals and alloys are shaped on occasion by founding or casting. This includes especially cast iron, steel, brass, bronze, lead, gold, silver, zinc alloys, aluminum alloys, and magnesium alloys. For cast iron, steel, brass, and other metals which melt at a high temperature, the mold is usually made of sand (see Fig. 14).

Foundry Operations. The founding of metallic bodies usually involves making a pattern of wood or metal, embedding this in sand to produce the desired mold, withdrawing the pattern from the mold, and pouring in liquid metal. One pattern will make a great many molds, but the mold is destroyed each time a casting is removed from the sand. Many efforts have been made to find a sand mold which will withstand several casting operations, and some progress has been made.

Design of Patterns for Castings. In designing structures or machines, engineers often design the castings in just the shape most convenient for fabrication or erection, without due regard to the effects such shape might have on the price or properties of the castings. Badly designed castings cost more, because they cost more to make and result in more defective castings. Of even more importance to the engineer is the fact that badly designed castings may contain invisible defects, such as porous spots, weak spots in the interior, segregation, and cracks, especially in the corners. If a casting must be designed with heavy and light sections in conjunction, such as a pulley, it will often be found that the spoke has

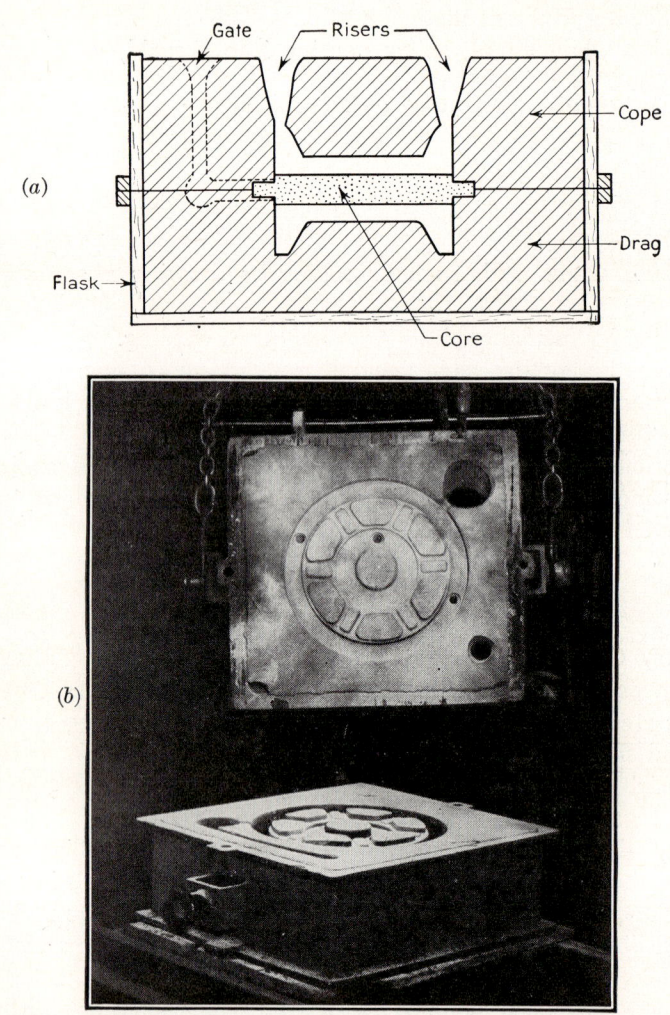

FIG. 14(a). Cross section of sand mold for casting. (b). Photograph of sand mold for casting.

torn itself in two in cooling or has developed microscopic cracks, especially where it joins the face. Also, the point of junction of the heavy with the light section will doubtless contain a spot of lower density in the interior, which may even amount to sponginess or porosity. All heavy sections will have spongy spots in the last portion of the metal to freeze, and there will be a tendency for segregation to show at that point, unless the casting is so designed that the heavy sections may be "fed" with a reservoir of liquid metal. Long portions, in shrinking, will tend to crush the sand, provided that they have arms, or projections, at the end. In such an event, the metal may give way before the sand, because it is weak at high temperatures.

Centrifugal Casting. Many cylindrical shapes are made commercially by pouring liquid metal into a permanent mold consisting of a rapidly rotating metal cylinder which may be lined with sand. Examples are cast-iron pipe; hollow projectiles and other ordnance such as gun tubes; stainless and heat-resisting steels for tubing and pipe, which are difficult to pierce and roll by conventional methods; aircraft cylinder barrels; bronze cylinder linings or rolls; copper slip rings; and squirrel-cage rotors. Centrifugal force carries the metal to the inner periphery of the cylinder and produces a hollow casting, which can be removed from the mold after it has solidified and shrunk. The centrifugal force under which the metal is frozen increases the density and strength of the metal.

Permanent-mold Casting. In another process, the metals and alloys which melt at low temperatures, such as lead, aluminum, or magnesium, are cast in permanent iron or steel molds. These molds are built in two or more parts, so that the casting can be removed after solidification.

Liquid Shaping. Some alloys cannot be shaped except while liquid. For example, cast iron cannot be forced through a die while pasty, because it is too "mushy"; it cannot be rolled at any temperature, because it will break apart instead of yielding plastically. Antimony behaves in a similar manner so far as rolling is concerned, and so do some of the alloys used for small cast parts, such as aluminum-silicon alloys. Another reason for casting is a very large size of object. For example, one can readily understand that the bedplate of an engine, weighing 100 tons or more, could not be forged or rolled in any apparatus of economical size. Another example is a complicated shape which does not permit shaping by pressure. Car wheels can be rolled in a specially designed mill which brings several rolls into action at one time, and crankshafts can be hammered out in dies, for which see Figs. 15 and 16, and page 76, but a spur gear or an eight-cylinder gas engine obviously could not be rolled or economically forged to shape. Finally, there is the question of relative cost, and this depends chiefly on the quantity to be made.

As noted above, ordinary castings destroy the mold each time they are removed from the sand. This and the cost of the pattern are the chief equipment expenses for a series of sand castings. But to make a drop forging (see Fig. 16), one or more pairs of striking dies costing hundreds of dollars each are required. Therefore, it is expensive to make drop forgings except in large numbers. Likewise, each individual rolled shape (see

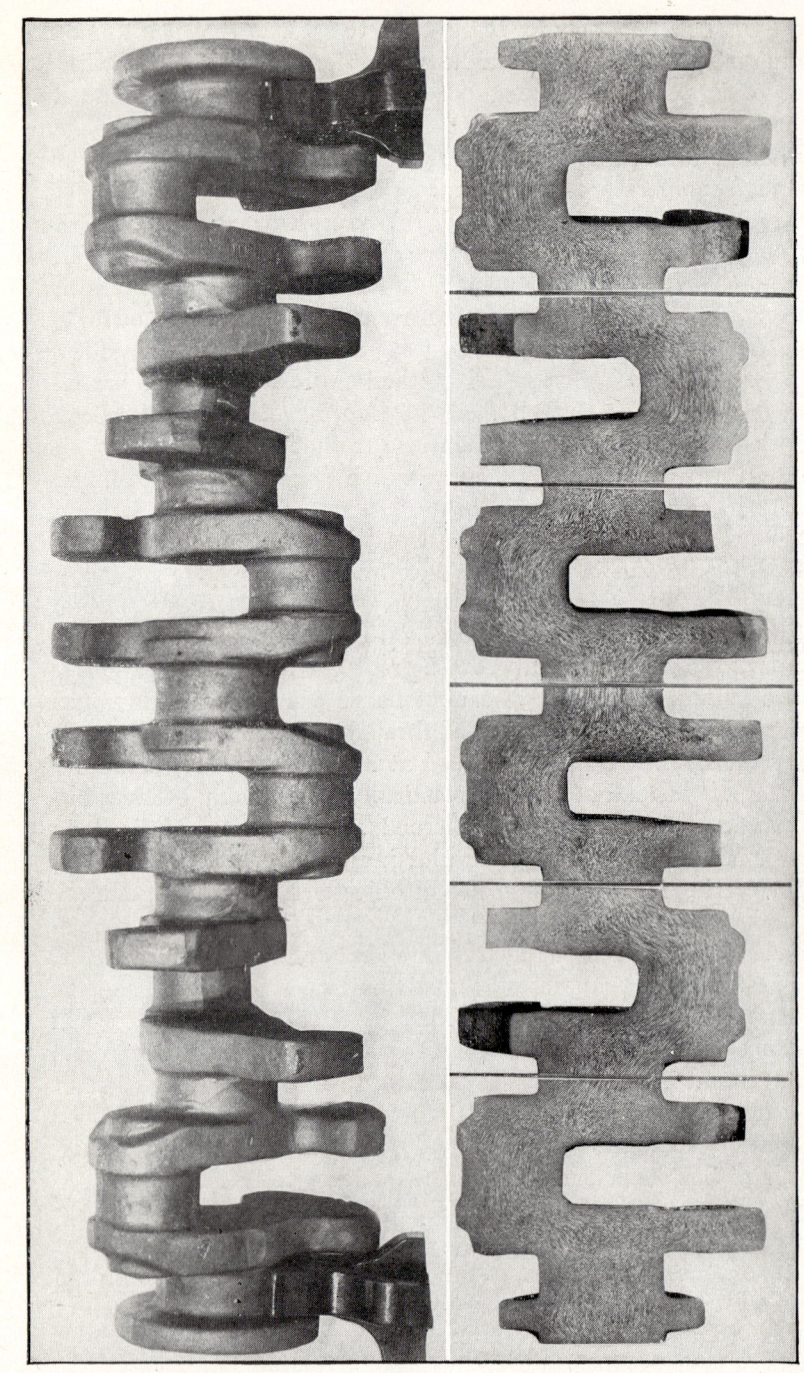

Fig. 15. Example of modern forging technique. An etched longitudinal section through an inline aircraft engine crankshaft forging. Starting as a straight bar of alloy steel, the material is successively worked through the various forging operations to produce the final shape, having flow lines carefully directed to provide the greatest strength in the critical sections. (*Courtesy of Wyman-Gordon Company.*)

SIZING AND SHAPING METALLIC BODIES 69

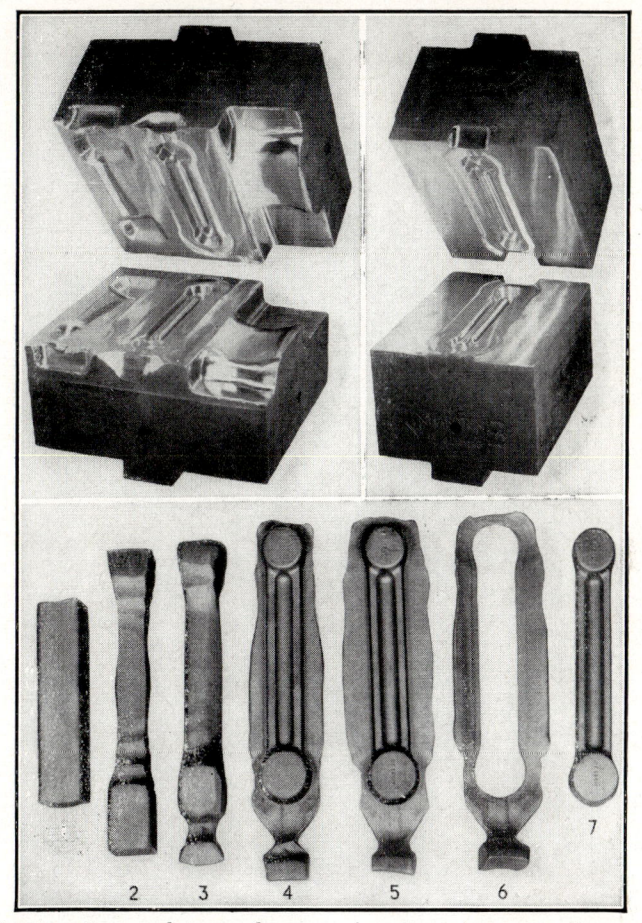

Fig. 16. Forging dies used to produce an aircraft engine connecting rod forging. Left, the blocking die for preliminary operations, and right, the finish die for the final or finish forging operation. The trimming dies are not shown.

The various operations in the evolution from a bar of steel to the completed forging are as follows: (1) 2-in. square bar stock as received from the steel mill and cut to a length of 9 in. Weight 10 lb. (2) The first operation, performed in the impression in the right-hand side of the die blocks shown at the left, consists in drawing out the stock in the center of the forging leaving heavier masses at each end, as required. (3) The second operation, performed in the impression on the left side of the dies illustrated at the left, rounds up and smooths the blank as received from the first operation correcting uneven distribution of material. (4) The breakdown operation performed in the center impression of the die blocks shown at the left. The contour of the piece in this operation approximates that of the finished forging, the principal difference being that all corners are rounded off. (5) The finished forging as it comes from the finish forging die shown at the right. The final contour has been formed and all of the surplus metal squeezed out into flash. (6) The trimmed flash (surplus material squeezed out during the forging operation). (7) The completed forging. Over-all length 12 in. Weight 6¾ lb. (*Courtesy of Wyman-Gordon Company.*)

Fig. 17) uses a specially cut set of rolls, and steel makers usually demand orders of some thousands of tons before agreeing to roll a special shape.

In this connection, note should be made of the circumstance that cast metals have a larger grain structure and are less homogeneous than the same metals which have been mechanically worked. By comparing the grain structure in Fig. 18 with that in Fig. 23, page 78, this will be evident. The smaller grains in Fig. 23 are indicative of better strength and

Fig. 17. Hot rolling steel. This is a so-called "universal mill," having horizontal rolls for thickness and vertical rolls for edging.

better ductility. Working under a hammer or press gives a structure similar to that formed in rolling, but with minor differences to be discussed later.

To summarize: Metals are cast if the shape to be made is very large, or very complicated, or if there are only a few identical objects to be made. But when there is a medium number to be made so that the cost is not greatly in favor of casting, forging or rolling is applied on account of the better mechanical properties obtained thereby.

Die Casting. Alloys that melt at low temperatures may be cast under pressure in metal molds. The process is known as *die casting*, because the molds are made with great care, so as to resemble forging dies in their accuracy and operation. The castings are usually small in size, and the die-casting machines are automatic in their operation. The dies come together to form the mold cavity into which the liquid alloy is forced by air pressure; it freezes very rapidly and is pushed or dropped out of the dies when they automatically separate. Sometimes the whole machinery containing the dies is enclosed in an evacuated chamber so that the alloys are cast in a way to give the maximum assurance of their density and freedom from gases and oxides. The most expensive die-

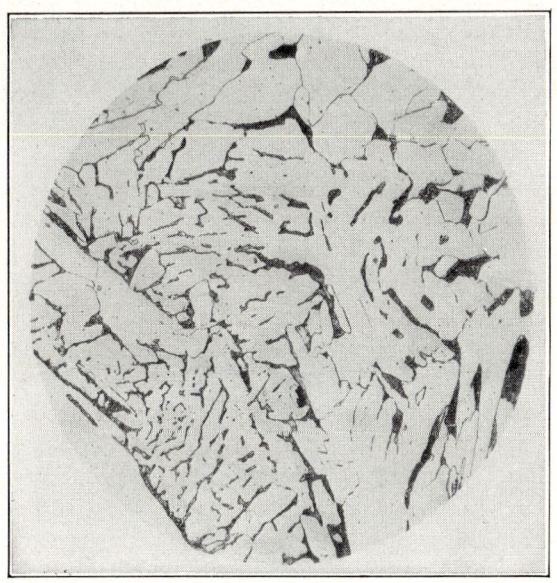

Fig. 18. The metallographic structure of low-carbon cast steel. Magnification 250 ×. Compare these crystals with those of structural steel that has been rolled at a bright red heat (see Fig. 23). (*Courtesy of Bausch & Lomb.*)

casting alloys are those which contain 80 per cent or more of tin; they are not readily tarnished and are especially suitable for bearings, but are not strong. The zinc-base alloys have increased rapidly in use (see page 272). They are low in cost and much stronger than the tin alloys, though more brittle under shock. The lead-base alloys are low in tensile strength and in price and are relatively heavy. The die-casting alloys consisting chiefly of aluminum or of magnesium are next to the zinc alloys in strength and have the lightest weight per unit volume.

Investment Casting. Investment casting is also called precision casting, because the process often produces castings of such accuracy that very little subsequent machining or grinding is necessary. It is a development of the old "lost-wax" process used for so many years for making castings for jewelry, dentures, and the like. It is essentially adapted to making small and intricate castings. In the modern investment process a pattern is first made, without taper, and is then covered with some quick-setting material such as plaster of paris, using partings which allow the pattern to be removed. The plaster of paris is applied in such a thick covering that it makes a mold into which wax or a plastic is later poured and removed to make as many patterns as are needed. For large production runs cast alloy dies may be used for making the wax patterns, instead of plaster-of-paris molds. However made, the patterns are fitted with wax or plastic sprues and joined to a central runner. Around this assembly is then poured a mold material, which may be a ceramic, or silica sand with ethyl silicate as a binder, or some material appropriate to the metal or alloy which is to be cast. After the assembly is "set" or "cured," the wax or plastic is melted out and the metal or alloy poured into the hot mold. The most important application of the process is the making of castings which are difficult or impossible to forge or machine. New techniques have made possible the casting of blades for gas and steam turbines. The surfaces are smoother than obtainable by the ordinary casting process, especially if the patterns have been dipped or sprayed with a fine refractory slurry. The accuracy can be within 0.005 in. per in. or less, and considerable intricacy of design is obtainable. Usually castings of less than 1-lb weight are made, but castings of 10-lb weight have been successfully produced. The cost of the process is high.

Shell Molding. A recent innovation in casting employs molds in the form of thin shells made of a mixture of sand with 5 to 10 per cent resin, which is baked hard by heat from a hot metal pattern over which the mixture is applied by a molding machine. The patterns, precision-made of cast iron or aluminum alloy, are heated to about 200°C (400°F). The thermosetting resin in the mix causes it to harden in a half-minute or less, after which it is conveyed from the molding machine to an oven for completing the "cure" at higher temperature. The shells are then joined to make a shell mold. The molds can be used for pouring most of the metals used in foundry practice. Advantages of the method include high dimensional accuracy and good surface finish, which may eliminate subsequent machining, and mechanization of the process, with a high production rate. The initial cost of the patterns and the machines is high and the resin is also expensive, so that the process is suitable only for a high volume of work. Applications have been primarily for small parts of close tolerance.

Continuous Casting. Continuous casting consists of a technique whereby an ingot is continuously solidified while it is being poured. Liquid metal enters one end of a mold continuously (*i.e.*, usually the top of a vertical, water-cooled mold), and solid metal emerges from the other end. Sometimes a pair of rolls receives the ingot as it emerges from the mold and works it to a smaller size, at the same time exerting a pull and control over the travel. Finally, the finished ingot or billet is cut into predetermined lengths by means of a moving shear or by flame cutting. The concept of continuous casting is very old, but the process has been commercially practiced for only about 15 years in the nonferrous metals and alloys industry in Europe and America. Several attempts have been made to employ it in the steel industry, but without success until early in 1948, when a development by several American steel companies gave promise of commercial possibilities. In the case of copper, aluminum, silver, lead, magnesium, and their alloys, the size and number of installations is increasing. The disadvantages of the process are (1) the high cost of installation, which, in the case of steel, at least, is counteracted (especially in a new plant) by the elimination of the cost of ingot molds and ingot-casting and handling equipment, soaking pits, and blooming mills; and (2) the obvious lack of flexibility of alloy changes. The advantages are no shrinkage or shrinkage porosity, less segregation because of smaller molds and also more rapid solidification, greater density, no gate scrap, lower pouring temperatures.

Shaping While Pasty: Pasty, or Semiliquid, Compression. Steel and most of the relatively pure metals contract during freezing, resulting in the formation of a cavity in the interior or at the top of the frozen mass. If the metals are placed under compression during the freezing period, this shrinkage cavity will be avoided or minimized. The pressure may be applied by having a side of the ingot mold movable so it can be forced against the ingot, or else by casting the metal into a tapered mold and then forcing it by hydraulic pressure into the narrow part of the mold. This consolidation of the structure and the prevention of formation of large crystals have a beneficial effect on the strength and other qualities of the metal.

SHAPING WHILE HOT AND PLASTIC

Most of the metals of commerce are plastic enough at atmospheric temperature for cold shaping under pressure, but some are not. Even when cold shaping is possible, hot working requires much less power expenditure, and is therefore cheaper. For example, the strength of steel at atmospheric temperature may be 75,000 psi, whereas the same steel may have only 2,000 to 4,000 lb strength at a rolling temperature of 1100°C (2010°F). Consequently most mechanical work is done at elevated temperatures. The metals so treated and the appropriate temperatures are given in Table 12. Iron, steel, aluminum, copper, and brass are shaped mostly by hot work, but often the hot work is followed by

TABLE 12. TEMPERATURES OF MECHANICAL TREATMENT OF SOME METALS AND ALLOYS

Metal	Can it be worked cold?	Best temperatures for working, °C	Best finishing temperature, °C	Softening temperature, °C	Temperatures of non-malleability, °C
Aluminum	Yes[1]	450– 425[2]	....	350– 500	550 up
Antimony	No	....	....	None	All
Bismuth	No	....	....	None	All
Brass (copper and zinc)	Yes	Usually cold	....	250– 500	600 up
Bronze (copper and tin)	Yes	Usually cold	....	....	....
Cobalt	No	500– 600	....	None	All
Copper	Easily[1]	800– 750	....	200– 325	800 up
Duralumin (aluminum, copper, and a little manganese and magnesium)	Yes[3]	450– 350	Cold[3]	530	[3]
Iron and steel	Yes[1]	1100– 900	900	250– 900	350–900
Lead	Very easily	Cold	Cold	....	None
Magnesium	Yes[4]	500– 300[5,2]	380	....	420 up
Molybdenum	[6]	....	....	....	....
Monel metal (nickel and copper)	Yes	1150– 900	900	850–1000	540–870
Nickel	Yes	1200–1100	900	700– 900	540–870
Steel—structural	Yes	1100– 900	900	250– 850	350–900
Steel—high-carbon	Yes	1100– 700	700	250– 700	350–700
Stellite (cobalt, chromium, and tungsten)	No	1000[7]	....	Cannot be softened	....
Tin	Very easily	Cold	Cold	....	All[8]
Tungsten (wolfram)	No[9]	1600– 600	600	....	200
Zinc	No[10]	200– 110	110–200	60– 150	Cold 260

[1] Large pieces rolled hot, then finished cold. [2] Rods and other appropriate shapes are extruded in preference to rolling. [3] After heat-treatment, duralumin can be worked cold for about 45 min. [4] Magnesium can be worked down to 200°C. [5] Must be exactly within this range. [6] Molybdenum is ductile at atmospheric temperature, and is malleable if it has been vacuum cast. [7] The softer varieties. [8] The harder varieties. [9] Ductile at atmospheric temperature, but not malleable. [10] Except after first hot rolling.

rolling at atmospheric temperature, which gives most metals hardness, improved strength, a brighter surface, and more exact size. Cold working is discussed in a later section of this chapter. Table 12 also shows that some metals—for example, antimony, bismuth, and cobalt—are brittle and nonmalleable at all temperatures and, therefore, cannot be worked at all. The same is true of cast iron and some other alloys.

Rolling. Rolling is an advantageous method of shaping metals, especially in large tonnages, because of its rapidity and low cost. The reduction of metal in rolls is diagrammatically illustrated in Fig. 19. The metal piece passes between two rolls revolving at the same speed but in opposite directions. In some cases three rolls are used so that pieces may be passed back and forth between the rolls without changing the direction of revolution, as shown in the figure. In other cases two reversible rolls are used, or else the piece is passed back above the rolls and then between them again in the original direction. The effect of the operation is to pull the metal forward at the surface in contact with the rolls relative to the rest of the metal. The magnitude of this effect depends in part on the relative temperature at the surface and the interior of the piece. If the cohesive stresses at the central plane are sufficiently low, the material will "alligator," as indicated in Fig. 19. In other cases this effect is negligible, especially in rolling thin sections. In general, reduction from the original to the desired thickness requires many passes, each accomplishing further reduction. When the pressure is first applied, the amount of reduction should be moderate; otherwise the metal may crack or the surface may be torn and a permanent defect be produced.

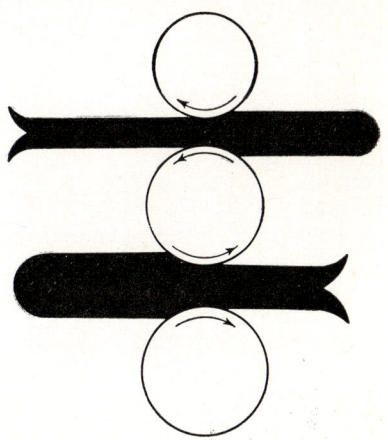

FIG. 19. Action of three-high rolling mills.

Defects in Rolling or Forging. There are many defects which inspection may disclose in metals after they have been worked, and these are not always the result of improper procedure in rolling or forging, *e.g.*, segregation or excessive inclusions which may be due to lack of expertness in the melting or pouring practices. Segregation in steel may be indicated by a banded structure. Inclusions may be disclosed by deep etching and may appear on the rolled product as slag lines, hairlines, etc. Or they may be the cause of internal cracks which, even though they may be produced by working the metal while it is too cold or by cooling it too fast from a high working temperature, would nevertheless not have developed if an inclusion had not weakened the metal. Gas bubbles, or *blowholes*, near the skin of an ingot may break out during the rolling operation to appear as marks known as tears, scabs, or seams. A weak structure in the ingot, the primary structure formed during solidification, may not be sufficiently broken up. It is commonly specified that the reduction must be 4 to 1, but it is believed that 3 to 1 is adequate and gives better material, because if the reduction from primary to finished member is too great, banding may result. Banded steel will give a poorer tensile test when pulled transversely to the direction of rolling than it will longitudinally. The strength and elastic limit may not suffer by the banding, but ductility in a transverse test may be much less, as indicated by unit elongation and reduction of area. Banding may result from various other causes in manufacture also.

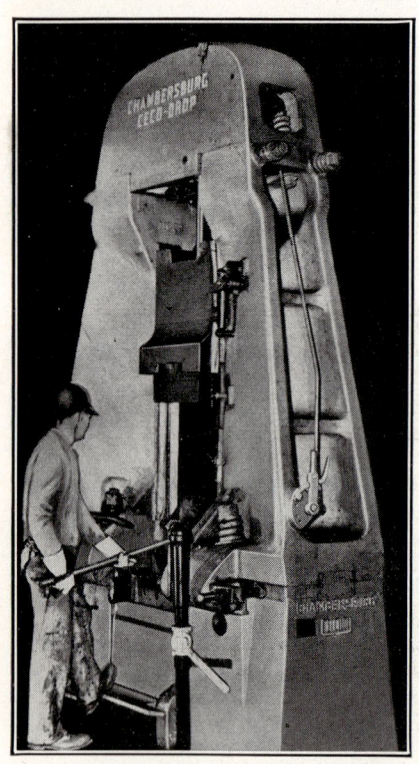

Fig. 20. Steam hammer used in making drop forgings. (*Courtesy of Chambersburg Engineering Company.*)

Forging. Metals may be forged hot, either under a hammer, which acts as a sudden blow, or under a press, which acts slowly and therefore requires greater force to produce the same amount of deformation or reduction (see Fig. 21). The same precautions must be taken in forging as in rolling, *viz.*, the metal must be treated carefully until it has been toughened by some degree of working.

Drop Forging. Metals can be formed into somewhat complicated shapes by forging under a hammer or press between an upper and a lower die (see Figs. 16 and 20).

Rolling vs. Hammer Forging in Its Effect on Properties. Hammer forging of metals expends the greater part of its force on the upper and lower surfaces and tends to spread the metal away from the point of contact of the blow. Its effect does not extend so deeply into the interior of the body as does the effect of rolling or press forging. On the other hand, the finishing temperature is likely to be much nearer the desired temperature than it is in rolling, because the operation is slower and the metal is under the direct observation of the operator. Hot rolling is the cheapest and most rapid method of reducing metallic objects.

Press Forging vs. Hammer Forging. The slow application of force in press forging results in less dissipation of the energy along the surface than in hammer forging, avoids shock due to blows, and works the metal

FIG. 21. Forging press having a capacity to exert a total pressure of 14,000 tons. (*Courtesy of Bethlehem Steel Company.*)

more deeply with attendant beneficial effects. The sizing and shaping of very large pieces should therefore always be done on a press rather than by a hammer or rolls. The great overhead expense of forge presses and the relative slowness of their operation render pressing a costlier process than either rolling or hammering.

Temperatures at Which Metals Are Worked. The temperatures at which the work may best be performed on many of the metals are shown in Table 12, and also the temperatures of nonmalleability—the temperatures at which the metal may crack in working. Most of the metals and alloys will be *hot short*, *i.e.*, brittle when hot, if worked at temperatures above the best working temperature. In addition, steel is liable to be cracked if worked between 900 and 200°C (1650 and 390°F) for low-carbon steel, or between 700 and 200°C (1290 and 390°F) for steels containing over 0.8 per cent of carbon. If steel is worked at temperatures of 400 to 200°C (750 to 390°F), it is especially liable to be brittle and hard thereafter. The effect is greater than if the metal is worked cold. Tin, which is one of the most malleable of all the metallic substances at atmospheric temperature, is brittle at 200°C. Nickel and monel metal are hot short at temperatures of 540 to 870°C (1000 to 1600°F). The extraordinary behavior of tungsten is described in the section devoted to that metal.

Effect of Finishing Temperatures in Hot Mechanical Work. The great advantage of mechanical work is that it improves the properties of

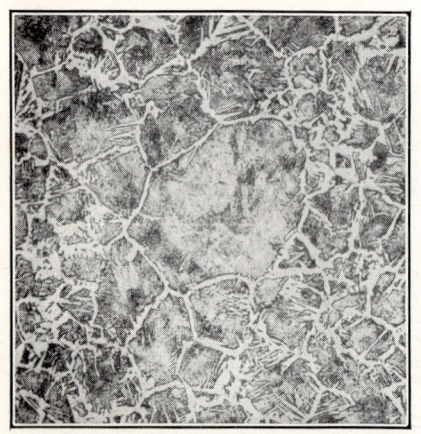

FIG. 22. Constructional steel (No. 1035) the rolling of which was finished at too high a temperature. Magnification 100 ×. Compare with Fig. 23. (*H. W. Cooper, author's laboratory.*)

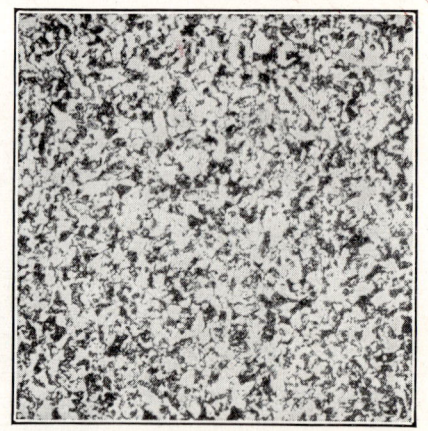

FIG. 23. The same steel as in Fig. 22, at the same magnification. This specimen was rolled to a correct finishing temperature. Note the smaller size of the crystals. (*H. W. Cooper, author's laboratory.*)

all metallic substances by refining their structure. In hot mechanical work the temperature to which the alloy is heated in order to give it the desired malleability often produces a large crystalline size, which is detrimental unless the crystals are broken up by rolling or forging. This is especially liable to happen in working steel. It has already been noted that mechanical work does break down the crystals, but it is important to note that the crystals grow again very rapidly at the rolling temperatures. Therefore the temperature at which the work is finished should be one at which the crystal size is normally small. For steel the temperature corresponding to small crystal size is from about 900 to 700°C (1650 to 1290°F), depending on the carbon content of the steel. In rolling steel, finishing temperatures are too apt to be 100 to 200°C above the desired point, while in forging they are much nearer the best temperature. Relative grain sizes produced by correct and incorrect rolling temperatures are shown in Figs. 22 and 23.

Automatic Control in Rolling. An important development, which is still in the process of improvement and wider adoption, is electric automatic control of rolling operations, including the use of photoelectric cells. A recent application of this is photoelectric-pyrometer indication of the temperature of bars being rolled, directly in front of the roller at his control pulpit. Even more recently, automatic control of thickness in rolling sheets has been developed, using X rays or beta rays which are passed through the sheet. By means of the beta gage, thickness of aluminum sheet can be controlled within 0.0002 in.

Extrusion. Bars and various shapes of aluminum, magnesium, copper, brass, and other metals and alloys are often made by forcing ahead under pressure through a die. Some of the aluminum and magnesium alloys are also extruded in the form of hollow tubes and similar shapes so that they go into service immediately as structural parts. Lead pipe is also customarily formed by extrusion, and tubes of brass and other copper alloys are often so made. Electric cables are encased in lead by a process in which the freezing metal is forced through a die around the outside of the electric cable. In recent years, all tubes of nickel, monel, inconel, K monel, and some analyses of stainless steel are made by extrusion, and the importance of the extrusion process is growing yearly. Currently (1952) a number of large installations for the extrusion of alloy and tool steels into tubular and special bar shapes are being completed.

COLD SHAPING

All manner of shapes are produced by cold shaping. Besides rolling, the operations include drawing, stamping, flanging, spinning, dishing, and cupping. For example, cartridge shells are made out of sheet brass by forcing it through a die by means of a plunger (see Fig. 24); steel gas cylinders and other containers are made in a similar way. Structural shapes in the form of channels, angles, etc., are produced cold in dies by a process known as flanging. Cylinders are made into vase shapes for various purposes by applying pressure to the side while they are rapidly rotated. This process is known as *spinning*. It is applied frequently for making objects of art. It is also used, both cold and hot, for making the ends of cylinders, tanks, boilers, and similar articles.

Effects of Cold Working. Cold working greatly alters the mechanical and physical properties of metals, the effects increasing with increasing amounts of cold work. Tensile strength, yield strength, and hardness are increased, while the ductility is decreased. Physical properties such as electrical conductivity and magnetic characteristics are often considerably altered. The primary purposes of cold-working processes are (1) to improve surface finish, (2) to achieve very close dimensional accuracy, (3) to adjust or improve mechanical properties, and (4) to improve machinability.

Cold-working methods are usually confined to the last few operations because the methods are generally more expensive than hot working

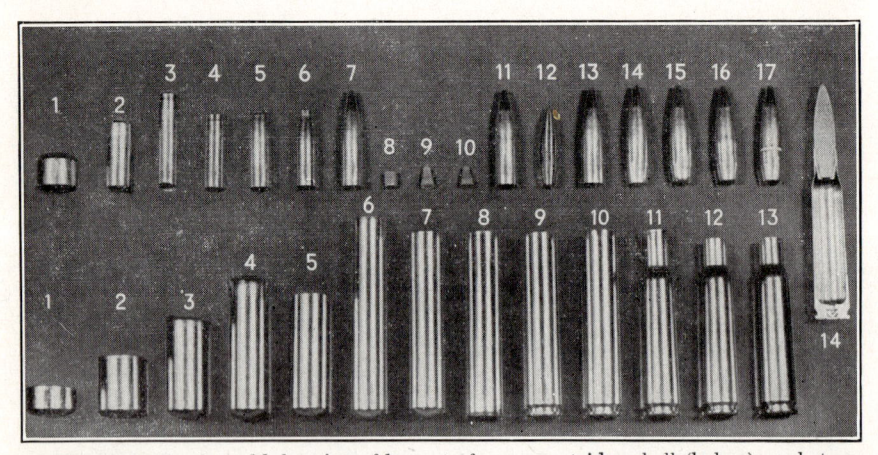

Fig. 24. Steps in the cold drawing of brass to form a cartridge shell (below), and steps in the manufacture of the bullet (above).
Below. .50 caliber cartridge case: (1) cup; (2) first draw; (3) second draw; (4) third draw; (5) first cutoff; (6) fourth draw; (7) second cutoff; (8) head and stamp; (9) head turn; (10) first mouth anneal; (11) taper; (12) mouth trim; (13) second mouth anneal; (14) sectional cartridge. *Above.* .50 caliber ball bullet: (1) cup; (2) first draw; (3) second draw; (4) cutoff; (5) first point; (6) second point; (7) third point; (8) lead slug before swaging; (9) lead core before tumbling; (10) lead point fully swaged and tumbled; (11) lead insert; (12) steel core; (13) steel core insert; (14) first boat tail; (15) crimp; (16) finish bullet; (17) groove and resize. (*Courtesy of Remington Arms Company, Inc.*)

and only a few of the metals can be severely reduced in section cold without being softened by heat-treatment at intervals. Gold, tin, lead, copper, aluminum, and silver are the easiest to cold work. The working of tin and lead at room temperatures is, for these metals, equivalent to hot working since their recrystallization temperatures are at, or slightly below, room temperature. The temperature at which a metal recrystallizes after cold work is considerably affected by the amount of such work, decreasing with increasing cold work or strain. Thus, a low-carbon steel which recrystallizes at 680°C (1250°F) after a small amount of cold work will, after very heavy cold reductions, recrystallize at temperatures as low as 565°C (1050°F). Complete recrystallization by annealing softens the metal again so that it may be further worked.

TABLE 13. RECRYSTALLIZATION TEMPERATURES[1]

Metal	Approx. lowest recrystallization temp. °C	°F	Metal	Approx. lowest recrystallization temp. °C	°F
Iron	450	840	Magnesium	150	300
Nickel	600	1110[2]	Tantalum	1000	1830
Gold	200	390	Tungsten	1200	2190
Silver	200	390[3]	Molybdenum	900	1650
Copper	200	390	Zinc	Below room temperature	
Aluminum	150	300	Lead	Below room temperature	
Platinum	450	840	Tin	Below room temperature	
			Cadmium	About room temperature	

[1] Jeffries and Archer, "The Science of Metals," McGraw-Hill Book Company, Inc., New York, 1924.

[2] A recent monograph states that very pure nickel recrystallizes around 800°F when severely cold worked.

[3] Indications are that under certain conditions silver will recrystallize at lower temperatures.

Cold work is applied by rolling, drawing, "deep drawing," spinning, stamping, and coining. Such processes accomplish the purposes mentioned above and also change the shape of the piece as in the deep drawing of automobile fenders, parts of aircraft and railroad cars, refrigerators, etc., and the cold heading of nails, bolts, and other fasteners. Almost all metal consumer goods are finished or shaped by one or another cold-working process.

When metals are reduced in cross section more than about 15 per cent, the grain structure is severely changed and after several such reductions may be greatly refined by fragmentation. This effect on the grain size and orientation is shown in Fig. 25, which illustrates the effect of severe cold drawing of stainless-steel tubing. Of particular practical interest is the fact that cold working increases the yield strength considerably more than the ultimate strength, and it is, after all, the yield strength which determines the load-carrying ability of a metal part. This effect in three commonly used steels is shown in Fig. 26, which illustrates the mechanical properties of these steels in the hot-worked and cold-drawn condition by means of stress-strain diagrams. Table 14 gives illustrations of the range of mechanical properties which may be conferred on cold-drawn steel and nonferrous tubing. It is also interesting to note that the softest and most ductile condition in steel is achieved by severe cold working followed by subcritical annealing, i.e., annealing below 715°C (1320°F). Severe cold working, of course, increases the endurance limit (fatigue limit) of metals also, for which special forms of cold work such as shot blasting, shot peening, autofrettage, or other prestressing are applied. If one takes as a definition of toughness the area under the stress-strain curve which represents the energy absorbed for fracture, then cold work actually increases the toughness of the metal. The

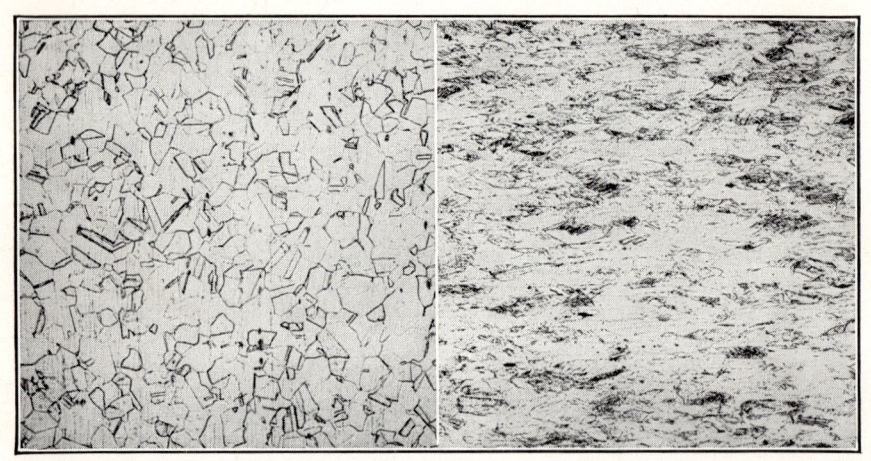

Fig. 25. Effect of cold drawing on crystal structure: (*a*) longitudinal section of stainless steel tube, annealed. Magnification 100 ×; (*b*) same tube after cold drawing to 40 per cent reduction in area; same magnification. (*H. W. Cooper, author's laboratory.*)

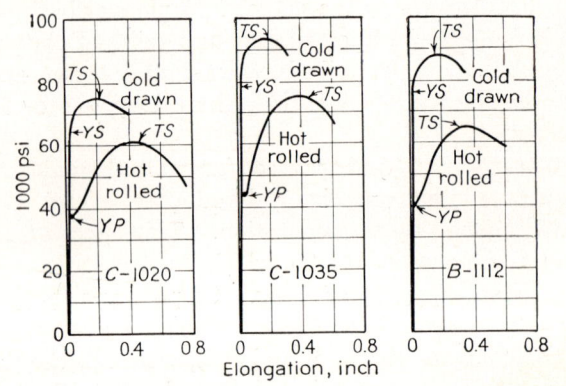

Fig. 26. Typical stress-strain diagrams of hot-rolled and cold-drawn steels. (TS = tensile strength, YS = yield strength, YP = yield point). (*From "Metals Handbook," 1948.*)

increase in yield strength and ultimate strength more than compensate for the decrease in elongation and reduction in area caused by cold working.

Cold Rolling. Thin sheets, strip, and foil made from all the metals are produced by cold rolling the rough hot-finished product. A number of cold-rolling and annealing operations may be required to achieve the desired bright, smooth surface condition, close dimensional accuracy, and mechanical properties. For utmost softness of steel sheets for subsequent deep drawing, stamping, and spinning operations, the sheets must first be cold-rolled and then annealed at temperatures less than 715°C (1320°F) so that the carbides become spheroidized. This is done in a controlled atmosphere to prevent scaling. In this condition they are amenable

TABLE 14. THE EFFECT OF COLD DRAWING ON THE MECHANICAL PROPERTIES OF TUBING

Material	Condition	Ultimate tensile strength, psi	Yield strength, psi	Per cent elongation in 2 in.	Hardness, Rockwell
AISI 1015 steel	Annealed	55,000	30,000	38	B-58
	Half-hard	65,000	53,000	19	B-75
	Hard-drawn	80,000	70,000	10	B-85
AISI 1095 steel	Annealed	83,000	55,000	28	B-85
	Half-hard	105,000	85,000	15	B-98
	Hard-drawn	125,000	110,000	6	C-28
Stainless steel type 304 (18-8)	Annealed	90,000	38,000	50	B-85
	Half-hard	125,000	90,000	25	C-22
	Hard-drawn	170,000	140,000	12	C-34
Pure nickel	Annealed	70,000	28,000	38	B-65
	Half-hard	90,000	55,000	18	B-85
	Hard-drawn	110,000	90,000	7	B-100
Monel (67 Ni, 28 Cu, 5 Fe + Mn)	Annealed	75,000	35,000	38	B-68
	Half-hard	95,000	65,000	22	B-90
	Hard-drawn	120,000	105,000	6	C-22
Red brass (90 Cu, 10 Zn)	Annealed	45,000	....	50	F-65
	Half-hard	61,000	45,000	28	B-35
	Hard-drawn	75,000	63,000	10	B-80
52S aluminum alloy (Al with 2.5 Mg, 0.25 Cr)	Annealed	27,000	15,000	24	
	Half-hard	37,000	30,000	10	
	Hard-drawn	44,000	38,000	4	

to the most drastic forms of further cold forming. Steel and nonferrous bars are also cold-rolled for improvement of surface, dimensional accuracy, and mechanical properties.

Cold Drawing. Bars and rods, wire, and tubing made from all the ductile metals are commonly finished by cold drawing. Practically, rods cannot be hot-rolled much smaller than ⅜ in. and tubing no smaller than about 1¼ in. diameter. All smaller sizes of rod, wire, and tubing are made by cold drawing, but larger sizes also are finished by cold drawing in order to achieve control of surface finish, size, machinability, and mechanical properties.

Wire is drawn cold through a cemented-carbide, hardened-steel, or white cast-iron die, slightly smaller than the original wirebar, onto a rotating drum called a *wire block* which furnishes the power. The metal must be thoroughly lubricated, often by means of a previously applied lime coating plus dry soaps or extreme pressure lubricants applied as the wire passes through the die. Some metals which have a very high work-hardening rate, such as stainless steel, may be coated with lead or copper to act as a lubricant and prevent galling and seizing between the wire and the die. Cold drawing of larger bars is done by the same general method, except that the power to pull the rods through the dies is supplied

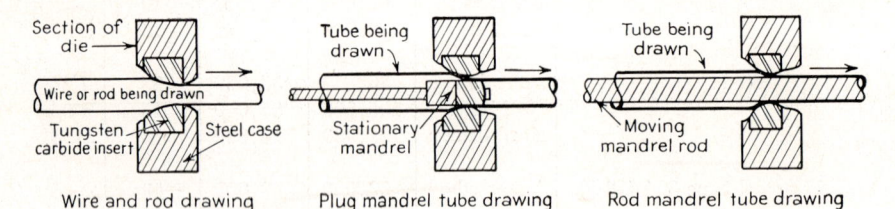

FIG. 27. Diagrammatic representation of wire, rod, and tube drawing.

by a moving chain through tongs which engage the previously pointed end of the rod and thus draw it through the die in a straight length. Such an apparatus is called a *drawbench,* and some drawbenches capable of drawing large rods and tubes have been built to exert a pull of as much as 300,000 lb.

Figure 27 shows in diagram form the related processes of wire drawing, rod or bar drawing, and tube drawing. Two basic methods of tube drawing are in common use. One is the *plug* or *stationary-mandrel* method employing a mandrel of cylindrical section, usually made from a cemented carbide, which is held stationary in the die opening on the end of a long rod. Thus, the tube is forced to pass between the die on the outside and the mandrel on the inside so that both the outside diameter and wall thickness are reduced. Another method generally used on tubes smaller than 1 in. diameter is the rod mandrel process. A hardened, accurately ground and polished alloy-steel rod is inserted into the tube before drawing, and both the tube and the rod are drawn through the die together. After drawing, the tube must be expanded slightly by rolling so that the rod may be withdrawn and used in the next tube.

The advent of cemented-carbide dies has considerably reduced the costs and increased the speed of cold-drawing processes, as have also many innovations in lubrication practice. Wire and tubing smaller than $1/16$ in. in diameter are commonly drawn through diamond dies, and wire up to $3/16$ in. as well as tubing and rod up to 2 in. or more are drawn through cemented-carbide dies. Drawing dies for tubes as large as 8 in. in diameter are made from hardened tool steel and are commonly chrom-

Fig. 28. Welded stainless steel tubes ready for cold drawing. Half size. (*E. J. Callahan, author's laboratory.*)

Fig. 29. Same tube as in Fig. 28 after several drawing and annealing treatments. Magnification 25 ×. (*E. J. Callahan, author's laboratory.*)

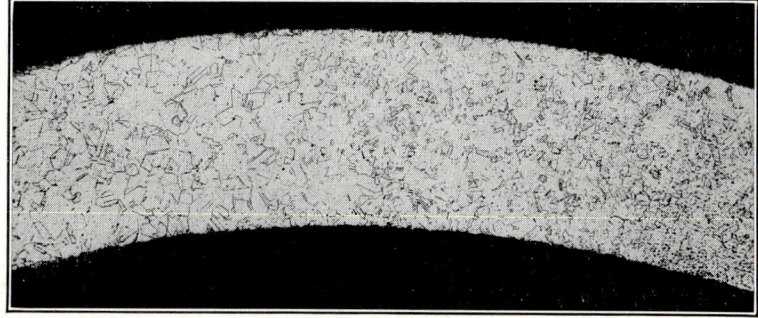

Fig. 30. Finished thin-wall welded and drawn tube, annealed. The weld area is at the right. Magnification 50 ×. (*E. J. Callahan, author's laboratory.*)

ium plated on the wearing surfaces in order to increase their life and decrease friction.

An interesting example of the effects of cold working is shown in Figs. 28 to 30. By repeated cold working and annealing, the cast structure of a welded tube (stainless 18-8) is made to recrystallize so that in the final product the weld can scarcely be distinguished from the original wrought structure.

By far the strongest forms of any metal are made by wire drawing. Thus, tungsten wire of 600,000-psi tensile strength has been produced, and high-carbon steel wire (often called music wire) is made by judicious combination of heat-treatment and cold drawing to exceed 300,000-psi ultimate strength. Austenitic stainless-steel wire can be drawn to surpass the latter figure. The cables for suspension bridges as well as the load-carrying cores of high-tension electrical cables are made from high-strength steel wire made in a similar manner. As in the case of cold-rolled sheet and strip, the softest condition in steel wire, rods, and tubing is also achieved by severe cold drawing followed by relatively low-temperature annealing.

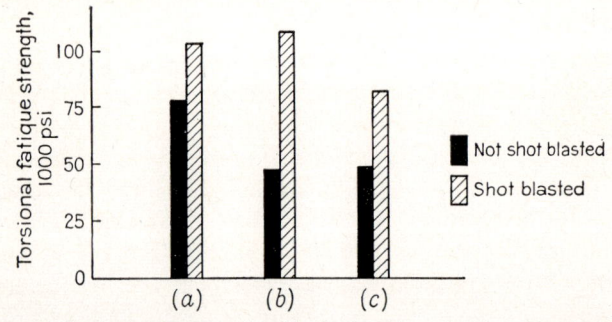

Fig. 31. Increase in fatigue strength of helical springs by shot-blasting oil-quenched and tempered steel wire, 0.118 in. in diameter with tensile strength of 205,000 to 235,000 psi; (a) without surface defects, (b) with small surface defects, (c) with surface laps. (*From Lüpfert, "Metals Handbook," 1948.*)

Shot Blasting or Shot Peening. The fatigue resistance and the endurance limit of steel are discussed on page 18. Any member of a vehicle or structure which rotates, vibrates, or is alternately stressed in any manner is subject to fatigue failure, and it is a matter of observation that a fatigue failure generally starts at the surface. Whatever increases the ultimate strength of a member, especially if it increases the strength at the surface, will increase its resistance to fatigue. It is found that subjecting the surface of a metal or alloy, either ferrous or nonferrous, to the impact of hard particles will increase its fatigue strength, even though it has already been strengthened by cold rolling or heat-treatment. The hard particles are sometimes sand or, more usually, hard pellets of white cast iron (shot), and they may be projected against the surface by a blast of air or, more frequently, by mechanical means of propulsion. The method, which started on springs about ten years ago, is now very general (see Fig. 31). Automobile axle shafts, connecting rods, steering arms, center and support arms, clutch-spring disks, and valve springs have been shot-blasted with great advantage from the standpoint of increased resistance to fatigue. Shot blasting not only increases the strength of the surface, but also puts it in compression, so that it is a form of prestressing.

Prestressing. Prestressing is the introduction of residual stress in a member of the opposite sign to the stress which the member is to experience in service; for example, a compressive residual stress may be established in a member which is to undergo tensile stresses in service, and vice versa. For instance, it has long been the practice to shrink tubes on the outer surface of gun barrels in order to put the barrels under a compressive stress which better enables them to withstand the tensile stress produced when the gun is fired. Since the First World War a similar result has been achieved by autofrettage, *i.e.*, by subjecting the interior of the gun tube to a very high hydraulic pressure at atmospheric temperature, whereby the inner bore is increased about 6 per cent and the outer diameter is increased 1 per cent. In this way, the elastic limit in tension at the bore is almost doubled as a combination of increase due to cold work and residual compressive stresses. This is offered only as an illustration of the general principle of prestressing. The oldest and commonest example of prestressing (although it was not originally so styled) is the initial overloading or "setting" of springs.

Hot Mechanical Work vs. Cold Mechanical Work. Hot mechanical work improves both the strength and the ductility of the cast metal. For each metal or alloy, however, there are usually certain ranges of temperature within which mechanical work must not be applied (see Table 12). If hot mechanical work on metals is followed by mechanical work at atmospheric temperature, the latter increases strength, decreases crystal size, and usually produces hardness roughly proportional to the amount of cold work. This necessitates frequent softening by heat between successive cold operations. In general, the purer the metal, the less is the intensity of the effects which are produced by cold work. For example, pure iron and pure copper can be cold-wrought almost indefinitely, while steel and brass will be hardened more rapidly. Low- and medium-carbon steel are not rapidly hardened provided that the cementite is in the spheroidized condition, but are so if the cementite is in lamellar form.

Properties as Affected by the Amount of Mechanical Work. Castings which have not been subjected to any mechanical work are composed of crystals of relatively large size (see Fig. 18). The result is that their strength and ductility are less than those of the same kind of metal which has been subjected to mechanical work (see Fig. 23). The amount of mechanical work should be sufficient to reduce the cross section of the casting to at least one-third or one-quarter of its original size, if a satisfactory improvement in crystalline structure is to be produced. Metal that is cast under pressure, as in die casting, centrifugal casting, and semiliquid compression, has better crystalline structure and better properties than the same metal cast without pressure, even though the latter has been subsequently worked. In other words, the crystals which form unhindered during freezing are seldom completely broken down by the amounts of hot work usually applied.

MACHINING AND MACHINABILITY

Machining is a method of sizing and shaping metals by cutting with some form of cutting tool. The principal operations included in the term "machining" are broaching, tapping, threading, reaming, drilling, milling, boring, planing, turning, sawing, and grinding. In this list the operations are given not in order of importance, but in order of severity of requirements for the cutting tool.

Machinability is a general term denoting for a material its relative capability of being machined or the ease with which it may be machined. Ease of machining may be considered in terms of rate of removal of metal by the operation, or in terms of cost of the operation. Machinability is not a single property, but is determined by combinations of other properties and varies with the type of operation as listed above and the conditions under which it is performed. Because of this variability it cannot be exactly defined or measured.

Although machining may be regarded as bordering on or overlapping the field of mechanical metallurgy, more strictly the operations and equipment of machining belong in the field of mechanical engineering and its subdivision tool engineering; accordingly they will not be discussed here. Machinability, on the other hand, is closely related to the properties and structure of metals, and it deserves the attention of metallurgists, particularly as regards the properties and conditions that affect it and the machinability ratings of metals and alloys.

The cutting tools used in machining are most often made of high-speed steel. Plain carbon tool steels are used to some extent at lower cutting speeds, for light cuts, and on free-cutting materials. Sintered carbides, especially tungsten carbide, are increasingly used for turning and certain other cutting operations on hard materials and for very high speeds. Cast cobalt-base alloys typified by stellite are also used. These materials are discussed in Chaps. 9 and 10. Industrial diamonds are also used occasionally.

During machining operations a "cutting fluid" is usually applied at the point where the cut is being made. This has the primary purpose of keeping both the cutting tool and the material being cut from being overheated. Besides carrying away heat it reduces the power requirement and wear on the tool through its lubricating effect, aids in proper forming and washing away of the metal chips, and sometimes prevents oxidation. The cutting fluid may be called a "coolant" or a "lubricant." Cutting fluids include various oils, emulsions, water, and air provided by blast or suction. The optimum choice of fluid depends on the type of operation, the material cut, the cutting tool, the cutting speed, and other conditions. The most recent method of drastically cooling the tool is by application of a stream of very cold carbon dioxide as it expands from a cylinder of the liquefied gas.

Among the important factors in machining are the manner of formation of the metal chips, their types and geometry, and the quality of surface finish desired. Removal of the chips of ductile metals is due to plastic flow. Tool angles and the mechanics of the forces acting on the tool and on the work are other important considerations.

Machinability is affected by several variables having to do with the machine and several having to do with the work material.[1] The former include cutting speed, dimensions of the cut, material and design of the tool, cutting fluid, rigidity of the tool and the work holder, and shape of the work. The latter include hardness, rate of work hardening, tensile properties, toughness and brittleness, chemical composition, and microstructure. Optimum conditions as to cutting speed, feed, depth, shape and material of the tool, and cutting fluid usually apply in machining a given metal of a given metallurgical structure.[2]

To make the machining time as short as possible, the work should be designed for simplified machining, the proper tool and tool material should be used, and machinability should be considered in the choice of the work material. Surfaces for milling and broaching should be flat and in a single plane, and free from shoulders. Surfaces to be turned should not contain tapers and fillets. While carbide tools permit higher machining rates, many drilling, broaching, and forming operations necessitate the use of high-speed steel. It has been found that wide differences in machining properties exist between similar steels and iron of a given category. Cast iron of given analysis may be cast and subsequently treated to provide differences in tool life of 50 to 1 at a constant cutting speed, or differences in productivity of 10 to 1 for a given tool life. Even with a single steel, differences in tool life of 10 to 1 can exist by choice of metallurgical structure through suitable annealing and by selection of a suitable grade of carbide for that particular microstructure.[3]

[1] Tool Engineers' Handbook," p. 319, McGraw-Hill Book Company, Inc., New York, 1949.
[2] Boston, O. W., "Metals Handbook," 1948, p. 360.
[3] Field, M., and N. Zlatin, Metcut Research Associates, SAE paper No. 561, 1950.

Additions of small percentages of certain elements are often made to improve machinability or confer free-cutting qualities. This is done especially with copper and its alloys and with various steels. Lead is the usual addition to copper, brass, bronze, and nickel silver; selenium is also used in these metals, and occasionally tellurium. For steels sulfur is the most common agent, and may be used in amounts up to 0.30 per cent. Selenium, sulfur, and sometimes tellurium may be added to stainless steel. Manganese as manganese sulfide or oxysulfide is effective for free-machining steels. Phosphorus may be used up to 0.10 per cent. These additions act in several ways, such as making the metal more brittle, breaking up the continuity of the microstructure, acting as lubricants either internally or in coating the cutting edge of the tool, or counteracting seizing. Inclusions of iron oxide are beneficial, and other inclusions may be likewise, but silicates and hard oxide inclusions are to be avoided because they dull the cutting edge.

Relation of the Properties and Structure of Metals and Alloys to Machinability. The action of machining is produced by plastic flow in metals with ensuing rupture in tension or in shear. The properties that are most conducive to good machinability are low hardness and low tensile strength with low ductility. Machinability often bears a direct relation to Brinell hardness, but this is not necessarily the case because of other factors involved. The hardness and the structure, even in the same metal or alloy, that are best for one type of machining operation may not be the best for another type.

It will be observed that the above properties which tend to improve machinability are the opposite of those which are usually desired for metals in service. Some sacrifice of these properties may be necessary to secure good machinability. If machining is required, the relative importance of the different properties must be decided and a proper balance struck. Thus, if only moderate strength or ductility is required for the service in view, it would be unwise to sacrifice machinability for greater strength or ductility than is needed.

The homogeneous structure of pure metals and solid solutions is unfavorable for good machinability. The chips formed in cutting these metals are likely to be more ductile and to cling to the tool. Tearing and galling may occur. On the other hand, the heterogeneous structure of gray cast iron and copper alloys to which some lead has been added makes them easily machinable.

In wrought metals directional properties affect machinability considerably. This is particularly true when good machinability is due to inclusions. When the inclusions are elongated in rolling, they break up the continuity of the microstructure to a greater extent, and they lower the ductility in the transverse direction with little effect in the longitudinal direction.

Hard spots in steel resulting from welding or from poor heat-treating practice are undesirable for machinability. In castings, a rough surface or one with imbedded sand causes poor machinability.

Machinability varies widely in different types of cast iron. Graphite flakes confer good machinability, which generally increases with graphite content and decreases with combined carbon content. The machinability of plain carbon steels improves up to 0.10 per cent carbon for bessemer steel and 0.20 per cent carbon for open-hearth steel because of the decreasing homogeneity of the structure, but above 0.15 and 0.30 per cent carbon, respectively, this factor is outweighed by increasing strength and toughness, with the result that machinability declines.

Machinability Ratings. Although there is no precise way of expressing or measuring machinability, a number of methods of determining it

Table 15. Machinability Ratings of Metals and Alloys[1]

Ferrous	Rating	Nonferrous	Rating
Malleable iron	80–120	Magnesium alloys	500–2000
Cast steel	70	Aluminum, 2S, O to H temper	300–1500
Cast iron	50–80	17S-T	300–1500
Wrought iron	50	Zinc	200
Steels (AISI Nos.):		Brass, yellow	80
B 1112	100	Brass, yellow, leaded	200–400
B 1113	135	Brass, red	60
C 1020	65	Brass, red, leaded	180
C 1045, annealed	60	Phosphor bronze	40
C 1050, annealed	50	Phosphor bronze, leaded	100
C 1070, annealed	45	Silicon bronze	60
C 1120	80	Silicon bronze, leaded	120
A 2317	55	Aluminum bronze	60
A 3120	60	Manganese bronze	60
A 4130, annealed	65	Copper, ¼ H	60
A 5120	65	Nickel	55
A 8620	60	Monel, as cast	40
A 9420	60	Monel, rolled	55
Stainless 18-8	25	Inconel, cold drawn	35
Stainless 18-8 (free-cutting)	45		

[1] Relative to 100 per cent rating for B 1112, cold-rolled or cold-drawn, machined with a suitable cutting fluid at 180 ft per min using high-speed steel tools. Except where otherwise indicated, the ratings refer to specimens in the cold-drawn condition. The same metals heat-treated or processed in another way will have different ratings.

for comparative purposes have been used. These include determination of the amount of power consumed in the operation, the resulting rise in temperature, the rate of penetration of a standard drill under fixed pressure, and the cutting speed that causes failure of the cutting tool in a given time. None of the methods gives results that can be applied generally to different conditions and types of machining. They do, however, permit "machinability ratings" of different materials for the conditions and process used, and these are useful for qualitative comparisons.

Machinability ratings may differ for the same material under different types of operations, and may differ even more radically with different conditions of the material, *e.g.*, whether steel is fully annealed, normalized, process annealed, or hardened and tempered, and whether nonferrous metals are soft or cold-worked.

Several experimenters and committees have developed tables of machinability ratings, some covering the alloys of a single base metal, others being more comprehensive. All these are largely qualitative, though some are expressed on a numerical scale in which some material is arbitrarily rated as 100. Table 15 gives the ratings for some materials selected from tables in the "Metals Handbook," 1948. The very high ratings for magnesium alloys and for aluminum and most aluminum alloys, especially when hardened, are noteworthy, as is also the marked effect of lead in copper and copper-base alloys.

Spark Machining. Machining of sintered carbides, titanium, some hardened steels, and nonferrous alloys of exceptional hardness and toughness is a difficult problem. Spark machining is a new electrical method of accomplishing this. A dielectric fluid flows onto the surface of the piece to be machined as a negatively charged electrode is advanced toward it. When it is close enough the dielectric breaks down, causing a spark discharge. Electrons rush through the ionized path, exerting a pull on positively charged particles in the piece. The force exerted exceeds the tensile strength of the metal, causing small particles to break away. As these float off in the dielectric fluid the surface is machined without change in the physical or chemical properties of the piece.

POWDER METALLURGY

Powder metallurgy is the art of producing metal or alloy powders and of compacting them by sintering (heating to a high temperature, but below the melting point) and compressing them into massive materials and shaped objects. The particles of metal powder are usually 0.001 to 1 mm in diameter. Sintering does not involve melting, except that in some cases a minor constituent may become molten. Compressing employs total pressures of 10 to 500 tons in mechanical presses and 1,000 to 3,000 tons in hydraulic presses.[1]

The purpose of pressing the powders is to secure such intimate contact between the particles that, during the subsequent sintering, diffusion

---

[1] For most of the data in this section we are indebted to an article by C. H. Samans, "Metals Handbook," 1948, pp. 47–52.

may take place across the boundaries between one particle and another, thus causing the boundaries to disappear and the powder to be consolidated into a continuous mass of metal. Pressing is usually done at room temperature, although hot pressing is also practiced. The purpose of heating or sintering following pressing is to increase the rate of diffusion, assist in providing close contact, and bring about the resulting consolidation. The action between the particles is similar to that which takes place between two surfaces in joining them by pressure welding, although in powder metallurgy the pressure and heat are not often applied simultaneously. In some cases either sintering or com-

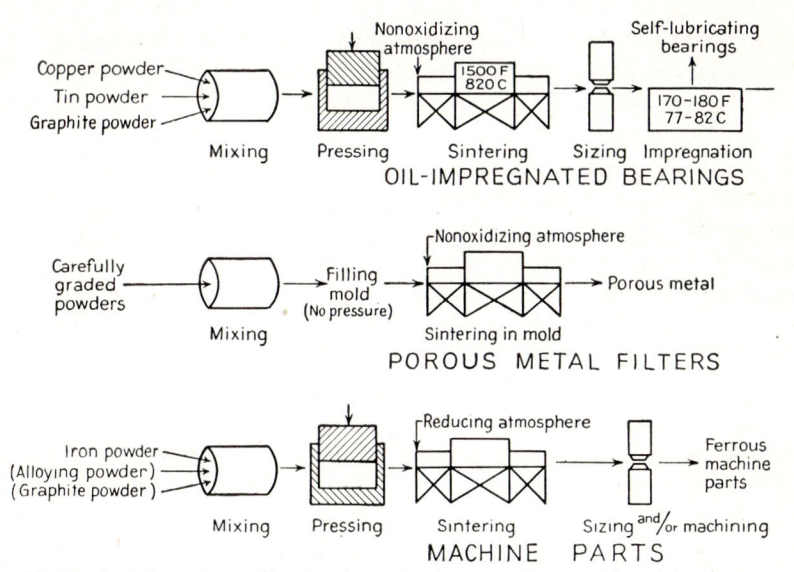

FIG. 32. Typical flow sheets showing steps in the manufacture of articles from metal powders. (*From C. H. Samans, "Metals Handbook," 1948.*)

pressing may be omitted; in others these operations may be repeated alternately. Increase in density of the metal object occurs progressively as consolidation takes place. Repressing and resintering adds to the cost of the process and ordinarily is not feasible in commercial work, so that some degree of porosity is economically unavoidable (see Fig. 32).

The temperatures of sintering may vary from 700 to 900°C (1290 to 1650°F) for brass and bronze; 800 to 1100°C (1475 to 2010°F) for iron; 900 to 1200°C (1650 to 2190°F) for electrical contacts; 1000 to 1200°C (1830 to 2190°F) for noble metals; 1200 to 1300°C (2190 to 2370°F) for permanent magnets; 1300 to 1500°C (2370 to 2730°F) for refractory carbides; 2500 to 3200°C (4530 to 5800°F) for some high-melting metals. Sintering must usually be done in a controlled atmosphere, or even in a vacuum, because of the very large area of particle surface in the powders. The atmosphere is commonly hydrogen, or dissociated ammonia (75 per cent hydrogen, 25 per cent nitrogen). Partly burned fuel gases, carbon monoxide, and natural gas may be used in some cases. The time of sintering is usually 10 to 90 min, depending on the metal or alloy and the density desired. Longer sintering will give increased density, but is usually uneconomic.

Pressing dies are usually of tool steel, and must be carefully made. The pressures range from 20,000 to 100,000 psi for most work, but may be as high as 200,000 psi.

The cost of the processes is relatively high, and economy must be the ruling factor if the parts are to be used to eliminate machining and other operations required by other manufacturing methods. Sometimes, however, properties can be produced which are not obtainable—or not economically obtainable—in metals and alloys by other methods. These factors are illustrated by the following typical examples of products produced by powder metallurgy:

1. The refractory metals, including tungsten, molybdenum, and tantalum, for which the method is necessary because of their high melting points and the undesirable coarse grain structure produced by fusion.

2. The superhard materials, including the cemented-carbides and diamond-impregnated tools, for which the method is also necessary to produce the structures desired (see also page 319).

3. Bearings and porous metallic parts, in which controlled porosity, the possibility of oil impregnation, and the use of nonmetallic additions are required.

4. Electrical and magnetic parts, such as contacts, motor brushes, commutator segments, permanent magnets, and cores for inductance coils, in which characteristics or combinations of materials impossible to secure by other methods can be produced (see also page 217).

5. Machine parts, in which the mechanical properties may be somewhat inferior to those of wrought metals, but in which the necessary tolerances and shapes can be attained at a reduced cost, by the elimination of machining operations.

6. Clad and duplexed parts, either all metallic, as in thermostatic bimetal, or both metallic and nonmetallic, as in friction materials.

The mechanical properties of compacted metal powders are fair; the yield strength (both in tension and in compression), the ductility, and the hardness are usually about one-third that of the same product in cast form, and may be made higher when the cost is justified. Controlled porosity in the finished material may be accomplished by incorporating a volatile substance in the powder mixture before pressing, which will be vaporized and eliminated during the subsequent sintering.

Methods of Making Metal Powders. There are five principal methods of producing metal powder: (1) The method used for the largest tonnage of powder production is reduction of the metal oxide by means of carbon monoxide or hydrogen. The metal oxide may be mill scale, or it may be made by a chemical process, such as precipitation. After reduction, the powder is usually ground and sized. (2) Atomization is commonly used for metals of low melting point. This is accomplished by impingement of a blast of compressed air, steam, or an inert gas on a stream of the molten metal forced through an orifice. (3) Electrolytic deposition is used for some metals, especially copper. The metal is deposited at high current density from an electrolyte of low concentration, which causes it to deposit as a loose powder instead of an adherent plating. (4) Direct milling or grinding of metals is also used to convert them to powder, but in this case a flake form of powder usually results, which is desired for paint such as aluminum paint, but is useless for most applications of powder metallurgy. (5) Finally, the carbonyl process is used, chiefly for iron and nickel. This produces a spherical particle, usually of high purity, but is more expensive. The metal is caused to combine with carbon monoxide, forming carbonyl vapor, which on heating to a somewhat higher temperature decomposes with deposition of the metal powder and regeneration of the carbon monoxide. This method is derived from the carbonyl process of refining nickel, which is described on page 392.

Bibliography

See also references following Chaps. 1 and 13.

ADAM, A. T.: "Wire-drawing and the Cold Working of Steel," 2d ed., H. F. and G. Witherby, London, 1936; The Sherwood Press, Cleveland, Ohio.

AMERICAN FOUNDRYMEN'S ASSOCIATION: "Cast Metals Handbook," 3d ed., Chicago, 1944.

AMERICAN SOCIETY FOR METALS: "Working of Metals," Cleveland, Ohio, 1937.

———: "Machining—Theory and Practice," Cleveland, Ohio, 1950.

AMERICAN SOCIETY FOR TESTING MATERIALS: "Symposium on Powder Metallurgy," Philadelphia, 1943.

AMERICAN SOCIETY OF TOOL ENGINEERS: "Tool Engineers' Handbook," McGraw-Hill Book Company, Inc., New York, 1949.

BAEZA, W. J.: "A Course in Powder Metallurgy," Reinhold Publishing Corporation, New York, 1943.

BRIGGS, C. W.: "The Metallurgy of Steel Castings," McGraw-Hill Book Company, Inc., New York, 1946.

CADY, E. L.: "Precision Investment Castings," Reinhold Publishing Corporation, New York, 1948.

CAMPBELL, H. L.: "Metal Castings," John Wiley & Sons, Inc., New York, 1936.

CRANE, E. V.: "Plastic Working of Metals and Non-Metallic Materials in Presses," 3d ed., John Wiley & Sons, Inc., New York, 1944.

GOETZEL, C. G.: "Treatise on Powder Metallurgy," 3 vols., Vol. I, "Technology of Metal Powders and Their Products," Inter-Science Publishers, Inc., New York, 1949.

GREGORY, E., and E. N. SIMONS: "Mechanical Working of Steel," Sir Isaac Pitman & Sons, Ltd., London, 1943.

HAUSNER, H. H.: "Powder Metallurgy, Principles and Methods," Reinhold Publishing Corporation, New York, 1947.

HERB, C. O.: "Die Casting," Penton Publishing Company, Cleveland, 1936.

HINMAN, C. W.: "Presswokring of Metals," 2d ed., McGraw-Hill Book Company, Inc., New York, 1950.

JONES, W. D.: "Principles of Powder Metallurgy," Edward Arnold & Co., London, 1937.

NAUJOKS, W., and D. C. FABEL: "Forging Handbook," American Society for Metals, Cleveland, 1939.

NEW JERSEY ZINC COMPANY: "Practical Considerations in Die Casting Design," New Jersey Zinc Company, New York, 1948.

PEARSON, C. E.: "The Extrusion of Metals," Chapman & Hall, Ltd., London, 1944.

PUPPE, J. (editor): "Walzwerkswesen," Vol. III, Verlag Julius Springer, Berlin, 1939.

SACHS, G.: "Plastische Verformung," Akademische Verlagsgesellschaft m.b.H., Leipsig, 1930.

SCHWARZKOPF, P.: "Powder Metallurgy," The Macmillan Company, New York, 1947.

SIMONDS, H. R., and A. BREGMAN: "Finishing Metal Products," 2d ed., McGraw-Hill Book Company, Inc., New York, 1946.

TRINKS, W.: "Roll Pass Design," 2d ed., Penton Publishing Company, Cleveland, 1934.

WOLDMAN, N. E., and R. C. GIBBONS: "Machinability and Machining of Metals," McGraw-Hill Book Company, Inc., New York, 1951.

WULFF, J.: "Powder Metallurgy," American Society for Metals, Cleveland, Ohio, 1942.

———, H. F. TAYLOR, and A. J. SHALER: "Metallurgy for Engineers—Casting, Welding, and Working," John Wiley & Sons, Inc., New York, 1852.

CHAPTER 5

WELDING AND JOINING METALLIC BODIES

If two metals are brought into such close contact that there is actual union of the interatomic bonds, they will be completely joined. Thus, if two pieces of a soft metal like lead or gold are pressed together for a considerable period of time at atmospheric temperature, mutual diffusion will produce a firm bond. The cold (atmospheric temperature) welding of some nonferrous metals has been done experimentally for years, and has recently been applied industrially, especially to aluminum and aluminum alloys, cadmium, lead, copper, nickel, zinc, and silver (see Fig. 33). The aluminum surfaces to be welded must be entirely freed

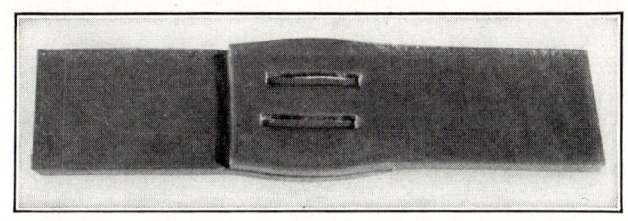

Fig. 33. Cold weld of aluminum strip, made by the Koldweld Corporation, New York. Weld efficiency said to be 75 per cent.

from oxide, as, for example, by scratch brushing; even contamination by handling will prevent formation of a satisfactory weld. In the case of iron and other hard metals, the pieces to be welded by application of pressure must be heated to a point where they are soft (actually near the melting point) and forced together, with care that no oxide intervenes in the joint. In practice the metals listed above are also usually heated for welding, since the plasticity brought about by heating results in more intimate contact of the surfaces and thus facilitates the welding by diffusion across the joint. The rate of diffusion also increases with temperature. Electric methods of heating are now common for all metals. For temperatures of welding, brazing, and soldering see Fig. 34.

Metals may be joined by pressure when the metals are plastic, or else by adding molten metal to the joint under such circumstances that the molten pool will fuse the metal on both sides and so adhere, as shown in Fig. 40. In either way, a joint may be made which is fully as strong as the parent metal; there are, however, two important considerations which must here be noted:

ENGINEERING METALLURGY

1. If the metal must be heated to make it plastic, its properties may be affected by the high temperature necessary, and also by the rate of subsequent cooling, particularly in the case of steel cooling through the critical range.

2. When metals freeze and cool slowly, they assume a coarse grain size and other characteristics of a casting, which gives less strength and less ductility than when the same metal has been wrought. Therefore, it is now the practice in the manufacture of tubing, wire, strip, and in a few other cases to cold-work and anneal the deposited metal.

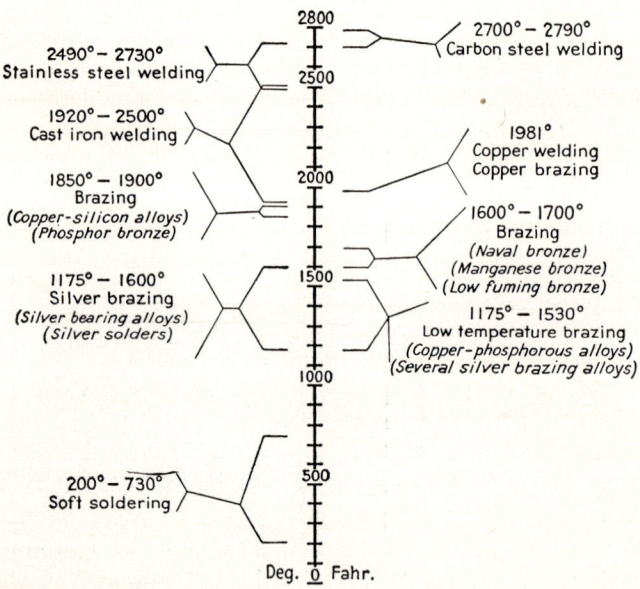

FIG. 34. Approximate ranges of various metal-joining processes. (*From "Welding Handbook," American Welding Society.*)

Expertness in welding takes into consideration these two circumstances, and also the following:

3. The molten pool of metal must be free from oxide, dirt, gases, and other foreign matter.

4. In planning the operation, provision must be made for taking care of the expansion and contraction stresses which are set up in the structure.

Joining processes may be summarized as in Table 16.

HAMMER WELDING OR FORGE WELDING

The oldest method of making a metallic joint was by uniting clean surfaces of metals or alloys under pressure—usually by heating them, cleaning the surfaces, and then uniting them under the blows of a hammer

TABLE 16. METAL-JOINING PROCESSES

A. Pressure processes:
  1. Hammer welding: The original and old-fashioned method which is seldom practiced today. Slow in operation and low in efficiency.[1]
  2. Electric welding without full fusion: Usually the heat comes from electrical resistance at the place where the pieces are butted together. Rapid and high in efficiency.[1]
  3. Solid-phase welding, also called pressure gas welding: Used in the manufacture of butt-welded pipe. High in efficiency.[1]
  4. Pressure after heating by the "thermit" reaction (see page 106). High in efficiency.[1]
B. Fusion processes: The deposited metal has the structure of a casting, but may, under special cases mentioned later, be worked and annealed. Its properties will also depend on what metal (or alloy) is deposited. It may be strong, or it may be ductile, and it may be both if it has been cold worked after deposition (see page 79).
  1. Soldering: The deposited metal has low melting point and low strength.
  2. Brazing: The filler metal is a nonferrous metal or alloy whose melting point is higher than 540°C (1000°F), but lower than that of the pieces to be joined.
  3. Fusion of welding rod by burning gas:
    a. Oxyhydrogen gas, or else city gas with oxygen. These gases serve for welding with lead, brass, bronze, and the like, but do not give high enough temperatures for fusing steel welding rods. Usually the welding-rod alloys which have high melting points have also higher strength.
    b. Where higher temperatures are required, there are now available in commercial form propane, butane, natural gas, acetylene, and other gases, which give temperatures up to 3500°C (6330°F).
  4. Fusion of welding rod by electric arc:
    a. Carbon arc, i.e., using a carbon electrode and striking an arc with the parent metal.
    b. Metal arc, i.e., using the welding rod itself as one electrode.
    c. Shielded arc. The arc is surrounded by a gas which keeps the deposited metal, as well as other heated metal, from becoming oxidized.
    d. Inert-gas shielded arc. The arc is maintained in an inert gas.
    e. Submerged melt. The weld is formed in a pool of molten flux.
  5. Fusion by combination of electric arc and an exothermic reaction:
    f. Atomic hydrogen arc welding (see page 104).
  6. Fusion by the thermit reaction (see page 106).

[1] By efficiency is meant both the strength and ductility of the joint, as compared to the same properties of the pieces welded, i.e., the parent metal.

(Fig. 35). This was performed by the blacksmith on wrought iron and other metals, but is now almost entirely replaced by other methods.

Efficiency of Hammer-welded Iron Joints. If a properly made hammer weld is put into a tensile machine and pulled, the actual line of junction is usually found to be stronger than the metal on either side of it. This fact might lead to the assertion that the weld is stronger than the original metal, but subsequent investigation proves that this is not the case. The weld itself is almost always stronger than the metal on either side of it, but only because the crystalline structure of the metal near the weld has been coarsened by the heat to which it has been subjected. The crystal structure at the weld is refined owing to the rapid and continuous hammering which is applied, but the structure on either side has suffered through overheating; no method has yet been devised of economically and commercially making hammer welds so that all the overheated metal will be refined by continuous forging until it reaches the proper finishing temperature, which is red heat. It is a safe rule that hammer-welded parts should never be used in structures or other positions where they must give reliable service under stress.

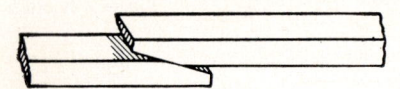

FIG. 35. Bars in position for hammer welding.

PRESSURE WELDING

Electric Resistance Heating for Pressure Welding. The more closely the heat can be confined to the parts of the metals which are to be actu-

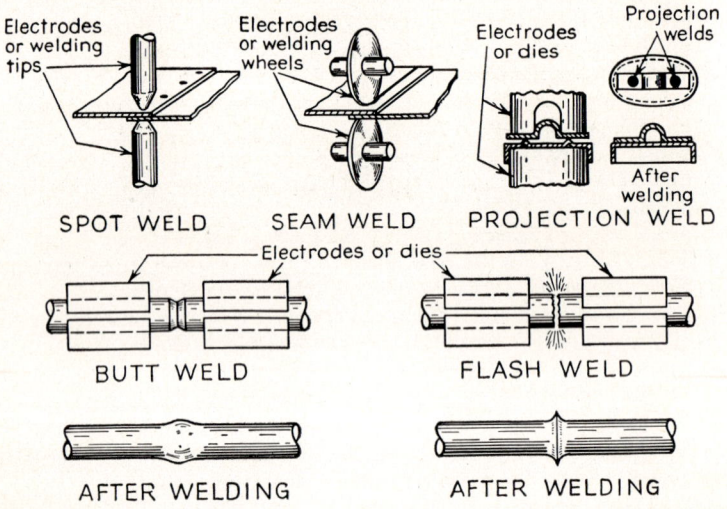

FIG. 36. Principal types of resistance welds. (*From "Resistance Welding Manual."*)

ally welded together, the less damage is liable to be produced to the properties of the welded bar. It has been found that electric heating, chiefly because of the intense temperature available, has advantages in this respect. Of several methods used, the one chosen for illustration is the electric butt-welding process, which is illustrated in Fig. 36. The parts to be welded are cleaned and placed together and tightly clamped in copper jaws. Electric connections are made so that a current of high amperage flows through the parts. The metal begins to heat from the joint outward, because of the high resistance at the joint itself. After it has reached a welding temperature, pressure is applied to bring the jaws together so as to compress and upset the metal at the joint. The jaws are then released, and the partially welded piece is rolled in rotating rolls to complete the weld. In another form, this type of welding is used for joining railroad or streetcar rails. For heavy work the joint is *flashed*. This uses a much heavier current, and a much shorter time is taken. In percussion welding, contact is made by abutting the pieces;

Fig. 37. Spot-welding machine. Welding collar on tube. (*Lewis Lodge, author's laboratory.*)

then contact is broken and made again. This heats to welding temperature, but does not give deep penetration of heat.

Wrought iron, steel, stainless steel, copper, brass, bronze, aluminum, monel, Inconel, and nickel can be welded by the butt-welding process just described. Also these metals may be welded to one another whenever a pair alloys readily. Copper and iron are easily welded together, and also copper and aluminum.

Efficiency of Resistance Butt Welds. Several tests have been made on the strength of electric-resistance butt welds. It would appear that the strength of the joint is 82 to 100 per cent of the strength of the original metal. Sometimes the metal adjacent to, but not in, the line of junction is of larger crystal size. One authority says that the efficiency of the welds is 93 per cent (average). If the assembly is annealed or normalized after welding, the efficiency may be 100 per cent, or better.

Electric Spot Welding. Electric spot welding is a type of electric resistance welding which is in some respects superior to riveting, because it does not reduce the section of the metal or injure its structure by punching rivet holes. It is especially applicable to thin plates, and consists of pressing two electrodes against the plates at the point where the spot weld is to be made. The electric current produces a high temperature at the point of contact, and the application of pressure completes the weld. The general principle is indicated by Figs. 36 and 37. The weld may be completed in as little as 0.1 sec, and, in this case, little or no oxide is formed, and therefore no flux is required. Spot welding can be used for almost all metals and alloys, and even for joining dissimilar alloys to one another. An automatic process of electric spot welding called shot welding is used on very thin alloys which are injured

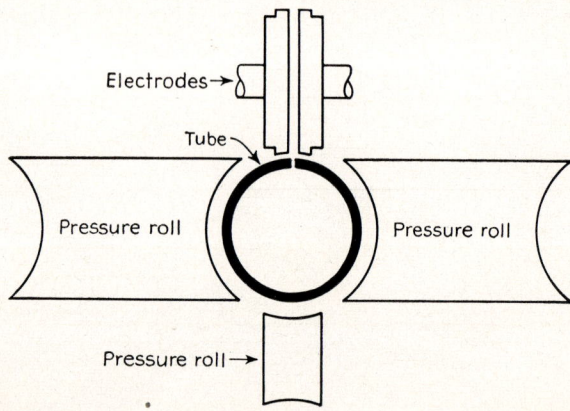

Fig. 38. Position of pressure rolls and electrodes for welding tube. (*From "Resistance Welding Manual."*)

if heated for more than a fraction of a second, notably stainless steel, as in the fabrication of lightweight railroad trains.

A pair of plates joined by spot welding will bear twice the load of the same couple joined by riveting. This does not mean that welding is stronger than riveting, but that about one-half of the parent metal has been removed for rivet holes and its strength correspondingly reduced.

Seam Welding. Using the same principle as in spot welding, a continuous seam may be produced, as indicated in Fig. 36. This will make pressure-tight welds. A somewhat similar process, illustrated in Fig. 38 and known as continuous-resistance butt welding, is used somewhat extensively at the present time for the production of welded pipe.

FUSION-WELDING PROCESSES

Fusion welding consists of depositing molten metal into a joint formed by two pieces of metal to be joined. Some of the different forms of joint are shown in Fig. 39 to illustrate the principle involved. It is customary to deposit a metal bead from a rod, whose analysis is frequently similar to that of the metal which is being welded (called the "parent metal"). The electric arc is the commonest source of heat used for melting, and the metal is deposited from the rod onto or into the joint, the sides of which are also melted superficially (see Fig. 40). A gas flame may equally well be used as the source of heat, and sometimes an exothermic chemical reaction may supply or supplement the heat, as in the thermit and atomic hydrogen methods. In all processes of

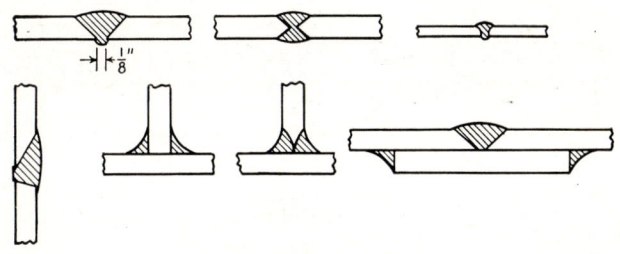

Fig. 39. Single-V, double-V, and other forms of scarf welds.

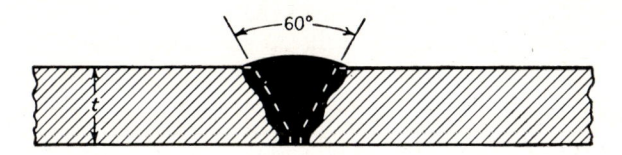

Fig. 40. Cross section of fusion weld after the bead has been deposited.

fusion welding the surfaces to be welded must be clean and free from dirt, grease, and all foreign matter.

Carbon-arc Process. In the carbon-arc process, which is now little used, the rod of welding metal is melted by an electric arc formed at the welding point between a carbon electrode and the metal to be welded. It is customary to make the metal to be welded the positive pole of the arc, and the electrode the negative pole, because the positive terminal is the hotter, and because this arrangement makes a more stable arc.

Metal-arc Process. In the metal-arc process one electrode is the metal rod which is to be melted; the parent metal is the other terminal. Both direct and alternating currents are used. When direct current is used, the rod may be either the positive or the negative electrode, depending upon the type of metal to be melted, and its thickness. Most rods are heavily coated with an appropriate solid flux material, but lightly coated or bare rods may be used. The coating stabilizes the arc as well as melting to form a flux or slag. It also forms a gas over the weld, shielding arc and weld from oxidation and, most particularly, from nitriding. It increases the rate of deposition of weld metal. Widely different types of rod are used to allow for different conditions and material. Obviously, a strong rod will deposit a strong metal bead; a ductile rod, a ductile bead; and so on. But the most important feature is the chemical composition of the deposited metal. The metal-arc process is probably today the most commonly used welding process (Figs. 39 to 42).

Instead of depositing melted metal into a joint, the edges to be welded may be abutted together and melted. This is especially applicable for

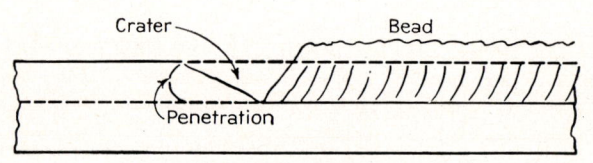

Fig. 41. Longitudinal section of bead.

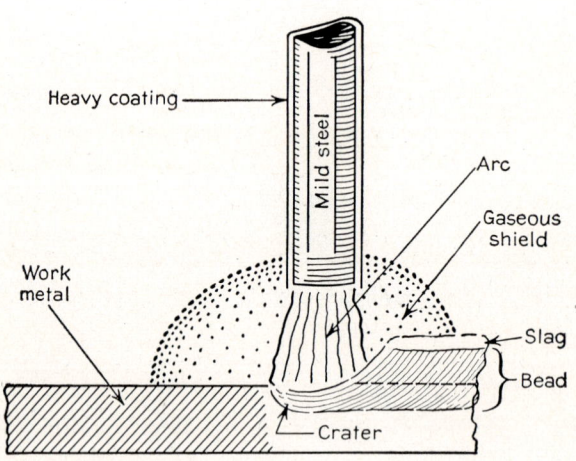

Fig. 42. Diagram of the shielded metallic arc. (*From Chaffee's "Practical Arc Welding," Hobart Trade School, Inc.*)

welding thin pieces and for welding flat pieces into tubes. Welded tubes are often cold-drawn and annealed, whereby grain refinement of the weld is accomplished. After such treatment the weld metal may have properties superior to those of the parent metal, especially if it has been deposited under inert or controlled atmosphere (see Figs. 28, 29, and 30).

Atomic Hydrogen Arc Welding. In this process (see Fig. 43), an arc is struck between the two electrodes; hydrogen passes through orifices in the clamps which hold the electrodes; when it comes in contact with the arc, most of its molecules dissociate into atoms ($H_2 \rightarrow 2H$), absorbing heat. When these atoms get beyond the arc, they recombine, forming molecules and releasing heat. This heat, plus the intense heat of the arc, produces a temperature higher than either the arc or gas flame. The greatest heat is generated at the boundary of the arc stream, the edge of which is brought into contact with the work. Therefore the work is protected by an envelope of hydrogen gas, and the process is used largely for oxidizable metals, such as stainless steel, aluminum, Inconel, monel metal, brass, and bronze; for hard-to-weld metals and alloys, such as chrome, nickel, and molybdenum steels; and for small and thin, light sections. The deposited bead is sound, free from scale, and smooth. The operating cost is higher than that of most other fusion-welding processes.

Inert Gas Welding. In this process a tungsten electrode is used and argon or helium is supplied to envelop the arc formed between the

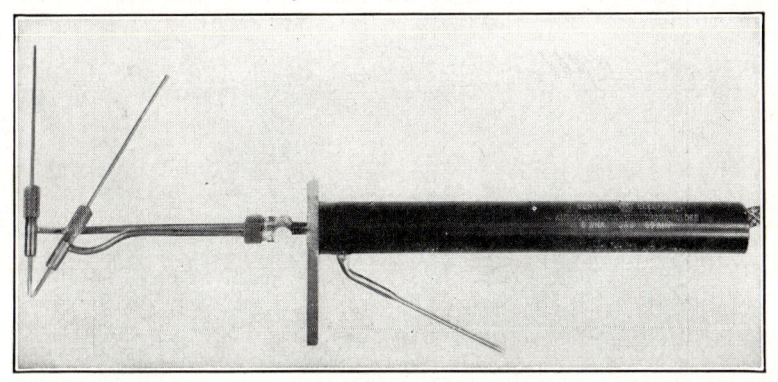

FIG. 43. Electrode holder for atomic-hydrogen arc welding. (*Courtesy of General Electric Company.*)

electrode and the work. This exclusion of air makes possible welding of such highly oxidizable metals as magnesium, aluminum, titanium, and zirconium; also stainless steel and K monel. Alternating current or direct current may be used, except that the latter may not be used with aluminum. Higher speeds than those obtainable with the atomic hydrogen method are achieved, and nickel, which absorbs hydrogen, may be welded by this process.

Submerged Melt Welding. This process uses a granular flux that is laid down on the joint to be welded, deep enough to cover the completed weld. A bare electrode is power-fed into this flux, and its rate of feed is automatically controlled by the length of the arc. High currents are used, and the resultant heat fuses the electrode and the base plate. The flux adjacent to the arc melts and floats to the weld surface, where it solidifies. The arc is completely covered at all times by the flux and is protected from contact with the air. Either direct or alternating currents may be used. The high current results in high welding speeds, and the process is of particular advantage where repetitive or heavy welding is to be performed in the horizontal position. An example is shown in Fig. 44.

Thermit Welding. Goldschmidt was the first to employ the very large amount of heat of oxidation of powdered aluminum for the purpose of reducing other metals from their compounds, chiefly oxides. The oxide of any metal below aluminum in the electropotential series will be reduced by aluminum, and the temperature of the reduced metal will be very high,

Fig. 44. Automatic submerged arc welding of 30-in. pipe. This step welds the outside of the pipe, which later goes to another machine that welds the inside. (*Courtesy of National Tube Company.*)

provided that the compound reduced has a much lower heat of formation than the compound formed. A typical example is the one used in the thermit welding process:

$$Fe_2O_3 + 2Al \rightarrow 2Fe + Al_2O_3 + 181{,}500 \text{ Cal}$$

The heat so produced may be used for welding in the following manner: The reaction is carried on in a suitable crucible. If the metal to be welded is steel, the mold must be so made that the steel can be preheated by some form of torch or blowpipe. The reduced iron at a temperature too high to be conveniently measured, but usually between 2300 and 2500°C (4170 and 4530°F), is tapped into the mold, unites itself to the metal on both sides, and upon freezing forms a strong joint. The contents of the crucible are so adjusted that the casting produced is a metal of specified analysis, which sometimes may be actually stronger than the parent metal.[1] The two parts that are being welded are separated slightly, so as to permit a suitable volume of the liquid metal to flow between and give its heat for the formation of a thin area of dissolved metal on either side.

One of the great advantages of thermit welding is that broken parts can be repaired without removing them from the machine in which they occur. Thermit welds have been made up to a size using 2 tons or more of metal, and are made in all manner of machines and structures, such as sternposts of vessels, side frames on locomotives, crossheads, connecting rods, crankshafts, driving wheels, teeth broken out of pinions, necks on broken steel-mill rolls, driving shafts, railroad rails, etc. Defective parts of castings, such as shrinkage cavities, misruns, etc., are successfully filled up with thermit metal. Cast iron may be welded by this process, but usually has to be annealed afterward, because the carbon in the cast iron makes the iron of the weld hard and brittle unless it is very slowly cooled from a red heat. Nonferrous metals and alloys may be welded by the thermit process, using a mixture of oxides which will be reduced by powdered aluminum to produce a mixture approximating the analysis of the metal to be welded. Also one of the outstanding characteristics of thermit fusion welding is the capacity to produce welds of very large size.

The strength of the metal deposited in a thermit weld will depend on its analysis. The efficiency of fusion welds will depend on the strength and the ductility of the welded piece and also whether the weld is left of larger cross section than the original parts joined, or whether it is machined off to the same size. Obviously, metal deposited at a high temperature will have approximately the crystalline structure and strength of a casting poured at a high temperature.

Applications of Fusion Welding. Fusion welding is applicable to all the metals and alloys except zinc and tin, as far as has been attempted, but the difficulties are much greater with some than with others. Copper is one of the most difficult metals, because it dissolves gases so readily when molten and gives them off on freezing, producing a porous weld, and also because it dissolves its own oxide, which injures its strength and ductility. These objections can be overcome by incorporating a little phosphorus or silicon in the copper welding rod. Copper may be welded to iron or steel, it being necessary only to preheat the iron and then melt the copper in contact with it, when an alloy forms at once. Although cast iron is difficult to weld, under some circumstances it may

[1] Though not usually both stronger and more ductile together.

be welded to itself, using steel or high-nickel alloys as a welding metal, or it may be welded to steel. Malleable cast iron, brass, bronze, monel, nickel, Inconel, aluminum, magnesium, and their alloys are all weldable by the fusion method. But the commonest application is the welding of steel and of alloy steels.

The welding of lead ("lead burning") is much practiced in storage-battery work and in lining tanks with lead. It is like soldering, using a gas flame and a solder of pure lead sticks or lead hardened with antimony when a harder metal is wanted for threading. The base metal to which the deposited metal is attached is not melted.

During the past few years, a number of large buildings have been erected in which fusion welding has been used instead of riveting. Boilers and pressure vessels are now often made by welding, and some bridges and many ships have been so fabricated. Most of the Liberty ships of the Second World War were fabricated by welding. Electric-arc fusion processes, and, to a less extent, gas fusion welding processes have been employed for all these procedures. It is prophesied that welding will completely replace riveting for these types of fabrication if, and when, there is greater confidence in the soundness of welds, especially if reliable methods of testing the finished weld in place are available.

Strength of Electric and Gas-torch Fusion Welds. The strength of all fusion welds will obviously depend on the kind of metal deposited in the weld. For the sake of ductility it is common to deposit pure metals in the joints, but where higher strength is important it is usual to deposit an alloy, or a joining metal of higher strength. It must be remembered that the deposited metal will not make a good joint unless it will alloy with the parts being joined—*i.e.*, unless it forms a liquid solution with them. In steel fusion welds, the strength of the deposited metal will be 40,000 to 120,000 psi.

Ductility of Fusion Welds. Many welding rods of alloy steel are now made which give deposits of high strength and ductility. Some alloying elements, such as vanadium, for example, have the effect of partly counteracting the undesirable crystal structure liable to be present in cast steel. Metallic deposits may therefore be made which are both stronger and more ductile than the parent metal itself. The shielded-arc process and, more recently, the inert-gas process and the submerged-melt process, which, as described before, exclude the air from the molten metal by gas or flux, have been largely responsible for material improvement in these respects, which have in turn been largely responsible for the acceptance by engineers of welding instead of riveting in joints of great importance, such as in high-pressure boilers for the Navy. The efficiency of fusion-welded joints is affected by rather complex metallurgical considerations. Actually, the deposited metal may be stronger and better in structure than the parent metal, but, as will be indicated in the next paragraph, the deposited metal is never so good as it would be if it could be hammered or otherwise worked after it had solidified.

The Structure of Fusion Welds. The deposited metal in electric arc, gas, and thermit welds solidifies with the structure of a casting. This calls to mind the columnar crystals, porosity, internal stresses, and even shrinkage cracks ordinarily associated with the cast condition in metals. The older "bare-wire" arc welds were, in addition, highly charged with oxygen and nitrogen both in solid solution and in precipitated form, these gases having been absorbed from the air while the weld metal was molten. Owing largely to changes occurring after cooling, welds of this type often have low ductility, perhaps 5 to 10 per cent elongation in 2 in., and a Charpy impact value of only a few foot-pounds, although their tensile strength is often as high as 60,000 psi.

With the advent of the shielding process now used in both carbon and metal-electrode welding, the metal is low in both oxygen and nitrogen and the ductility has risen to 20 and even 30 per cent elongation in 2 in., with little if any loss of strength. The Charpy impact value is greatly increased. The cast columnar structure is retained in single-layer welds, but, as is usually the case, where layers of weld metal are deposited on top of each other, the heating action of the superincumbent layer causes structural changes to occur in the layer beneath it, and when the weld is finished, all the layers (except, of course, the top one) possess a more desirable structure. Thus in the multilayer shielded arc welding of steel, mechanical properties as good as those of rolled boiler plate are attainable.

Effects in the Metal Adjacent to the Fusion Zone. Of equal importance are the effects of the heat produced in the base metal adjacent to the weld, called the "heat-affected zone." Especially in steel, marked changes in structure and properties take place, which depend on the composition of the metal, the temperature reached, the time at a given temperature, and the rate of cooling. Improved properties may result because of recrystallization and consequent grain refinement in the steel at a certain temperature, while at a higher temperature undesirable overheating and coarse grain growth may result. Rapid cooling may form hard brittle transformation products in the steel, and this may be prevented or alleviated by supplying heat after the welding operation to alter the rate of cooling ("postheating"). An understanding of these metallurgical effects can be had only after study of Chaps. 7 and 8. Postheating is also used to bring about stress relief. Preheating, too, is frequently used in welding. This reduces the temperature gradient from the weld to the adjacent metal, thus reducing the cooling rate. Preheating is sometimes essential to attain proper welding temperature with copper and other metals or alloys of high thermal conductivity. The necessity for and effects of these treatments are greatly dependent on the method of welding employed and the size of section being welded.

Comparison of Carbon Arc, Metallic Arc, and Gas Fusion Welding. The metal-electrode arc process gives less heat penetration into the parent metal than do the carbon-electrode arc and the gas-fusion processes. Sometimes this is a benefit, and sometimes not. For example, much heat penetration is purposely avoided on light work, like welding locomotive boiler tubes to flue sheets, for parts of which expansion would be undesirable, etc. Gas is better for thin-sheet welding, the carbon arc is next best. Gas welding is usually slower on work above $\frac{1}{8}$ in. in thickness. The expenditure of heat energy in gas welding is much

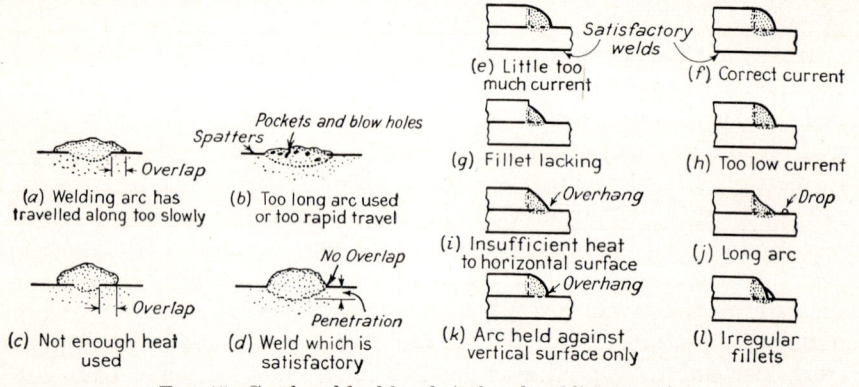

FIG. 45. Good and bad beads in hand-welding practice.

greater than in electric arc welding, on account of the greater heat dispersion. For easily oxidizable metals, the atomic-arc or inert-gas processes are most commonly used.

Automatic Welding Practice. The disadvantages in hand-welding practice, either electric or gas, are so great that automatic practice is now almost universal. The defective beads deposited, as mentioned below, are almost never encountered in automatic practice. The strength of the weld usually exceeds that of the parent metal.

Efficiency in Hand Arc-welding Practice. Where hand arc welding is employed, experience has now convinced administrators that the price paid for employing only expert welders is more than returned (see Fig. 45). Bad beads may be deposited for several reasons, such as the following:

1. Dirt, pockets, and blowholes in the metal.
2. Not enough metal deposited, because of too rapid travel of the welding rod.
3. Too much metal deposited.

4. Not enough heat, so that the deposited metal has not cut into the parent metal sufficiently.

5. Heat not applied in all places.

6. Too much heat.

7. Incorrect electric curent.

8. Deposited metal not welded to the parent metal.

Testing Welds. Welds may be cut open and inspected. They may be pulled, twisted, sheared, or tested under impact, or for hardness or corrosion resistance, using the customary testing methods in each case. Wherever the service involves vibration or alternation of stresses, fatigue tests are necessary. A special fatigue test sometimes used is the so-called "breathing test," in which a closed welded vessel (perhaps a boiler) is subjected to repetitions of internal pressure tending to cause swelling and then relaxing. A bend test is also often applied (Fig. 46). Destructive tests are generally used in order to determine whether the welding procedure and/or the ability of the operator meet the requirements (physical and chemical) of the service conditions. They may require the destruction of a complete weldment, or quantitative information may be obtained from a representative specimen. But the most desirable tests are nondestructive ones, which assure that the weld is sound and reliable, and then leave it in service. The commonest causes of failure of welds in service are internal cracks and lack of fusion. These are much less liable to occur in automatic welding.

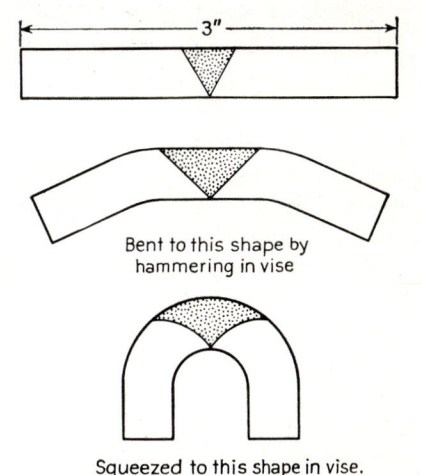

FIG. 46. Bend test of a single fusion weld.

Nondestructive tests are of value to prove the quality of the weld metal, and may consist of X-ray, gamma-ray, magnetic, hydrostatic-pressure, air-pressure, stethoscopic, penetrating oil, and supersonic testing. The hydrostatic-pressure and air-pressure tests are those mentioned in the previous paragraph as "breathing tests." The stethoscopic test consists in striking the weld and its neighboring metal with a hammer and listening through a stethoscope to the ringing sound produced. In the hands of an experienced person, this test gives excellent results as to soundness. The other tests are described in Chap. 6.

Economy of Welding. The joining of metal parts in the building of an automobile, for example, is an expensive part of its manufacture.

When the various "parts" are manufactured, often in small-town plants, and shipped to the factory for assembly in large numbers, welding machines, especially of the butt-, spot-, and seam-welding types, cut the time and the labor costs sometimes to one-tenth of the older methods of bolting and riveting. Of course an expensive welding machine cannot pay for its keep unless the quantity of work is large and of one general type. Where miscellaneous "job" welding is done, as in small repair shops, the gas and arc processes are most useful. When the welding must be done in the field, as in structural and pipe-line construction, the fusion processes also are more useful because of their flexibility and portability.

Fields of the Different Welding Processes. There are millions of pressure-welding operations performed per year, especially in the automobile and airplane industries. But, for heavy shapes, field fabrication, and similar outside-the-factory work, fusion welding probably represents the greatest tonnage, though not the greatest number of operations. Fusion welding comprises electric welding, gas welding, atomic hydrogen arc welding, thermit welding, and others listed in Table 16. There is no sharp line of demarcation between the fields of usefulness of these fusion processes, although the atomic hydrogen and the thermit processes each have certain special fields of their own, as indicated on pages 105 and 107. Both the electric-fusion and the gas processes cover satisfactorily the large-tonnage field of pipe-line welding, heavy machine building, erection of structures, and like operations. Each has its advocates, and probably each is best and/or cheapest under certain conditions, but neither is best for all. Under many circumstances it is cheaper and easier to lead electricity to the welding location, and, under others, to supply the appropriate gases in cylinders and tubes. For metals which oxidize readily, the gas flame is usually easier to use. It avoids the necessity of expertness in maintaining steady arcs of proper length and temperature. The question of relative heat penetration is discussed on page 110. Both electric and gas methods have been developed for automatic operation.

SOLDERING AND BRAZING

Soldering. The operation of soldering consists of joining two metallic surfaces by causing a molten alloy to adhere to the surfaces by a process of diffusion or alloying. In the common soldering process used in plumbing, for example, the surface is first cleaned with a flux to remove grease, oxide, and dirt, and then melted solder, commonly an alloy of 50 per cent lead and 50 per cent tin, is applied. The composition is such as to have a very low melting point and to alloy readily with the clean metal surface. The melting point of the solder is always lower than that of the surfaces to be joined. Soldering is much used in electrical, radio, and television work for joining or attaching wires; sheet-metal parts of steel and other metals are also often made or repaired by soldering. Special solders are used for aluminum and other metals, and when aluminum is soldered the clean surface is often first coated with tin. Solders are usually weak alloys, and the joints are not only weak but may also give rise to rapid corrosion in moist surroundings because of the large difference in electric potential between the metal surfaces and the solder (see Chap. 12).

Brazing. Brazing is a method of joining metal surfaces wherein another metal or alloy, of lower melting point than the surfaces to be joined, is melted or caused to flow while molten between the surfaces, bonding them together when it solidifies. The surfaces themselves are not fused, and in this respect brazing differs from welding and is basically the same as soldering, differing from ordinary soldering in that higher temperatures and stronger, higher-melting metals are used for the joint. The bond is obtained by diffusion or alloying between the brazing alloy and the surface. Brazing cannot correctly be called welding, and it is well to differentiate it from soldering because of the much stronger joints obtained than in ordinary soldering and the consequently greater usefulness of the process from an engineering standpoint.

Brazing is commonly and increasingly employed, and is especially useful where either the metallic composition or the shape and position of the parts to be joined would make welding difficult. For example, cast iron is commonly brazed because it is not readily welded.

Brazing alloys are of two types, the silver brazing alloys, often called "silver solders," and the copper or zinc-copper brazing alloys, often called "spelter solders" or "brazing solders." The most commonly used silver brazing alloys range in composition from 10 to 80 per cent silver, with the remainder chiefly copper and zinc in varying proportions. Some may thus be regarded as brass with added silver. Small amounts of other metals are sometimes added, and other compositions, including pure silver, are occasionally used for special purposes. Among the advantages of the silver brazing alloys are lower melting points than the copper or zinc-copper alloys, better corrosion resistance of the alloy, strong joints, and high electrical conductivity.

The base-metal brazing alloys range from pure copper to high-zinc brasses and bronzes. The commonest is approximately half copper, half zinc. Several per cent of tin or nickel is sometimes added.

In the brazing operation the alloy may be placed between the surfaces in solid form and melted in place, or it may be melted separately and caused to flow into the joint. A proper jig or assembly is employed, and a flux is also used. The flux is generally melted borax and boric acid. The various brazing methods include:

1. Melting by gas or torch, as in gas welding. This is probably most widely used.

2. Furnace brazing. The assembly is placed in a furnace already heated so as to melt the alloy quickly. This method is growing in use.

3. Dip brazing. The assembly is dipped in the molten alloy.

4. Electric brazing. Heating by resistance or by induction is generally employed. The latter is illustrated on page 424.

SURFACE APPLICATIONS

Hard Surfacing. Welding is used to coat with a hard surface both new parts and those worn in service. Alloys are applied to the surface to be protected, or built up, by arc or gas welding. These alloys may be made of ferrous or nonferrous material, and they commonly possess resistance to impact, corrosion, abrasion, and scouring.

Metallizing. In metallizing, or metal spraying, a hand gun is employed to which the metal, in the form of wire or powder, is automatically fed. It is there melted by an oxygen-gas flame and forced out of the nozzle of the gun in the form of a fine, dense spray, which is caused to impinge upon the surface to be metallized, where it chills instantly in stratified layers. Any molten metal may be sprayed by this process, which may be applied to parts of any shape or size, and can be used for both new and worn parts.

CUTTING METALS WITH A FLAME

Besides the shaping and finishing of metals in machine shops, there is a large amount of cutting done on a much larger and rougher scale, as in the cutting up of structures to wreck buildings, bridges, etc. There is also the cutting up of scrap in fabricating shops and steel mills, cutting gates and risers off castings in foundries, etc. Rotating saws, sometimes with hardened teeth and a relatively slow speed, and sometimes without teeth but revolving so fast as practically to melt their path through the metal, are used. The process of cutting by means of heat has increased rapidly with the use of gas and electric welding. This operation is applied according to two methods: In the arc process a current of 350 to 800 amp is used with a carbon electrode to melt its way through plates of steel or other metal. The arc is advanced across the plate, or other object, as fast as the metal melts and flows out of the path. A method used much more extensively for iron, steel, and other easily burned metals and alloys which do not have very high heat conductivity is to burn a

FIG. 47. Powder-cutting stainless steel. (*Courtesy of Lukens Steel Company.*)

FIG. 48. Multiple flame cutting with pantagraph. (*Courtesy of Lukens Steel Company.*)

path through the metal with a stream of oxygen (see Figs. 47 to 49). In practice the gas-cutting method is applied industrially only to iron and steel; if there were a demand, it doubtless could be applied to nickel, monel, and zinc. Brass may be cut, but not with commercial efficiency, and copper, because of its high thermal conductivity and low heat of oxidation, is not economically amenable to gas-cutting methods. The cutting of cast iron is not industrially satisfactory, because the carbon (especially graphite) interferes with the propagation of the chemical reaction of oxidation of iron. It is the heat from this reaction which

Fig. 49. Oxygen lance cutting "hot top" from a steel ingot 24 by 66 in. This is a regular production operation in a certain large steel plant and takes only 15 min. (*Courtesy of Linde Air Products Company, through E. E. Thum, Metal Progress.*)

enables the cutting to continue. The cutting of steel consists in heating a spot to a bright-red heat and then projecting on it a thin jet of oxygen. This readily unites with the hot steel, forming a fusible oxide, which flows out of the way under the impact of the oxygen, leaving a fresh surface for attack. The heat generated by the chemical reaction between iron and oxygen is sufficient to propagate the action actively after it is once started, but it is usually more economical in time and labor to have a pilot flame of gas and oxygen preheating the metal in advance of the main oxygen jet. Hydrogen, acetylene, or propane gas may be used with oxygen for the preheating flame.

The cutting of stainless steel with the oxyacetylene torch has been hitherto impossible, because of the refractory chromium oxide film which quickly coats the cut surface. Recently the blowing of fluxing powders through the gas nozzle has obviated this difficulty. The powder both erodes the film mechanically and reduces its melting point.

Flame Machining. Gas cutting in its later developments has become a tool of remarkable precision and value. In its most refined form it is called *flame machining*. Much of the cutting of structural-steel shapes, later to be welded into one of many useful articles, is now done by flame methods. Where intricate designs are to be cut, the flame is guided automatically by a pantograph device. An electronic tracer has been developed which guides the cutting flame, accurately following a drawing of the shape to which the steel plate is to be cut. Thus, flame cutting of structural steel, followed by welding of the cut parts, makes possible the cheap fabrication of a strong, tough structure at a low cost, without the necessity for the more expensive casting procedure which it replaces. It might be thought that extreme temperature might injure the properties of the metal on its surface, but investigations seem to show that low-carbon steels, up to at least 0.25 per cent carbon, are less injured by heat cutting than by the tearing action of tool machining. On the other hand, steels of higher carbon and alloy steels, especially those containing chromium or tungsten, may be injured to a depth of $\frac{1}{8}$ to $\frac{3}{8}$ in., which should be cut off with tools after flame cutting.

Bibliography

Books

Allegheny-Ludlum Steel Corporation: "Welding Stainless Steels," Brackenridge, Pa., 1943.
American Welding Society: "Welding Handbook," 3d ed., New York, 1950.
British Welding Research Association: "Symposium on Metallurgy of Steel Welding," London, 1947.
Boston, O. W.: "A Bibliography on Cutting of Metals, 1864 to 1943," American Society of Mechanical Engineers, New York, 1945.
Chaffee, W. J.: "Practical Arc Welding," Hobart Trade School, Inc., Troy, Ohio, 1942.
Grover, La Motte: "Manual of Design for Arc Welded Steel Structures," Air Reduction Sales Co., New York, 1946.
Henry, O. H., and G. F. Claussen: "Welding Metallurgy," American Welding Society, New York, 1940.
Jefferson, T. B.: "The Welding Engineer," McGraw-Hill Publishing Company, Inc., New York, 1948.
Jennings, R. F.: "General Shop Gas and AC Arc Welding and Cutting," rev. ed., McKnight & McKnight, Bloomington, Ill., 1946.
Lincoln Electric Company: "Procedure Handbook of Arc Welding Design and Practice," 9th ed., Cleveland, Ohio, 1950.

———: "Arc Welding in Design, Manufacture, and Construction," Cleveland, Ohio, 1939.
———: "Maintenance Arc Welding," Cleveland, Ohio, 1943.
———: "Studies in Arc Welding," Cleveland, Ohio, 1945.
———: "Lessons in Arc Welding," Cleveland, Ohio, 1947.
———: "Design for Welding," Cleveland, Ohio, 1949.
LINDE AIR PRODUCTS COMPANY: "The Oxy-Acetylene Handbook," New York, 1946.
MACKENZIE, L. B., AND OTHERS: "Welding Encyclopedia," 11th ed., Welding Engineer Publishing Company, Chicago, 1943.
MARKS, LIONEL S. (editor): "Steel Plates and Their Fabrication," Lukens Steel Company, Coatesville, Pa., 1947.
PRIEST, H. M.: "The Practical Design of Welded Steel Structures," American Welding Society, New York, 1943.
RESISTANCE WELDER MANUFACTURERS ASSOCIATION: "Resistance Welding Manual," Philadelphia, 1946.
ROSSI, B. E.: "Welding and Its Application," McGraw-Hill Book Company, Inc., New York, 1941.

PERIODICALS AND TRANSACTIONS

Industry and Welding.   Monthly, The Industrial Publishing Co., Cleveland, Ohio.
International Acetylene Association, *Proceedings.*   Annual, New York.
Transactions of the Institute of Welding.   Bimonthly, London.
Welding Engineer.   Monthly, The McGraw-Hill Publishing Company, Inc., New York.
Welding and Metal Fabrication.   Monthly, The Louis Cassier Co., Ltd., London.
Welding Journal.   Monthly, American Welding Society, New York.
Zeitschrift für Schweisstechnik, Journal de la soudure.   Monthly, Luzern, Switzerland.

CHAPTER 6

METALLURGICAL INSPECTION AND TESTING

Metallurgical inspection includes comprehensive inspection of the product and surveillance of methods and processes of manufacture used in the production of metals and alloys. Such inspection and supervision is ordinarily provided by the manufacturer himself, often through an independent organization responsible only to a top-ranking executive, so that standards of quality may not be influenced by the exigencies of production. Customs and practices in the various branches of the metal-working industry are quite different in so far as the rights and privileges of the purchaser's inspector are concerned. Where a large, important, and expensive steel forging is to be produced, as for instance a large oil-cracking still, the purchaser's agent commonly oversees the entire process from melting to finishing, and his collaboration is welcomed by the producer. On the other hand, many metal producers and fabricators feel rather strongly that the purchaser's prerogative is the specification of the analysis and grade of metal to be used and the various mechanical, physical, or microscopic tests to be applied to the finished product to prove its soundness and fitness for the service intended, and there should be no interference with the producer or fabricator as to methods of production.

Undoubtedly the best specification is the simplest one which will encompass all the necessary qualities in the finished article without limiting the producer as to his method of arriving at such an end product. An example of the simplest type of metallurgical specification, and perhaps the best type, is the proof firing of an armor-piercing shell. Either the shell penetrates the standard armor-plate section or it does not, and it is up to the producer to choose analysis and grade of steel, rolling and forging practices, and heat-treatment methods that will accomplish the desired result. Unfortunately, metallurgical inspection and acceptance tests can seldom be reduced to such an ideal single test, and it is often necessary to employ a variety of chemical, mechanical, and physical tests to ensure the quality and suitability of the part.

Such examinations and tests range from ordinary visual inspection through chemical etching tests, mechanical tests of tensile, yield, compressive, transverse, torsional, and impact strength, to the testing of ductility, bending, hardness, hardenability, grain size, machinability, magnetic and/or electrical properties. Precise dimensional inspection also is often included in the general term "metallurgical inspection."

Metals and alloys should be bought and sold on the basis of written specifications which state the composition limits, including the maximum allowable impurities, and the desired mechanical and physical properties. Standard specifications have been formulated for almost all types of materials by committees of the American Standards Association and the American Society for Testing Materials, which contain in their membership an approximately equal number of consumers and producers. Such specifications are regularly revised and kept up to date. The Society of Automotive Engineers, a consumer organization, has formulated specifications as has also the American Iron and Steel Institute, an association of producers of steel products. The American Society for Metals publishes in its "Metals Handbook" recommendations and suggestions for processes, tests, and materials suited to various purposes. Chemical analyses are liberally employed by manufacturers at many steps in the processing, and the purchaser of large quantities of metals and parts commonly makes his own analysis of the product. Descriptions of standardized and routine tests are published in many reference books and will not be elaborated here in detail, except to indicate the usefulness and limitations of such procedures.

The production of metals and alloys and parts produced from them is a vastly complex and detailed procedure of which this book is but the barest outline. Ordinarily the consumer relies upon the specialized knowledge of the producer's technical organization to ensure that the best and most economical metal or alloy is used for his particular application. The most suitable quality (not necessarily the highest quality) is best determined through consultation between producer and consumer, with the producer in full possession of the details of further processing and the end use intended. Often, where human life and safety are not involved, it is more economical for the consumer to put up with a few rejections of individual parts than to pay the higher costs which necessarily accompany higher quality. Thus the *quality level* is a very important area of preagreement, particularly with respect to large numbers of mass-produced parts. In recent years statistical analysis has been applied to test data with increasing fruitfulness. A brief discussion of modern statistical quality control is given toward the end of this chapter.

Résumé of Manufacture. In order that one may understand the purpose of inspection, it is necessary at this point to anticipate briefly the processes of production of metals, with possibilities of defects arising. A brief description of the production of steel will serve as a background, because irregularities occuring in steel manufacture are typical.

Iron ore is smelted to produce pig iron, which is an impure product containing about 94 per cent iron. Melted pig iron with about an equal amount of melted steel scrap added is refined in an open-hearth steel furnace to produce steel containing roughly 99 per cent iron. After purification, as much as possible of the excess oxygen in the steel is removed by adding silicon and manganese. This is a source of SiO_2 and MnO and $2FeO.SiO_2$ in the form of inclusions which may be entangled in the solid steel. About 150 tons of steel may be cast into molds, where it solidifies into ingots which are, for example, 7 ft long and 24 in. square. During solidification, there is a tendency for steel somewhat lower in impurities than the average to solidify first on the outside and impurities to concentrate slightly in the top center. This concentration of impurities is known as *segregation*. The top center also contains a shrinkage cavity.

The ingot is heated to a uniform temperature inside and out and rolled or hammered into the desired shape. Correct temperature at the beginning and end of this mechanical forming has an important influence on the quality of the product. A part of the top of the ingot is cut off with the object of removing the worst of the segregated metal and the shrinkage cavity.

If tool or aircraft steel of special quality is to be made instead of ordinary structural steel, an electric furnace will be used for the refining and the liquid steel will be cast into ingots of smaller size. Then, after being brought to the desired finished form, the steel may be heated to the correct temperature, quenched, and tempered to the desired hardness or strength as the case may be.

Inspecting Manufacturing Processes and Material in Process. All manufacturing processes should be watched with care by one who understands the meaning of the different precautions and the relative importance of abnormal appearance of the alloy at any stage. The refining and ingot-forming operations are important for practically all metals and alloys; the cropping of partially rolled ingots must be watched to see that all the shrinkage cavity has been cut off; the top of an ingot is usually inferior to the bottom, especially where long ingots are cast; the temperature at which one begins rolling or forging must not be too high, and the finishing temperature must be appropriate to the material to give the best grain size and structure; the amount of reduction in the plastic state must be sufficient to eliminate completely the crystal structure formed during freezing; the cooling after rolling must not be so rapid, especially in large-sized ingots, as to produce unequalized external or internal stresses. Usually the chief attention is given to inspecting the final rolling or forging operation of any product. Where heat-treating operations are performed, the heating must be gradual: the temperature must be uniform from exterior to interior, with suitable soaking; the temperatures of the piece quenched and of the quenching bath must be correct. Many other precautions could be mentioned, but enough is said to indicate the importance of expert inspection by one who understands correct procedure. The user of metals must understand what he needs and what inspections, specifications, and tests are necessary to secure it.

If an intermediate product is not up to standard, it may be converted into a final product which is of inferior quality. For example, there are certain types of pig iron the analysis of which may be off-grade. If this pig iron is converted into steel, we may find that the steel is inferior. It is obviously important to eliminate such material from the process of manufacture before it has gone too far. Likewise, impurities may be introduced unintentionally into copper or aluminum when remelted. Furthermore, even though the final product is tested exhaustively, the test is usually on supposedly representative samples, and other parts of the same lot may by chance be defective and not be detected. Therefore, inspection of the final product is only one step in the purchaser's assurance of specification quality in all the materials bought.

Inspecting the Final Product. Although it has been customary to classify testing and inspection methods by whether or not they were destructive of the product, such a classification has little to do with the basic testing principles used. We shall discuss testing methods under the headings of Chemical Analysis, Determination of Mechanical Properties, Optical Examination, and Testing by Methods of Physics which may employ X-ray or magnetic methods, electric fields, and the like.

Chemical Analysis. While the methods of chemical analysis are the field of the chemist, the metallurgical engineer may deduce many facts concerning metal quality and processing history from the analysis of well-chosen samples. Besides the routine chemical analysis to determine that the composition of a piece is correct and impurity levels have not been exceeded, individual pieces of finished products may be analyzed to determine that segregation or decarburization has not been excessive. Because of variations like segregation and because there is a definite limit of accuracy for each analytical method, check analysis tolerances have been established for many products which are in addition to the stated permissible ranges of the elements and impurities. These tolerances take care of the expected slight differences in results obtained by different chemical laboratories.

Because of their rapidity and sensitivity to minute traces of some impurities, spectrographic methods of analysis are becoming increasingly important. If a spark is struck between a very pure carbon electrode and the sample of metal to be tested, and the light from this arc is projected onto a diffraction grating, the light is separated into its component wavelengths and a series of wavelengths or a *spectrum* may be photographed. The position and density of the spectrum lines of the sample to be analyzed, compared with a known standard, will indicate which elements are present, and their proportion. For small amounts of alloying constituents, *e.g.* less than about 5 per cent, this procedure shows an error of less than 10 per cent, takes a very short time as compared with ordinary analytical methods, and will often determine proportions of impurities present in quantities so small that they could not be detected by ordinary chemical analysis. Once a set procedure is established nonprofessional laboratory assistants are capable of handling such work.

Recently automatic spectrographic equipment which handles the whole procedure mechanically has been introduced. Many metal producers now use spectrographic analytical methods, particularly for routine control purposes.

Spark Test. Sparks thrown off when grinding a metal will indicate qualitatively the composition. This test is commonly used at many plants and scrap yards for grading steel into low-carbon, high-carbon, tungsten steel, nickel steel, chrome steel, etc. Different spark characteristics are illustrated in Fig. 50.

Other Means of Qualitative Analysis. Occasionally pieces of metal of the same form and size but of different alloys become mixed in manufacture. When this occurs, steel parts can sometimes be separated by the spark test described above, but there are now a number of methods which do not require defacing the part by grinding. These methods depend upon the comparison of standard pieces of known analysis with the unknown sample, so that the difference or identity with the known sample may be detected. Different analyses of steels show different magnetic properties such as permeability or hysteresis, and thus a magnetic comparison may be made. When like pieces of metal are joined by welding and the joint is heated, no significant thermoelectric potential is generated, but if the pieces are different a small and detectable voltage is produced. If two identical high-frequency electric fields are established and like pieces of metal put into each, the resulting small eddy currents generated in each piece will be identical. However, if the pieces

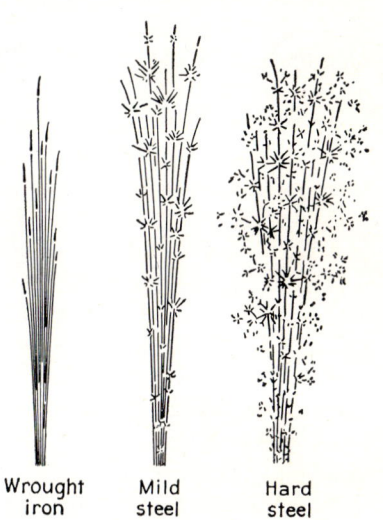

Wrought iron   Mild steel   Hard steel

Fig. 50. Character of sparks with different carbon contents in iron or steel. (*From Brearley's "Heat Treatment of Tool Steel," Longmans, Green & Co., Inc.*)

are of different analysis they will not be identical, and the difference may be detected by electronic methods.

DETERMINATION OF MECHANICAL PROPERTIES

Tensile Tests. The tensile properties of metals have been defined and described in a preceding chapter; now let us consider the methods of mak-

FIG. 51. Universal hydraulic testing machine, 200,000 lb capacity. (*Courtesy of Tinius Olsen Testing Machine Company.*)

ing such tests. A Universal testing machine has a stationary and a movable head, the latter being given a slow vertical straight-line motion by means of a hydraulic cylinder and ram, or by means of screws which are driven through a set of reduction gears. The speed of testing may be quite important and generally is defined in the specifications for the material being tested. It will vary from as little as 0.005 in. to as much as 6 in. per min. Such a machine, capable of exerting a pull of 200,000 lb, is shown in Fig. 51. The load or tension on the specimen is measured in pounds by means of hydraulic, mechanical, or electric weighing systems.

METALLURGICAL INSPECTION AND TESTING

Tensile specimens may be of a variety of shapes and range in size from fine wire to structural sections. Wherever possible tensile properties are determined on full-size sections, but where the product is of large dimensions standard round tensile specimens 0.505 in. in diameter (0.2 sq in. in area) are machined from it. In foundry work it is the usual practice to cast tensile samples in special molds, or attached to the production casting, which are poured from the same ladle as the casting itself. Examples of such standard tensile specimens are shown in Fig. 52. The central section is called the gage or parallel section and is the part really tested. It is necessary to have a portion of metal of definite

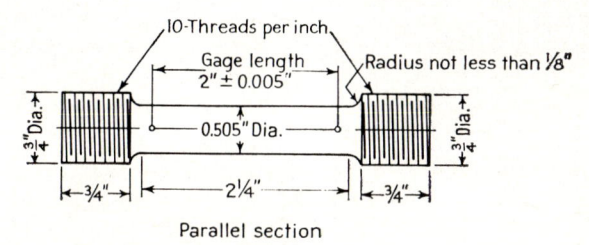

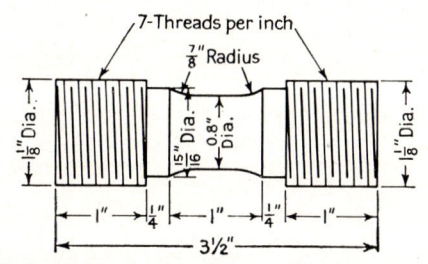

FIG. 52. Standard tension test specimens. The upper one is for wrought materials such as steel and nonferrous metals; the lower is for cast iron and other cast metals.

length and cross section throughout over which the load will be uniformly distributed. The specimen must be machined smoothly, because toolmarks and abrupt changes of cross section produce local concentrations of stress when the load is applied.

Before placing the specimen in the machine, marks are made with a prick punch or scriber at definite distances apart on the central parallel section, generally 2 in.; these are called gage marks. The distance between them is called gage length, and varies with the specimen size (see ASTM specification E8-46). The specimen also is accurately measured with a micrometer and the area of the cross section calculated. The load at any time, divided by this original area, is called the unit stress and is expressed in pounds per square inch.

As soon as a load, even a very small one, is applied to the specimen, it elongates slightly. Although this elongation is very slight, it can be measured by attaching to the specimen a sensitive instrument called an "extensometer" which reads to 0.0001 in. or less (see Fig. 53). This instrument measures the *strain* in inches per inch of gage length. Simultaneous readings of stress and strain in the specimen permit the construction of stress-strain curves as shown in Fig. 1, page 14. Most tensile-testing machines can be supplied with auxiliary equipment to permit automatic tracing of the stress-strain curve during the course of the test. Typical tensile fractures are shown in Fig. 54.

The Universal testing machine may also be used for flexural or transverse tests (bend tests), and a bend test of wrought iron is shown in Fig. 55. Nonmetallic materials such as concrete usually show very poor tensile strength but very large compressive strength, and the same Universal machines may be used to apply compressive loads for the testing of such products.

FIG. 53. Extensometer for measuring strain. (*Courtesy of Tinius Olsen Testing Machine Company.*)

Hardness Tests. The common hardness tests depend upon resistance to indentation, which is the property generally implied by hardness. Tests for this property are the Brinell, Rockwell, Vickers, and similar

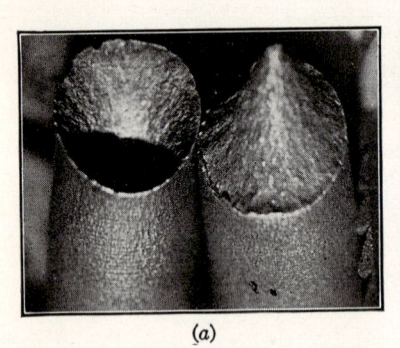

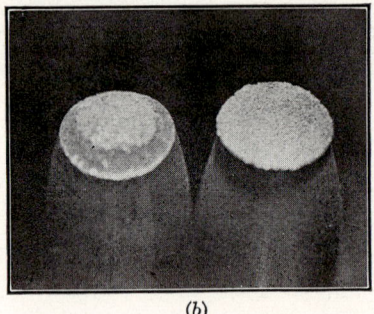

FIG. 54. Tensile fracture of (*a*) manganese bronze, and (*b*) steel. (*From F. W. Roys, "Materials of Engineering Construction," The Ronald Press Company.*)

methods. In research work very tiny impressions may be made on individual grains; such tests are called *microhardness* tests. Machines used in this work are the Vickers, Eberbach, Tukon, Bergsman, and others. The scratch-hardness method, which may employ the microcharacter tester, is also sometimes used for microhardness determination. For elastic hardness the Shore scleroscope is the only test still in common use.

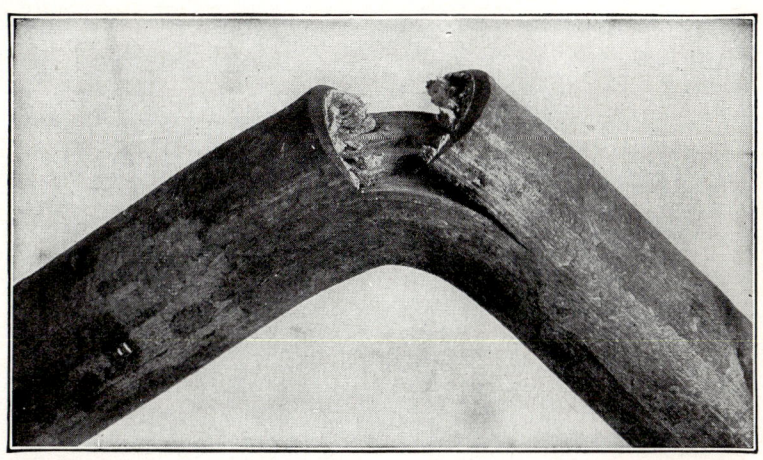

Fig. 55. Fibrous fracture of wrought iron. (*From F. W. Roys, "Materials of Engineering Construction," The Ronald Press Company.*)

Brinell Hardness Tester. The Brinell tester consists of a hand- or power-operated vertical hydraulic press designed to force a ball indenter into the test specimen. The standard procedure requires a ball of 10 mm diameter under a load of 3,000 kg for ferrous and 500 kg for nonferrous metals. The diameter of the impression is measured under a special microscope and directly converted to the Brinell hardness number (Bhn) (see Fig. 56).

Rockwell Hardness Tester. The Rockwell test employs first a minor load applied to the specimen by elevating it against the indenter. Then a major load is applied, being slowly released, and leaving the minor load still applied. After an impression has been made by application of the major load, the major load is removed and the Rockwell hardness is read on a gage. The reading is based upon the depth of penetration, less the elastic recovery following removal of the major load, less the penetration resulting from the minor load (see Fig. 57).

Fig. 56. Brinell hardness tester.

Vickers Test. The Vickers-Armstrong, as well as the Amsler-Vickers tester, employs a square-base diamond pyramid indenter which is pressed into the specimen by a load of 1 to 120 kg. The diagonal of the impression made is measured under a special microscope and converted to the diamond pyramid hardness number (DPH). Because of the shape of the indenter the diagonal of the impression is actually a measure of the area of impression.

Shore Scleroscope. The scleroscope measures loss in kinetic energy of a falling "tup," absorbed by indentation upon impact of the tup on

FIG. 57. Rockwell hardness tester. (*Courtesy of American Chain & Cable Company.*)

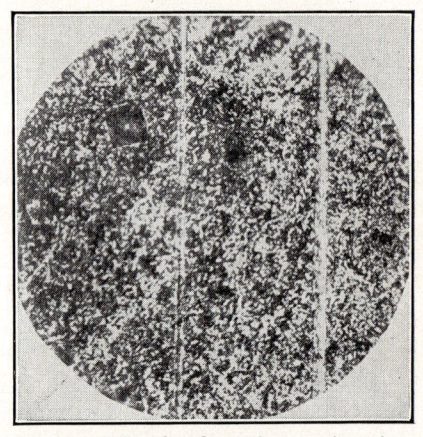

FIG. 58. Microhardness impressions in a slightly decarburized alloy steel (AISI 4130). Scratch hardness under two different pressures (of the order of 1 g and 5 g) and a diamond pyramid impression, which is only 0.002 in. from the edge. (*Author's laboratory.*)

the metal being tested, and as indicated by the rebound of the tup. The apparatus is portable, and the test is most useful on smooth surfaces that must not be deeply marked by an indentation. On rough or uneven surfaces the test gives low readings.

Conversions. Conversion tables (see Table 5, page 21) are published for comparison of Brinell, Rockwell, Vickers, and sometimes scleroscope readings. The tables must be used with considerable caution, as they are not always applicable, especially on different kinds of metals. Most of the conversion tables published are based on steel products. The hardness is also an *indication* of the ultimate tensile strength and the fatigue strength of ferrous metals. It is sometimes used as such, and especially when it can be used as a nondestructive acceptance test.

Microhardness Tests. If an alloy contains hard and soft particles, it is often desirable to measure the hardness of microscopic points in order to determine the hardness of each kind of constituent. A crude scratch-hardness tester has been used for many years for such a purpose, but the Bierbaum microcharacter tester, which draws a diamond point across the surface under a given load, is a more refined method. The width of the resulting scratch is measured under a special microscope. The Eberbach, Tukon, and Bergsman testers use the DPH scales, and

Fig. 59. Universal impact testing machine. (*Courtesy of Tinius Olsen Testing Machine Company.*)

indent in a microscopic field. In addition, the Tukon tester employs a specially shaped diamond penetrator, known as the Knoop indenter, and consequently, a special hardness scale (see Fig. 58).

Toughness Tests. The Charpy and Izod notched-bar impact tests have been previously described, and a Universal machine for performing either test is shown in Fig. 59. Both types of specimen contain a notch which causes a stress concentration and ensures fracture of the specimen. The test has been subjected to criticism because it determines the resistance of a material to impact *when a notch is present* rather than the impact resistance in the absence of stress raisers. The tension impact test is probably a better indication of the true toughness of a material, and it may be expected that this method will receive increased attention in the future.

Ductility or "Cup" Testing. Although the elongation in a tensile test specimen is a good indication of ductility, it indicates only how much stretch a metal will take in one direction before failure. Stamping and deep-drawing operations require the metal to stretch in two directions

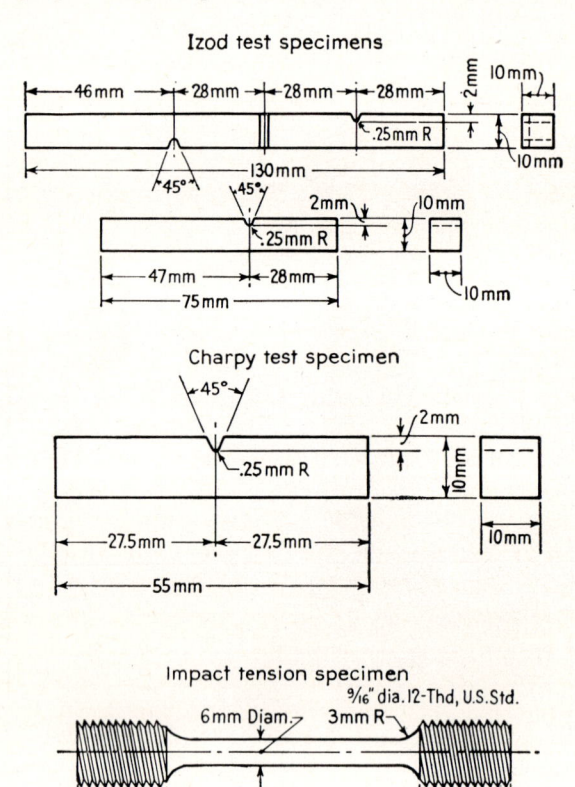

FIG. 60. Impact test specimens.

at once, and the Olsen and Erichsen ductility tests have been developed to simulate the deep drawing of a cup. By either hydraulic or mechanical means a standard ball forces sheet metal through a die, which also is standardized, until the cup thus formed cracks. The depth of the cup formed before fracture is taken as a measure of the type of ductility required for deep drawing and stamping.

Abrasion Tests. Tool steels, railroad rails, bearings, brake shoes, and other objects are often tested for wear resistance or abrasion. Attempts to establish a standard test for this purpose have not been successful, but the loss of weight over a unit surface area after a definite number of abrasions under a definite pressure is sometimes used as an indication. Usually this is a destructive test, but the article tested may be put into service subsequently.

Step-down Test. If a rolled "round" is turned down to various diameters, as shown in Fig. 61, and ground to a very smooth surface, the various surfaces may be examined by eye or by magnifying glass, and occasionally there will be found extremely small marks or hairlines. Obviously in this way one can inspect areas representing different portions of the material from almost the center to the outside.

Other Tests Commonly Used on Metals. Creep tests to measure the plastic flow of metals held for a long time at stresses lower than the normal yield strength and fatigue tests to measure endurance limit are

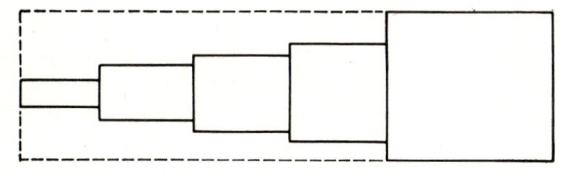

FIG. 61. Step-down test.

mentioned on pages 31 and 20. Stress-to-rupture is now a common test on metals for high-temperature service. Dilatometers are used to measure the expansion and contraction of metals with changes in temperature or phase. Many other specialized mechanical property tests have been devised to determine the suitability of a metal product for peculiar service conditions. In general, all the mechanical property tests are destructive ones, *i.e.*, samples of the product are destroyed in order to determine accurately their properties.

The P-F Test. The P-F test was developed by B. F. Shepherd for the purpose of testing the quality of tool steel.[1] Round specimens ¾ in. in diameter are quenched in brine from temperatures of 790, 815, 845, and 870°C (1450, 1500, 1550, and 1600°F), respectively. They are then notched and broken, and their grain size is compared with a standard set of like analysis. The other halves of the specimens are then smoothed off and etched in dilute hydrochloric acid at 80°C (180°F), which shows the depth of hardening in the steel. The combination of penetration and fracture grain size is an excellent measure of the quality of the steel for use in tools and similar purposes.

---

[1] Palmer, F. R., and G. V. Luerssen, "Tool Steel Simplified," Carpenter Steel Company, Reading, Pa., 1948, pp. 416 and 424.

The cone test also is used to determine the hardenability of tool steels (see Fig. 62), as well as the Jominy end test, described on page 179.

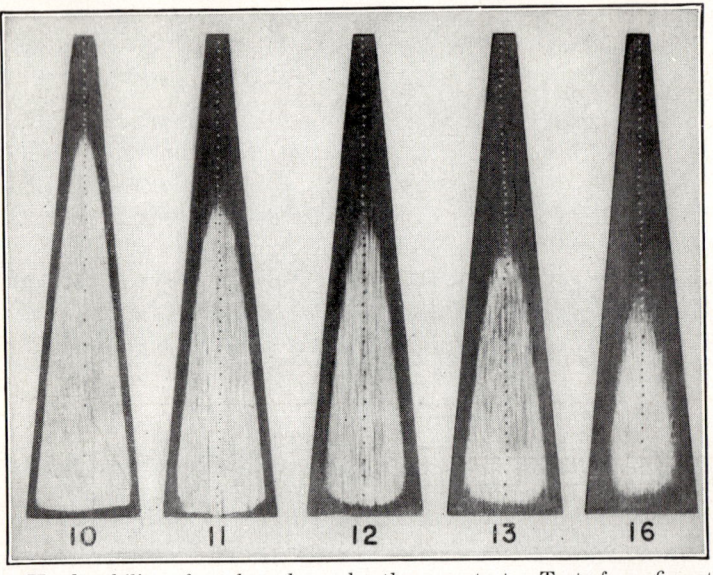

FIG. 62. Hardenability of steel as shown by the cone test. Tests from five steels of different hardenabilities, quenched in brine from 1190°C (1450°F), split lengthwise, and etched. (*Courtesy of Carpenter Steel Company.*)

OPTICAL EXAMINATION

Finished products, of course, are visually examined to detect flaws or imperfections which might be due to tearing of the metal during rolling, or some other irregularity to be discussed later. In order to examine hollow forgings or bored shafts, it is customary to examine the inside surface by means of a boroscope. By observation of broken specimens, a metallurgist can often tell much about the qualities of steel and other metals. For example, the cup and cone fractures in Fig. 54 are an indication of uniformity and ductility; the fibrous fracture in Fig. 55 is an indication of toughness and impact resistance. The grain size, which is important in its effect on the strength and ductility of steel, often varies sufficiently to be distinguished by the eye without magnification, as shown in Fig. 63. The unaided eye may be assisted by means of the microscope, as shown in Figs. 67 to 71 and others.

Deep-etch Test. This is sometimes called also the macro etch or the hot-acid etch. It is illustrated in Figs. 64 and 65. A slab or disk of steel is cut for examination and its surface made fairly smooth. This surface is then subjected for 15 to 30 min., depending on the kind of steel, to hydrochloric acid of about half strength,[1] at a temperature of 70°C (160°F). It is cleaned and the surface examined. The result will show the presence of surface cracks caused by rolling, grinding, or heat-treatment; internal cracks or flakes caused by too rapid cooling after rolling or forging; shrinkage cavities not entirely cut off; segregated material; dendritic patterns; porosity and gas bubbles too small to be seen by the unaided eye. A deep-etch test made on a slab cut from a piece rolled from the upper part of an ingot, which is the part most likely to contain porosity, segregation, or inclusions, will indicate the expertness of the refining process and of the making of the ingot. The temperature of the metal poured into the mold, the speed of pouring, and the amount of top metal cropped off subsequently will all affect

FIG. 63. Metcalf test: fractures of steel showing different sizes of crystals. A bar of steel has been heated to different temperatures along its length, thus producing different grain sizes.

quality, and will often be indicated by visual examination used in conjunction with the deep-etch test. The result of flow of the metal under pressure may also be seen, as in Fig. 15, page 68.

Sulfur Prints. If a smooth surface of steel is brought into contact with photographic bromide paper that has been wet with dilute sulfuric acid, dark spots may appear on the paper, owing to the production of sulfide of silver wherever sulfur in the steel is concentrated (see Fig. 66). Steel which shows segregation of sulfur is liable to be segregated with respect to other impurities. Moreover, the concentration of sulfur is itself injurious to the steel.

Microscopic Examination. Next in importance to chemical, mechanical, and visual inspection is examination with the microscope at magnifications of usually 50 to 500 diameters, with the general average of about 100 diameters. For this purpose a specimen is cut from a suitable location, for example, a $\frac{3}{4}$-in. cube or $\frac{1}{2}$-in. round from a test specimen, and a flat surface is brought to a mirrorlike polish by a series of steps as

---

[1] Commercial HCl 50 per cent, water 50 per cent.

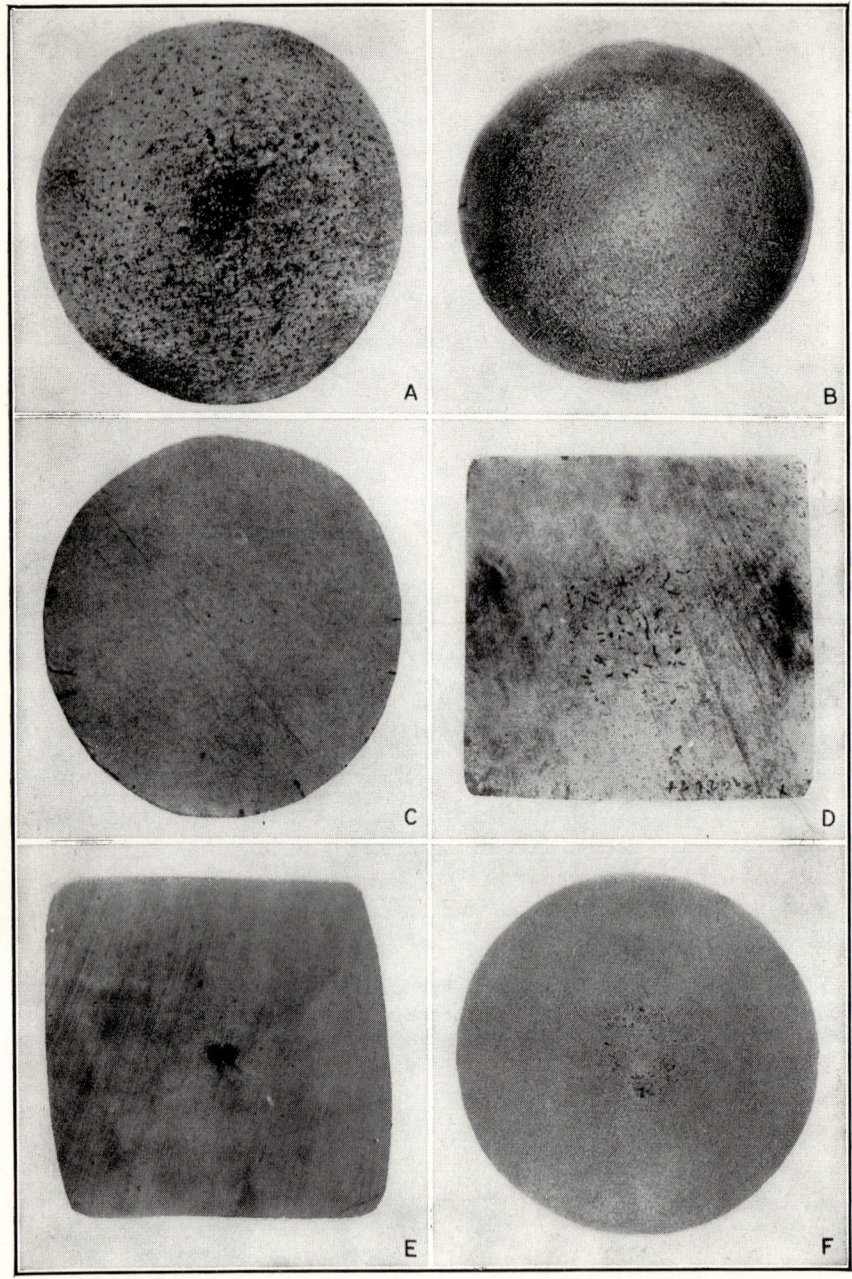

FIG. 64. Some typical defects in steel as revealed by deep etching. *A*. Blowholes. *B*. Dendritic structure. *C*. Surface seams. *D*. Internal cracks or flakes. *E*. A "piped" billet. *F*. Porous center. (*Courtesy of Carpenter Steel Company.*)

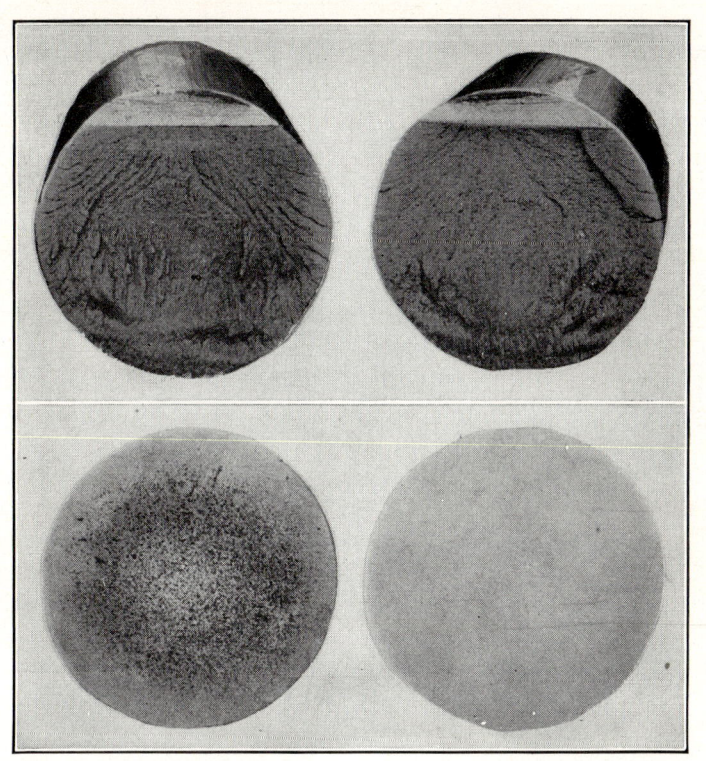

Fig. 65. Top: crop test on tool-steel bars. Bottom: hot-acid disk inspection of the same two bars. Defects appear in the left bar while the right bar is sound.

described in the standard reference books. This surface will then reveal under the microscope any inclusions of foreign bodies, such as those shown in Fig. 67. The amount of inclusions discernible under the microscope at a magnification of 100 diameters is usually limited by purchase specifications. Sample micrographs are frequently included in specifications to illustrate the maximum allowable impurities (see also page 204). Even the nature of the inclusions may be determined under suitable conditions.[1] A microscopic specimen of steel may be etched lightly with nitric or picric acid, and the grain size will be revealed by the outlining of the ferrite grain boundaries. In Fig. 68 are shown two grain sizes of brass of identical composition. Figure 69 shows a steel used for construction. The importance of inclusions upon the fatigue resistance of steel, and of grain size upon its strength, formability, impact resistance, and ductility, makes these two determinations valuable observations by means of the microscope. Purchase specifications frequently demand grain size of a given number, and standard charts are available showing

[1] See "Metals Handbook," 1948, pp. 445–449.

grain sizes from No. 1, which is approximately 1.25 in. in diameter of grain in a micrograph of 100 diameters magnification, down to size No. 10, which has 100 grains in a square inch of micrograph (see Fig. 121, page 208).

Standard procedures have also been established for revealing the grain size of the austenite which existed in the steel at some high temperature but has decomposed on cooling (see page 206). It is possible to make steel in the open-hearth furnace with a coarse, medium, or fine austenitic grain size. The response of steel to heat-treatment and some of its mechanical properties are directly related to the austenitic grain size established at an appropriate heat-treating temperature. The austenitic grain size should not be confused with the grain size of ferrite. Austenite is stable only at elevated temperatures (above the upper critical temperature), but this notwithstanding, its size prior to cooling will influence the behavior of the steel.

McQuaid-Ehn Test. Austenitic grain size may be determined by the McQuaid-Ehn test, which is used for constructional and other steels and is especially useful for steels that are to be carburized for casehardening. If a piece of steel contains over 1 per cent carbon and is slowly cooled to atmospheric temperature, it will have an appearance under the microscope, after etching lightly, somewhat similar to Fig. 103. If the steel contains less than 1 per cent carbon, a sample of it is packed in a compound consisting largely of charcoal and heated to about 925°C (1700°F) for several hours, after which it is cooled slowly. The results for two steels having a coarse and a fine austenitic grain size, respectively, are shown in Figs. 70 and 71.

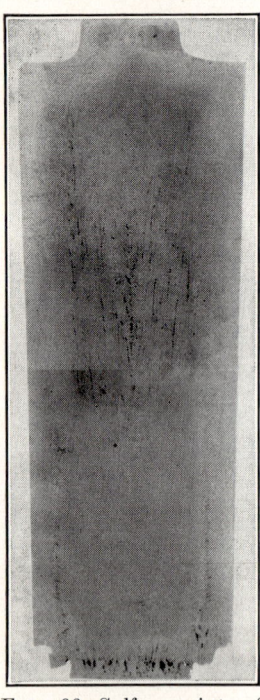

FIG. 66. Sulfur print of section of steel ingot.

Other Determinations by Means of the Microscope. With suitable polishing and etching, it is possible to distinguish under the microscope the nature of the crystals in a metal. This is common procedure and is illustrated by numerous micrographs in this book. With etching and expert examination, it is also possible to tell the difference between an alloy that has been rapidly cooled and one that has been slowly cooled.

Metallographic examination of samples of finished metals and alloys is commonly specified as a routine acceptance test. In nonferrous metals grain size, oxide and dross content, complete solution of alloying ele-

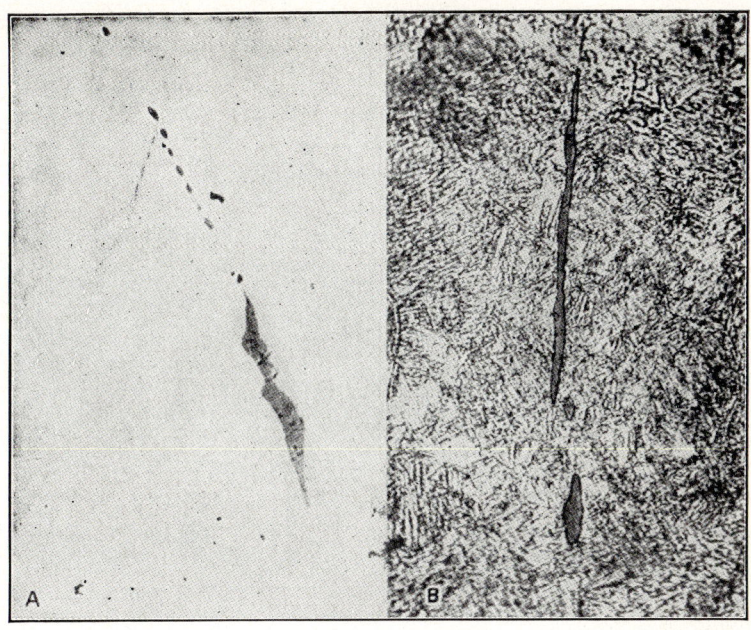

FIG. 67. (A) Photomicrograph of slag particles at one end of crack in airplane cylinder. Magnification 100 ×. Not etched. (B) Slag particles at the other end of crack. Magnification 100 ×. Etched in nitol.

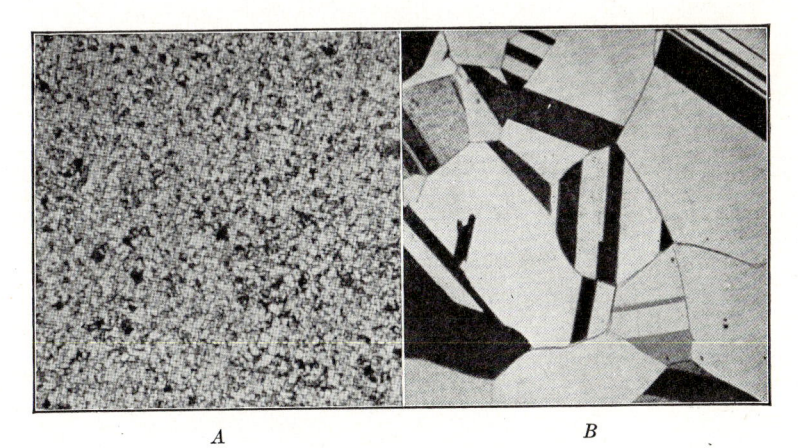

FIG. 68. Grain structure of brass (70 Cu : 30 Zn). The brass has the same composition in both cases, and the magnification is the same (100 ×), but the temperature to which the brass has been heated is different.

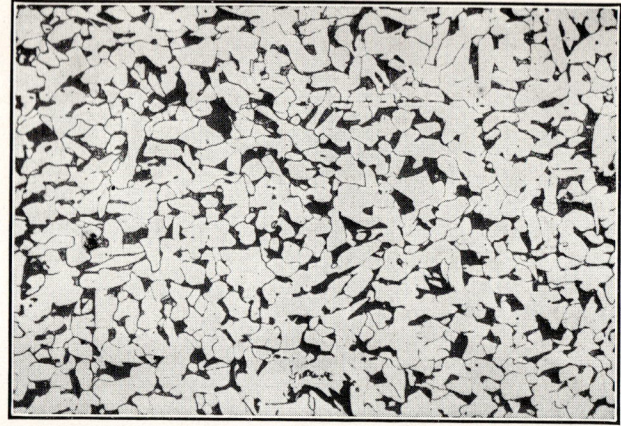

Fig. 69. Structural steel. Magnification 100 ×. The white crystals are of ferrite. The dark crystals are composed of a conglomerate; each is made of fine crystals of Fe and Fe_3C, so small that they are invisible at this magnification. (*A. Scotchbrook, author's laboratory.*)

Fig. 70. Steel of coarse inherent grain size after McQuaid-Ehn test. Magnification 100 ×. (*From H. W. McQuaid, "Metals Handbook," 1936.*)

METALLURGICAL INSPECTION AND TESTING 139

ments, and similar features are indicated by the microscope. Steels are similarly examined for grain size, decarburization (see Fig. 73), and carburization (see Figs. 74 and 75). The presence of tiny cracks, laps, and similar processing or inherent defects may thus be revealed on a

Fig. 71. Steel of same composition as that shown in Fig. 70, but having fine inherent grain size. Magnification 100 ×. (*From H. W. McQuaid,*" *Metals Handbook,*" 1936.)

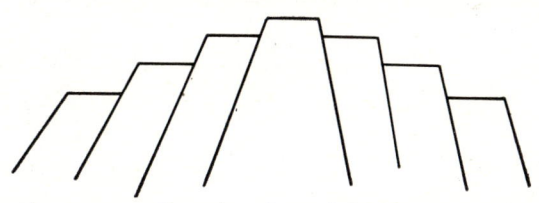

Fig. 72. Schematic representation of surface of ductile metal which has been permanently deformed. This shows how slipping within the metallic crystals produces unevenness on the surface. The uneven blocks throw shadows which appear as "slipbands" on the surface of an unetched specimen viewed under the microscope (see Fig. 8).

sampling basis. The metallurgical microscope is today less of a research tool and more a means of routine inspection for quality than it has been in the past.

Fractography. Fractography, developed by C. A. Zapffe, is the study at high magnification of nascent unpolished and unetched fracture surfaces of metals and other solids. It supplements conventional metallography. Of first importance is the circumstance that it is a direct

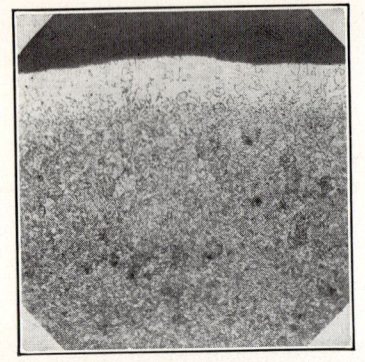

FIG. 73. Alloy-steel instrument spring decarburized at surface during heat-treatment. Magnification 100 ×. (*H. W. Cooper, author's laboratory.*)

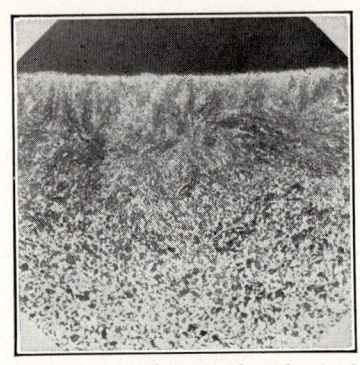

FIG. 74. Low-carbon steel carburized at surface during annealing. Magnification 100 ×. (*E. J. Callahan, author's laboratory.*)

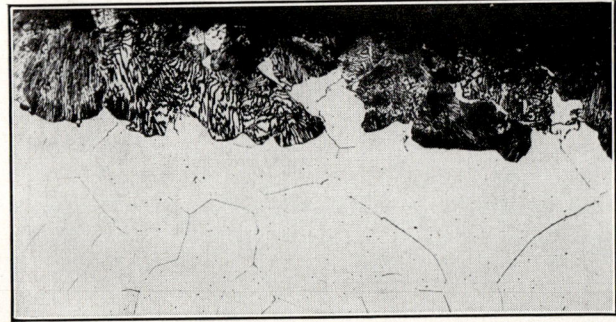

FIG. 75. Stainless steel carburized at surface during annealing. Magnification 100 ×. (*J. B. Giacobbe, author's laboratory.*)

FIG. 76. Fractograph of cast molybdenum, showing oxides in grain boundaries, advancing in treelike formation into a field of featherlike markings representing carbide. The oxides destroy the carbide and, advancing far enough, would also destroy forgeability of the molybdenum. Magnification 200 ×. (*Courtesy of C. A. Zapffe.*)

study of failures. The body is fractured, and a broken end is mounted in a fractographic stage. A metal cleaves along planes of weakness and, in so doing, often discloses the fundamental cause of that weakness. For example, Fig. 76 discloses a subtle grain-boundary phenomenon whose recognition was fundamental to success in casting molybdenum. Fractography is providing new information on the internal architecture of the individual grain, and sometimes offers an explanation of toughness and brittleness in metals.

INSPECTION BY METHODS OF PHYSICS

Most of the tests mentioned previously are of the destructive type, that is to say, a sample is tested to destruction and cannot be put into service thereafter. For such tests a sample is chosen from a supposedly uniform batch, and its characteristics as determined by the tests are supposedly representative of the characteristics of the remainder of the batch. Chemical, mechanical, microscopic, and some other tests are, in general, destructive ones.

The tendency today, both among manufacturers and consumers, is to apply *nondestructive* methods of inspection, *i.e.*, tests which determine the characteristics of the representative piece, but still allow it to be used in service. In this category are included visual inspection; hardness tests (usually); radiography by X rays, beta rays, and gamma rays; magnetic characteristics; influence of discontinuities on the passage of electric current; examination in high-frequency fields; magnetic particle inspection (Magnaflux test); acoustic and supersonic tests; fluorescent penetration (Magnaglow test); spark, pressure, and other tests. It may be seen that almost all of these are dependent upon methods associated with the physics laboratory.

Radiography. Radiography, or the penetration of shorter-than-light waves through a metallic body, should not be confused with X-ray spectrometry or diffraction, by which the atomic structure of a material is determined. Radiography consists in causing X rays or gamma rays to pass through a metallic body and then impinge on a photographic plate. The absorption of such rays by a specimen is roughly proportional to the density of the materials through which the rays pass, and the resulting negative photograph is therefore a shadow picture of the object. It is possible to locate blowholes, inclusions, hot tears, misruns, shrinkage cavities, segregation (sometimes), and other inhomogeneities which differ in density from that of the piece. X-ray apparatus up to 1 million volts potential is used and can penetrate 7 in. of steel. Gamma rays emanate from a number of natural or artificial radioactive elements and can penetrate to at least as great a depth. Some "shadowgraphs" are shown in Figs. 77 to 79. The much less penetrating beta rays have been used recently to measure the thickness of thin strip and sheet metal in rapid motion during manufacture.

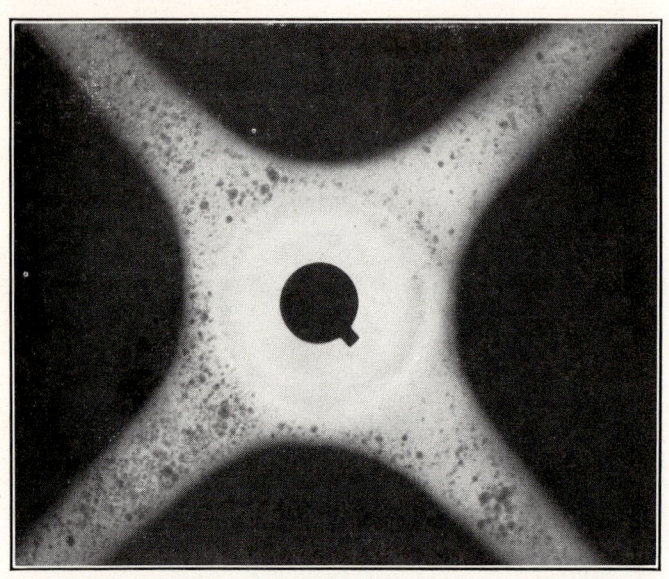

FIG. 77. Radiograph of die-cast aluminum alloy steering wheel, showing blowholes revealed by X ray. (*Courtesy of General Electric Co.*)

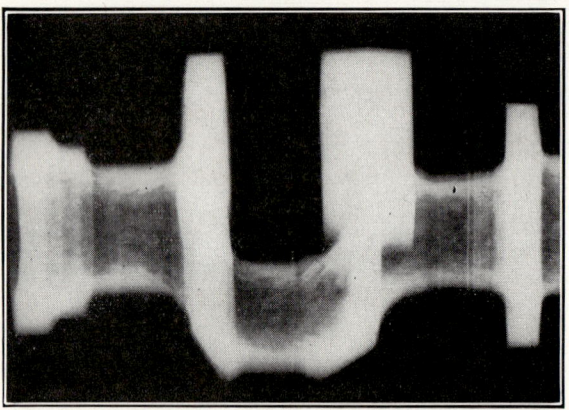

FIG. 78. Radiograph of crankshaft revealing complete "runout" of metal from center. (*Courtesy of General Electric Co.*)

Magnetic Particle Inspection. If discontinuities exist on or near the surface of a magnetic metal, such as laminations, heating or forging cracks, laps, tears, and similar defects too small to be seen by the eye and sometimes even invisible under the microscope, they may often be disclosed by magnetic particle inspection. Other inhomogeneities such as blowholes, inclusions, and sometimes segregation are revealed by this test. The piece is magnetized and covered with fine iron particles which adhere to and build up on it wherever the magnetic field is interrupted by a discontinuity. This technique is also used for the discovery of incipient cracks (usually the start of a fatigue crack) in locomotive axles and in airplane structures and engines, both of which are disassembled at intervals at considerable expense for inspection purposes (see Fig. 80).

Fluorescent Penetrant Test. It has long been known that, if a part such as a locomotive axle suspected of containing a crack is rubbed with an oily rag, the excess oil wiped off, and then "whiting" spread on the surface, the crack will reveal itself by discoloring the whiting. A more

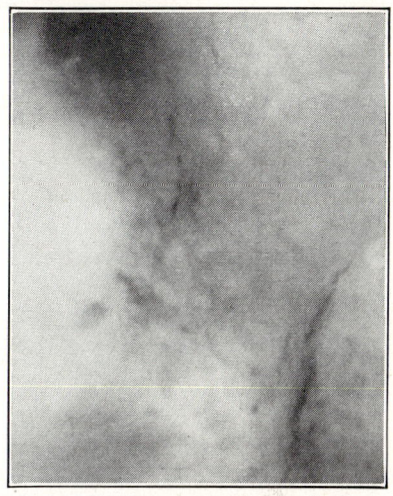

FIG. 79. Gamma-ray radiograph showing crack and possibly pipe in a casting. (*Courtesy of G. E. Doan.*)

FIG. 80. Cracks in an airplane gear, located by magnetic particle technique. (*Courtesy of Magnaflux Corporation.*)

delicate test, still sometimes used, is to wipe the surface of the metal with a cloth which has been wet with sodium sulfide solution, rub the surface dry, and apply a piece of photographic paper which has been soaked in sulfuric acid. Even an invisible crack soaks up enough sulfide to make a brownish line on the photographic paper. A more recent innovation is the spreading of fluorescent penetrant on the surface, or immersing the piece in a fluorescent liquid and allowing it to drain, then washing and drying and inspecting the piece under near-ultraviolet light in the dark. The fluorescence of the penetrant under ultraviolet rays shows up in a dark room, and the reemergence of the penetrant from any crack, pinhole, or other inhomogeneity may be aided by the application of a film of developer material which acts as a blotter (see Fig. 81).

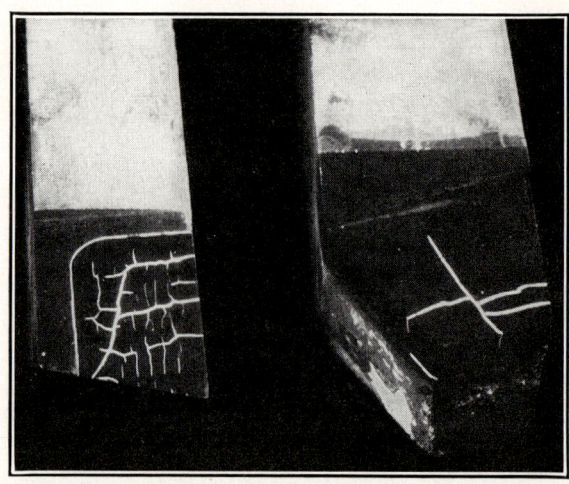

Fig. 81. Carbide-tipped tools with cracks identified positively under black light. Visual inspection, under high-power magnification, fails to disclose many such cracks, and confuses scratches with cracks. (*Courtesy of Magnaflux Corporation.*)

Invisible cracks or other surface defects may often be discovered by deep etching, but this is inadvisable for a nondestructive test, because the hydrogen generated by the reaction with acid may diffuse into the steel and embrittle it.

Magnetic Field Testing. If a magnetic flux is passed through all parts of a steel member and the flux density measured, a discontinuity, shrinkage cavity, blowhole, or other defect will cause a reduction in the flux value and thereby give an indication of the presence of the defect. A more refined testing method is magnetic analysis using waveform distortion; this is used for detecting many discontinuities but is chiefly employed in detecting flaws not more than $\frac{1}{4}$ in. deep in bar stock and tubing, including weld defects in resistance-welded tubing. As previously discussed, the method is also used for separating steel of different chemical analysis, or of different metallographic structure. Figure 82 is a schematic diagram of the process: Two solenoids are energized by alternating current of 110 volts and 60 cycles. In the solenoid in the center of the diagram is first inserted a steel sample free of defects and of exactly the same analysis as that of the steel in which defects are to be detected. This piece is used for balancing the circuits and indicators. It may also be used to balance against a bar of steel in the solenoid at the left of the diagram, for the purpose of separating steels of different chemical analysis or structure. In the solenoid is a secondary or "pickup" coil which registers the magnetism induced in the bar. In the solenoid at the left-hand side of the diagram are two secondary coils, $2\frac{1}{2}$ in. apart, and balanced against each other. Through this solenoid

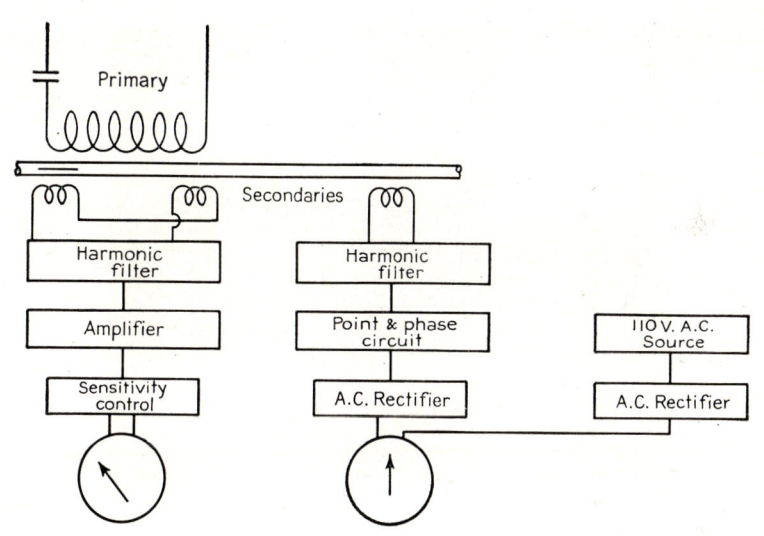

FIG. 82. A schematic diagram of the magnetic analysis principle, showing two testing circuits. (*From C. M. Lichy, "Electronic Methods of Inspection of Metals," American Society for Metals, 1946.*)

are passed bars or tubes which are to be tested for flaws. These can vary in size from $\frac{1}{4}$ in. to over 4 in. in diameter and can be tested at rates averaging about 120 ft per min. Discontinuities such as seams, cracks, and incomplete welds cause a disturbance in the magnetic field which may be recorded on suitable apparatus or by a warning light. Such a test is used by several steel producers and consumers as a 100 per cent inspection method.

Acoustic and Supersonic Tests. Sound waves travel 245,000 in. per sec in aluminum; 229,000 in steel, 174,000 in brass, and only 13,000 in air. Thus when sound waves are propagated in a metal and strike an air gap, the majority of the waves are reflected from the air-metal interface and very little sound energy is transmitted through the gap. This is familiar to all in the "dead" sound given off when a piece of cracked metal is struck. Advantage is taken of this circumstance in the testing of welds (page 111) with a hammer and a stethoscope to detect cracks and other unsoundness.

In supersonic testing, high-frequency waves are propagated in metal samples and the reflected waves are picked up by the same or a different crystal when they are reflected back to the surface of origin. Internal discontinuities are thus detected. Heavy pieces such as blooms and billets may thus be tested before further work is done on them. Development work is progressing on the testing of railroad axles by this method, and there is some indication that the method can indicate the grain size of the sample.

Penetration by Electric Current. The Sperry transverse-fissure test car is officially accepted by the American Railway Association as a

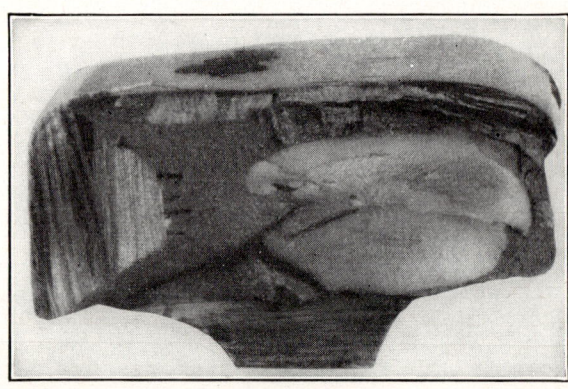

Fig. 83. First transverse fissure ever apprehended by the electrical method of Sperry. (*Courtesy of Sperry Products, Inc.*)

standard test for transverse fissures in rails. These are among the most dangerous defects in railroad rails, and they frequently develop after the rail has been laid in the track, probably due to repeated shocks from the unbalanced weight on the driving wheels of locomotives. The detector car can be run at several miles an hour over the roadbed and will automatically record the presence of fissures in the rails (see Fig. 83). The principle is based upon the fact that, if the rail is made to conduct a very heavy current, all internal inhomogeneities encountered present obstructions in the path of the current, the variations of which are recorded through suitable equipment.

Sperry Products, Inc., has also developed a high-frequency electrical process for the inspection of bar and tube stock, both ferrous and nonferrous, by inducing a current to flow within the material and by measuring the extent to which the current deviates from its normal path because of the presence of a defect. The instrument was designed to detect seams, discontinuities, and similar defects and to reduce all other indications to a negligible level.

High-intensity Light for Pinhole Detection. Some procedures for electronic testing of metals are discussed in the references listed at the end of this chapter, but a method recently developed for detecting pinholes in strip is not included there. Pinholes as small as 0.01 in. in diameter in strip 6 to 62 in. wide and traveling at a rate of 1,000 ft per min may be detected. This equipment consists of a source of intense light mounted above the strip, a phototube housing below the strip, and a control device. Pinholes cannot be tolerated in black plate intended for the manufacture of tin cans, and thus the pinhole detector makes possible an improvement in steel for the canning industry.

STATISTICAL QUALITY CONTROL

Although the purchaser of metals may be protected from receiving defective material and parts by rigid metallurgical inspection procedures, it does the producer little good to discover that a quantity of his product must be rejected after a great deal of money has been spent in its manufacture. Wherever definitive numbers can be obtained by testing a product as it is being made, it is possible by statistical methods to predict trends by sampling on a time instead of a batch basis. Thus the operation may be stopped before actual rejectable parts are made. The method is particularly applicable to dimensional inspection of parts made by mass-production methods, but it is equally effective wherever the desired qualities may be expressed by numbers. H. W. Poole of the American Society for Quality Control has written the following short résumé, and it is hoped that the student may find the technique of sufficient interest to follow it up in the references cited.

Analysis of test data must employ a mathematical consideration based on the laws of probability if the data are to be of practical value. The data obtained from a few tests produce a limited amount of information unless they can be evaluated mathematically in the light of similar tests on the same or similar material. It is just as impractical to arrive at conclusions based on a small number of tests as it would be to attempt to evaluate some characteristic of the human race after meeting a few people.

Modern quality control techniques employ the mathematical laws of probability to evaluate test data in terms of data obtained from previous tests compared with the test data under consideration, and to evaluate the accuracy of the data based on the number of observations taken with respect to the difference between individual observations.

Where tests for one property are used to obtain a measure of another, for example, using hardness tests to indicate tensile strength, the mathematics of correlation must be applied to prove the reliability and accuracy of the test. Such testing has been employed to a much greater extent in recent years because the mathematics for testing correlation have been extensively developed. For example, it is much more convenient and economical to test spring wire for fatigue properties as a wire, rather than test the finished springs for fatigue. It will be appreciated that a high degree of correlation exists in this case, even though it is reasonable to expect the endurance limit of the material to be decreased because of the work the material receives in the coiling of the spring.

Space does not permit publication of even the few simple formulae and instructions for their use. The American Society for Quality Control, the American Society for Testing Materials, the American Society of Mechanical Engineers, and the American Standards Association have many publications which cover the subject. A number of good texts such as E. L. Grant's "Statistical Quality Control" and L. E. Simon's "Engineers' Manual of Statistical Methods" have been published.

Bibliography

See also references following Chaps. 1, 2, and 8.

AMERICAN IRON AND STEEL INSTITUTE: "Steel Products Manual," New York, biennial. Twenty-nine booklets covering each distinct steel product.

AMERICAN SOCIETY FOR METALS: "Electronic Methods of Inspection of Metals," Cleveland, Ohio, 1946.

AMERICAN SOCIETY FOR TESTING MATERIALS: "ASTM Standards," Philadelphia. Published every three years, with "Supplement" in intervening years.

BEAUMONT, R. A.: "Mechanical Testing of Metallic Materials," 2d ed., Sir Isaac Pitman & Sons, Ltd., London, 1944.

BURTON, E. F., and W. H. KOHL: "The Electron Microscope," 2d ed., Reinhold Publishing Corporation, New York, 1946.

COPPER AND BRASS RESEARCH ASSOCIATION: "Standards," New York, 1947.

COWDREY, I. H., and R. G. ADAMS: "Materials Testing: Theory and Practice," John Wiley & Sons, Inc., New York, 1944.

DESCH, C. H.: "Metallography," 6th ed., Longmans, Green, & Co., Inc., New York, 1945.

DOANE, F. B.: "Principles of Magnaflux Inspection," 2d ed., Photopress, Inc., Chicago, 1940.

GABOR, D.: "The Electron Microscope, Its Development, Present Performance, and Future Possibilities," Hulton Press, London, 1945.

GILLETT, H. W.: "Impact Resistance and Tensile Properties of Metals at Subatmospheric Temperatures," American Society for Testing Materials, Philadelphia, 1941.

———: "An Engineering Approach to the Selection, Evaluation, and Specification of Metallic Materials," Penton Publishing Company, Cleveland, Ohio, 1944.

GOUGH, H. J.: "Fatigue of Metals," D. Van Nostrand Company, Inc., New York, 1924.

GRANT, E. L.: "Statistical Quality Control," 2d ed., McGraw-Hill Book Company, Inc., New York, 1952.

HIRST, HENRY: "X-Rays in Research and Industry," 2d ed., Chapman & Hall, Ltd., London, 1946.

ISENBURGER, HERBERT R.: "Bibliography on X-Ray Stress Analysis," St. John X-Ray Laboratory, Califon, N.J., 1949.

KEHL, G. L.: "The Principles of Metallographic Laboratory Practice," 3d ed., McGraw-Hill Book Company, Inc., New York, 1949.

LYSACHT, V. E.: "Indentation Hardness Testing," Reinhold Publishing Corporation, New York, 1949.

MOORE, H. F.: "Manual of the Endurance of Metals under Repeated Stress," Engineering Foundation, New York, 1927.

MUHLENBRUCH, C. W.: "Testing of Engineering Materials," D. Van Nostrand Company, Inc., New York, 1944.

PULSIFER, H. B.: "Inspection of Metals," American Society for Metals, Cleveland, Ohio, 1941.

ROLFE, R. T.: "A Dictionary of Metallography," Chapman & Hall, Ltd., London, 1945.

SHILLABER, C. P.: "Photomicrography in Theory and Practice," John Wiley & Sons, Inc., New York, 1944.

SIMON, L. E.: "Engineers' Manual of Statistical Methods," John Wiley & Sons, Inc., New York, 1941.

ST. JOHN, ANCEL, and H. R. ISENBURGER: "Industrial Radiography, X-Rays, and Gamma Rays," 2d ed., John Wiley & Sons, Inc., New York, 1943.

VILELLA, J. R.: "Metallographic Techniques for Steel," American Society for Metals, Cleveland, Ohio, 1938.

WILLIAMS, S. R.: "Hardness and Hardness Measurements," American Society for Metals, Cleveland, Ohio, 1942.

CHAPTER 7

THE THEORY OF ALLOYS

In this chapter will be discussed the principles involved when metals are mixed and combined to form alloys, and examples of industrial alloys will be cited to clarify the principles. The alloys themselves, or such of them as are of considerable importance to engineers, will be discussed as regards composition, properties, and uses in Chaps. 9 to 11. The industrial use of alloys far exceeds the use of unalloyed metals.

Definition of an Alloy. It is generally considered that an alloy is formed when two or more metals are mixed or united, either by melting them together and allowing the melt to freeze, or in some other way, such as consolidation of metal powders as in powder metallurgy or by depositing them together by electrolysis. Melting is by far the most important way of making alloys, and for the purposes of this chapter we may define an alloy as a substance formed by the solidification of a metallic solution. In this sense, if metals will not dissolve in each other when molten, and remain undissolved until the mass has cooled to the freezing point, they will not form a solid alloy. To the unaided eye an alloy looks like a homogeneous union of metals, but under the microscope it is seen to be an aggregation of crystals which may or may not be chemically alike; sometimes they differ from one another in chemical composition and in size, hardness, shape, and other properties, such as their individual strengths or their strength of adherence to one another.

Most metals dissolve in each other when liquid, but there are a few exceptions. For example, molten lead and aluminum will separate into two liquid layers, each of which contains only a trace of the other metal, similar to the behavior of oil and water. Aluminum when molten is almost insoluble in many other metals. Bismuth and iron are also entirely insoluble in each other when liquid. Very important in the lead industry is the fact that molten lead will dissolve only a small amount of molten zinc. Molten copper will dissolve only a little molten iron, and, conversely, molten iron will dissolve only a little copper. If it were not for this fact, it is possible that some exceedingly valuable alloys of iron and copper might be formed, since these two metals are so useful and common.

Making Alloys. In industrial work alloys are nearly always made by melting one of the metals and dissolving the other in it while liquid, or else by melting two or more metals and mixing them. When one metal is considerably more volatile than the other, it is almost universal practice to melt the least volatile and dissolve the other in it as quickly as possible, so as to save loss in fume. This is the case in making brass, when the copper is melted and the zinc added to the liquid bath. Brass and other alloys are sometimes melted from scrap material, in which the two or more metals pure already joined; in this case we may have a loss of a part of the more volatile metal.

Properties of Alloys. A striking feature about alloys is that they often differ materially in their properties from the properties of the metals composing them. When metals form an alloy, the result is often a surprise. For example, two soft metals frequently make a very hard alloy, and two ductile metals often make a brittle alloy. Brass is stronger than either of its constituents, copper and zinc. Permalloy is more magnetic at low magnetizing forces than either the iron or the nickel of which it is composed, while Heussler's alloy is as magnetic as nickel, although none of its components—copper, manganese, and aluminum—is a magnetic metal. However, it is in the study of variations in such properties as electrical conductivity, hardness, toughness, strength, and ductility that a comprehension of the theory of alloys is most helpful. An understanding of this theory is demanded now in industry from all those who buy and use metals, as well as from those who supply them. Commercial metals are in a sense alloys on account of the impurities which they contain. As little as 0.10 per cent phosphorus in steel will ruin its ductility, and less than 0.01 per cent arsenic in copper will make it unfit for electrical conductors.

Solid Metals and Alloys Are Crystalline Aggregates. Solidified alloys are composed of crystals, and it is the chemical composition and the size, shape, and interrelation of these crystals with one another which determine the characteristics and properties of the alloy, even more than the characteristics or properties of the metals which form the alloy. No means has yet been found of predicting with certainty what property one metal will confer upon another, but the study of the structure of metallic bodies explains many of the observed results and makes it possible to form alloys with a much greater knowledge of the probable result. Crystals form from a liquid metallic mass when it freezes. In metallography the size, form, and interrelation of these crystals to one another is studied. These characteristics, and the chemical composition of the crystals, depend not only upon the elements present, but also upon the action which occurs when a liquid metallic mass changes into the solid state. The study of the solidification, or freezing, of alloys is therefore essential to an understanding of their properties and uses.

The Freezing of a Pure Metal. This is the simplest process of freezing and is illustrated in Fig. 84. The pure molten metal cools from the temperature represented by point *c* to the temperature of *a*, where freezing takes place. A momentary fall below the actual freezing temperature occurs; then, owing to release of the latent heat of fusion, the temperature of the metal rises to the freezing point and remains there a short time as indicated by the line *ab*. As soon as freezing is complete, the temperature of the solid metal falls along line *bd*. All the freezing occurs at practically the same temperature, and is represented on the graph by a horizontal line.

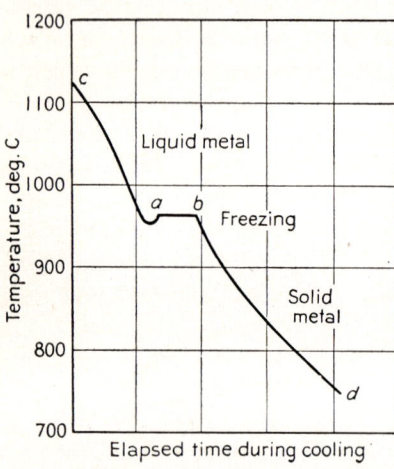

FIG. 84. Freezing-point curve of a pure metal, for example, silver.

Chemical Relations in Liquid Alloys. All alloys when molten are in a state of chemical solution. The state of molten solution is analogous to the solution of sugar in water. For the sake of simplicity we shall discuss here only two-metal (binary) alloys; the theories applying to them can be extended to alloys of three or more metals.

THE FREEZING OF ALLOYS

Binary alloys may be classified in four types, according to the ways in which they freeze. Type I, in which the liquid solution freezes to form crystals of a solid solution; Type II, in which the component metals are entirely soluble in each other in the liquid state, and practically insoluble[1] in the solid (crystalline) state; Type III, in which the component metals are mutually soluble in the liquid state, but only partially soluble in the solid state; and Type IV, in which a chemical compound between the two metals exists after solidification of the solution.

Freezing of Type I Alloys. Figure 99 shows a microscopic view of a solid solution. Here each crystal is identical in composition (or nearly so) with every other crystal and with the composition of the liquid solution from which they froze. The alloys of gold and silver belong to this type, and also many important industrial alloys, such as the alloys of nickel and copper, those of iron and manganese, gold and platinum, nickel and cobalt, tungsten and molybdenum—in number these represent somewhat less than one-third of the important alloys.

[1] Almost nothing in nature is complete in the chemical sense. For example, we do not have in nature 100 per cent pure water or pure air. But we regard Type II alloys as those in which the metals are insoluble in each other in the solid state, a condition which is approximated in many alloys.

THE THEORY OF ALLOYS

The freezing-point curve of this type of alloy is shown in Fig. 85. It will be noted that the freezing does not all occur at one and the same temperature. Only a fraction of the alloy freezes at each decrement of temperature as it cools, and if the temperature were not allowed to fall the alloy would remain partly frozen and partly liquid. This results in a sloping line xy. At the point y the last of the alloy crystallizes from a liquid droplet. From this point onward the temperature of the solidified

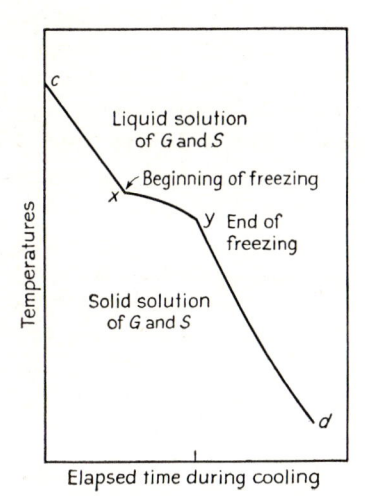

FIG. 85. Freezing-point curve of an alloy which freezes as a solid solution: for example, 50 per cent gold (G) and 50 per cent silver (S).

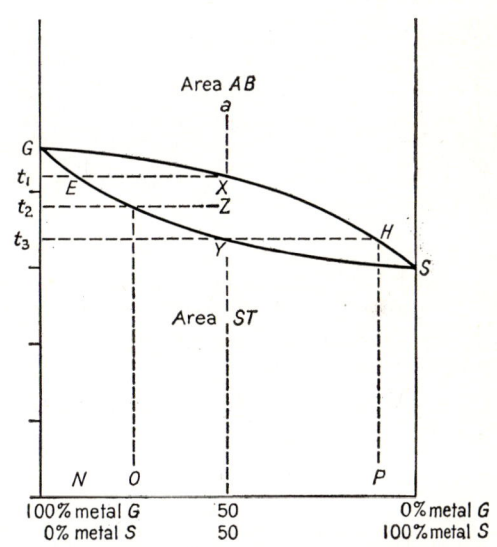

FIG. 86. The mechanism of freezing of Type I alloys.

alloy drops more rapidly because there is now no heat of fusion evolved. This results in the steeper line yd.

The mechanism of freezing of alloys of Type I is explained in Fig. 86. In such a diagram the line above which the alloy is entirely liquid (GXS) is called the *liquidus*, and the line below which the alloy is entirely solid (GYS) is called the *solidus*. Consider any alloy of the series, for example, the one containing 50 per cent of each metal. If it is at a temperature above the liquidus (area AB), it may be indicated on the diagram by the point a. Assume that it cools until it meets the line GXS at X. As this line marks the beginning of the freezing, one might at first thought suppose that crystals of an alloy containing 50 per cent of each metal would form. This is not the case, however, because the energy of chemical solution affects the freezing process. The crystal which does form is one having the composition at the *end* of freezing corresponding to that of the temperature of X. Its composition can be determined by drawing the line XEt_1 and then the line EN, showing that in this case the composition is 90 per cent of metal G and 10 per cent of metal S. Each succeeding fall in temperature results in a new crystal being frozen. When the temperature has fallen to the point Z in the diagram, the crystal that freezes has the composition 75 per cent G and 25 per cent S. The action is continuous, and finally the solidus GYS is reached at the point Y. Here freezing is completed, and obviously the last portion of the alloy to freeze is that portion which has the composition corresponding to

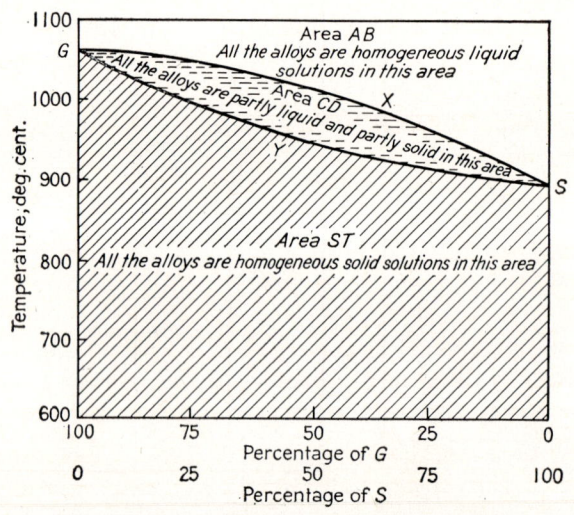

FIG. 87. Equilibrium diagram of Type I alloys.

The line GXS is the locus of the beginning of freezing of each of the various alloys, as indicated in Fig. 85; the line GYS is the locus of the ending of freezing, as determined from the same freezing-point curves.

the abscissas of the point H in the diagram, which is 10 per cent G and 90 per cent S.

Many different crystals have frozen, of many different compositions, but the temperature is high so that diffusion readily takes place between the small crystals of the mutually soluble metals, tending to make the composition become uniform throughout the alloy. If diffusion takes place too slowly or for an insufficient time, the crystals of different compositions may separate as dendrites, producing a "cored" structure. This inhomogeneity may be eliminated by further heating (annealing).

Equilibrium Diagram of Type I Alloys. A complete binary alloy series will extend from 100 per cent of one metal to 100 per cent of the other. The freezing of all the alloys of such a series can be represented in a diagram which will represent equilibrium between the liquid and the solid states, as indicated in Fig. 87. Such a diagram is a comprehensive and graphic way of illustrating the collected experimental data. Such a diagram can be built up from the freezing-point curves of the two pure metals and from the beginning and ending of freezing of several alloys of intermediate composition. This is illustrated in Fig. 89. (The details shown in Fig. 89 are for an alloy of Type II, but the same procedure is employed in building an equilibrium diagram of Type I alloys.) Referring now to Fig. 87: The beginning and end of freezing of the two pure metals and of each alloy of the series whose freezing-point curve has been determined are plotted at an ordinate representing temperature and an abscissa representing composition, and then the line GXS is drawn through the points representing beginning, and the line GYS through the points representing ending, of freezing.

Freezing of Type II Alloys. In alloys of Type II the mutual solubility of the component metals in the liquid state ceases to exist when the alloy solidifies. Therefore, in the process of freezing there is a breaking down, or decomposition, of the solution, with formation of crystals of one or the other of the two metals. From this fact the freezing-point curve of an alloy of Type II, as shown in Figs. 88 and 89, can be understood. Let us assume an alloy of the series, such as the one containing 60 per cent of metal A and 40 per cent of metal B.

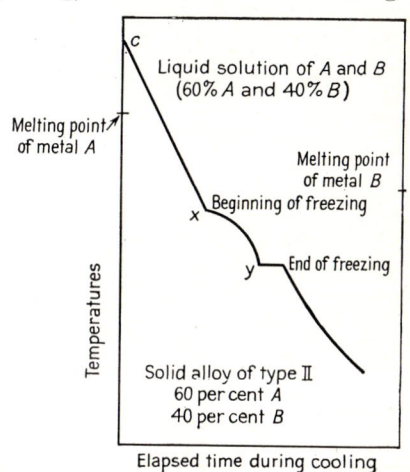

Fig. 88. Freezing-point curve of a Type II alloy.

When liquid, it is a solution of A and B; the solution is of such nature in this alloy that it will cool below the freezing points of both the pure metals before either will start to crystallize. At some temperature related to the precise composition of the alloy, freezing will begin with precipitation of one of the metals from solution, for example, metal A. Further drop in temperature results in more crystals of A forming, with a corresponding decrease of metal A in the remaining liquid solution of A and B.

Before considering the end of freezing of the preceding alloy, let us discuss the freezing of another alloy in the same series, for example, one containing 20 per cent A and 80 per cent B. Here metal B, being overwhelmingly predominant, will be the first to begin freezing; further drop in temperature will result in more crystals of B forming, with the consequence that the liquid remaining becomes poorer and poorer in B and richer and richer in A.

Eutectic. During freezing of an alloy of Type II, that metal which is

156   ENGINEERING METALLURGY

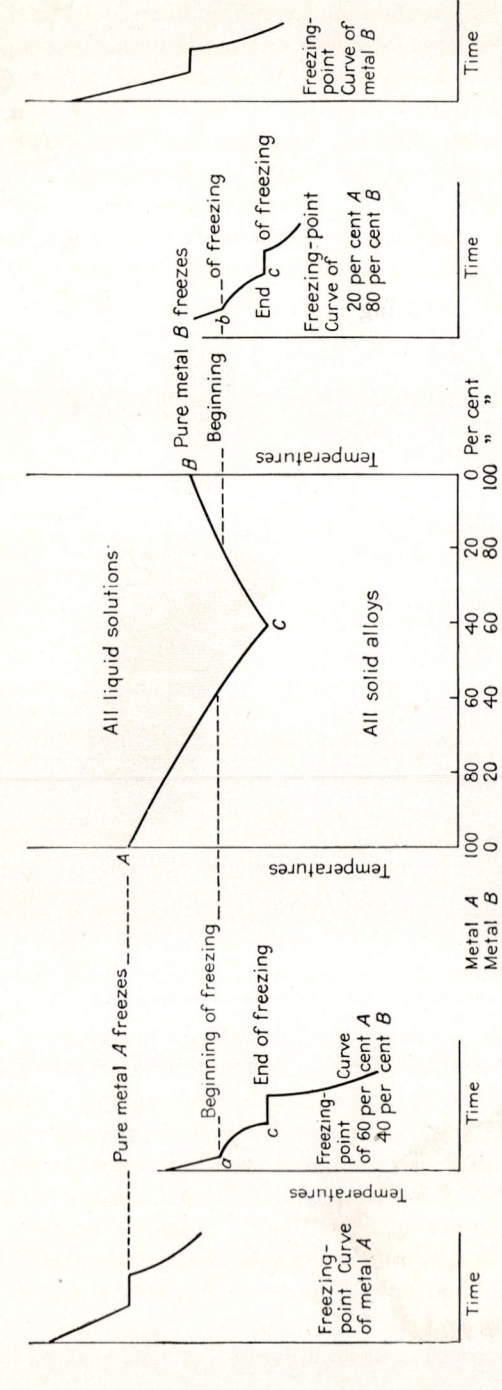

FIG. 89. A method commonly employed for constructing an equilibrium diagram of alloys from freezing-point curves of individual alloys of the series.

The example used is that of Type II alloys. Along the line *ac* in the left-middle figure, crystals of metal *A* separate; along the line *bc* in the right-middle figure, crystals of metal *B* separate.

present in excess of the amount contained in the most fusible alloy of the series will separate and crystallize first. The liquid portion will thus approach the composition of lowest freezing point, represented by C in Fig. 90. The abscissas of the point C therefore indicate the composition of the most fusible alloy of the series; to this the name *eutectic* is given, a name derived from the Greek word meaning "well melting." Every alloy series of Types II and III has a eutectic.

An Equilibrium Diagram of a Type II Alloy. In any series of alloys, whether of Type I, II, or III, the temperature of the beginning of freezing

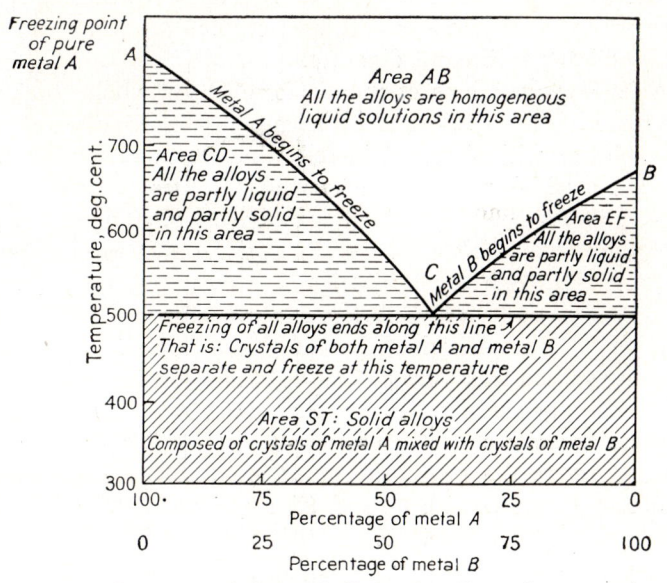

Fig. 90. Equilibrium diagram of Type II alloys: the alloys of two metals which are soluble in each other when molten but insoluble in each other when solid.

of any composition cannot be predicted by theory, but it must be determined by experiment. The results of the determinations for many compositions can be assembled in an equilibrium diagram which illustrates equilibrium between liquid and solid for any composition in the series. These diagrams are also called "phase diagrams," because they show what phases are present in any alloy of the series at any temperature. These diagrams represent, and are intended to represent, equilibrium conditions resulting from extremely slow cooling, in nonreactive surroundings. These conditions seldom fully prevail in actual practice.

The building of an equilibrium diagram may be illustrated as follows, a Type II alloy being used as an example: In Fig. 89 the line AC represents the locus of the beginnings of freezing where metal A separates (crystallizes), and the line BC likewise represents the locus of the beginnings of freezing where metal B separates. The two lines must cross. Evidently this crossing fixes a point at which both A and B are precipitating from the liquid solution together, and fixes the temperature at which freezing must end. It is also evident that any alloy of the series must be concentrated during freezing to a composition represented by the abscissas of the point C. A line drawn horizontally through C will, therefore, represent the temperature of the ending of freezing for any alloy in the series. Thus there can be shown for all alloys of the series the beginning and ending of freezing and the presence of a pasty stage in which solid crystals are mixed with still-liquid alloy. The temperatures and lines in this diagram will depend on the component metals; every combination of metals will have a different diagram.

Only a few combinations of metals form alloys wholly of Type II, because most metals will take at least a small proportion of another metal into solid solution with them. The following are examples of pairs that will form alloys which separate on freezing into (nearly) pure individual metals: lead and antimony, cadmium and zinc, aluminum and silicon, bismuth and cadmium, bismuth and silver, silver and lead. These pairs will not mix in the same crystal lattice.

Type III Alloys, and an Equilibrium Diagram Thereof. Formation of the Type III alloy results when the constituent metals do not separate from molten solution in a pure state, but rather form limited solid solutions. In this type there are two series of solid solutions, as illustrated in Fig. 91: (1) a series of solid solutions of metal P in metal O in all the compositions where the proportion of P is equal to or less than that which would saturate O with P; and (2) a series of solid solutions of O in P provided that the proportion of O in the liquid is equal to or less than the limiting solid saturation of O in P. Between these two limits, the solid alloys are composed of two kinds of crystals, namely, saturated solid solution of P in O, and a saturated solid solution of O in P. The equilibrium diagram is built up from freezing-point curves in the same way as described in Fig. 89, except that the constituent which precipitates along the line AC is not a pure metal, but is a saturated solid solution. An alloy of Type III is a combination of solid solution and of selective freezing. It will be seen in Fig. 91 that the compositions on both ends form solid solutions, whereas those between the saturated solid-solution limits form a series of alloys similar to Type II alloys, except that the constituents precipitating to produce selective freezing are saturated solid solutions instead of pure metals. In other words, the area $abdc$ is like that of an equilibrium diagram of a Type II alloy.

The most important industrial alloys belong essentially to Type III, including steel, brass, bronze, aluminum-copper alloys, and many others; but their diagrams have many complicating factors. The solid solutions which crystallize upon freezing of Type III alloys do not usually remain unchanged as the temperature falls. Most often the proportion of the solute decreases; rarely, it increases. In other words, the compositions of the solid-solution crystals do not remain constant, but change as the temperature falls. Or some other change in relation may occur. Instead of only two types of solid solution, several may form. Also there is formed by selective precipitation and freezing a most fusible alloy, or eutectic, in many Type III alloys, as well as in all Type II alloys. Furthermore, some of the solid solutions in Type III alloys are not stable at

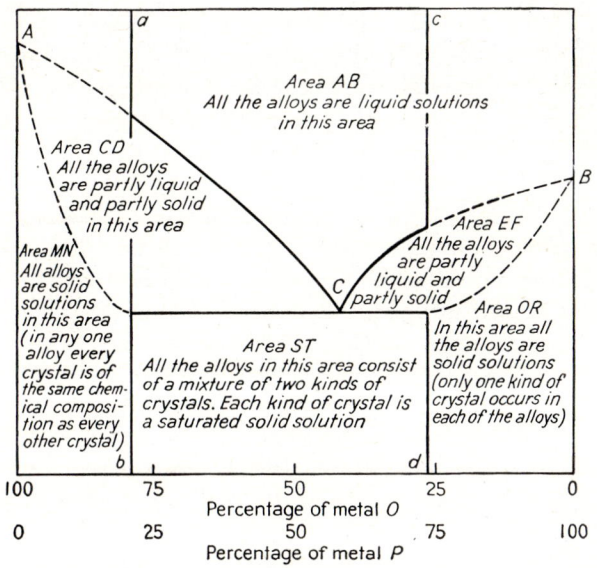

FIG. 91. Equilibrium diagram of Type III alloys: the alloys of two metals which are soluble in each other when liquid, and each dissolves a limited percentage of the other when solid.

lower temperatures but on cooling undergo a process of selective precipitation in the solid state which is analogous to the process of freezing when a eutectic forms. The solid solution decomposes in the solid state and is replaced by a mixture of two kinds of crystals, just as the liquid solution in the freezing of alloys of Type II is replaced by two kinds of solid crystals. For example, the solid solutions in steel,[1] formed upon solidification and varying from almost no carbon to 2 per cent carbon, decompose upon cooling, with precipitation of crystals of nearly pure iron and of Fe_3C. To a constituent forming from solid solution in the same way as the eutectic is formed from liquid solution, the name of *eutectoid* is given. A micrograph of a eutectoid is shown in Fig. 101, page 172.

[1] Disregarding the impurities which are commonly found in commercial steels.

Type IV Alloys. Type IV alloys are those in which chemical compounds are formed between the alloying constituents. This is a very common occurrence. Other types of alloys are frequently combined with Type IV. Thus, since Fe_3C is formed in steel and $CuAl_2$ in duralumin, these alloys belong to Type IV as well as to Type III. When both the constituents are metals, the compound is an "intermetallic compound."

When a compound is formed in an alloy system, sharp breaks usually occur in the lines which form the equilibrium diagram. Just as the properties of the compound NaCl have no relation to the properties of either Na or Cl, abrupt changes in properties occur in Type IV alloys. If the constituents of the alloy are the metals A and B, the diagram is no longer concerned with equilibrium between A and B, but perhaps between A and the new substance A_xB_y at one end of the diagram and between A_xB_y and B at the other end. Thus the diagram is divided into two halves at the point at which A_xB_y occurs. Instead of pure A or B, we may have solid solutions as in Type III alloys. In some alloy series more than one compound is formed. The diagrams may become very complicated, and it will not be profitable to discuss them further here.

Binary and Ternary Alloys. The types of alloys discussed so far are made up of two metals. This is the simplest case, and the only kind that can be fully represented in curves on plane surfaces. Alloys are often made with three metals, and are then called *ternary alloys*. The freezing points of such alloys would have to be represented by a system of three-dimensional coordinates. Many alloys contain four or more metals, and the use of multicomponent alloys is becoming more and more common.

Size of Crystals in Type II and Type III Alloys. With reference to Fig. 90, the crystals which form in freezing between the liquidus and solidus will be larger than those comprising the eutectic, formed at 500°C (930°F). This difference seems to be due to the fact that the crystals which form earlier have a chance to grow while they are suspended in the liquid solution. Therefore, all the alloys represented in Fig. 90 which contain more than 60 per cent of the metal B will be composed, after freezing, of large crystals of metal B together with the small crystals of metal A and small crystals of metal B. The alloy containing exactly 60 per cent of B and 40 per cent of A will contain, after freezing, small crystals of both metals. Finally, the alloys containing more than 40 per cent of metal A will be composed, after freezing, of large crystals of metal A, mixed with small crystals of A and B. The crystals which form along the lines AC and BC in Figs. 89 and 90—that is to say, the large crystals—are known as "primary" crystals. Since small crystals make for strength, everything else being eliminated, this explains why the strongest alloys are often those which have a composition corresponding to the eutectic in alloys of Types II and III.

Strength, Hardness, and Electrical Conductivity. A very small proportion of one element in *solid solution* in another will increase its strength and hardness and will decrease its electrical conductivity. This is illustrated in Fig. 92 giving the compositions and below it Fig. 93 showing the variation of certain physical properties with this variation of composi-

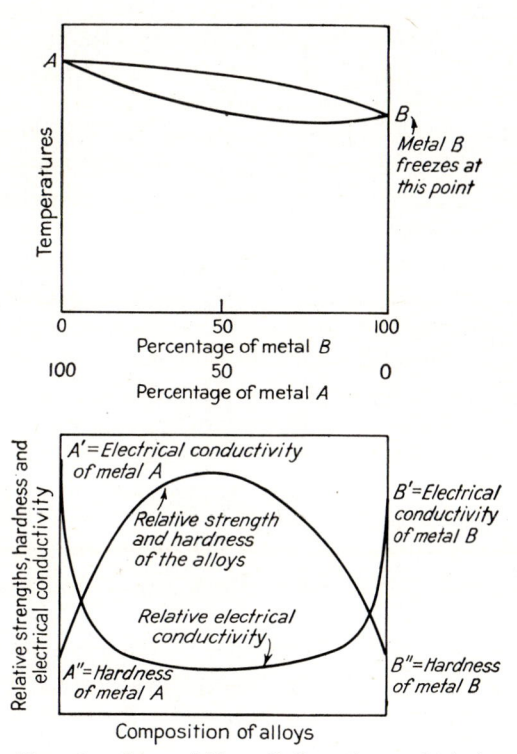

FIGS. 92 and 93. How the alloys of Type I (*i.e.*, those which form solid solutions throughout the series) vary in some of their physical properties from the corresponding properties of the pure metals.

The curves for strength and for hardness follow roughly the same general trend in this type of alloy.

tion. Strength and hardness are shown in the same curve because they follow almost the same pattern. It should be observed that these graphs are only approximate and given for illustration of the principles. It has also been shown that an appreciable proportion of solute or solvent, as the case may be, will raise the strength and/or hardness well above that of either of the metals. This is indicated in Fig. 93. The illustration refers to solid solutions, but the question of the size of crystals also has some bearing here, because (other things being equal) the smaller the crystal size, the greater the strength, hardness, and to a lesser extent electrical resistivity. A new situation will arise in alloys of Type II, shown in Fig. 94, because the primary crystals are relatively large in size and the eutectic crystals are much smaller. These are the general facts as to the size, shape, arrangement, and composition of the crystals, and in applying them to an alloy, it must be remembered that strength depends not only on the strength of the crystals, but also, under some conditions, upon the force required to tear the crystals apart from each other.

Practical Illustrations of the Theory of Alloys. Some interesting examples may be cited to illustrate some of the foregoing theory. Fusible alloys, solder, and bearing metals will be chosen for this purpose.

The common metals which melt at relatively low temperatures are the following:

Zinc	419°C (786°F)
Lead	327°C (621°F)
Cadmium	321°C (609°F)
Bismuth	271°C (520°F)
Tin	232°C (449°F)

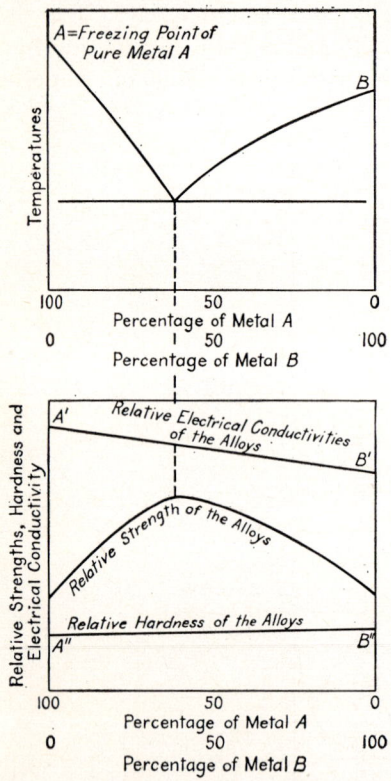

Fig. 94. How the alloys of Type II (*i.e.*, those which consist of two metals which are insoluble in each other when solid) vary in some of their physical properties from the corresponding properties of the pure metals.

The high point in the relative strengths of the alloys corresponds to the apex of the V in the freezing point curve. This is typical of this type of alloy and illustrates again the importance of the occurrences during freezing on the properties of the solid alloy.

These metals may be combined into a series of alloys called "fusible alloys" whose eutectics melt at temperatures as low as 70°C (158°F) and upward. Such alloys are used for safety plugs in boilers, electric fuses, automatic sprinkling apparatus, and the like.

Solder is an alloy of lead and tin and is valued because of the long pasty stage which it passes through during solidification, as well as because it will stick to lead pipe during this period, thus making it very useful for wiping a joint. Finally, its low melting point is an advantage. Figure 95 illustrates the action of the lead-tin alloys during freezing. Take, for example, the solder which the plumber may use for wiping purposes, say one containing 67 per cent lead and 33 per cent tin. Such an alloy will be fully melted below 300°C (572°F). If wiped over the

THE THEORY OF ALLOYS 163

joint, it will cool, and will begin to form solid crystals at about 240°C (464°F). The diagram shows that these crystals will be mostly lead; so they will stick well to the lead pipe. The separation of the crystals will

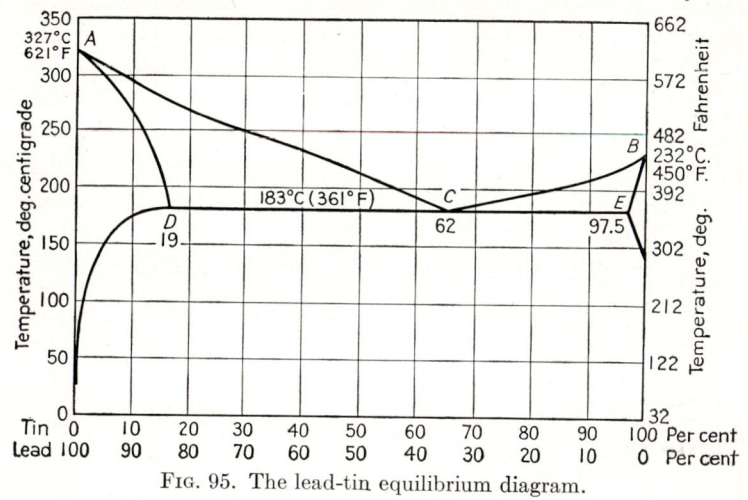

FIG. 95. The lead-tin equilibrium diagram.

form a pasty mass, which will continue during cooling until a temperature of 183°C (361°F) is reached.

Bearing metals required to support heavy pressures are commonly made of bronze, containing about 88 per cent copper and 11 per cent tin, with a little phosphorus added just before pouring in order to produce a deoxidized casting, and less than 0.5 per cent of lead. This lead unites with some of the tin and forms a fusible component, which is soft and flows more easily than the majority of the matrix. These bearings must be very strong in order to support the weight resting on the axle. The introduction of a soft component like lead causes enough unevenness on the surface of the bearing to prevent it from binding and to permit oil to circulate. Under certain conditions,

FIG. 96. Bearing alloy containing 82 per cent tin, 11 per cent antimony 6 per cent copper, and 1 per cent lead. Magnification 50 ×. (*Guillet.*)

it is customary to increase the proportion of lead up to 20 per cent.

"White bearing metals" are alloys of tin, lead, and antimony suitable for purposes where heavy pressure does not have to be supported. They are also unsuitable where high temperature is likely to occur. These alloys are often hardened with copper. The purpose of the alloy is to form a reasonably soft matrix carrying cubic crystals of a hard compound of either copper or lead with antimony. After a short period of use, these hard crystals project from the matrix and support the axle. This decreases the frictional area and permits circulation of the lubricant. Figure 96 shows some of these cubic crystals in the softer groundmass. They are, of course, primary crystals. (Not all bearing metals have this type of structure, however. Smooth homogeneous surfaces, such as those of silver-plated bearings, may hold a lubricating film of oil and provide strong support with minimum friction.)

IRON, STEEL, AND IRON-CARBON ALLOYS

The equilibrium diagram of the iron-carbon alloys up to 5 per cent carbon is shown in Fig. 97. The diagram given is that for equilibrium between iron and iron carbide (Fe_3C). The latter contains 6.67 per cent carbon, but becomes unstable at very high temperatures, before it melts; therefore, little is known about the diagram above about 5 per cent carbon. Probably more research has been devoted to the iron-carbon alloys than to all the other metallic alloys collectively. The iron-carbon equilibrium diagram belongs to Type IV because there is a chemical compound present; it also belongs to Type III in that one constituent carries a limited proportion of the other into solid solution with it when it freezes. The alloy is called *steel* when it contains carbon up to 2 per cent, 2 per cent being the maximum solid solubility of carbon in gamma iron (see Fig. 97). *Ferrite* is the name given to iron having not more than 0.025 per cent carbon in solid solution in it, this being the maximum solid solubility of carbon in alpha iron.[1]

Steel is made, then, by incorporating carbon in liquid iron to the desired percentage. For example, for a structural steel 0.25 per cent carbon is added, and when this freezes a solid solution of iron and carbon is obtained, containing 0.25 per cent carbon.[2] If a machinery steel is desired, about 0.40 per cent carbon is dissolved in the liquid iron; for a spring steel, 0.75 per cent; and for a file steel, about 1.20 per cent. The amounts of carbon in different steels is given in Table 18, page 200. The point to be made clear here is that the upper limit of the amount of carbon that can be got in a solid solution in iron is 2 per cent, and that up to this percentage all the carbon added to the liquid iron will be in solid solution immediately after freezing, before the steel has cooled.

The iron carbide Fe_3C is named *cementite*.

[1] Alpha and gamma are two allotropic forms of the element iron, differing in the form of crystal lattice in which they exist and in the temperature at which they are stable (see p. 167).

[2] Disregarding impurities.

Cooling of Steel after Freezing. It should be pointed out that all commercial steels have other elements in them besides carbon. Some occur as impurities, such as phosphorus, sulfur, oxygen, nitrogen, and the like; others are intentionally added, such as manganese and silicon;

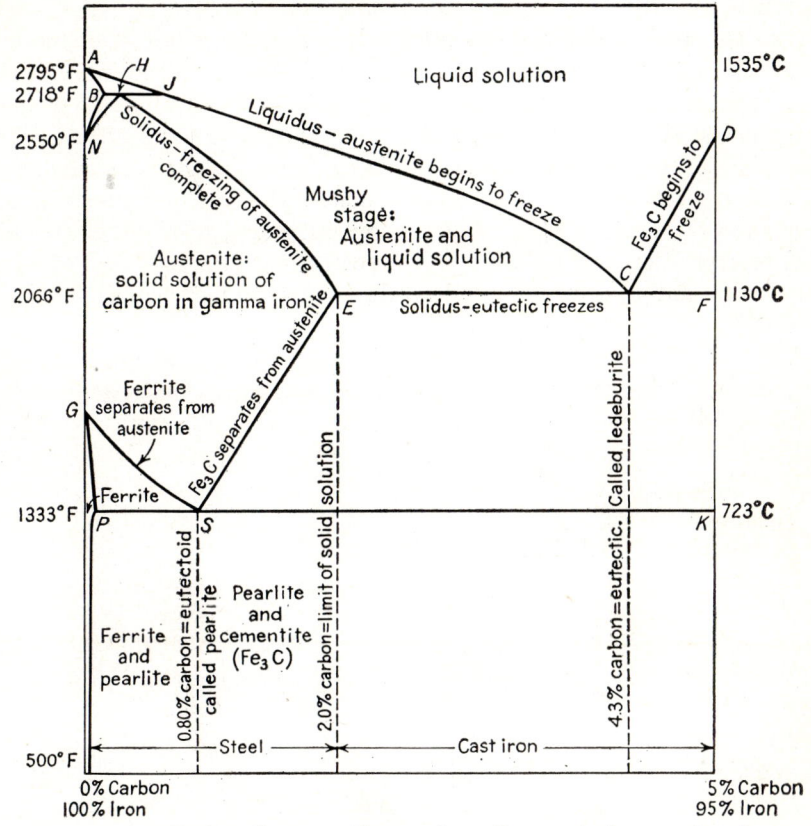

Fig. 97. Equilibrium diagram of iron-carbon alloys up to 5 per cent carbon.

The iron-carbon diagram is of Type IV. The left-hand side consists of ferrite and iron carbide, Fe_3C. Iron will separate from the liquid solution carrying into solid solution with it up to 2 per cent carbon (as Fe_3C). The iron is then in the "gamma" modification; it is formed of crystals built in space lattices of the face-centered cubic type (see page 26). At a lower temperature the iron changes to the "alpha" type, consisting of crystals built up in body-centered cubic lattices. It then will dissolve almost no carbon, and, consequently, the solid solution (austenite), will decompose, as shown. Another allotropic modification known as "delta" iron is in equilibrium near the melting point and results in the lines shown near AN.

Note: There is a small departure from scale in plotting certain of the points in order that the areas may be shown more clearly. Following are the carbon percentages for these points: B, 0.10 per cent; H, 0.18 per cent; J, 0.50 per cent; P, 0.025 per cent.

while still others occur as "residuals," which are elements which remain in the steel in whatever amounts they were present in the charge to the steelmaking furnace. Among the "residuals" should be especially mentioned copper and nickel. All these elements have an effect on freezing and subsequent cooling after freezing, and this is taken into account in commercial manufacture; but in order to bring out the principles involved, there is considered at this point only iron and its principal alloying element, namely, carbon. The effect of other elements on freezing and subsequent cooling will be discussed briefly in a later chapter. When we speak of cooling, it is assumed that slow cooling is intended, because only very slow cooling will result in equilibrium conditions being achieved.

All steels, then, are solid solutions immediately after freezing, but the solid solution does not remain as such as the temperature slowly falls. Just as liquid solutions may break up into different compositions when they freeze, so the solid solution of iron and carbon breaks up into component parts when it cools. This is a new thought to those who are familiar with ordinary chemistry, and one must understand that a chemical precipitation and a decomposition can occur in a solid state just as definitely and completely as they do in a liquid state (see Figs. 97 and 98).

The Most Stable Alloy. A solid solution consisting of 99.20 per cent iron and 0.80 per cent carbon will cool to approximately 723°C (1333°F) without decomposing. But at this temperature the alloy will completely decompose (being in a solid state both before and after precipitation) into separate crystals of ferrite and Fe_3C. There are many interesting things about this alloy which contains 0.80 per cent carbon. It is the strongest slowly cooled alloy of iron and carbon, and it is the only one composed entirely of alternate lamellae of ferrite and Fe_3C with no primary crystals of either. A micrograph of it is shown in Fig. 101. It is the eutectoid of the series, and to it is given the name *pearlite*. Then, to repeat, the only solid solution which will cool unchanged to as low a temperature as 723°C is the one containing 99.20 per cent iron and 0.80 per cent carbon. Every other alloy in the steel series will undergo a change before cooling to 723°C.

Cooling of a Structural Steel. If a structural steel containing 99.75 per cent iron and 0.25 per cent carbon is manufactured and solidified in the usual way, it will be a solid solution of its two components. But this solid solution will not remain unchanged to as low a temperature as 723°C. When it has cooled to a temperature of approximately 830°C (1526°F), it has reached the lowest temperature at which the solid solution is stable. Any further cooling will result in the separation of ferrite crystals (nearly pure iron). Therefore the piece of steel at yellow heat will consist of crystals of solid solution with separated grains of ferrite disseminated through them. As the cooling progresses there will be a constantly increasing number of grains of ferrite among the solid-solution crystals and a corresponding increase in the carbon content of the solid solution until 723°C is reached. At this point there will be a mixture of a solid solution containing 0.80 per cent carbon and grains of ferrite.

The proportion of carbon in the solid solution and in the grains taken together will be 0.25 per cent, but practically all this carbon will be in the solid-solution component since the ferrite grains are almost free from it. This situation will exist only so long as the metal remains at 723°C. It cannot cool below this point without a complete decomposition of all the solid solution into crystals of ferrite and Fe_3C (see Figs. 97 and 98).

In summary, (1) a solid solution exists immediately after freezing; (2) crystals of iron separate out from 830° down to 723°C; (3) at 723°C, the solid solution decomposes completely into crystals of ferrite and Fe_3C. A microscopic section of such an alloy is shown in Fig. 69, page 138. The large white meshes are the grains of ferrite which separated between 830 and 723°C; these are the primary crystals. The gray portions show the conglomerate consisting of lamellae of ferrite and Fe_3C, which separated out at 723°C.

The Cooling of File Steel. When steel for files, containing 1.20 per cent carbon, is first frozen, it is a solution of iron and carbon. When it cools, however, it soon reaches the temperature where so much carbon cannot be held in solid solution. This results in the separation of Fe_3C, and, since Fe_3C contains a relatively large proportion of carbon, the amount of carbon remaining in the solid solution becomes progressively less. When 723°C is reached, the file steel is composed of part solid solution containing 0.80 per cent carbon and part Fe_3C containing 6.67 per cent carbon (see Fig. 103).

Allotropic Modifications of Iron. Iron undergoes four allotropic modifications: Delta iron has a body-centered space lattice and is stable from about 1400 to 1533°C (2550 to 2790°F). It is interesting scientifically, but we shall not discuss it further here. It changes to gamma iron, which will hold carbon in solid solution up to a maximum of 2 per cent at 1130°C (2066°F). All solid solutions of carbon in gamma iron are known as *austenite*. Gamma iron and austenite have a face-centered cubic lattice and are nonmagnetic. The decomposition of the solid solution austenite is discussed in the previous four paragraphs. When pure, gamma iron upon cooling to 910°C (1670°F) changes to another modification, alpha iron, which will hold almost no carbon in solid solution. Alpha iron has a body-centered lattice. Also, it is nonmagnetic until it cools to a temperature of about 768°C (1414°F), at which temperature it becomes magnetic, without a change in crystal structure; this change is not considered an allotropic change, although it was once so considered, and the name "beta iron" was given to the nonmagnetic face-centered iron. The temperature at which certain metals change from a nonmagnetic to a magnetic form on cooling, or from a magnetic to a nonmagnetic form on heating, is called the "Curie point." For pure iron, then, the Curie point is 768°C.

As indicated on the diagram, alpha iron will hold only 0.025 per cent carbon in solution at 723°C, and 0.008 per cent at atmospheric temperature. We shall see, however, that even this small proportion in solid solution is important in magnetic and electrical alloys. It is evident that the change to the alpha from the gamma modification is the cause of the breaking up of the solid solution. Alpha iron when pure is almost as soft and ductile as copper. Its presence in steels has an important influence in making them tough.

Summary of the Formation of Structures in Steel

1. Steel, when molten, is a liquid solution of iron and carbon, up to a limit of 2 per cent carbon.

2. All liquid iron-carbon alloys up to 2 per cent carbon freeze as solutions of carbon in iron in the solid state.

3. The only solid solution of iron and carbon that will cool as far as 723°C without decomposing is the one containing 99.20 per cent iron and 0.80 per cent carbon.

4. From all solid solutions with more than 0.80 per cent carbon, Fe_3C will crystallize out until the solution remaining when the alloy has cooled to 723°C contains only 0.80 per cent carbon.

5. From all solid solutions with more than 99.20 per cent iron, ferrite will crystallize out until the solution remaining when the alloy has cooled to 723°C contains only 99.20 per cent iron.

6. At 723°C every solid solution of iron and carbon decomposes into ferrite and Fe_3C.

Critical Temperatures; A_c and A_r Points. The temperatures at which the phase changes occur in iron and iron-carbon alloys are known as *critical temperatures;* they vary with the carbon content. The critical temperatures in heating are designated by the symbol A_c, and the critical temperatures in cooling are designated by the symbol A_r. In practice the A_r temperatures are slightly lower than the A_c temperatures, although in equilibrium they would coincide. The symbol A_e is often used for the critical temperature in equilibrium diagrams.

The A_{c1} point is the temperature at which austenite begins to form during heating. The A_{c3} point is the temperature at which the transformation of ferrite to austenite is completed during heating. $A_{c_{cm}}$ point is the temperature at which, in heating a hypereutectoid steel, the solution of cementite in austenite is completed. A_{r1}, A_{r3}, and $A_{r_{cm}}$ are the corresponding points in cooling.

Variation of the Properties of Iron, Steel, and Cast Iron. Gamma iron is believed to be hard owing to the carbon in solid solution; alpha iron is ductile, tough, and soft; cementite (Fe_3C) is hard and brittle. The proportion and grain size of the alpha iron and the cementite phase in any slowly cooled steel will determine its properties. Primary (large) grains of alpha will evidently have more effect in producing ductility in a steel than will the small grains of alpha in pearlite, while the small grains tend to promote strength and lack of ductility. Gamma iron does not occur in equilibrium in slowly cooled carbon steel, but by rapidly cooling from the temperatures where austenite is stable, as in quenching, properties very different from those of slowly cooled steel can be produced, as will be discussed in Chap. 8. We can also add alloying elements to the steel, such as nickel plus chromium, which will result in the existence of austenite at atmospheric temperatures on normal cooling. Large grains of pure alpha ferrite have good magnetic permeability and better electrical conductivity than any other entities in iron-carbon alloys. Moreover, electrical conductivity is better in one direction of the grains than in another. Thus it is evident that, by control of the components and by their size, arrangement, and like attributes, a variety of properties can be secured.

According to the equilibrium diagram, cast iron, which contains more than 2 per cent carbon, will consist of ferrite and cementite, with cementite greatly predominating; this would make the mass hard and brittle. But an element can be added to liquid cast iron, such as silicon, which will cause Fe_3C to decompose into iron and a soft, flocculent graphite. The resulting "gray cast iron" will not be very brittle and can be readily machined. Iron castings were made in this way long before the reasons for it were understood, both as a result of chance and by means of blast-furnace control.

NONFERROUS ALLOYS

The principal nonferrous alloys are discussed in Chap. 10. The equilibrium diagrams of some nonferrous alloy series are shown in the following figures: copper-zinc alloys, Fig. 144; aluminum-copper alloys, Fig. 155; antimony-lead alloys, Fig. 12; lead-tin alloys, Fig. 95.

Bibliography

See also references following Chap. 8.

AMERICAN SOCIETY FOR METALS: "The Metals Handbook," Cleveland, Ohio, 1948. The theory of alloys is discussed in this book, which also gives the most comprehensive compilation of the alloy phase diagrams published up to the end of 1947.

BOWDEN, S. T.: "The Phase Rule and Phase Reactions: Theoretical and Practical," Macmillan & Co., Ltd., London, 1938.

FINDLAY, A., and A. N. CAMPBELL: "The Phase Rule and Its Applications," 8th ed., Longmans, Green & Co., Inc., New York, 1938.

LORD, J. O.: "Alloy Systems," Pitman Publishing Corp., New York, 1949.

MARSH, J. S.: "Principles of Phase Diagrams," McGraw-Hill Book Company, Inc., New York, 1935.

WILLIAMS, R. S., and V. O. HOMERBERG: "Principles of Metallography," 5th ed., McGraw-Hill Book Company, Inc., New York, 1948.

CHAPTER 8

HEAT-TREATMENT OF METALS AND ALLOYS

HEAT-TREATMENT OF STEEL

Steel may be heated to a previously determined temperature and then cooled at a rapid, or slow, or moderate rate, in order to secure one or more of the following: (1) hardness, (2) softness, (3) a combination of strength and useful ductility (*i.e.*, toughness), and (4) desired grain size. Since before the dawn of history it has been known that some steels are greatly hardened if they are heated to a bright-red heat and then cooled rapidly, such as by plunging into water or oil. A hardened steel cutting tool over 3,000 years old is in the British Museum. For a long time it has been known that steel must contain at least about 0.65 per cent carbon in order to have effective cutting hardness in the quenched condition, and it is now known that it must also be quenched from above the temperature of the line PSK in Fig. 98, or it will not be hardened at all by the rapid cooling.

Critical Temperature. For relatively pure carbon steels, the temperature of the line PSK in Fig. 98 is known as the "lower critical temperature," because the necessary proportion of carbon together with rapid cooling from above the line PSK will produce hardness, whereas slow cooling (whatever the carbon) from above PSK will produce relative softness. Several alloying elements displace this line either upward or downward. Any pronounced lowering will result in retention of austenite, giving austenitic steel, which cannot be hardened by rapid cooling.

Austenite. Austenite is the name given to the stable solid solution above the line PSK in Fig. 98, in which gamma iron is the solvent and the solute is carbon. The proportion of carbon in solution may be from about 0.02 up to 2 per cent. If austenite is cooled slowly to the line PSK, it decomposes into ferrite and pearlite, pearlite alone, or pearlite and cementite depending on the carbon content. If the solid solution contains 0.80 per cent of carbon (*i.e.*, the point S in Fig. 98) and is slowly cooled under equilibrium conditions from that temperature, it will become 100 per cent pearlite (eutectoid). If it contains less than 0.80 per cent carbon, and is cooled under like conditions, it will consist of pearlite with ferrite and is known as "hypoeutectoid steel." If it contains more than 0.80 per cent of carbon, it will consist of pearlite with cementite and is known as "hypereutectoid steel." In any of the three events, it will consist of ferrite and cementite, for pearlite is, of course, composed of these two constituents.

Austenite has a face-centered cubic crystal structure. It is tough, but not nearly so hard as cementite. If, instead of cooling austenite slowly, we accelerate the cooling so as to suppress full transformation at the line *PSK*, we can obtain pearlitic structures of greater or less

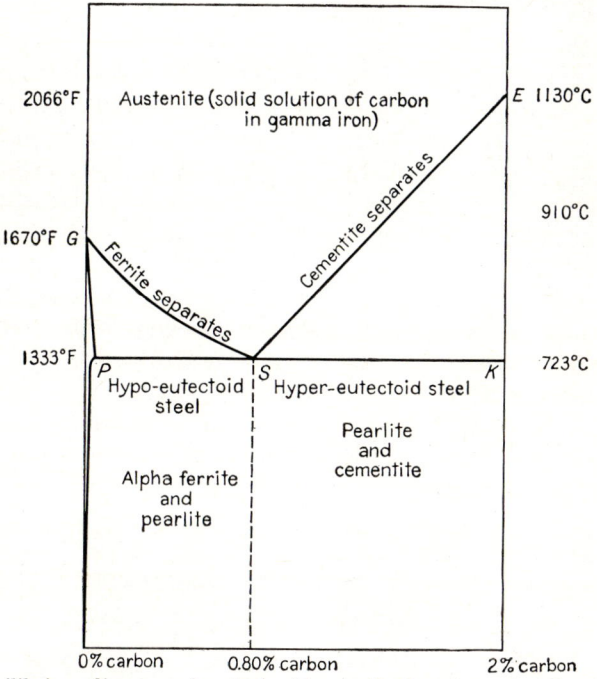

Fig. 98.—Equilibrium diagram of a steel without alloying elements other than carbon and without impurities (iron with carbon up to 2 per cent).

The temperatures of phase changes are higher on heating than on cooling, on account of lag; the temperatures here given are those determined for heating the alloys.

Upon cooling below the line *GS*, ferrite separates from solid solution.

Upon cooling below the line *SE*, cementite separates from solid solution.

The area *GPO* contains alpha iron with a very little carbon in solid solution (ferrite). The proportion of carbon in solution decreases as the temperature falls.

degree of fineness. By the procedure known as "interrupted quenching" we can control the structure obtained, as explained on page 175 and in Fig. 106. The most rapid cooling that can be accomplished in unalloyed iron-carbon alloys will produce martensite, the hardest constituent obtainable from the decomposition of austenite. Austenite is composed of structureless crystals, as will be evident from Fig. 99, whereas martensite, shown in Fig. 100, has a triangular, needlelike pattern which evidently has a structure, but it is submicroscopic and has never been fully revealed. Austenite is in equilibrium above the transformation range, and the most rapid cooling of plain carbon steels so far attained fails to perpetuate it (except in small proportions known as "residual austenite") in the cold steel. But some alloying elements have the effect of lowering the temperatures of the transformation range. In some alloy steels, the structure can be rendered austenitic at atmospheric temperature and often can then be partly or wholly converted to martensite by cold work.

The Nature of Martensite. Martensite is an unstable constituent in quenched steel. It is a supersaturated solid solution of cementite in alpha iron. It is more magnetic than is austenite; its space lattice is body-centered, and it is usually tetragonal in crystal form at ordinary temperature. A suggestion, now widely believed, is that the hardness of martensite is due to its being in a highly stressed condition, both because of being an unstable, supersaturated solid solution and because of the expansion resulting when austenite transforms to less-dense

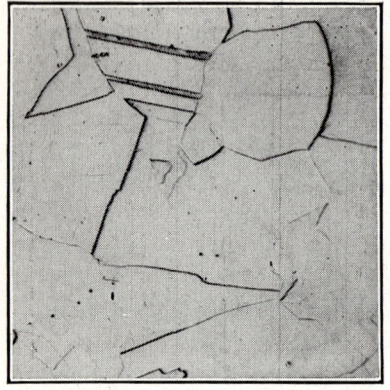

FIG. 99. Austenite. In steel with 18 per cent chromium, 12 nickel. Magnification 250 ×. Etched with glyceregia. (*George V. Luerssen.*)

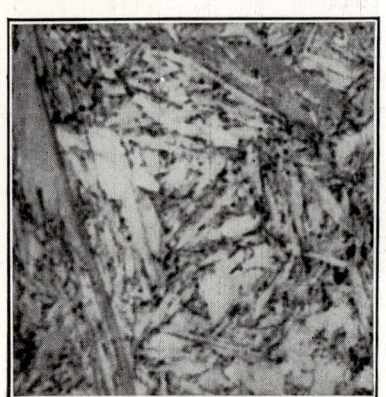

FIG. 100. Martensite. (Formed from rapidly cooled austenite.) Steel of 0.85 per cent carbon. Magnification 2,000 ×. (*Courtesy of Bausch & Lomb.*)

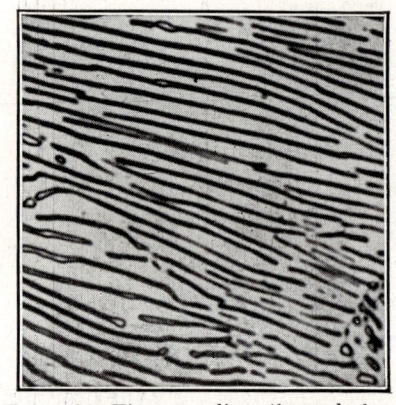

FIG. 101. Fine pearlite (formed from slowly cooled austenite or austenite otherwise completely decomposed into ferrite and cementite). In AISI 1095 steel. Magnification 1,500 ×. This structure was obtained by cooling the steel 25° per hour from 1700°F. (*M. W. Keenan and E. F. Shiner, author's laboratory.*)

martensite. This is the theory based upon residual stress. Martensite forms only on cooling, and while the temperatures of start and finish of martensite formation (M_s and M_f points, respectively, Fig. 104) depend

HEAT-TREATMENT OF METALS AND ALLOYS 173

FIG. 102. Hypoeutectoid steel. Ferrite plus pearlite. 0.50 per cent carbon. Magnification 1,000 ×. (*George V. Luerssen.*)

FIG. 103. Hypereutectoid steel. Pearlite plus cementite. File steel of about 1.20 per cent carbon. Magnification 750 ×. (*H. W. Cooper, author's laboratory.*)

The massive cementite precipitated in the grain boundaries etches white, whereas the same constituent is black when present in pearlite. This sometimes makes it difficult to distinguish between cementite in grain boundaries and grain-boundary ferrite typical of hypoeutectoid steels.

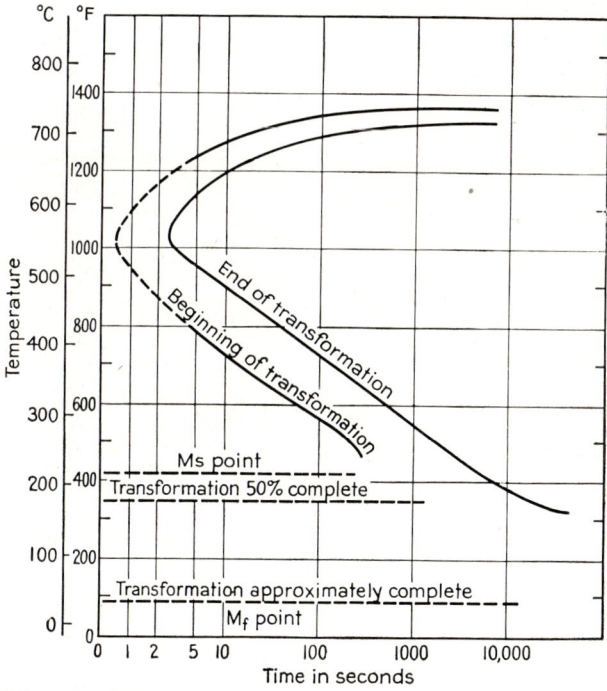

FIG. 104. "S" curve of steel containing 1.10 per cent carbon, showing time required for transformation at various temperatures after quenching from 790°C (1450°F) and holding at those temperatures.

upon the composition of the alloy, nevertheless the beginning is often at about 205 to 290°C (400 to 550°F). Therefore, to obtain the maximum proportion of martensite possible, one must cool austenite so rapidly that it does not decompose at all until a temperature of about 220°C

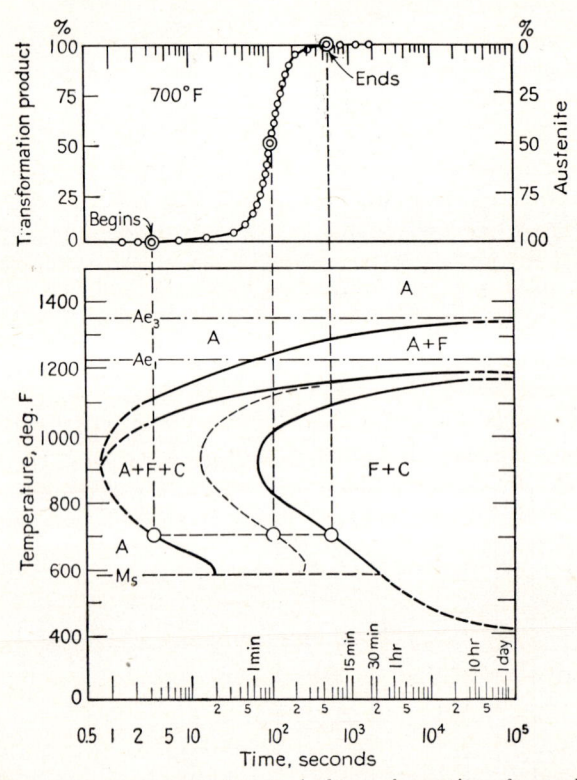

FIG. 105. The upper curve represents a typical transformation of a steel at a constant temperature, and the lower is a typical isothermal diagram of the same steel. (*Courtesy of E. S. Davenport.*)

The lower curve may be regarded as a kind of map or working drawing that enables one to visualize approximately how the steel will behave and what structural changes will take place when it undergoes transformation at any temperature from the austenitic state. It is obtained by determining by investigation the beginning and the time necessary for the completion of austenite decomposition at several different temperatures, when the steel in question is held in a molten bath at that temperature until transformation is complete. The vertical dotted lines indicate how the lower diagram may be obtained from a number of transformations of the steel at a single temperature, in this case, 700°F. A = austenite; F = ferrite; C = cementite; M_s = martensite starts to form; M_f = martensite finishes forming (not shown); Ae_3 (upper transformation line in Fig. 98) = austenite begins to deposit a proeutectoid constituent; Ae_1 (lower transformation line in Fig. 98) = austenite begins to deposit eutectoid. In the lower figure, the left-hand line is the beginning and the right-hand line is the ending of austenite transformation, whereas the middle, dotted, line represents 50 per cent of transformation.

(430°F) is reached. This means maintaining an unstable condition in the austenite during a cooling of about 500°C (900°F). This requisite speed of cooling for any given steel was long known as "the critical cooling speed" of that steel. This is now better explained by the "S curve," or the isothermal transformation curve, also called the transformation-temperature-time (or TTT) curve.

Isothermal Transformation Curves. The classic studies of Bain and Davenport, beginning before 1930, on the decomposition of austenite have thrown a flood of light upon the so-called "critical cooling curves" and transformed the heat-treatment of steel from an art into a science. To their work has been added that of Payson on annealing. A typical isothermal transformation diagram is shown in Fig. 104 on a logarithmic scale, and in Fig. 105 is shown in more detail the transformation of a steel at a single temperature, in order to illustrate how the isothermal curve is obtained. The explanation under this figure should be studied carefully. These curves provide a convenient means of showing the time required for austenite to begin and to finish transforming at any temperature below its range of stability. For example, a "critical cooling curve" must be so steep that it will bring the steel down from Ae_3 to M_s without touching the "nose" or "knee" of the S curve, which indicates decomposition of austenite. The "knee" shown in the graph is between 425 and 540°C (800 and 1000°F). The time in this case is shown to be about 0.5 sec. On the other hand, if we want to accomplish the complete decomposition of austenite, and thus secure a soft condition in the steel, we can cool at any speed which will bring us to the right of the right-hand line. In the case of alloy steels, the TTT curves are more complicated than those of plain carbon steel, and some alloy steels have two or (rarely) more "noses" or "knees."

In the patented process of *austempering*, one can operate somewhat according to the lower graph in Fig. 105; *i.e.*, the steel can be heated to a point above the Ae_3 line and then quenched in a bath maintained at, say, 370°C (700°F)[1] and held there until the austenite has been transformed into ferrite and cementite (in this case, called "bainite," described on page 180). In the process of *martempering*, the steel is heated until the solid solution is complete, then it is quenched in a bath slightly above or in the upper portion of the temperature range of martensite transformation, held there until it is substantially uniform in temperature, and then allowed to cool in air to below M_f. The common processes of quenching and tempering are shown schematically in Fig. 106.

Quenching Media. The hardening of steel is accomplished by having in it the requisite proportion of cementite, heating the steel until austenite is formed, and then immersing it in a quenching medium which will rapidly abstract heat from it. The effectiveness of a quenching medium

---

[1] The temperature must be low enough to produce ferrite plus cementite, but above that of martensite formation. The heat-abstracting character of the quenching bath must be high enough to prevent the formation of high-temperature transformation products.

will evidently depend upon its temperature, its heat conductivity, the continuity of contact between it and the steel, and other conditions. Many quenching media are used with the object of cooling with greater or less rapidity. Iced brine, water, hot water, oil, hot oil, metal plates, liquid air, atmospheric air, and a vacuum are some of these. We may have a quiet bath, a circulating bath, a spray, and so on. A spray

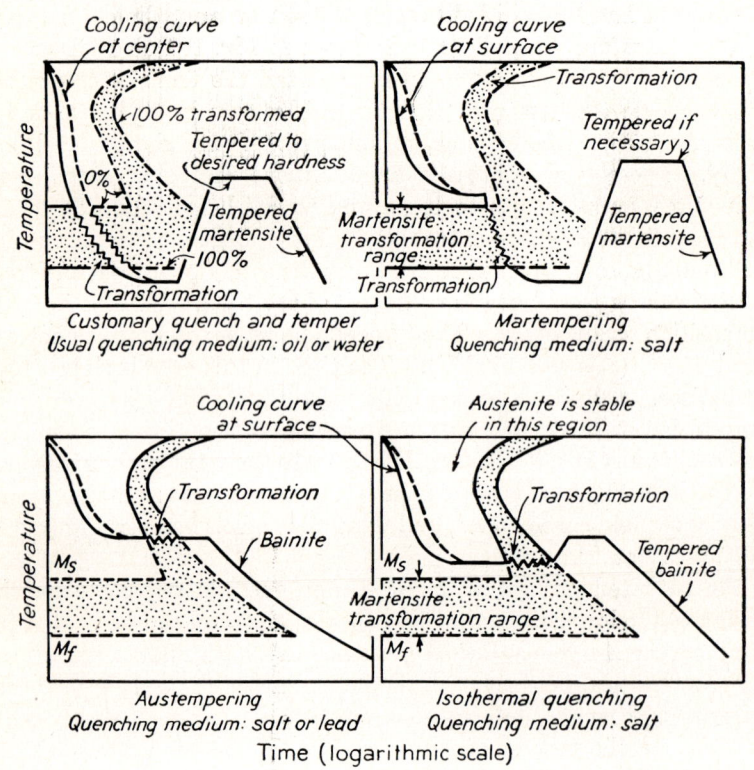

Fig. 106. Schematic representation of four important quenching methods related to the TTT or isothermal curve. The last three methods are known as "interrupted quenchings," because the cooling occurs in two stages.

prevents gases formed by the volatilization of the medium from collecting between it and the steel.

The Influence of Mass: Hardenability. Evidently the outside surface of any specimen will be cooled most rapidly by the quenching medium, and the interior will be cooled by conduction of heat from it to the outer layers and thence to the quenching medium. The hardness of the interior will therefore depend on the depth of hardening (called the "hardenability") of the steel in question (which is frequently a function of its composition) and the speed with which heat can be extracted from it. Some alloy steels harden deeply because their isothermal transformation curves are well to the right of the ordinate of the graph shown in Fig. 105, and therefore they transform with the passage of greater time than that shown. In other words, their austenite is relatively sluggish. A series of steels of different hardenability, in rods of 1-in. diameter, that were hardened, cut into two parts, polished on the cut surface, and etched, is shown in Fig. 107. The penetration of hardness is obvious. Another simple method of illustrating hardenability is to harden cylinders of

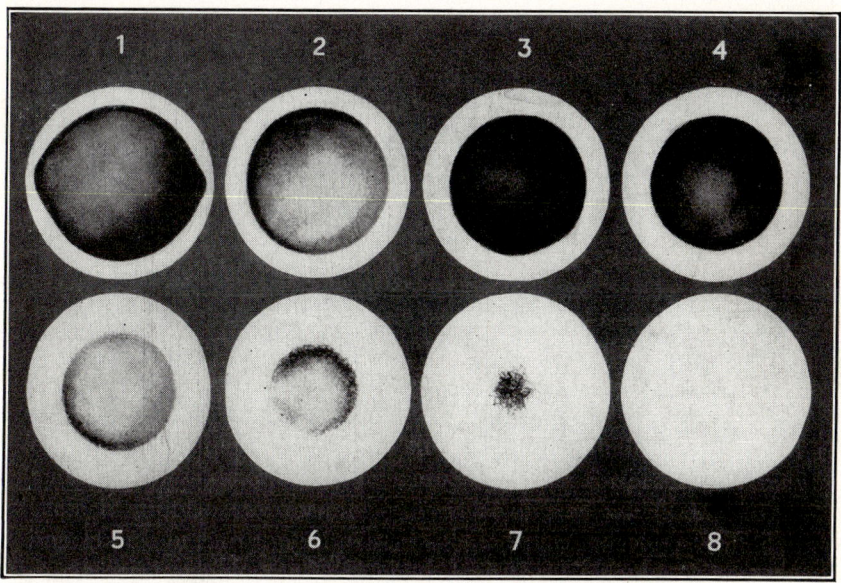

Fig. 107. Eight steels of continuously increasing depth of hardness. (*E. C. Bain.*)

The white portion is martensite, and the dark portion is unhardened structure, consisting chiefly of ferrite and cementite, some of the latter being associated in pearlite. The carbon content is almost the same in each one, and the total of alloying elements in each is not more than 1 per cent. The difference in hardenability is due chiefly to the larger grain size in those of greater hardenability.

differing diameters of the same steel, cut them diametrically, and then make hardness determinations across their cut surfaces. We may plot these in graphs, two examples of which are shown in Fig. 108. The importance of hardenability is great, and particularly is this so in the case of steels which are to be toughened by heat-treatment, for the reason that they are often under stress internally as well as externally. Another example of showing hardenability, particularly for tool steels, is illustrated in Fig. 62, page 132.

Hardenability Testing. The depth to which hardness (*i.e.*, a martensitic structure) will penetrate into the interior of a steel will evidently depend upon (1) the speed necessary to ensure the continuity of the austenitic structure down to the temperature at which the martensitic structure forms (*i.e.*, M_s), (2) the temperature of M_s, and (3) the speed with which heat may be extracted from the interior of the specimen through the surface. Numbers 1 and 2 can now be learned usually from isothermal diagrams (S curves) available for most alloy steels.

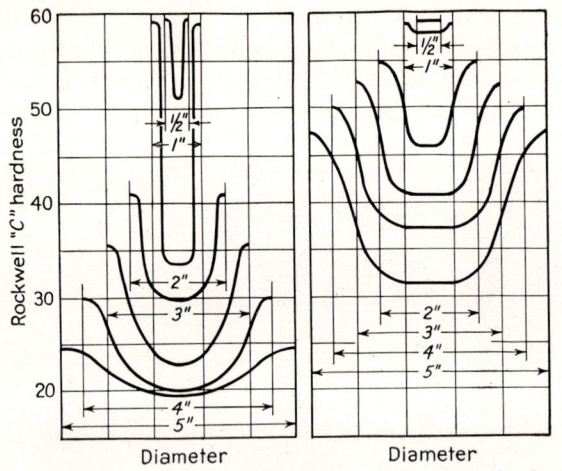

FIG. 108. Hardenability curves in which the Rockwell hardness is plotted against the diameter of the sections. (*M. A. Grossmann.*)

The left-hand series of curves shows the hardness across the section of various-sized bars of carbon steel of about 0.45 per cent carbon, and therefore not deep-hardening. The right-hand series shows the corresponding hardness figures for bars of a deeper-hardening steel containing chromium and vanadium.

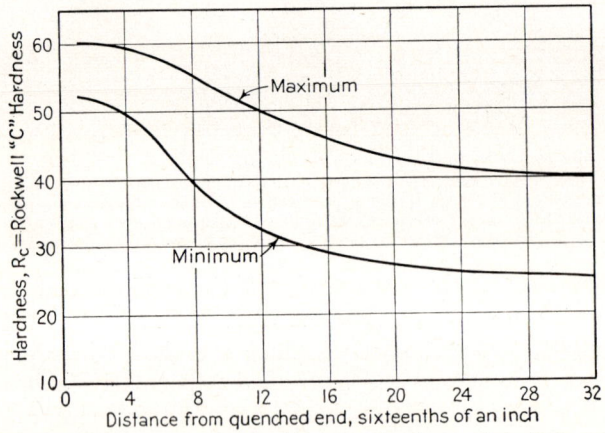

FIG. 109. Hardenability curves determined by Jominy end test for a given steel. (*Courtesy of U.S. Steel Corporation Research Laboratory.*)

The alloying elements which most strongly produce depth hardness in steel are molybdenum, tungsten, manganese, and chromium—especially chromium with nickel. Sometimes the hardenability of a steel may be calculated approximately from its composition, as has been described in the publications of Grossmann, but hardenability tests, some of which are discussed in the next two paragraphs, are now commonly used also.

The Jominy End Test for Hardenability. The Jominy test is described as follows: the bar is first normalized at about 85°C (150°F) above the Ac_3 point; it is then machined to remove the decarburized surface and to bring it to exactly 1 in. in diameter. Then it is heated in a non-oxidizing atmosphere to 40°C (75°F) above the Ac_3 point and quenched

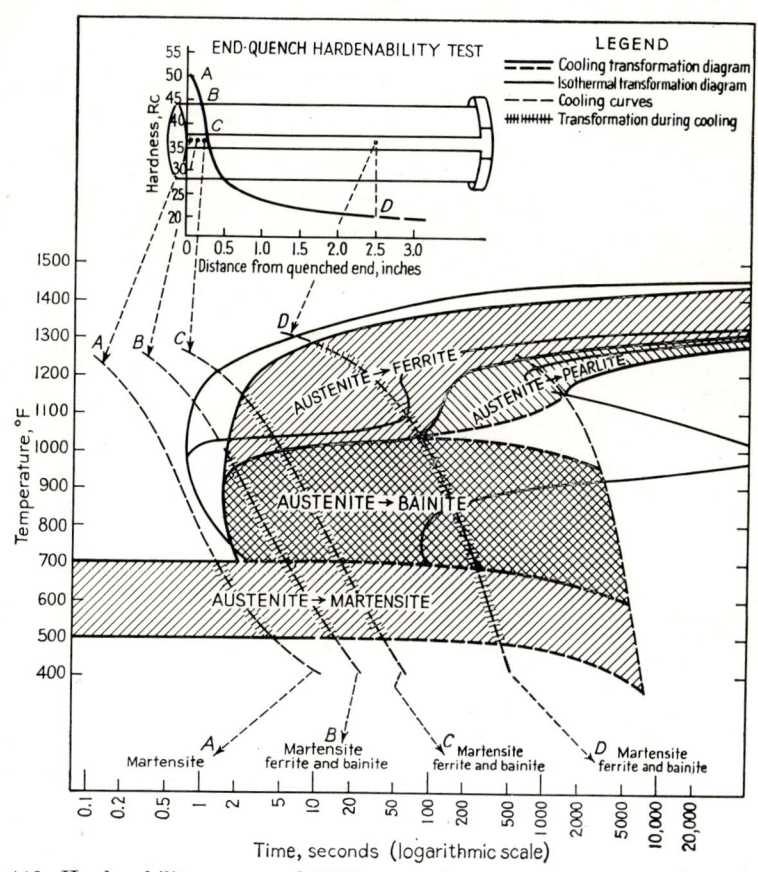

Fig. 110. Hardenability curve and TTT curve of same steel, showing how the speed of quenching produces different constituents and therefore differences in hardness. The steel used contained 0.30 per cent carbon, about 0.50 per cent each of nickel and chromium, and about 0.15 per cent molybdenum. The lower graph represents the TTT curve for the steel in question, and the lines *ABCD* and the transformations during cooling show why the hardnesses indicated at the points *ABCD* in the hardenability curve are obtained. (*Courtesy of U.S. Steel Corporation Research Laboratory.*)

in such a manner that only one end of the 4 in. long specimen comes in contact with a stream of water. Two flat surfaces are then ground longitudinally on the specimen to a depth of 0.015 in., and hardness determinations are made on these ground surfaces at intervals of $\frac{1}{16}$ in. from the quenched end. Thus we have hardness values ranging from those of a water quench to those representing relatively slow cooling, and a "hardenability curve" can be plotted as shown in Fig. 109. The relationship between the hardenability curve and the isothermal diagram of the same steel is shown in Fig. 110.

(*Bainite* is a structure named after E. C. Bain, who first encountered it in structures obtained by isothermal transformations. Low-temperature bainite is an austenite decomposition product that is apparently indistinguishable from tempered martensite. Both products consist of finely divided cementite in a matrix of ferrite and appear through the microscope as platelike regions that are confined to individual austenite grains or to areas of austenite grains which did not transform at higher temperature. The fundamental difference between the platelike structure of pearlite and of bainite is that pearlite grows by a process of Fe_3C nucleation followed by ferrite precipitation, while bainite grows by ferrite nucleation followed by the appearance of Fe_3C platelets. Thus, fundamentally, cause and effect are reversed.)

Other Hardenability Tests. The Carpenter cone test shows on one specimen the penetration to be expected in various diameters and the diameter which will just harden through. The B. F. Shepherd "P-F test" is more sensitive to shallow-hardening steels than is the Jominy end test. Both of these make it possible to convert the results into terms of specific hardenability expressed as critical quenching speed in degrees per second.[1] These tests are described on pages 131 and 132.

Air-hardening Steels. Evidently a steel that will become martensitic upon cooling in quiet air, without acceleration such as quenching or the like, will be an "air-hardening" steel. Such steels are sometimes called "self-hardening." Several alloy steels have this characteristic. All of them contain two or more alloying elements, with 0.40 to 1 per cent carbon. A common type is a nondeforming tool steel containing approximately 5 per cent chromium, 1 per cent molybdenum, and 1.00 per cent carbon.

Differential Hardening. Some objects require a combination of hard and tough parts. To cite a few examples: the surface of the teeth of a gear must be hard to resist wear, whereas the web must be tough, strong, and ductile; a crankshaft should be hard on its bearing surfaces, whereas the remainder should be tough to resist shocks; the nose of a projectile must be hard, but the shank must be tough. There are three principal ways in which this can be accomplished: (1) by heating to the austenite region only that part of the steel which is to be hardened by rapid cooling; (2) by using a low-carbon steel which will not be appreciably hardened by heat-treatment—say, 0.20 per cent carbon—and then carburizing the

---

[1] For more details, see "Tool Steel Simplified," Carpenter Steel Company, 1948, pp. 423–426.

parts which it is desired to harden; or (3) hardening some parts by nitriding (which requires no heat-treatment thereafter). *Flame hardening* is accomplished by causing a flame to impinge on that part of an object which it is desired to harden until it is heated above the critical temperature (*i.e.*, into the austenitic region) and then rapidly cooling at least that part. Another method of differential hardening is described in the next paragraph.

Induction Hardening. Since 1935, high-frequency induction heating has been extended to numerous commercial applications involving both surface and through hardening. Any material which is a conductor of electricity can be successfully heated by induction. The principle involved is similar to that of a transformer, wherein electric current passing through the primary induces flow of current in the secondary. The primary, called the load coil or inductor, is made from copper tubing, water-cooled during operation, and wound to conform to the area of the part that is desired to be heated. The secondary represents the part itself. High-frequency alternating current, *i.e.*, 3,000 to 500,000 cycles per sec, developed by motor-generator, spark-gap, or electronic-tube converters, passes through the load coil and induces the flow of eddy currents in the surface of the part to be heated. The resistance of the workpiece to the flow of these currents heats the metal. If the material is magnetic, heating occurs by hysteresis losses as well.

Since the penetration of induced current in the workpiece is inversely proportional to the square root of the frequency, it is possible to control the depth of heating by the frequency used, by the energy input, and by the time allowed for conduction of heat from the surface to the center of the part.

For surface hardening, medium plain-carbon steels of 0.35 to 0.60 per cent carbon are preferred, although alloy steels containing approximately 0.30 to 0.50 per cent carbon can be successfully treated. Such steels are heated rapidly above the critical temperature, at the surface, and immediately quenched in water or oil. Heating and quenching are generally performed progressively, the quench following the heating as the piece progresses through the work coil. Upon quenching, the localities which were heated above the critical temperature harden, while those which were not heated above that temperature remain soft. The bearing surfaces of crankshafts are commonly differentially hardened in this way, as are also the noses of armor-piercing or semi-armor-piercing projectiles. It is a very rapid method of heat-treatment, readily and accurately controlled. When through hardening is desired, steels are heated more slowly, and time is allowed for conduction of heat from the surface to the center. When the temperature is essentially uniform, the piece is quenched in the same manner as that employed with conventional heat-treating methods. An apparatus for induction heating is shown in Fig. 201, page 424.

Casehardening with Carbon. This is a type of differential hardening in which the outside is hard by virtue of being high in carbon, while the interior is soft because of being relatively low in carbon and is tough and ductile. It is used in making many objects, especially automobile parts, such as gears, crankshafts, pins, and the like. Casehardening steel contains about 0.20 to 0.30 per cent carbon, but often alloy steels are used in order to make the core stronger and tougher, and/or to increase the speed of penetration of carbon into the surface. The steel is heated well into the austenitic range and held there for some hours during which the carbon diffuses or "cements" into the austenitic solid solution. This "cementation process" is as old as history, although, of course, the terms "austenite" and "solid solution" were not known until this century.

There are four chief processes of casehardening, or "carburizing," as follows:

1. Pack carburizing, in which the steel is entirely surrounded with solid carburizing material, usually consisting of powdered charcoal with an "accelerator," which is often a carbonate, and packed into containers, inserted into a furnace, and heated to the appropriate temperature, say 960°C (1760°F), where it is held for some hours, depending upon the degree of carburization desired. It usually requires about 8 hr for the carbon on the surface to reach about 1 per cent. The boxes are then dumped and either the steel is quenched (see treatments E and G of Fig. 111), or else the pieces are cooled, reheated, and quenched (see treatments A, B, C, D and F, of Fig. 111). The outside ("case") is hard, and the inside ("core") is tough and ductile.

2. In gas carburizing the pieces are fed through a rotary gas retort[1] in which they are subjected to the necessary temperature in a forced circulation of carburizing gas, whereby the outer surface is brought to a well-controlled carbon content by suitable gas composition. Quenching follows as previously described.

3. In carbonitriding, a rotary retort is used,[1] and the carburizing gas is mixed with ammonia gas. The temperature is usually between 815 and 850°C (1500 and 1560°F). Both carbon and nitrogen penetrate into the case, which is usually only 0.003 to 0.10 in. in depth, and if sufficient ammonia gas has been used in the retort, carbon steel can usually be made file-hard on the surface without quenching.

4. In liquid carburizing, new equipment and salt baths are extensively

[1] In the automobile industry, gas carburizing is often done in continuous furnaces rather than in rotary gas retorts, and carbonitriding is also done in continuous furnaces or in salt baths.

replacing the old cyanide pots. The steel is immersed in the liquid salt bath until the outside is carburized. The salts consist of sodium cyanide, with alkaline-earth salts, such as barium and sodium chloride and sodium carbonate. The process is extremely flexible, gives low distortion and uniformity in control of the case, and is well adapted to small units, but is usually not employed for cases over 0.03 in. in depth. Both carbon and nitrogen penetrate into the case, and heat-treatment after carburiza-

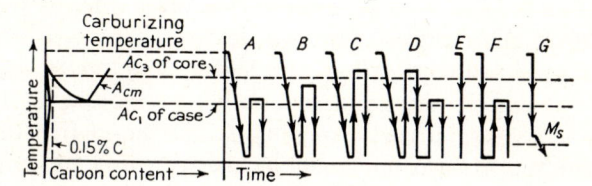

FIG. 111. Diagrammatic representation of the various hardening treatments following carburizing of steel, and summary of the properties of case and core provided adequate hardenability is assumed.

Treatment	Case	Core
A (Best adapted to fine-grained steels)	Refined; excess carbide not dissolved	Unrefined; soft and machinable
B (Best adapted to fine-grained steels)	Slightly coarsened; some solution of excess carbide	Partially refined; stronger than A; erratic
C (Best adapted to fine-grained steels)	Somewhat coarsened; solution of excess carbide favored; austenite retention promoted in highly alloyed steels	Refined; maximum core strength and hardness. Better combination of strength and ductility than B
D (Best treatment for coarse-grained steels)	Refined; solution of excess carbide favored; austenite retention minimized	Refined; soft and machinable; maximum toughness and resistance to impact
E (Adapted to fine-grained steels only)	Unrefined with excess carbide dissolved; austenite retained; distortion minimized; fileproof when carbon content is high	Fully hardened
F (Adapted to fine-grained steels only)	Refined; solution of excess carbide favored; austenite retention minimized	Low hardness; high toughness
G (Interrupted quench; martempering)	Unrefined with excess carbide dissolved; austenite retained; distortion minimized; file-hard when carbon content is high	Fully hardened

tion is commonly employed. The usual temperature of the bath is between 845 and 900°C (1550 and 1650°F).

Nitriding. Another method of casehardening steel is by the process known as nitriding. This is used for many parts of automobiles, airplanes, and machinery because it gives a surface which is much harder than that produced by casehardening with carbon, and also because it requires no rapid cooling after nitriding in order to produce the hardness. Rapid cooling (quenching) tends to distort some shapes of carburized parts. Nitriding is performed by heating the steel for several hours or even days in an atmosphere of ammonia at 510 to 535°C (950 to 1000°F), which is lower than employed in case carburizing. This results in an absorption of nitrogen by the surface of the steel, which makes it hard without any further heat-treatment. Many precautions must be taken in nitriding, and it is an operation requiring experience and skill.

Special Inspection Required for Carburized and Nitrided Parts. Because the case of a casehardened piece has different characteristics from those of the core, and also because a casehardened part is often subjected to fatigue stresses, there are special features which must be assured. In circumstances where the highest quality is required in a casehardened member, the grain size of both case and core should be determined. In a carburized part there must be no free cementite in the case, and the surface must not be decarburized by forging or by heat-treatment subsequent to carburization. A case which is too soft or too thin may not be disclosed by a Rockwell or other hardness test, but a soft surface may fail by scoring or galling and will have relatively low fatigue strength. The fatigue strength of the core is lower than that of the case, and if the latter is too thin, or if there is insufficient support of the case by the core, the fatigue strength of the part as a whole may be inadequate. There must be no surface irregularities from forging or heat-treatment or any other cause, because such irregularities will act as notches to reduce the fatigue strength.

If it is possible to test the completed member for residual stresses on both case and core, this should be done. Since fatigue failures result only from tension stresses, never from compression, it follows that a compression stress inherent in a part will increase its resistance to fatigue. Such a residual compression stress is normal to a carburized and quenched, or to a nitrided, surface. Many believe that this is one of the reasons why casehardened gear teeth, for example, survive so well in service.

Tempering or Drawing. The term "tempering" indicates a moderation of hardness. Although the terms *tempering* and *drawing* are practically synonymous as used in commercial practice, the term tempering is preferable. "Tempering," to mean the combined operation of hardening followed by reheating to moderate the hardness, is a usage which is illogical and confusing and should be discouraged. When cutting hardness is produced by rapid cooling, brittleness also results, and this must be corrected, or the steel will be fragile under shock. The brittleness is removed by heating the hardened steel to temperatures of 200 to 300°C (390 to 570°F). Where ductility is especially desired, as in constructional steels, the temperature of tempering may be as high as 600°C (1110°F) or more, but too high a temperature removes too much hardness and strength. Each increase in the temperature of tempering, and in the time at temperature, lowers the strength and hardness and increases

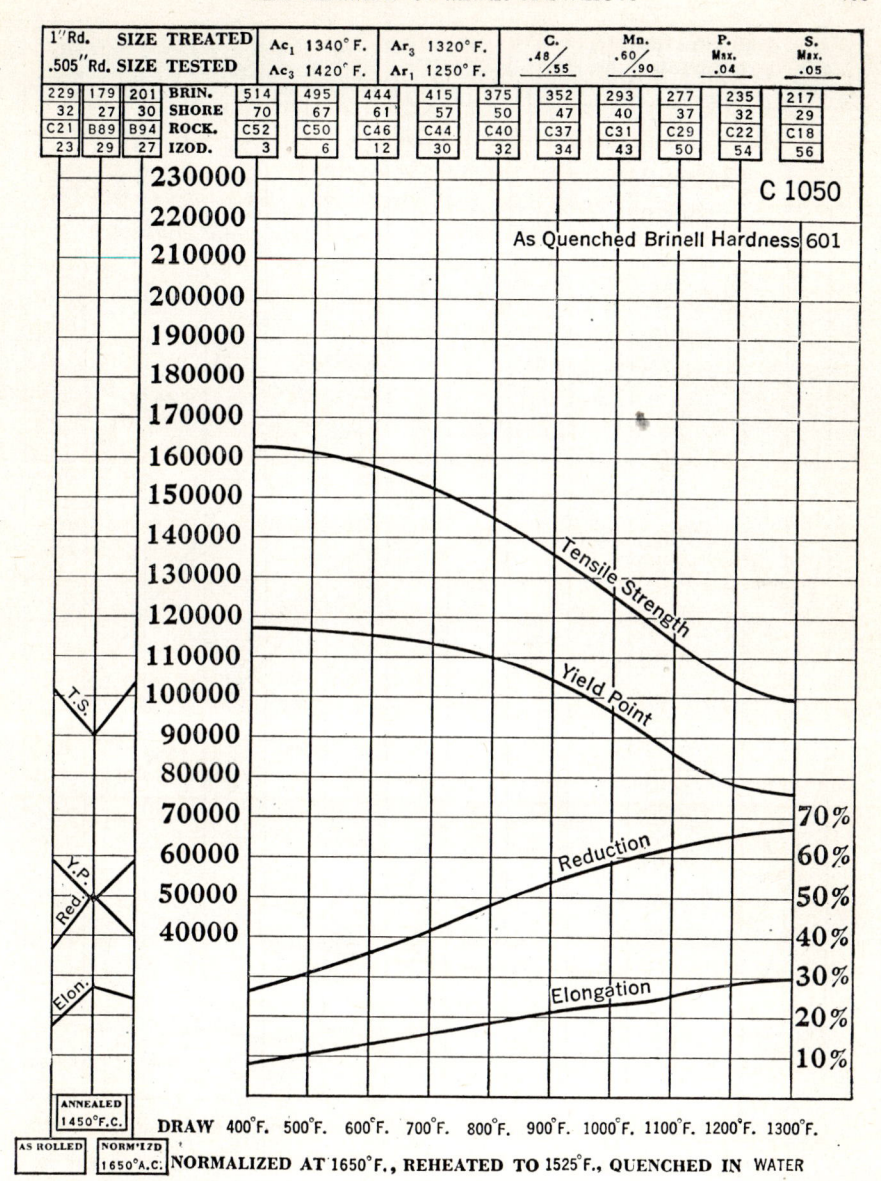

FIG. 112. Relation between temperature of drawing (tempering) and hardness, impact strength, tensile properties, and ductility of a carbon steel of about 0.50 per cent carbon. (*Courtesy of Bethlehem Steel Company; taken from their Handbook* 268, "*Modern Steels*.")

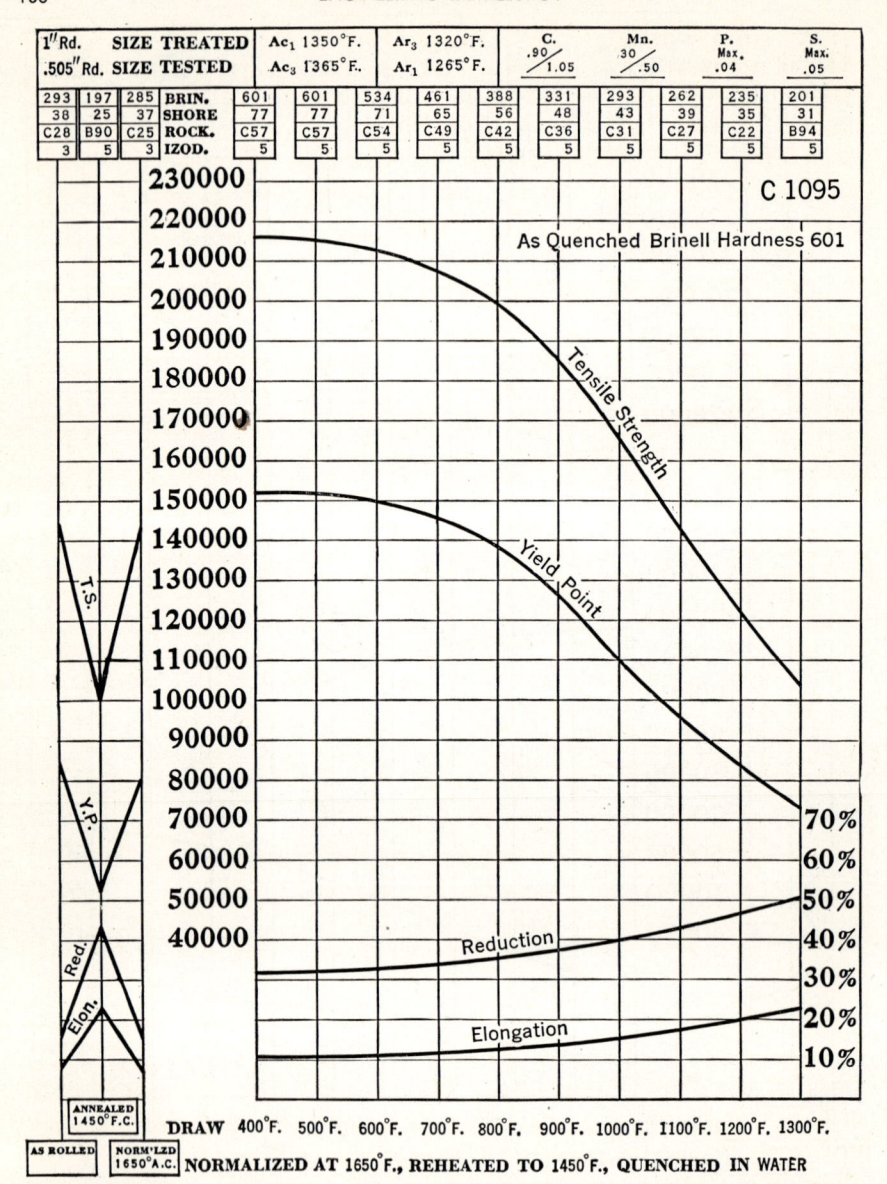

FIG. 113. Relation between temperature of drawing (tempering) and hardness, impact strength, tensile properties, and ductility of a carbon steel of about 1 per cent carbon. (*Courtesy of Bethlehem Steel Company; taken from their Handbook 268, "Modern Steels."*)

the ductility of carbon and alloy steels, as shown in Figs. 112 to 114. The impact strength is also improved by tempering, except that, when the tempering is in the neighborhood of 200 to 425°C (390 to 800°F), the impact strength suffers, as indicated for an alloy steel in Fig. 115 (see page 188). Many alloy steels show peculiarities in impact strength or toughness; they sometimes have high points in toughness which are also high points in hardness, and vice versa.

Temper Brittleness. This results when certain steels are held within, or cooled slowly through, a certain range of temperature below the

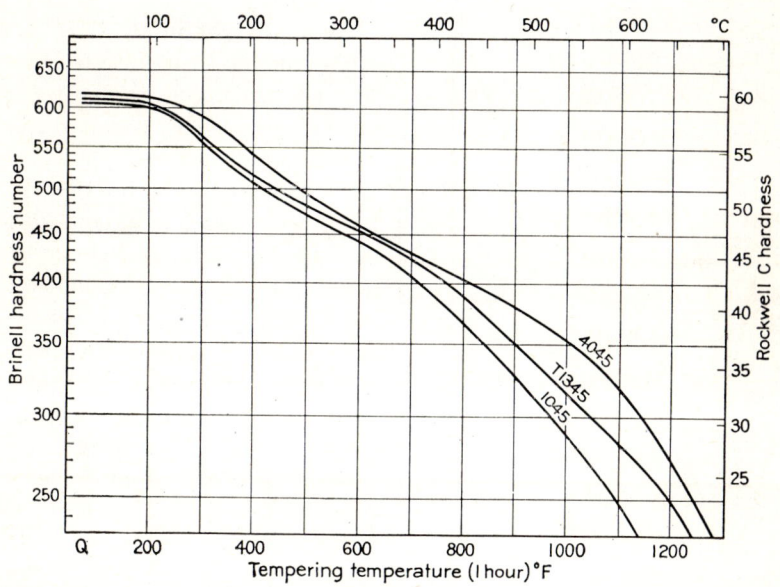

Fig. 114. Effect of tempering temperature on the hardness of a carbon steel and two alloy steels. (*Courtesy of Steel Publications, Inc.; taken from their "Watkins' Cyclopedia of the Steel Industry."*)

transformation range. The brittleness is revealed by notched-bar impact tests at room, or lower, temperature. The term arose because certain steels reheated for tempering and then allowed to cool slowly instead of being "quenched out" proved to be brittle. The reason for temper brittleness is not proved, although many believe it to be caused by the absorption of nitrogen. A small proportion of molybdenum (say, under 0.50 per cent) will lessen or eliminate temper brittleness.

Secondary Hardening. In quenching austenite, 100 per cent of martensite does not usually result, and if the quench is too fast, there may be some "retained austenite," which is not so hard as martensite and results in the steel being softer or having soft spots. During tempering, some or all of this residual austenite may change to martensite, with the result that the tempered steel is harder than before it was tempered. This is especially the case with some alloy steels that change rather sluggishly from austenite, notably high-speed steel and 5 per cent chromium steel. This hardness as a result of tempering is called "secondary hardness." Another cause of it is the precipitation of carbides of an alloying element. When the Fe₃C begins to coalesce in tempering, the hardness drops; but when the temperature rises to a point high enough to cause another carbide to precipitate, but not high enough to cause coalescence thereof, the hardness increases.

Annealing of Steel. Rapid cooling of austenite, by interfering with the change which normally occurs at 723°C (1333°F) and partially or wholly producing martensite, causes steel to be hard and brittle. If, on the other hand, it is cooled very slowly through this change, the austenite will transform into ferrite and cementite at and below the lower critical temperature and the new structure will be relatively soft and ductile. From a study of the isothermal or TTT diagram it is also evident that if, after complete austenitizing, the steel is cooled to a temperature below Ae_1 and held at that temperature (see Fig. 105) for a period of time long enough to cause the austenite to transform into ferrite and cementite, it may be equally soft and ductile if the constant temperature of austenite transformation is the correct one for that particular steel. The work of Peter Payson is especially to be noted in this connection, particularly on alloy steels.

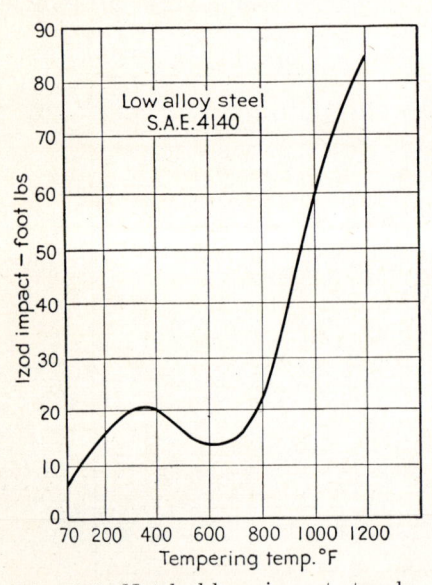

FIG. 115. Notched-bar impact toughness vs. tempering temperature. (Courtesy of Steel Publications, Inc.; taken from their "Watkins' Cyclopedia of the Steel Industry.")

The purposes of annealing steel may be the following:

1. To remove stresses (often called stress relieving).
2. To induce softness.
3. To alter ductility, toughness, electrical, magnetic, or other mechanical and physical properties.
4. To refine the crystalline structure.
5. To remove gases.
6. To produce a definite microstructure.

In annealing, the temperature of the operation and the rate of cooling depend upon the material being heat-treated and the purpose of the treatment.

Certain specific heat-treatments coming under the comprehensive term annealing are as follows:

Full Annealing. 1. Heating to a temperature above the transformation range and, after holding for a sufficient time at this temperature, cooling slowly to a temperature below the transformation range. The alloy is ordinarily allowed to cool slowly in the furnace, although it may be removed and cooled in some medium that ensures a slow rate of cooling.

NOTE. As stated above, a similar result may be accomplished by heating in a similar manner and then cooling rather rapidly to a temperature below the lower critical and holding at that constant temperature for a sufficient length of time to permit the complete transformation of austenite. The constant temperature of transformation is usually not more than 110°C (200°F) below the lower critical temperature.

2. The annealing temperature is generally about 55°C (100°F) above the upper limit of the critical temperature range, Ac_3, and the time of holding is usually not less than 1 hr for each inch of section of the heaviest objects being treated.

Process Annealing. In the sheet, wire, and tubing industries, a process by which steel is heated to a temperature close to, but below, the lower limit of its transformation range and subsequently cooled as desired. This process is also called "subcritical annealing" and produces the softest structures, softer than full annealing.

NOTE. With relatively slow cooling, the temperatures usually applied in process annealing are 550 to 650°C (1020 to 1200°F), but in continuous annealing the metal is usually heated in the range 690 to 720°C (1275 to 1325°F).

Normalizing. A process in which a ferrous alloy is heated to a suitable temperature (approximately 55°C, 100°F) above the upper critical temperature and is subsequently cooled in still air at room temperature. (Sometimes cooling is accelerated by an air blast and the process is still called normalizing, although it may be a misnomer.)

NOTE. Normalizing is rarely practiced with hypereutectoid steels because of the coarsening of the grain and the tendency to crystallize cementite at grain boundaries or in needles. However, it may sometimes be necessary to normalize the steels by heating them above the A_{cm} line of the iron-carbon diagram.

Patenting. In wiremaking, a heat-treatment applied to medium-carbon or high-carbon steel before the drawing of wire or between drafts. This process consists in heating to a temperature above the transformation range, and then cooling to a temperature below that range, in air or in a bath of molten lead or salt maintained at a temperature appropriate to the carbon content of the steel and to the properties required of the finished product.

Spheroidizing. Any process of heating and cooling that produces a rounded or globular form of carbide in steel. Spheroidizing methods frequently used are as follows:

1. Prolonged heating at a temperature just below Ae_1 (Fig. 105, page 174).
2. Heating and cooling alternately between temperatures that are just above and just below Ae_1.
3. Heating to a temperature above Ae_1 or Ae_3, and then cooling very slowly in a furnace or holding at a temperature just below Ae_1.
4. Cooling at a suitable rate from the minimum temperature at which all carbide is dissolved, to prevent the re-formation of a carbide network, and then reheating in accordance with method 1 or 2 above (applicable to hypereutectoid steel containing a carbide network).

NOTE. Alloy steels particularly may be spheroidized by heating above the transformation temperature for a sufficient length of time to dissolve all carbide followed by cooling fairly rapidly to a temperature just below the lower critical where the austenite is transformed at a constant temperature to ferrite and cementite. If the steel is held sufficiently long at this temperature, the cementite will spheroidize. For some alloy steels the process is speeded up by first soaking for a time just below the lower critical temperature.

Flame Softening. Differential softness can be produced in a hard steel, as well as differential hardness, by heating one or more locations with a flame and then cooling slowly to produce stress relief, softness, and other results of localized annealing and/or normalizing.

Heat-treating Steel for Strength or Toughness. Different practices are employed when heat-treating steel for strength than when heat-treating for hardness: Heat-treating for cutting hardness requires steel with more than 0.65 per cent of carbon; whereas, usually, steel of less than 0.50 per cent of carbon is heat-treated for optimum properties of toughness and strength, because the steel with higher carbon would be too brittle. To understand the rationale of this strengthening process, the mechanism of breaking of a metal should be reviewed:

If a metal is stretched beyond its elastic limit, slip will occur (see page 30), with the result that the metal is deformed and, perhaps, ultimately broken. Obviously, the more easily slip occurs, the less force will be required to deform the metal. This is lack of strength. Plain carbon steel with, say, 0.25 to 0.50 per cent carbon, does not have a great deal of strength, because a large portion of it consists of crystals of ferrite which precipitated while the steel was cooling from 890 to 690°C (1630 to 1270°F),[1] and these crystals are soft and slip easily along the slip planes. If this steel is heated above the upper critical temperature (line GS in Fig. 98), all the ferrite crystals will be in solid solution, and if the steel is then quenched, it may cool so fast that very little, if any, ferrite will have time or opportunity to separate from the solid solution. Quenching, then, will strengthen the steel by suppressing the component which allows easy slip under stress. This is the fundamental basis on which steel is heat-treated for strength.

In actual practice the steel is not always quenched, because quenching requires subsequent tempering to remove any residual stresses or brittleness; instead of the expensive process of quenching and tempering, the process of normalizing (see page 189) may be employed. This process diminishes slightly the amount of ferrite and introduces finer pearlite, as compared to full annealing. For medium-carbon steels, particularly those containing small alloying additions, normalizing increases strength and toughness very considerably, but it is not employed for axles and similar applications requiring maximum strength with good toughness. Steel which has been rapidly cooled from above the upper critical temper-

[1] The phase change occurs at a lower temperature on cooling than on heating.

ature and tempered at a temperature below the lower critical temperature will be both stronger and tougher than the same steel slowly cooled through the critical range (full annealed). For lighter sections, which are the ones most likely to warp during quenching and tempering, normalizing by cooling in still air or in an air blast often produces mechanical properties very similar to those for the same steel if quenched and then tempered above 540°C (1000°F).

The fundamental difference between heat-treating for hardness and heat-treating for toughness is that for hardness we transform austenite to martensite, and for optimum strength and toughness, we produce steel without large crystals of ferrite, either by quenching and tempering at a relatively high temperature or by cooling at an appropriate rate to assure the formation of very fine pearlite. Accelerating the speed of formation of pearlite at and below the lower critical temperature not only produces smaller crystals, but also reduces the size and increases the number of the lamellae which compose pearlite. For many years this very fine pearlite could not be resolved by the then existing microscopes, and it was thought that such a structure represented different constituents which were given names such as sorbite, troostite, etc. It has been shown that many of these structures consist of extremely fine pearlite of higher strength, hardness, and toughness than coarse pearlite.

By using the isothermal transformation diagrams in heat-treating for strength, much better control and more accurate results can be obtained. As one example of this procedure, instead of quenching austenite to martensite, with all the latter's internal stresses (and perhaps even incipient cracks), and then tempering to relieve hardness and stresses, we can heat-treat without forming martensite at all, by quenching the steel in a bath maintained at, say, 540°C (1000°F) or lower, holding it there until the desired decomposition of austenite occurs, and then cooling to atmospheric temperature either in the air or in another bath. The austenite is transformed to bainite. We can thus secure a combination of good strength, ductility, and toughness. This is a quenching method illustrated in Fig. 110, but unfortunately we cannot avoid the center of some thicknesses of steel passing through the "nose," or "knee," of the S curve and therefore suffering some transformation of the austenite before it reaches the temperature of the quenching bath. The exact thickness will obviously depend upon the hardenability of the steel, but we usually cannot get a bainite structure more than an inch or so thick.

HEAT-TREATING NONFERROUS ALLOYS FOR HARDNESS AND STRENGTH

When an alloy freezes in the form of a solid solution and then cools to room temperature, the solid solution may either (1) remain unchanged or (2) break down by the formation of precipitated particles. Thus in

Fig. 144 the solid solution α cools without change, but in Fig. 97 the solid solution, austenite, breaks down on cooling. In many alloys the amount of the element which can be held in solid solution under slow cooling without being precipitated is greater at some elevated temperature than at room temperature. For example, in Fig. 155 it is seen that the percentage of copper in solid solution at 548°C (1022°F) is 5.65, but at 300°C (572°F) it is only 0.5. If such an alloy is cooled rapidly (quenched), the normal precipitation may be prevented and there results a supersaturated solid solution at room temperature. Then if this solid solution *partially* breaks down, at relatively low temperature, the precipitate may form in it in a manner which will cause the alloy to become progressively harder and stronger.

Precipitation Hardening. This type of hardening and strengthening of an alloy is known as *precipitation hardening*. Since in some alloys the precipitation may occur slowly and spontaneously as the quenched alloy stands at room temperature, the term *aging* or *age hardening* is applied to the process. In the greater number of alloys it is necessary to reheat the quenched alloy (to a relatively low temperature) to cause the precipitation to occur. The terms "age hardening" and "precipitation hardening" are used interchangeably, but if it is desired to differentiate between the occurrence at room temperature and that taking place on reheating, as is often the case when the alloy would age harden in either way, the term *accelerated aging* is applied to age hardening through reheating.

The precipitated particles may be submicroscopic in size, or colloidal, or they may become much larger. In any case they are not all the same size, *i.e.*, in the same stage of formation (see Fig. 156, page 297). Hardening and strengthening are due to the particles too small to be seen under the microscope. It was at one time thought that the hardening resulted from the precipitated particles acting as keys to prevent slip. It is now generally believed that the mechanism of the process is one of three stages occurring in sequence. According to this theory, the first stage is segregation of the solute atoms, which form on certain planes of the crystals of the matrix. The second or transition stage is the critical one in the hardening process. During this stage the precipitating phase forms in a new lattice which, regardless of its normal dimensions, is forced to atomic conformity with the lattice of the matrix crystals. The enforced conformity between lattices of different spacings results in high elastic stress, as well as deformation in the matrix, manifested in increased hardness and strength. When the stress reaches a critical value, shearing occurs along the plane of conformity and the precipitate assumes stable dimensions and form. This is the third or stable stage.

While space does not permit a full discussion of the factors which make an alloy responsive to this type of heat-treatment, it should be noted that the first essential is solid solubility of one alloying element in the other, with the solubility greater at some elevated temperature than at room temperature. A second essential is that the alloy possess sufficient atomic mobility after quenching to allow precipitation to take place at the lower temperature. The manner in which the resulting hardness is affected by the temperature during aging and the acceleration of the time of hardening by rise in temperature are illustrated in Fig. 116. There is a short incubation period before precipitation starts, this being shorter the higher the temperature. Unless too high a temperature is used, a maximum hardness is reached after a time, since no further change then occurs in the coherency or size of the precipitating particles. If the temperature is too high (curves 4 and 5), after the particles have reached

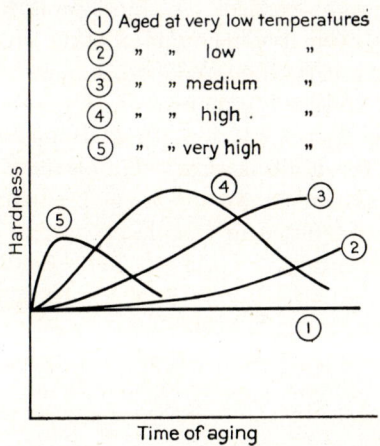

Fig. 116. Typical age-hardening curves. (*From Williams and Homerberg, "Principles of Metallography," McGraw-Hill Book Company, Inc.*)

the critical condition for maximum hardness they grow or coalesce until the resulting stress is sufficient to cause shearing of the nonstable plane of conformity and softening takes place. This is called *overaging*.

ANNEALING NONFERROUS METALS AND ALLOYS

Annealing is rarely employed with nonferrous alloys for the purpose of breaking down a solid solution in the manner that has been described for steel. On the other hand, annealing is a very frequent and very important process for softening nonferrous alloys, and the pure metals as well, after they have been hardened by cold work. Copper and its alloys and aluminum and its alloys, for example, are severely hardened with accompanying loss of ductility by cold rolling, wire drawing, etc. The ductility may then be restored and internal stresses relieved by reheating to or above the recrystallization temperature. During coldworking operations it is often necessary to anneal at intermediate stages of reduction; after a certain amount of cold work, the metal must be made soft and ductile again before further working; otherwise cracks would occur. Electrical conductivity is also restored, which is important in the case of copper. The annealing temperature for copper is commonly about 500°C (930°F) and for aluminum about 400°C (750°F), though copper may recrystallize after severe cold work at 200°C (390°F) and aluminum at 150°C (300°F). For alloys, lower annealing temperatures are used. If hard material is desired, annealing is omitted. If an intermediate hardness is desired, the annealing may be done after only part of the cold work has been performed, and the work completed after the annealing.

Annealing may also be employed with nonferrous metals and alloys in connection with grain-size control. Careful procedure with close temperature control has been developed to yield correct grain size, as is particularly necessary for the nonferrous metals and alloys. For annealed sheet, wire, and tubing made from copper and brass, grain size is now often a standard specification, this having been found to be an excellent measure of the usefulness of the material for a particular purpose. Examples of annealing, as well as of precipitation hardening, of nonferrous metals are included in the chapter on properties and uses of nonferrous metals and alloys.

Bibliography

See also references following Chaps. 7 and 9.

AMERICAN SOCIETY FOR METALS: "Age Hardening of Metals," Cleveland, Ohio, 1940.
———: "Carburizing," Cleveland, Ohio, 1938.
———: "Controlled Atmospheres," Cleveland, Ohio, 1942.
———: "Hardenability of Alloy Steels," Cleveland, Ohio, 1939.
———: "Grain Control in Industrial Metallurgy," Cleveland, Ohio, 1949.
BULLENS, D. K.: "Steel and Its Heat Treatment," 5th ed., with the Metallurgical Staff of the Battelle Memorial Institute, under the supervision of H. W. Gillett, 2 vols., John Wiley & Sons, Inc., New York, 1948.
GROSSMAN, M. A.: "Principles of Heat Treatment," 2d ed., American Society for Metals, Cleveland, Ohio, 1937.
HALL, J. J.: "Steel Hardening, Tempering, and Annealing," G. Newnes, Ltd., London, 1945.
JENKINS, I.: "Controlled Atmospheres for the Heat Treatment of Metals," Chapman & Hall, Ltd., London, 1946.
JOHNSON, F.: "Metal-working and Heat-treatment Manual," Vol. II, "Alloy Steels, Cast Iron, and Non-ferrous Metals," Paul Elek Publishers, Ltd., London, 1947.
———: "Heat Treatment of Carbon Steels," Chemical Publishing Company, Inc., Brooklyn, 1946.
PAYSON, PETER: "The Annealing of Steel," Crucible Steel Company of America, New York, 1944.
PORTEVIN, A.: "Introduction to the Study of Heat Treatment of Metallurgical Products," Penton Publishing Company, Cleveland, Ohio, 1939.
WINNING, J.: "Principles and Practices of Heat Treatment," 2d ed., Emmott & Company, Ltd., Manchester, England, 1945.

CHAPTER 9

PROPERTIES AND USES OF IRON AND STEEL

The iron-carbon alloys include all the products from wrought iron, which is a commercial product nearly approaching pure iron, through steel, to cast iron, which sometimes contains as much as 4.5 per cent carbon. Steel contains from almost none up to 2 per cent carbon. Those varieties which contain very little carbon (say, 0.05 per cent and less) are known as "ingot iron," indicating that they are finished in a liquid condition suitable to be cast into ingots and, therefore, distinguishable from wrought iron, which is finished in a pasty condition and so contains webs and strings of slag, which, together with its low carbon, give wrought iron its characteristic properties and uses. Most of the steel used in industry is of the type called "plain carbon steel," or "straight carbon steel," meaning an alloy essentially of iron and carbon, as distinguished from the so-called alloy steels, which have special qualities due to the presence of some additional alloying element, such as nickel, chromium, or molybdenum. In the straight carbon steels, the proportion of iron is always in excess of 95 per cent. Their mechanical properties will vary greatly with the proportion of carbon contained. For example, an iron-carbon alloy may be one of the strongest or one of the weakest of the metals or alloys; it may be very hard or a comparatively soft metal, one of the most ductile or one of the most brittle, of low or of somewhat higher electric conductivity, and so on. Iron is the most magnetic element, but, by varying its temperature, or by adding alloying elements, it may become as nonmagnetic as lead or copper. We have already seen how heat-treatment will make the same steel either hard or soft.

Tensile Strength and Hardness. There is an almost constant relation between the strength and hardness of steel. This is indicated for some alloy steels in Fig. 117 and is true also of plain carbon steels when their structures are similar. There is occasionally a deviation from the exact relation, but the relation is important.

The Most Frequently Used Properties of Steel. Strength, ductility, cheapness, and machinability are the four most important industrial and commercial properties of steel. Machinability is necessary for most commercial shapes. Cheapness is the dominant reason why steel is used nearly 75 times as much as any other metal. In strength, steel is exceeded by the tungsten filaments of electric lights; in strength per pound, it is exceeded by some of the aluminum and magnesium alloys. In ductility it is surpassed by several metals. Its combination of commercially valuable properties, including cheapness, makes it the chief metal of our civilization.

Of paramount importance in certain uses, depending on the type of steel, are hardness; resistance to wear or abrasion; resilience; resistance

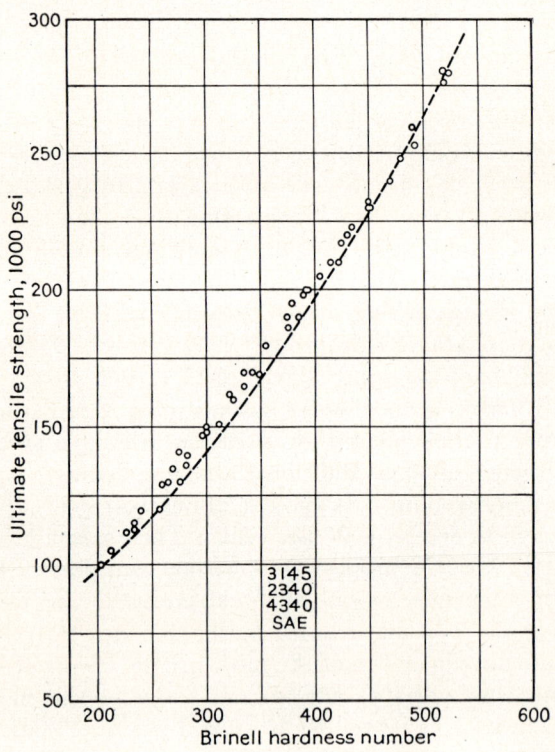

FIG. 117. Relation between hardness and tensile strength of some alloy steels. (*Courtesy of Steel Publications, Inc.; taken from their "Watkins' Cyclopedia of the Steel Industry."*)

to loss of strength, or to oxidation, at high temperatures; magnetic properties; electrical conductivity combined with low cost; fluidity for casting; constancy of dimensions with changes of temperature; lack of brittleness at low temperatures; resistance to rusting (stainless steels); and other properties in particular types of service. In certain cases these properties may be of prime importance, but it is usually desirable to have them in combination with one or more of the properties mentioned in the preceding paragraph.

MEANS OF VARYING THE PROPERTIES OF THE IRON-CARBON ALLOYS

There are three chief means of altering the properties of iron and steel:
1. By varying the chemical composition.
2. By variations in physical conditions, *i.e.*, grain size and other details of structure, heat-treatment, residual stresses, etc.
3. By mechanical means, *i.e.*, by hot work or cold work, by casting, forging, rolling, etc.

Variation Due to Chemical Composition

This section is devoted chiefly to steel and its composition. Wrought iron does not vary much in composition, and the properties of alloy steels and of cast iron will be discussed later. Carbon is the most influential element and the one most commonly used for adjusting the properties of steel, but small amounts of manganese and silicon are intentionally added, and unavoidable proportions of impurities, such as phosphorus, sulfur, oxygen, and nitrogen, have effects that must be considered. The process of manufacture is important in this connection, for crucible and electric steel are low in oxygen; basic open-hearth steel can be cheaply produced with low proportions of phosphorus; acid open-hearth steel is lower in oxygen than is basic; bessemer steel is usually higher in phosphorus and nitrogen; the electric steel process is better able to reduce sulfur to a very low point than is any other process.

Phosphorus causes brittleness, especially at atmospheric temperature and colder ("cold-shortness") and especially when the phosphorus plus the carbon is in excess of 0.25 per cent. Sulfur causes brittleness, especially at red heat ("red-shortness") and especially when copper and/or oxygen are present. Sulfur also interferes with weldability. Oxygen causes brittleness, and nitrogen causes brittleness and "aging." Both sulfur and nitrogen in causing brittleness increase machinability. Manganese is added to the steel when liquid to remove oxygen and to neutralize the embrittling effect of residual oxygen and sulfur, by forming MnO instead of FeO and MnS instead of FeS. Silicon is added to remove oxygen and to prevent gas bubbles (blowholes). In some cases it is added to increase strength. Homeopathic additions of aluminum are added to remove oxygen and to control grain size, and superhomeopathic additions of boron are made to increase hardenability.

Many defects in steel are the direct or indirect result of impurities or improper amounts of ingredients. For example, segregation, or the concentration of ingredients in one locality more than in another, may be caused by phosphorus, sulfur, or oxygen, and also by slow freezing. Blowholes and/or inclusions may be the result of highly oxidized liquid steel; surface or internal cracks may originate from an inclusion. While surface irregularities, such as laps, seams, and the like, are chiefly caused by rolling when the steel is too cold or too stiff to yield readily to the pressure applied, yet stiffness may be due to improper chemical composition.

TABLE 17. SOME EFFECTS OF CARBON ON IRON
(Other elements being low)

AISI No.[1]	Carbon, per cent	Steel	Tensile strength of annealed steel		Elongation, per cent in 2 in.[2]
			Ultimate, thousand pounds per square inch[2]	Yield, thousand pounds per square inch[2]	
C 1010	0.05–0.15	Very mild steel	40–55	24–30	34–28
C 1020	0.15–0.25	Mild steel	48–65	30–36	28–25
C 1030	0.25–0.40	Low-carbon steel	60–70	36–40	25–22
C 1050	0.40–0.65	Medium-carbon steel	70–80	40–48	22–18
C 1065	0.60–0.70	Higher-carbon steel	80–94	48–56	18–14
C 1075	0.70–0.80	Spring steel	94–118	56–64	14–8
C 1080	0.75–0.85	Pearlitic steel[3]	120	70	5±
	1.00–1.10	High-carbon steel	115–110	60–55	Slight
	1.10–1.70	Very high-carbon steel	110–90	55–50	Slight

[1] The AISI numbers are supplied for the so-called "structural" or "constructional" steels." These designations refer to the structural parts of machines and/or bridges, buildings, and the like.

[2] An approximation, dependent on amount of working, annealing, etc.

[3] Also called "eutectoid steel."

The Effect of Carbon on the Strength, Ductility, and Uses of Steel. The chief commercial classifications of plain carbon steel and the effect of carbon are shown in Table 17. This table illustrates that, with increasing carbon, the strength of the steel increases until 0.8 per cent of carbon is reached and that the ductility decreases with each increment of carbon. It will be seen later that the hardness of slowly cooled steel increases with each increment of carbon (owing to increase in amount of Fe_3C) from zero to the upper limit of carbon in steel (2 per cent).

Uses of Different Steels and Wrought Iron. The uses of ordinary commercial steels depend upon (1) the carbon content; (2) the process of manufacture; and (3) the kind of treatment, *i.e.*, whether cast, hot-rolled, or cold-rolled, and whether rapidly or slowly cooled. Thus wrought iron and very low-carbon steels are used for purposes requiring softness, ductility, electric conductivity, and magnetic permeability. For example, Table 18 shows that steel for rivets, for wire for electrical conductors, and for boiler tubes is very low in carbon. On the opposite end of the series stand the steels of high carbon—those used for purposes which require them to be greatly hardened by heat-treatment, such as, for instance, cutting tools. The harder the material to be cut, the more carbon will be put in the steel—compare stone-cutting tools and steel-cutting saws with carpenter's tools. But where hardness must be combined with resistance to shock, or some other service demanding at least a modicum of ductility, the permissible amount of carbon is limited. This requirement is exemplified in drills and chisels used for rock cutting by blows and in saws (such as band saws) which must be bent around in a circle.

Between such extremes of carbon content as exemplified by almost carbon-free wrought iron on the one hand and file steels on the other are found the steels which require ductility to a greater or less extent. The service demanded of structural steel which is exposed to shock does not permit the addition of more than 0.25 to 0.30 per cent carbon. However, where structural steel is used in the form of wire that is twisted into a cable, a carbon content of approximately eutectoid composition is used in order to assure maximum response to the patenting process, thus assuring a maximum combination of tensile strength and toughness. In such a steel there are no soft ferrite grains to cause weakness, nor are there any hard iron-carbide particles, other than those existing in the fine pearlite, to cause brittleness.

Concrete-reinforcement bars can contain as much carbon as will permit them to endure the requisite cold twisting and bending; cold-rolled steel must have enough toughness to endure cold deformation; for machinery steel and many parts of machines and shafting one can afford to sacrifice some ductility for strength. In this way one can select examples from Table 18 to illustrate how the use for which the steel is intended will determine the amount of carbon that is put in it.

The appropriate process of manufacture is also indicated in Table 18. This will be better understood after a study of Chap. 13. Electric steel is the highest in quality and price. Then follows acid open-hearth steel, then basic open-hearth steel, and lastly bessemer, which is lowest in quality and price. In choosing the process of manufacture for steel, the importance of quality and the price which it is permissible to pay for greater strength, ductility, and reliability must be considered.

Effect of Carbon on the Hardness of Unhardened Steel. Unhardened steel is that which has not been hardened by cold rolling, straining, heat-treatment, or other hardening procedure. When reasonably pure, it consists mainly of crystals of ferrite, which is soft and ductile, with some cementite, which is hard and brittle. The cementite contains the carbon, and, therefore, the hardness of unhardened steel will depend on the pro-

TABLE 18. CARBON CONTENT OF IRONS AND STEELS FOR DIFFERENT USES

Use	Material[1] Usual	Material[1] Preferred	Carbon, per cent Desired	Carbon, per cent Limits
Axles................................	B.O.H.	El.	0.40	0.25–0.70
Axles, cold-rolled.....................	B.O.H.	O.H.	....	Not over 0.40
Alternate stress, resistance to..........	B.O.H.	El.	0.50	0.45–0.75
Boiler plate, steel.....................	B.O.H.	A.O.H.	0.12	0.08–0.18
Boiler plate, wrought iron..............	W.I.	W.I.	0.10	0.08–0.18
Boiler tubes, steel.....................	O.H.	A.O.H.	0.10	0.08–0.18
Castings, steel........................	O.H.	El.	....	0.12–0.50
Carpenter's tools.....................	......	Steel	....	0.50–1.20
Carpenter's tools, hammers............	M.C.I.	Steel	....	0.50–0.80
Carpenter's tools, woodcutting tools....	Steel	El.	1.15	1.10–1.20
Casehardening stock..................	O.H.	......	0.12	0.08–0.25
Chain, steel..........................	B.O.H.	O.H.	Min.	0.04–0.15
Chisels, granite cutting................	El.	El.	1.05	1.00–1.10
Chisels, cold chisels...................	El.	El.	0.75	0.70–0.80
Cold-rolled steel......................	B.O.H.	......	....	Not over 0.35
Concrete-reinforcement bars...........	Bess.	O.H.	....	0.40–0.70
Culverts for water disposal............	O.H.	O.H.	Min.	0.00–0.10
Crankpins for wear resistance..........	O.H.	El.	0.30	0.25–0.35
Crankpins for resisting shocks and reversals of stress.....................	O.H.	El.	0.50	0.45–0.55
Dies, for making drop forgings.........	B.O.H.	O.H.	0.65	0.60–0.70
Dies, for metal cutting................	B.O.H.	El.	0.85	0.80–1.20
Dies, for thread cutting...............	El.	El.	1.15	1.10–1.20
Drills, rock drilling...................	B.O.H.	El.	0.85	0.80–0.90
Engraver's tools......................	El.	El.	1.35	1.30–1.40
Files for metal smoothing..............	El.	El.	1.25	1.20–1.50
Forgings, ordinary....................	B.O.H.	A.O.H.	0.25	0.20–0.30
Forgings, strong......................	B.O.H.	A.O.H.	0.40	0.35–0.60
Gears, except casehardened............	B.O.H.	O.H.	0.35	0.30–0.60
Lathe tools..........................	El.	El.	1.10	1.00–1.20
Machinery steel......................	B.O.H.	O.H.	0.35	0.25–0.40
Machinist's tools.....................	El.	El.	....	0.70–1.20
Nails, wire...........................	Bess.	Bess.	0.10	0.08–0.15
Pipe, steel (welded)...................	Bess.	......	Low	0.05–0.15
Pipe, wrought iron....................	W.I.	W.I.		
Plates, tank..........................	Bess.	O.H.	0.12	0.08–0.15
Plates, structural.....................	B.O.H.	A.O.H.	0.30	0.25–0.40
Punches.............................	B.O.H.	El.	....	0.80–1.00
Railroad-car wheels, steel.............	B.O.H.	O.H.	0.70	0.60–0.85
Railroad rails, small sizes.............	Bess.	B.O.H.	....	0.37–0.50
Railroad rails, large sizes.............	B.O.H.	O.H.	....	0.50–0.80
Rivets...............................	B.O.H.	B.O.H.	0.05	0.05–0.20
Screws for wood......................	Bess.	Bess.	0.10	0.08–0.16

TABLE 18. CARBON CONTENT OF IRONS AND STEELS FOR DIFFERENT USES. (*Continued*)

Use	Material[1] Usual	Material[1] Preferred	Carbon, per cent Desired	Carbon, per cent Limits
Setscrews	B.O.H.	El.	0.65	0.60–0.70
Saws, band	El.	El.	0.75	0.70–0.80
Saws, circular	O.H.	El.	0.85	0.80–0.90
Saws, for cutting steel	El.	El.	1.55	1.50–1.60
Shafting, for transmission purposes	B.O.H.	B.O.H.	....	Not over 0.40
Shafting, for crankshafts	O.H.	El.	0.50	0.50–0.60
Staybolts, wrought iron	W.I.	W.I.		
Shock-resisting steel	O.H.	O.H.	0.50	0.45–0.55
Stone-cutting tools	El.	El.	1.35	1.30–1.40
Structural shapes, small	Bess.	O.H.	0.22	
Structural shapes, important structures	O.H.	A.O.H.	0.22	
Springs	B.O.H.	El.	0.95	0.90–1.15
Tubing, steel, seamless	B.O.H.	B.O.H.	0.12	0.08–0.18
Tubing, steel, welded	B.O.H.	B.O.H.	0.08	0.06–0.15
Tubing, wrought iron	W.I.	W.I.		
Valves for resisting wear	B.O.H.	O.H.	0.30	0.25–0.35
Wire, for electric conductivity	Bess.	Bess.	Min.	0.05–0.10
Wire, for fencing and chicken wire	Bess.	Bess.	Low	
Wire, music[2]	El.	El.	....	0.90–1.10
Wire, structural steel	A.O.H.	A.O.H.	0.80	0.75–0.85

B.O.H. = basic open-hearth steel; A.O.H. = acid open-hearth steel; El. = electric furnace steel; M.C.I. = malleable cast iron; Bess. = bessemer steel; W.I. = wrought iron.

[1] Material refers to American practice.

[2] Music wire is so called because it was first used for pianos; it is now used for springs and similar purposes also.

portion of carbon present and will increase from pure iron to that containing 2 per cent carbon.

Effect of Carbon on the Hardness of Quenched Steel. If austenite contains more than about 1 per cent carbon, it may not change wholly into martensite on quenching, and therefore maximum hardness may be found in steel of 1 per cent carbon, or slightly less. There are several factors which cause steel of eutectoid composition (0.80 per cent carbon) to be as hard as steel of higher carbon content, although a 1 per cent carbon steel may have better cutting qualities or wear resistance. Cutting tools almost never contain less than 0.50 per cent and seldom more than 1.30 per cent carbon. The latter have excess cementite visible under the microscope and embedded in the martensite, serving as extra-hard particles which help with the cutting, as, for example, in the case of files. Figure 118 gives an approximate idea of the variation of the quenched hardness with the carbon content.

Summary. Tool steels, and in general those to be hardened by heat-treatment, are usually high in carbon, while general-purpose and high-ductility steels are generally low in carbon. Constructional steels for bridges, buildings, and like purposes are of medium carbon content; they contain sufficient carbon for strength, but not so much as to eliminate the ductility necessary for the member in question. Constructional steels for parts of airplanes and/or automobiles are usually made of alloy steels (see pages 228 to 241), in order to be both strong and reasonably

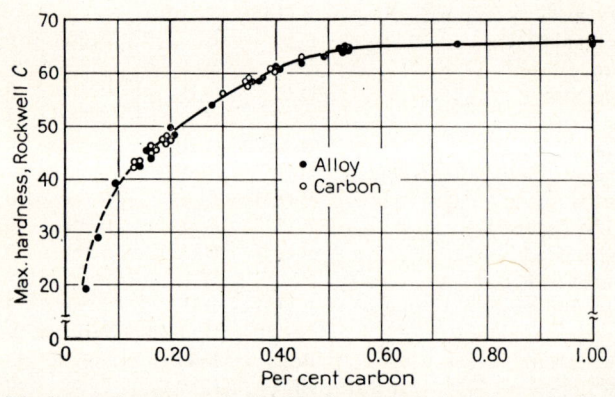

FIG. 118. Maximum hardness obtainable in quenched plain carbon and low-alloy steels. (*From Trans. Am. Soc. Metals, vol.* 26, 1938.)

ductile (tough). For purposes requiring ease of welding, carbon is generally limited to 0.35 per cent maximum.

Chemical Composition and Some Physical Properties. The purest iron has the highest electrical conductivity of any alloy of the series and the highest magnetic permeability of any known substance except for some alloys of iron and nickel (for low magnetizing forces). On the other hand, in order to secure magnetic retentivity (for permanent magnetism), we must have about 1 per cent of carbon and employ heat-treatment. In retentivity, some alloys and alloy steels excel carbon steel. Certain alloy steels also excel in resistance to corrosion, resilience, variability in thermal expansion and contraction with temperature, and in some other properties, notably in the various categories of strength, in combinations of strength with ductility, and in resistance to high temperatures.

Other Elements Intentionally Added to Carbon Steel. Manganese is added to molten steel at the end of the production process in order to remove as much oxygen as possible, and also to form a compound of manganese with any remaining oxygen, or any sulfur, which is in the steel (see page 367). The amount of manganese added for this purpose is the minimum required to do the desired work. Thus, electric steel will frequently contain less than 0.40 per cent manganese, because there is not so much oxygen and sulfur to counteract. Bessemer steel, on the other hand, will sometimes contain as much as 1.10 per cent. Manganese is also added where resistance to abrasion is desired, as in railroad rails. Silicon is another element added to steel at the end of the purification process for the purpose of removing oxygen and also gas bubbles or blowholes. It forms the compound FeSi, which dissolves in the ferrite and strengthens it. Steel castings, which must be as free as possible from gas bubbles, because there is no opportunity for these to become welded up and eliminated in rolling or forging, often contain as much as 0.4 per cent silicon. This has the effect of strengthening the steel, with practically no decrease in its ductility.

Impurities in Steel in Unoxidized Form. The commonest and most harmful impurities in steel are sulfur and phosphorus. Sulfur is especially harmful when in the form of FeS, because FeS is molten at rolling temperatures and forms planes of weakness which often cause the steel to crack badly during rolling or forging. Even MnS is harmful in this respect. Sulfur is harmful in any form, or in any amount above 0.03 per cent, particularly if weldability is desired. Phosphorus is especially notable as making steel brittle, fragile under shock, and unreliable in ductility. The behavior of phosphorus in iron alloys is discussed further under Cast Iron, page 220. The effect of phosphorus shows up more especially under an impact test. Under the ordinary static test, its effect is uncertain and unreliable. Phosphorus is a dangerous ingredient in steel and is valuable only because of the hardness which it produces. It is sometimes comparatively harmless in very soft and low-carbon steels. Phosphorus plus carbon should never exceed 0.25 per cent. A combination of high phosphorus and high sulfur, especially if oxygen is also high, is especially dangerous. It is safe practice to have the phosphorus below 0.04 per cent as a maximum in all steel that is to be subjected to shock or vibration. Phosphorus and sulfur, especially when both are high, also cause a concentration or segregation of impurities in one or more parts, thus producing points of more impure steel, which make localities of brittleness or hardness.

Oxidized Impurities in Steel. FeO, MnO, SiO_2, Al_2O_3, slag, dirt, and similar particles are sometimes entangled during solidification of steel, while sometimes FeO and MnO may be dissolved in, or combined with, the metal. All entangled particles are like so many stress raisers; *i.e.*, their presence may intensify the unit stress acting at any point and start a fracture. Their harmfulness is often dependent upon the fact that they may occur at a point which happens to be stressed to a dangerous degree, but which would safely meet the stress if it were not for the inclusion. These impurities frequently cause the failure of steel and have been the factors which in the past have sometimes produced so-called mysterious failures.

Excessive inclusions are nearly always due to cheap or improper steel manufacture, but may occur in spite of all reasonable care on the part of the steelmaker. For example, dirt may be washed from the sides of the steel runner or ladle and remain suspended in the steel until it is solid. Microscopic inclusions are most frequently caused by oxidation of silicon, manganese, aluminum, etc., added during the recarburizing of steel, and in such minute particles that the steel cannot clarify itself by gravity until it is too viscous to do so. Larger inclusions may be due to particles of slag or lining.

Determination of Amount of Inclusions. The harmful effect of inclusions is so important that the American Society for Testing Materials

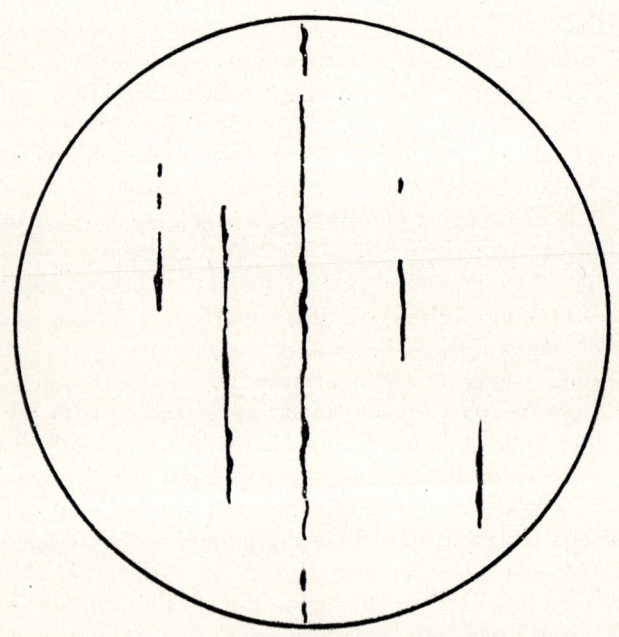

Fig. 119. Example of standard chart for determining the inclusion content of steel. The chart numbers range from 1 to 5, No. 1 representing the cleanest steel. The chart is used by comparing with a microscope field of 0.8 mm (0.03125 in.) diameter on the specimen at magnification of 100 diameters. The example shown is No. 5 of the silicate type (type C), heavy series. Actual thickness of inclusions is approximately 9 microns. (*Courtesy of American Society for Testing Materials.*)

has set up standards and methods of determining the inclusion content of steel, with reference to kind (*i.e.*, heavy or thin), type (*i.e.*, oxide, alumina, silicate, or sulfide), and amount. When the amount is small, the steel is said to be "clean," and when large, "dirty." Five standards are set up showing increasing amounts of inclusions. A sample approximately 1 by ½ in. in size is taken from the surface or central portion (as may be deemed advisable by the customer) of a bar or billet and polished on the surface parallel to the longitudinal axis. Its entire surface is examined at a magnification of 100 diameters, and the worst field of each type of inclusion is compared with standard micrographs, of which a sample is shown in Fig. 119. If desired, the predominant type of inclusions may be recorded.

Gaseous Impurities in Steel. Oxygen, carbon monoxide, hydrogen, and nitrogen may occur in gas bubbles in steel, or they may occur as dissolved or combined impurities. Unfortunately, the chemist has not yet developed a method of determining these elements with sufficient promptness and facility for the process to be universally accepted in industrial work. All the information at hand is that these gases are harmful and embrittling in their effect. They are most likely to occur in bessemer or basic open-hearth steel, and least often in crucible and electric steels. The amount of these gases present in a metal may be determined by the vacuum fusion method, a practice which is coming into wider use for expensive "specialty" steels. Steelmakers are also developing methods of making steel with lower hydrogen content.

Residuals. Some elements accumulate in steel because they are not removed by oxidation in the steelmaking furnace, and especially because they may be introduced from alloy-steel scrap used in the furnace charge. Notable among these elements are copper and nickel. Copper makes steel hot-short, *i.e.*, cracks are formed in the steel during mechanical treatment at red heat. Nickel lessens hot-shortness, but makes steel unnecessarily stronger than specifications require and therefore more costly to roll.

Variations in Physical Conditions

Physical conditions include structure, which involves the kind, shape, and size of crystals; residual stress, which may or may not be present; previous heat-treatment; the temperature at which the steel is to serve; and lesser conditions or variations.

Properties of Steel vs. Grain Size. All other things being equal, the smaller the crystals of steel, the greater will be its strength. Because the crystals in castings are larger than those in worked metal, and because they have not been crushed and kneaded together, the strength and the ductility of steel castings are less than those of wrought steel of the same composition. Furthermore, the hardness and the strength of cold-worked steel are due partly to the breaking up of the crystals.

Austenitic Grain Size. One must distinguish between two kinds of grain size in steel: that due either to composition or to mechanical treatment (both of which have been discussed above), and that resulting from the size of crystal which the steel had before it cooled, when it was in the austenite region. The latter is usually known as *austenitic grain*

1550°F.　　1625°F.　　1700°F.　　1825°F.　　1925°F.
Normalizing temperatures.　Temperature of McQuaid-Ehn Test

A.—Coarse grain

B.—Mixed grain, coarse tendency

C.—Mixed grain, fine tendency

D.—Fine grain

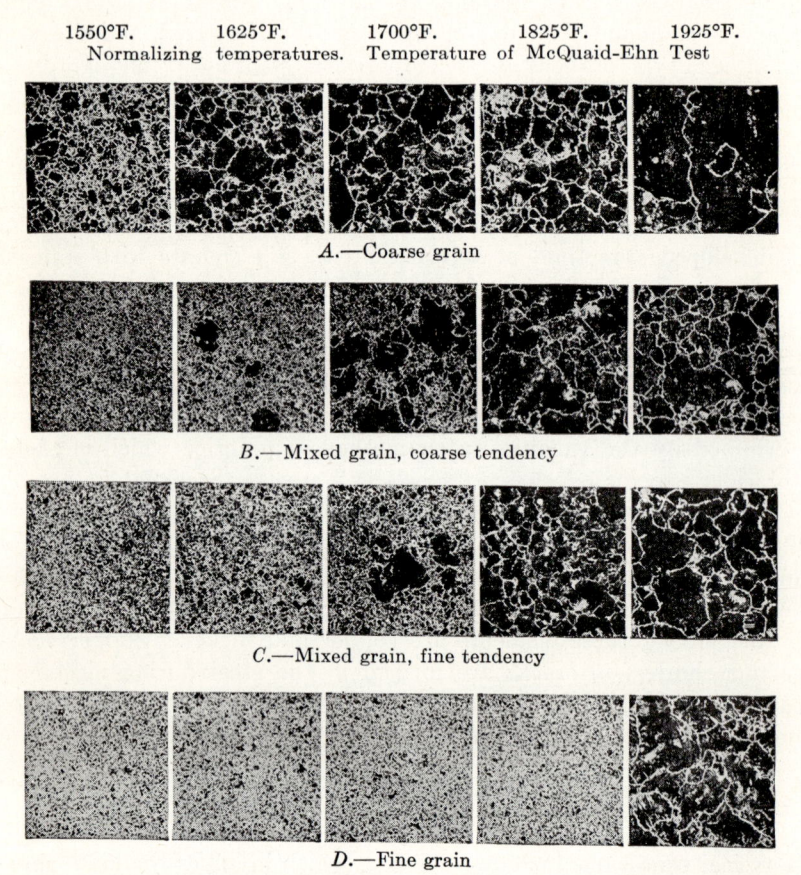

Fig. 120. Effect of temperature on the grain size of normalized steel. (*From Herty, McBride, and Hollenbeck, Iron Age, vol.* 139, *p.* 29, 1937.)

size, or *inherent grain size*, and is the one usually referred to when speaking of "coarse grain size" or "fine grain size" in steel. If steel is heated until the ferrite and cementite dissolve in one another, for which see Figs. 97 and 98, pages 165 and 171, the austenite crystals will at first be small, but will normally grow by the absorption of their neighbors, as the temperature rises. Hypoeutectoid steel is the kind usually considered with respect to the effect of grain size and the upper critical temperature (*i.e.*, the top of the critical range) is that above which austenite grains are considered to grow; but it should be observed that on heating pearlite changes to austenite at the lower critical temperature, although the ferrite is not all dissolved until the steel is heated above the upper critical line. It should also be carefully observed that once a grain has grown larger it will not become smaller on cooling. Foreign particles in the grain boundaries will oppose growth. In Fig. 120 are shown four steels with different austenitic grain sizes; it is seen that the grains in steel D do not begin to grow until it is some 220°C (400°F) above its upper critical temperature. The subject of grain size is further illustrated in Figs. 63, 70, and 71, pages 133 and 138, and Fig. 121.

Referring especially to hypoeutectoid steel, fine austenitic grain size is most often valued because it gives a better impact strength, but both coarse and fine-grained steel have other characteristics in which one is superior to the other, as shown by the accompanying list.

Effect of Austenitic Grain Size in Hypoeutectoid Steel

Property or characteristic	Fine grain[1]	Coarse grain[2]
Strength	Superior	Inferior
Ductility	Superior	Inferior
Toughness by impact test	Usually much superior	Inferior
Critical speed for hardening[3]	Faster	Slower
Depth of hardening	Lesser	Greater
During heat-treatment:		
Susceptibility to distortion	Superior	Inferior
Susceptibility to quenching cracks	Less	More
Susceptibility to retained austenite	Less	More
Residual stress	Lower	Higher
Grinding cracks	Less	More
Creep resistance at high temperature	Inferior	Superior
Electrical conductivity	Inferior	Superior
Permeability in magnetically soft material	Less	Greater
Coercive force in magnetically soft material	Greater	Less
Formability (usually)	Inferior	Superior
Rough machining	Inferior	Superior
Fine finish machining (usually)	Superior	Inferior

[1] Fine grain sizes are here considered as Nos. 5 to 8 (see Fig. 121).

[2] Coarse grain sizes are here considered as Nos. 1 to 5.

[3] This is "the critical cooling curve" discussed on p. 175. The slower the speed necessary for hardening, the more completely may the heat-treatment be accomplished. In other words, a coarse grain size pushes the isothermal transformation curve (TTT curve) to the right.

Dendritic Structures. Dendrites form when a liquid metal freezes. Theoretically, these dendrites near the solidus form more or less equiaxed grains; but actually, castings and steel which has not been sufficiently wrought at the forging temperature, say, 1150 to 1260°C (2100 to 2300°F), may contain some columnar crystals which do not adhere firmly together and therefore lower the strength and ductility. (See Fig. 122 for residual dendritic structure which, in that case, is not so pronounced as to be harmful.)

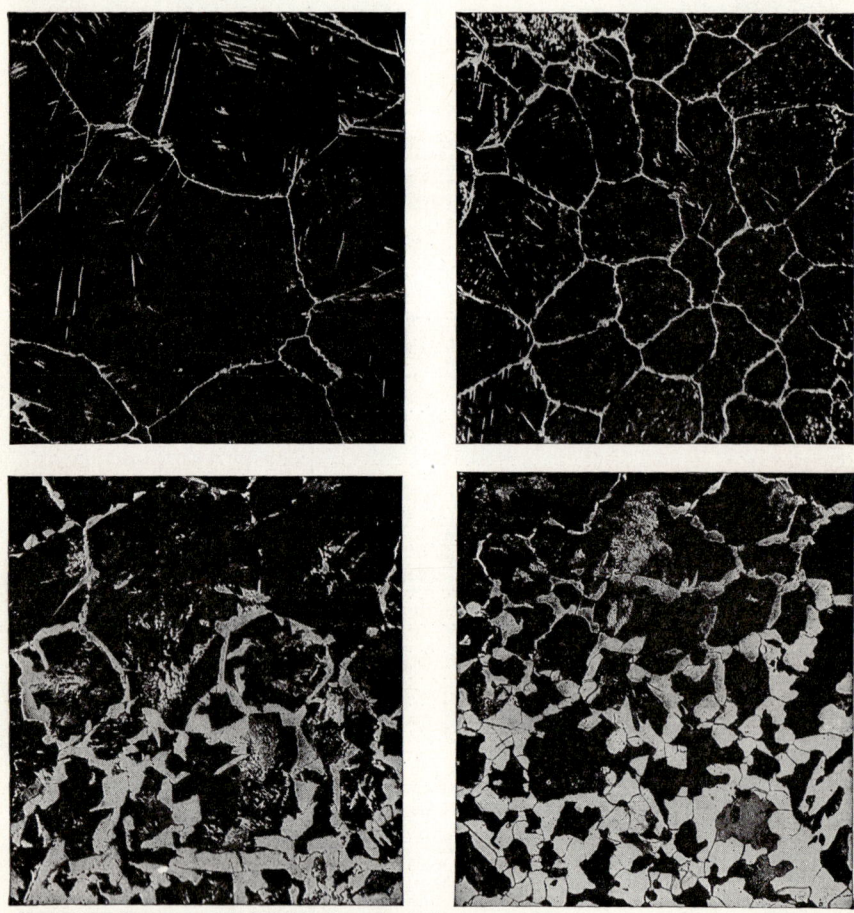

Fig. 121. Portion of A.S.T.M. Standard Grain-size Chart, nos. 1, 3, 5, and 7 (up to 1½, 3 to 6, 12 to 24, and 48 to 96 grains per sq in., respectively). Samples carburized at 1700°F (927°C) for 8 hr. Upper and lower micrographs refer to hypereutectoid and

Residual Stresses. A metal or alloy may contain residual stresses, or unequalized internal stresses, because of nonuniform plastic deformation as a result of cold rolling, rapid cooling (as from heat-treating, welding, or similar causes). These may be removed by heating for an hour or more at the temperature at which the distorted structure is replaced by a stress-free structure, and then cooling slowly. Temperatures vary from that of "stress relieving," say about 480°C (900°F), to "full annealing," which is in or above the transformation range, say 720°C (1325°F) and above.

Precipitation Hardening or Aging. Some metals will dissolve a constituent at one temperature and then precipitate it in submicroscopic particles which increase strength and hardness at the expense of ductility

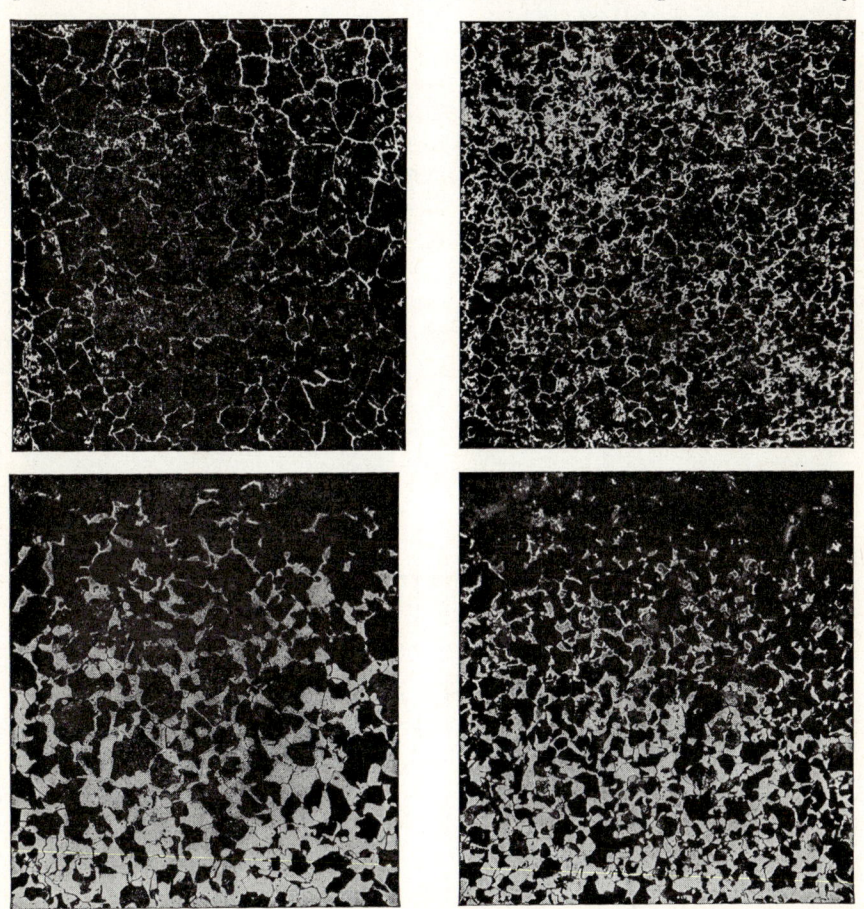

hypoeutectoid zones, respectively. Magnification 100 ×. (*By permission of American Society for Testing Materials.*)

(see page 192). Certain nonferrous alloys are most responsive to this effect, but iron-carbon alloys also may be precipitation hardened.

Properties of Steel at Subzero Temperatures. Steel, like most other metals, becomes stronger and more brittle at low temperatures. It is especially brittle and fragile under shock, and usually only special alloy steels are suitable for the construction of refrigerating machinery and the like. Nickel and nickel steels retain their toughness to a notable extent at low temperatures, and austenitic steels are remarkably stable. Thorough deoxidation improves toughness at low temperatures.

Properties of Steel at High Temperatures. As indicated in Figs. 123 and 124, steel becomes more plastic as the temperature rises, except only at the so-called "blue heat" (about 260°C or 500°F), where there seems to be an aging effect, since non-aging steels do not show this irregularity. Advantage is taken of the plasticity and decreased strength of steel at high temperatures by hot forging and rolling, which is usually done above the critical temperature, and more often at temperatures of about, or slightly above, 1210°C (2210°F). If steel is to be used for superheated steam equipment, tie rods in furnaces, oil-cracking retorts, and other

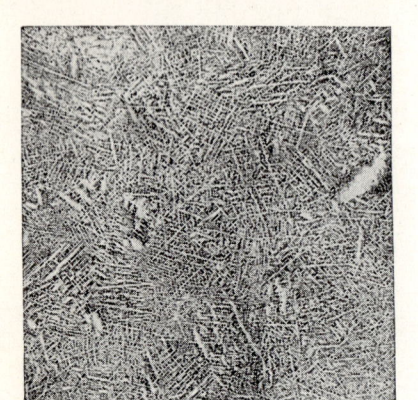

Fig. 122. Dendritic structure in one end of steel bar containing 1 per cent carbon.

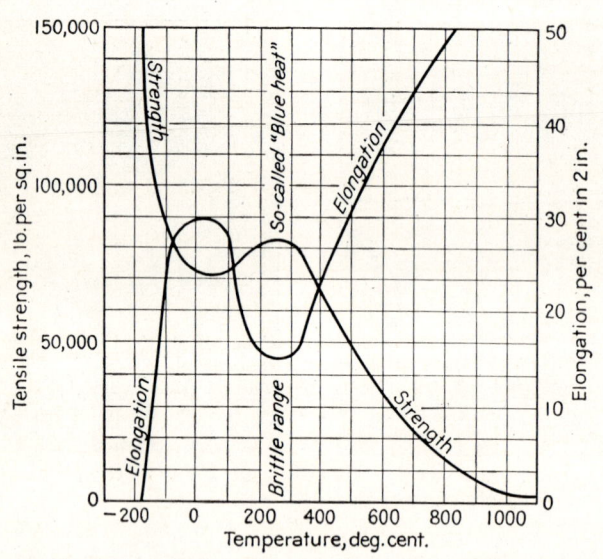

Fig. 123. Approximate tensile strength and elongation in 2 in. of structural steel at various temperatures from that of liquid air to the usual rolling temperatures.

purposes where the service temperatures are between 200 and 700°C (390 to 1290°F)—in other words, below the critical temperature—then carbon steel will have sufficient strength; but where the service tempera-

PROPERTIES AND USES OF IRON AND STEEL 211

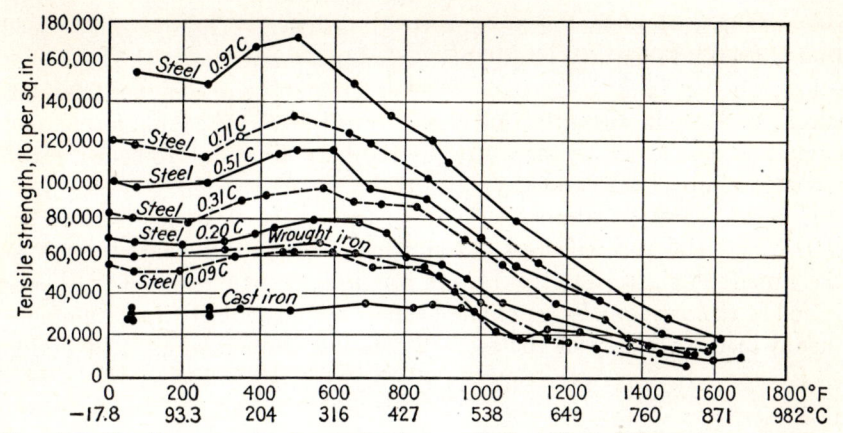

FIG. 124. Tensile strength of wrought iron and of steel at different temperatures. (*Watertown Arsenal Tests of Metals,* 1888.)

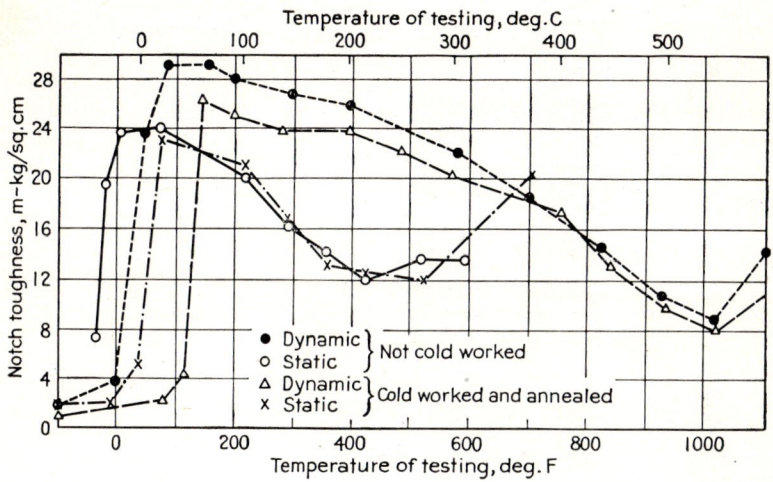

FIG. 125. Static and dynamic notched-bar tests at various temperatures with annealed and with cold-worked and aged mild steel. During slow bending, the energy absorption is at a minimum in the "blue-heat" region, but in the impact test the minimum in energy absorption occurs at a considerably higher temperature. In both the impact and slow bend tests, the specimens were of the following dimensions: 160 by 30 by 16 mm; keyhole notch with circle 4 mm in diameter, 15 mm deep. (*From "Metals Handbook,"* 1948.)

ture is above the critical (723°C or 1333°F) or where strength or resistance to creep must be combined with resistance to corrosion by air or gases, then one of the alloy steels or other heat-resistant alloys must be employed. In brief, it is usually considered that carbon steel should not be used above about 480 to 540°C (900 to 1000°F) on account of its tendency to scale.

Impact resistance and slow-bend ductility is shown in Fig. 125, which is from the work of E. Maurer and R. Mailender.[1] There it will be seen that slow-bend ductility (static test) reaches a minimum at the blue-heat range, whereas impact resistance reaches a minimum at a higher temperature. S. Epstein suggests that aging (precipitation) cannot occur fast enough at the lower temperature for the hardening due to cold work to lower the impact resistance.

Creep. Even at atmospheric temperatures steel is not a perfectly elastic material and will "creep" at stresses below the yield strength or the apparent elastic limit. This is important when members are subjected to stresses for a long period of time, and particularly if the temperature is in the vicinity of the recrystallization temperature. The action

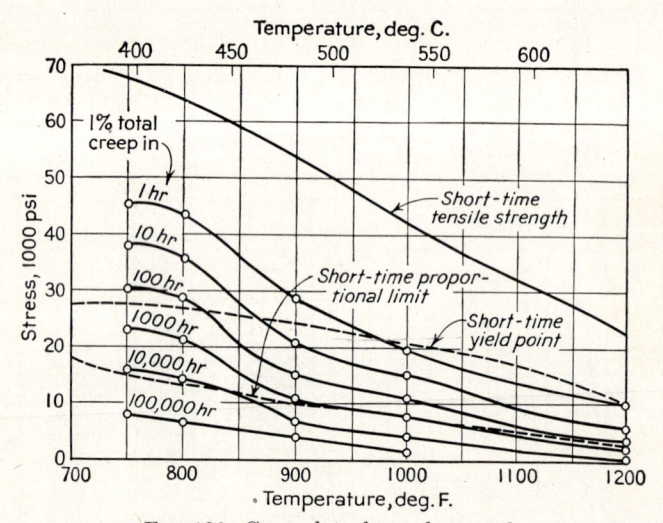

FIG. 126. Creep data for carbon steel.

of creep is illustrated in Figs. 9 and 10, page 31. Figure 126, taken from J. J. Kanter,[2] shows the creep limit for various periods of time and temperatures of a carbon steel, related to its static strength at the same temperatures.

Alteration by Means of Mechanical Work

In considering the kind of treatment which the different qualities of steel should have, hot and cold mechanical treatment, as outlined in Chap. 4, must be compared. Cast steel is lower in strength, ductility, and reliability than rolled steel, while cold-rolled steel is higher in strength but lower in ductility than hot-rolled steel. Cold rolling greatly increases both strength and hardness, and steel to be used for cutting purposes, if

[1] See "Metals Handbook," 1948, p. 442.
[2] "Metals Handbook," 1948.

in very thin sections, may be given a moderately serviceable hardness by cold mechanical treatment alone. But, if the maximum service as a cutting tool is desired, a steel fairly high in carbon must be selected, and it must be cooled rapidly from a red heat. On the other hand, if a soft, tough, and ductile steel is desired, it can be softened by cooling slowly.

Hot mechanical work often welds up deep-seated blowholes and makes the structure more compact and the grain size smaller, while cold working

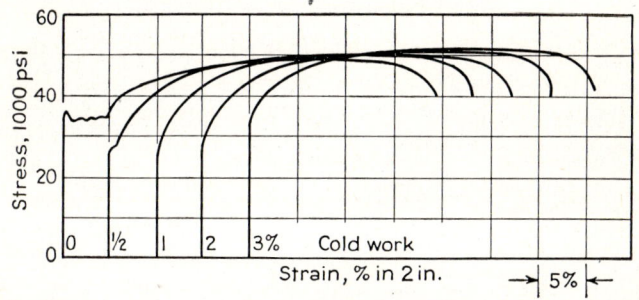

FIG. 127. Jogged stress-strain curve for annealed mild steel sheet. (*From "Metals Handbook,"* 1948.)

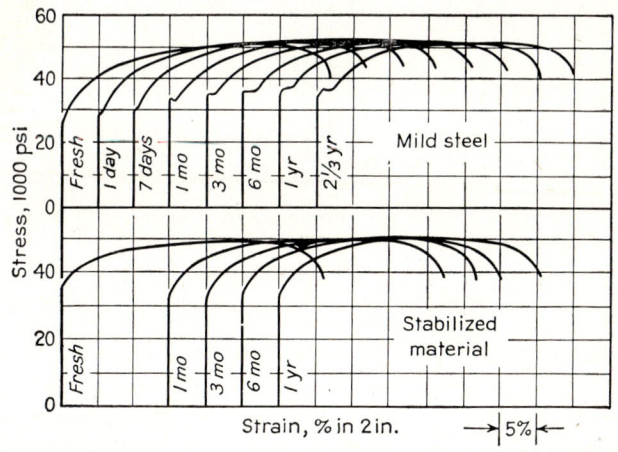

FIG. 128. Return of jogged stress-strain curve in ordinary mild steel during aging after straining. Retention of smooth rounded curve after aging in nonaging material. Both materials were rolled 1 per cent before aging. (*From "Metals Handbook,"* 1948.)

hardens and at the same time introduces residual stresses. Residual stress may be eliminated by "stress-relief" annealing, and grain size will be altered by annealing above the critical temperature. Cold work will cause traces of certain elements (notably nitrogen and/or carbon) to dissolve in ferrite, which, upon annealing or long standing ("aging"), will separate out as an iron compound in critical-dispersion size, causing an aberration in the stress-strain curve. This is known as "strain aging," and is illustrated in Figs. 127 and 128, taken from an article by

S. Epstein.[1] An aging steel is one containing more than 0.001 per cent nitrogen and/or more than 0.001 per cent unfixed carbon, *i.e.*, carbon which has not been fixed by titanium or some other element that would make it unavailable for solution in ferrite. With more nitrogen or carbon than this, it may show a jog in the stress-strain curve.

PROPERTIES OF STEEL

In general, the strength and hardness of steel increase together, whereas the tendency is for the ductility to decrease as the strength increases, although this is not universally true, especially in some alloy steels.

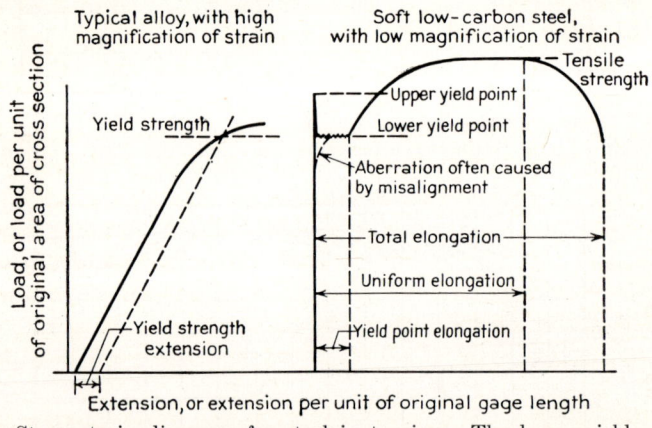

Fig. 129. Stress-strain diagrams for steel in tension. The lower yield point is as shown, and the upper yield point corresponds roughly to the familiar "drop of the beam" in the tensile testing machine.

The engineer must differentiate between several kinds of strength, appropriate to different types of service: for example, tensile, yield, compressive, fatigue, impact, shear, bending, and other types. As determined by the tensile test, the mechanical properties of a low-carbon steel are illustrated in Fig. 129, which is taken from an article by Maxwell Gensamer.[1]

Impact Strength. Brittleness is not the only quality which renders steel liable to failure under shock, although it is one of the worst attributes in this respect, so that phosphorus, oxygen, and large crystal structure—all of which tend to produce brittleness—increase the liability of steel to fail under a blow. But a very ductile low-carbon steel will not withstand so much of a blow as will a medium-carbon steel. This is doubtless due to the higher strength and usually smaller grain size of the

[1] "Metals Handbook," 1948.

medium-carbon steel. For shock-resisting purposes a steel is desired which is ductile enough to yield to the blow without being weak enough to be permanently deformed.

Fatigue Strength (Endurance Limit). If steel is subjected to frequently repeated stresses far below its ultimate strength, and even in some cases below its yield strength, or if it is subjected to corresponding alternating stresses (say, for example, tension and then compression), it will break in service or under test. Even vibration, as in a moving body, will cause fatigue stresses in a member. Designers are now alert to this danger, and many determinations have been made of fatigue limits of carbon and alloy steels. The fatigue limit, or endurance limit, is the maximum stress a metal can withstand for a predetermined number of cycles of repetition; 10,000,000 cycles of stress is generally accepted as defining the limit for steel. The determination is time-consuming, but no short cut has yet been devised. A fatigue crack will start where the repetition or alternation of stresses is most intense. It will start, for example, on the surface of a rotating axle. Any irregularity on the surface of the axle, or even a toolmark or scratch, or a blowhole or inclusion slightly below the surface, may be the nucleus for the start of the crack and will considerably reduce the endurance limit. Sharp corners, fillets with short radii, and other changes in contour which concentrate stresses will serve as stress raisers. Where such stress raisers are not present, the fatigue strength of steel generally ranges from 40 to 60 per cent of its ultimate strength. Typical values for different steels are given in Table 4, page 20.

Corrosion Fatigue. If a member is subjected to repeated or alternating stresses and concurrently to corrosive influences, the endurance limit may be reduced to only a portion of what it would be if corrosion were absent. A corrosion-fatigue endurance limit of only 24,000 psi is wise design practice for most steels, even for strong alloy steels (see page 19).

Modulus of Elasticity. Young's modulus in tension, in millions of pounds per square inch, is as follows for some ferrous materials:

Carbon steel	About 29
Alloy steels	About 28.5–30
Cast irons	About 14
Malleable cast iron	About 25
Wrought iron	About 28
Austenitic stainless steel	About 26–28
Graphite	About 0.7

Modulus of Rigidity. In a torsion test the modulus of rigidity corresponds to the modulus of elasticity in a tension test, and the *modulus* *of rupture* corresponds to ultimate strength. The modulus of rigidity is also called the torsional modulus (G) or the shear modulus; for most steels and alloy steels it is 11,500,000 psi.

Machinability. Normal gray cast iron, which, besides cutting easily, provides the lubrication of flakes of graphite, has high machinability. Soft steel is tough, but low-carbon bessemer steel with relatively high sulfur and nitrogen, although not having high strength or ductility, breaks off into chips and is very useful as stock for automatic screw-threading machines. Soft open-hearth steel to which lead has been added, the lead being held in suspension when the steel freezes (for lead and iron will not alloy), breaks off readily under the cutting tool and therefore machines with comparative ease (see also page 90).

Hardness. Carbon is the main factor in producing hardness in steel, although the intensity of its effect (and its penetration—"hardenability") is now often increased by alloying elements. Other elements will harden steel, but the brittleness and uncertainty which accompany hardness due to phosphorus, for example, discourage engineers from using it in structural steel. The same applies to manganese over 1.10 per cent. The usual alloying elements are too costly for use in ordinary rails. Pure iron is the softest of the ferrous materials; the effect of the addition of carbon on the hardness has been discussed on page 201.

Resilience. Resilience, the tendency of a material to return to its original shape after the removal of a stress that has produced elastic strain, is most often applied in springs. Steel springs vary in size from the minute strips used in watches to the heavy supports used under railroad coaches, etc. The latter are too thick to be hardened by cold work, but thin strips and wire are usually given resilience by rolling or drawing. The greater the degree of cold work and the higher the carbon in the steel, the greater the resilience; but carbon alone, without either work or heat-treatment, cannot produce resilience in steel.

Magnetic Permeability. For ordinary magnetizing forces, pure iron is the most magnetically permeable substance known. Carbon is a deleterious impurity in this respect, and carbon in dissolved form causes a greater decrease in magnetic induction and permeability than the same amount of carbon in the form of Fe_3C crystals. Ferrite dissolves traces of carbon, as shown in Fig. 98, and when so powerful an influence as the effect of dissolved carbon on permeability is considered, it is found that the carbon dissolved in commercial steels in amounts of 0.01 to 0.03 per cent is enough to produce a very important effect. The remedy is to remove the carbon, or else to precipitate it from solution. Silicon and aluminum will precipitate carbon from solid solution. This is one of the factors which contributes to the success of silicon steel in transformer sheets and other electromagnetic equipment.

All impurities are injurious, but sulfur, phosphorus, and oxygen exert a powerful decrease in permeability and an increase in hysteresis loss in proportion to the amount of impurity present. The usual amounts of manganese produce little effect. Mechanical work has a strong effect, and strained metal is lower in magnetic permeability and higher in hysteresis. Annealed steel is much superior in magnetic permeability to that which has cooled without attention, and rapidly cooled steel is unfit for use for electromagnetic purposes. The hysteresis curves in Fig. 130 show some of the effects of carbon and of strain on the magnetic properties of iron. Electromagnets are made of the purest forms of commercial iron, *viz.*, wrought iron, ingot iron, and electrolytic iron, or of silicon steel. Recently iron powder obtained from iron carbonyl and

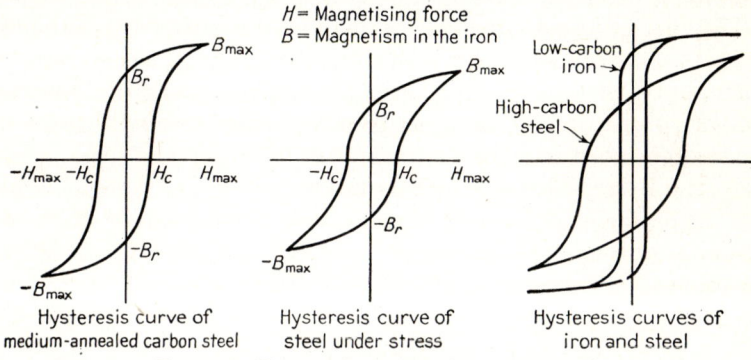

FIG. 130. Hysteresis curves of iron and steel.

the particles insulated by shellac, then compressed under 100 tons pressure into forms suitable for magnet cores, although costly, has been used to give high magnetic permeability combined with high electrical resistivity.

Permanent-magnet Steel. The best steel permanent magnets are made of alloy steels, but cheaper grades are made of high-carbon steel. The desired properties of permanent magnets are retentivity, hysteresis, and coercive force. These can best be secured by rapidly cooling a high-carbon steel from above the line PSK in Fig. 98—in other words, hardening the steel. After it has been hardened, the steel is subjected to a magnetizing force.

Permanent magnets made of alnico, Vicalloy, and other nonferrous alloys are far stronger than those made of any kind of steel.

Electrical Conductivity. The purer the iron, the greater will be its conductivity. Silicon, tin, and nickel especially reduce the conductivity of iron. Iron is like other metals in that it conducts electricity better through its crystals than across the crystal boundaries; therefore heat-treatment which reduces the size of crystals in any steel increases its electric resistance. In third rails for electric conductors a conflict of desiderata is met; electric conductivity is desired, which means that a pure iron should be supplied, but pure iron is soft and will not stand the abrasion of the contact shoe. To overcome this double difficulty the steel is hardened with phosphorus, which gives the greatest hardness for the least proportion of impurity and does not decrease crystal size so much as carbon does.

Directional Properties. If a metal is tested parallel to its direction of rolling or working, it will show higher strength and particularly higher ductility than if it is tested transverse to this direction. A fibrous structure may be caused by working, as in the case of the drawing out of slag particles in wrought iron or of inclusions in the case of steel, or by banding due to differences in carbon, manganese, phosphorus, or other impurity in individual crystals. Likewise, steel and some other metals conduct electricity better in one direction through their crystals than in another direction. This characteristic is of minor importance when a steel bar is made up of many crystals heterogeneously aggregated. However, directional properties with respect to tensile strength and ductility are sometimes of major importance, and it is customary that specifications for important stressed parts, such as turbine rotors, for example, require that test specimens be cut with a hollow drill in longitudinal, transverse, and axial directions. The difference in tensile strength is not so marked, but differences in ductility and impact resistance caused by directionality are very noticeable.

GRAY AND CHILLED IRON CASTINGS

Purchasers may specify the properties which iron castings are to have to be acceptable, and the tests which they must pass; also the allowable limit of harmful impurities, such as sulfur and phosphorus, and the visible and invisible defects, such as flaws or cracks. The manufacturer must then produce the composition and treatment which will give the desired result. It is the amount of silicon and manganese which is usually adjusted to produce this result. The former acts by regulating the proportion of carbon in the form of graphite (see page 362). In Table 19 are shown recommended analyses of gray and chilled iron castings as given in the "Metals Handbook," 1948, by H. Bornstein and J. W. Bolton.

The most important properties of gray iron castings are transverse strength and machinability, but shrinkage also is important, and density and resistance to abrasion require consideration.

Effect of Graphite on Properties. The total carbon in iron castings is seldom far from 3.0 per cent. This is usually partly in the form of graphite, the remainder being combined as Fe_3C, which may be Fe_3C alone or contained in pearlite. The more of the carbon that is in the

TABLE 19. SOME TYPICAL COMPOSITIONS OF IRON CASTINGS

Casting	Composition, per cent							
	TC	Si	Mn	P	S	Ni	Cr	Mo
Auto cylinder, plain iron	3.25	2.25	0.65	0.15	0.10			
Auto cylinder, Ni-Cr iron	3.25	2.25	0.65	0.15	0.10	0.75	0.30	
Auto cylinder, Ni-Cr iron, heavy duty	3.25	1.90	0.65	0.15	0.10	1.75	0.45	
Auto cylinder, Ni iron	3.25	1.80	0.65	0.15	0.10	1.25		
Auto pistons, plain iron	3.35	2.25	0.65	0.15	0.10			
Auto pistons, Mo iron	3.35	2.25	0.65	0.15	0.10	....	....	0.50
General castings (auto), soft iron	3.40	2.60	0.65	0.30	0.10			
Piston rings (auto), individually cast	3.50	2.90	0.65	0.50	0.06			
Brake drums (auto)	3.30	1.90	0.65	0.15	0.08	1.25	0.50	
Brake drums (auto)	2.75	2.25	0.70	0.15	0.08	....	....	0.50
Cams	3.10	1.50	0.65	0.15	0.10	2.00	0.60	
Machinery iron:								
Light service or thin section	3.25	2.25	0.50	0.35	0.10			
Medium service or heavy section	3.25	1.75	0.50	0.35	0.10			
Heavy service with heavy section	3.25	1.25	0.50	0.35	0.10			
Water pipe, sand-cast:								
Light and medium	3.60	1.75	0.50	0.80	1.08			
Heavy	3.40	1.40	0.50	0.80	0.08			
Chilled plowshares	3.60	1.25	0.55	0.40	0.10			
High-strength iron, plain	2.75	2.25	0.80	0.10	0.09			
High-strength Ni iron	2.75	2.25	0.80	0.10	0.09	1.00		
High-strength Mo iron	2.75	2.25	0.80	0.10	0.09	....	....	0.35
Heat-resistant iron, fire pots, and kettles	3.50	1.15	0.80	0.10	0.07			
Pots for caustic, Ni-Cr	3.30	0.70	0.50	0.10	0.08	1.50	0.60	
Pots for caustic, plain iron	3.60	1.00	0.75	0.20	0.07			
Ingot molds	3.50	1.00	0.90	0.20	0.07			
Car wheels	3.35	0.65	0.60	0.35	0.12			
Air cylinders, ammonia cylinders, plain iron	3.25	1.25	0.65	0.20	0.10			
Heavy compressor cylinders, Ni iron	3.00	1.10	0.80	0.20	0.10	2.00		
Light compressor cylinders, Ni-Cr	3.30	2.10	0.55	0.25	0.10	1.25	0.45	
Light forming and stamping or forging dies, Ni-Cr iron	3.30	1.50	0.60	0.20	0.10	2.00	0.60	
Heavy forming and stamping or forging dies, Ni-Cr iron	3.00	1.25	0.60	0.20	0.10	2.75	0.80	
Light forging dies, Mo iron	3.30	2.00	0.60	0.20	0.10	....	....	1.00
Heavy forging dies, Mo iron	3.10	1.50	0.60	0.20	0.08	....	....	1.00
Valves and fittings (medium)	3.30	2.00	0.50	0.35	0.10			

form of graphite, the lower will be the strength and the better the machining qualities (see Fig. 131). Indeed, white cast iron, which has practically all the carbon in dissolved or combined form, cannot be commercially machined. White cast iron is too hard and brittle for most purposes, and usually a white surface with a gray core to provide a backing of greater toughness (chilled iron) is produced (see Fig. 132). But all-white cast iron has some uses, as, for example, balls in grinding mills. Graphite causes an expansion of iron during the freezing period, which makes the total shrinkage between the size of the mold and the size of the cold casting about $\frac{1}{8}$ in. per linear foot, instead of $\frac{1}{4}$ in. as in the case of white cast iron and steel, from which no graphite separates. This lesser shrinkage reduces the tendency of the casting to crack (or *check*, as it is called). The separation of graphite also tends to increase porosity and decrease density, which is important in castings for hydraulic and high-pressure work (see Fig. 131).

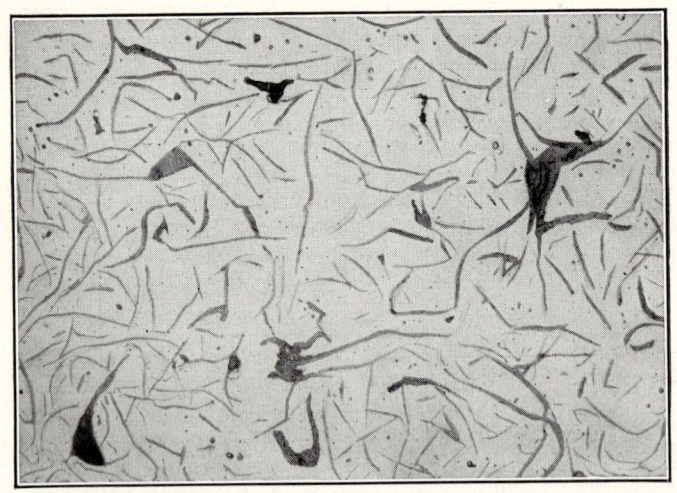

Fig. 131. Gray cast iron, showing graphite flakes. Magnification 50 ×. Unetched. (*Courtesy of Bausch & Lomb.*)

Fig. 132. Fracture of chilled cast-iron roll. (*Courtesy of Robt. S. Lukens, Bethlehem Steel Company.*)

Controlling the Properties of Iron Castings. Since silicon tends to precipitate graphite during freezing, and sulfur tends to keep it in solution or combination, the purchaser formulates his specifications for castings with due attention to these two elements. When density is important, it is customary to limit the phosphorus very closely, as this causes both porosity and segregation. However, phosphorus is often added to increase fluidity.

Phosphorus in iron alloys forms a compound with the formula Fe_3P. This in turn forms a series of alloys with iron, having a fusible eutectic containing 10 per cent phosphorus and 90 per cent iron. This eutectic will form in accordance with the amount of phosphorus present; *i.e.*, 0.1 per cent of phosphorus will result in 1 per cent of eutectic. This eutectic melts at a lower temperature than the remainder of the alloy. The phosphorus eutectic migrates to the grain boundaries during freezing and produces planes of weakness under shock.

Properties of Chilled Iron Castings. Chilled cast iron is composed of white iron, in which all the carbon exists in the combined form, *i.e.*, as Fe_3C, making it hard and wear-resistant, together with unchilled parts composed of gray cast iron, which is less brittle and resists shocks better. The iron castings are made with just that proportion of silicon and sulfur which will cause the carbon to separate during freezing in those portions which are slowly cooled and to remain combined in those portions which are rapidly cooled (chilled) (see Fig. 132). The rapid cooling is effected on the surface by casting the metal against a metal "chill," which conducts the heat away from the surface rapidly, while the interior cools more slowly. Parts that are cast in sand will also cool more slowly. Such castings are used for rolls for rolling metals, grain, paper, etc., which require a hard, highly polished exterior, but must not be brittle throughout; for railroad freight-car wheels, which must resist wear and abrasion in those portions which come in contact with the rails, but must not be brittle in the web; also for plowshares and other objects.

Castings to Resist Corrosion. Iron castings to resist chemical attack, even from acids, are sometimes made with about 13 per cent silicon. They are white and brittle and are difficult to make on account of excessive shrinkage in freezing and cooling. Cast iron with 25 per cent or more chromium is also often used for corrosion resistance. It is not much harder than some gray cast irons. A series of cast irons containing nickel, copper, and chromium, known as the Ni-resist series, are often used to resist corrosion. The microstructure of Ni-resist is shown in Fig. 133.

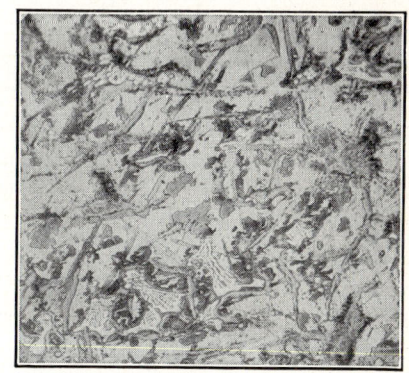

FIG. 133. Ni-resist cast iron. Magnification 150 ×. This sample contains 3.2 per cent C, 15.5 Ni, 6.5 Cu, 2.0 Cr, 1.5 Si, and 1.3 Mn. (*Author's laboratory.*)

High-strength Cast Iron. High-strength cast iron has been defined as cast iron with a tensile strength of at least 50,000 psi. It may be made without alloying elements, but high-strength properties are obtained more easily with alloys of nickel, chromium, molybdenum, or a combination thereof. It may be made in an electric furnace (with or without duplexing from the cupola), in an air furnace, in a special type of high-temperature oil-burning furnace, or in a cupola. Since high temperature is needed for high-strength compositions, the result is more easily achieved in an electric furnace and least easily in a cupola.

Composition and Properties. High-strength cast iron must be low in total carbon. The combined carbon must be about 0.80 per cent or less, giving essentially a pearlitic matrix, which may be obtained either by control of composition or by heat-treatment. It must have a close and compact grain, preferably with spheroidal cementite in the pearlite, and especially with small nodules of graphite isolated from one another. Compositions of high-strength cast iron, both alloyed and unalloyed, are shown in Table 19. In special cases, tensile strength up to 100,000 psi has been obtained. A dendritic structure of the metallic matrix must be avoided. This is often accomplished by adding ferrosilicon, with or without some chromium, to the forehearth or ladle. Vanadium also lessens the tendency to form dendrites.

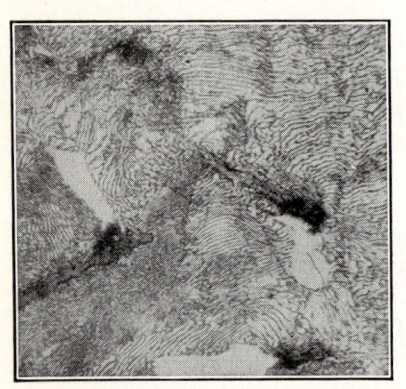

FIG. 134. Pearlitic cast iron, 3.60 per cent carbon, at center of 2¼-in. roller. Magnification 400 ×. (*Author's laboratory.*)

The size, shape, and distribution of the graphite particles have a predominating influence on the physical and mechanical properties. These characteristics are controlled by decreasing the total carbon content, superheating the cast iron to a maximum of 1650°C (3000°F), and then cooling to about 1480°C (2700) before pouring. The object of the superheating is to dissolve all the graphite, and when this is accomplished, the graphite will not be precipitated in the molten mass. Its precipitation during cooling may be controlled by controlling the cooling rate, as by preheating the sand molds. Instead of superheating to 1650°C, a relatively lower temperature with a longer time of soaking will accomplish the result. It is also said that agitating the molten iron assists in effecting the solution. It is best not to use in the charge pig iron or cast-iron scrap having large graphite flakes. The use of fluxes, such as soda ash, calcium silicide, etc., in the forehearth or ladle is also said to produce fine graphite particles.

High-strength unalloyed cast iron can be made with an average tensile strength of 55,000 psi, a modulus of elasticity of 19,000,000, and a fatigue strength of 24,000 psi.

A high-strength gray cast iron with a pearlitic structure is shown in Fig. 134. It has 3.60 per cent total carbon.

Uses of High-strength Carbon and Alloy Cast-iron Castings. Cast-iron automobile crankshafts and camshafts have the advantages of lower initial cost, lower machining and finishing costs, better wearing qualities, and higher endurance ratio on account of better stress-damping properties than if made of steel. The better damping capacity also produces a more smoothly running engine.

Damping. Some metals give a resonant sound when struck with a hammer; others have the capacity of changing the mechanical energy of vibration into heat. They give out a dull sound when struck. Cast iron has high damping capacity. This suppression of vibration will reduce the fatigue stresses generated thereby. The use of cast-iron crankshafts in automobiles is successfully practiced by some manufacturers, because torsional vibration is absorbed by the damping capacity of cast iron.

Cast iron has a much greater damping capacity than steel. This is especially important in resistance to fatigue stresses. It is especially noticeable in lessening the unfavorable effect of a corner or insufficient fillet.

Meehanite. Meehanite is a patented material often called "pearlitic cast iron," although meehanite is not always (though usually) pearlitic, and there is pearlitic cast iron which is not meehanite. Meehanite has a tensile strength of about 60,000 to 70,000 psi and often an elongation in 2 in. of 2 per cent. It has good transverse strength and a modulus of elasticity in tension of about 22,000,000. It has a Brinell hardness of 200 to 280, depending upon the kind of material desired, and this can be raised to 650 by heat-treatment. It is compact, and the grains are of small size, with the free carbon mostly in the form of nodules. The total carbon is 2.40 to 2.70 per cent, with no alloying elements. It is used for locomotive castings, high-quality piston rings, oil-refinery parts, and many other purposes where resistance to pressure, temperature, and wear are required.

Alloy Cast Irons. The use of nickel with or without chromium or molybdenum, or the use of molybdenum alone, accomplishes the desired fineness of size and isolated distribution of the graphite particles; and a proper composition results in the pearlitic metallic matrix, which gives greater strength and abrasion hardness. Surface hardness is also obtained frequently by nitriding the cast iron. Two difficulties are encountered in the manufacture of alloy cast iron, *viz.*, the dissolving of the alloy additions, which is best accomplished by the use of the electric furnace or an electric forehearth furnace receiving the metal from the cupola, and the contamination of the foundry scrap with alloying elements, such as nickel, which do not oxidize when the scrap is used for subsequent charges.

Heat-treatment of Cast Iron. Sometimes white cast iron is heat-treated to produce graphite. This is similar to the production of malle-

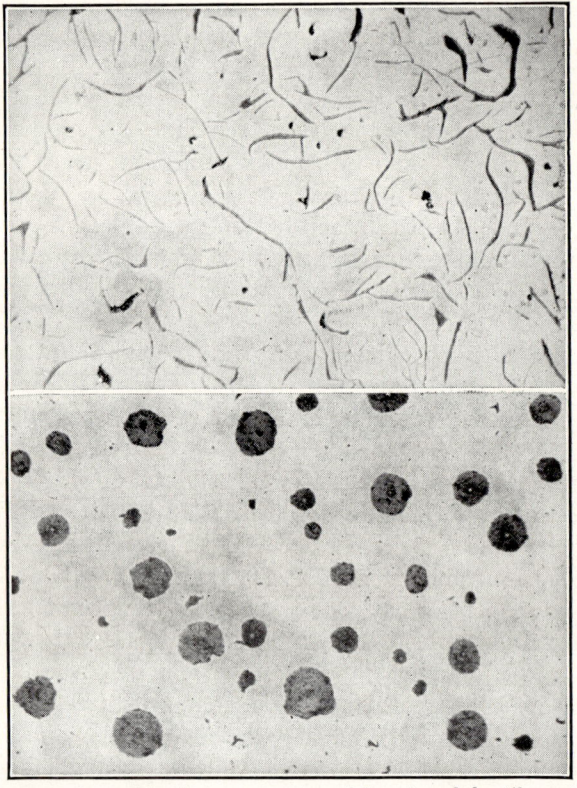

Fig. 135. Structure of graphite in gray cast iron (above) and ductile cast iron (below). Magnification 100 ×. Unetched. (*Courtesy of International Nickel Company.*)

able cast iron, and tensile strengths of 60,000 to 110,000 psi may be obtained, with elongations up to 15 per cent. Other methods of heat-treatment have the following objectives: (1) Stress relieving by heating for several hours below the critical temperature, which causes only a slight decrease in hardness, in strength, and in the amount of cementite. (2) Full annealing above the critical temperature, or about 650 to 815°C (1200 to 1500°F) for ordinary gray cast iron, by which the hardness is reduced to 120 to 130 Brinell; or up to 980°C (1800°F) for alloy cast irons, by which the hardness is reduced to about 130 to 180. This softening for machining is accompanied by a decrease in strength and in the amount of cementite. (3) Quenching and tempering, which is usually applied to alloy cast irons having a pearlitic matrix and small well-distributed graphite flakes. Hardness is increased and strength decreased by quenching, but both are improved by tempering at about 300°C (570°F), and the strength of quenched and tempered alloy cast iron should be greater than that of the iron as cast. A fourth class of methods includes special heat-treatments, such as flame hardening or induction hardening, where special localities are to be hardened for wear

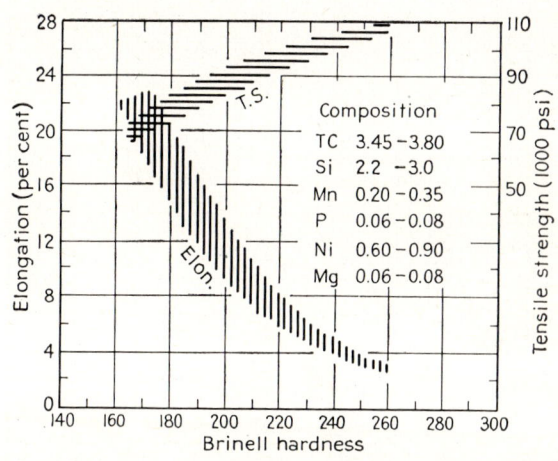

FIG. 136. Relationship between elongation, tensile strength, and hardness of ductile cast iron in 1-in. sections as cast. These properties apply to this composition only. (*From Machine Design, January, 1950; courtesy of International Nickel Company.*)

resistance; austempering for strength and wear resistance; and nitriding of alloy iron castings for wear resistance.

Ductile Cast Iron. Flake graphite in ordinary cast iron causes discontinuities in the matrix which are primarily responsible for relative weakness and brittleness. The International Nickel Company's research department has developed a so-called "ductile cast iron," in which the flakes are partially or completely converted into spheroids, as shown in Fig. 135, and consequently a wide range of properties is achieved, as partially shown in Figs. 136 and 137. This product is patented, and the spheroid result is accomplished by means of magnesium, usually (but not necessarily) added in the form of a nickel-magnesium alloy. Less than 0.1 per cent magnesium usually remains in the metal. With suitable composition and rate of cooling from the mold, or of heat-treatment, structures obtainable are pearlitic, ferritic, martensitic, or austenitic, depending upon the properties desired.

Ductile cast iron is less porous than gray cast iron and does not have its damping quality. Unlike gray cast iron, its properties are only slightly affected by thickness of section. It has properties comparable to steel, including good hardenability, with the process advantages of gray iron. It has a modulus of elasticity approaching that of steel, namely, 24.5 to 26.5 million psi. Available since 1948, it is already used for many purposes, such as pressure and ductile pipe castings, agricultural and general machinery and tractor parts requiring moderate toughness combined with high yield strength, and the like. It appears to machine

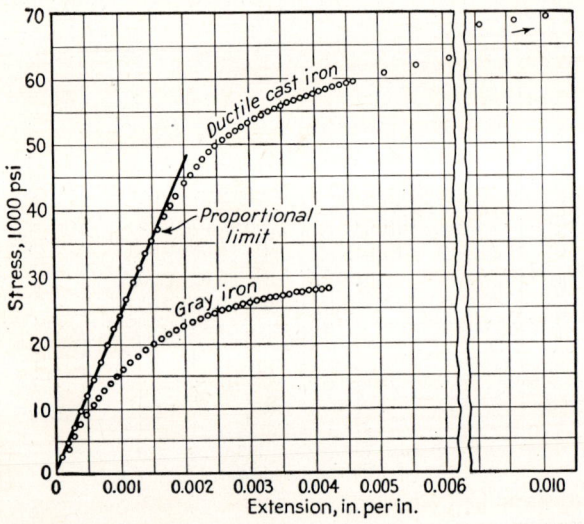

FIG. 137. Comparison of stress-strain curves of plain gray iron (3.45 per cent C, 1.8 per cent Si) and ductile cast iron (3.7 per cent C, 1.8 per cent Si). (*Courtesy of International Nickel Company.*)

as easily as gray cast iron, and has a better machined surface, resembling steel in this respect. Preliminary tests indicate that it will wear as well without lubrication as will gray cast iron. It is possible to cast it against a chill and produce a surface of 52 to 60 Rockwell C hardness with a moderately ductile core. It also has a good response to surface hardening by induction heating and quenching.

MALLEABLE IRON

Malleable iron is made from white cast iron by a special process. It contains particles of graphite differing from the flakes of graphite in gray cast iron in that they are present in a fine nodular form. Its strength approaches that of constructional steel (50,000 to 60,000 psi). It has an elongation in 2 in. of 10 to 18 per cent. It is fairly tough, having an impact strength of 10 to 16 ft-lb. Its yield strength is about 65 per cent of its ultimate strength, and its fatigue endurance limit is 22,000 to 31,000 psi. It is the most easily machined of any ferrous alloy, and it has many uses in automobiles, railroad rolling stock, agricultural machinery, pipe fittings, etc., where a material of moderate strength, toughness (especially under shock or unusual stress), and resistance to rusting is required. Special types of malleable iron have tensile strengths of 60,000 to 90,000 psi, with elongation in 2 in. of 12 to 2 per cent. These are known as "pearlitic malleable," having much of their carbon content in combined form. These also have higher yield strengths and better wearing qualities.

Briefly, malleable iron castings are made as follows: Cast iron of suitably adjusted composition is poured into molds in which it will cool moderately fast, producing a white-iron casting. The metal has high fluidity, resulting in good casting qualities. The sections should not be more than 4 in. in thickness. Malleable iron is specified on the basis of mechanical tests rather than chemical analysis, which is rather variable. Carbon in the iron as cast ranges from about 2.0 to 2.65 per cent; silicon, usually 1.0 to 1.3; sulfur, 0.06 to 0.16; manganese, 0.25 with low sulfur to 0.50 with high sulfur; phosphorus, 0.08 when silicon is high to 0.18 when silicon is low. In the final product the carbon content is

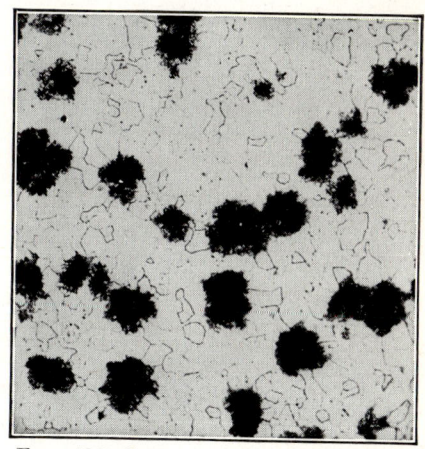

FIG. 138. Structure of malleable cast-iron pipe fitting. Magnification 50 ×. Etched with nital. (*Author's laboratory.*)

0.25 to 0.75 per cent less than in the iron as cast. The casting is cooled, cleaned, and usually packed in some granular material to keep it from sagging at the high temperature in the treatment furnace. Packing is not always necessary, however, and some furnaces are provided with special atmosphere that will not cause the castings to scale and through which the castings are passed from one end to the other. The maximum temperature is about 870°C (1600°F), and the time to reach this temperature in the furnace may be 24 to 36 hr. A typical treatment cycle is 40 hr at 870°C, cool to 760°C (1400°F) in 15 hr, cool to 690°C (1275°F) in another 15 hr, hold at 690° for 20 hr, and cool to handling temperature in 15 hr. In short-cycle annealing, the maximum temperature may be as high as 955°C (1750°F) and the time at that temperature only 10 hr, while the total time above red heat may be about 30 to 35 hr. Castings suitable for this process must be relatively high in silicon. The result of the annealing is that the carbon, which was all in a dissolved or combined form in the white casting, is precipitated in the form of fine particles known as temper carbon (see Fig. 138). The particles of carbon are well separated, so that fracture must take place through the low-carbon iron matrix. It is this which gives malleable iron its strength, toughness under shock, and ductility. Recent practice involves the use of alloying elements, chiefly molybdenum and copper, whereby strength and/or ductility and/or corrosion resistance are obtained.

ALLOY STEELS

As already noted, several elements, such as manganese, silicon, aluminum, and titanium, are added to straight carbon steel in relatively small amounts for remedial purposes. An alloy steel, on the other hand, is a steel to which sufficient alloying element has been added to produce properties unobtainable in carbon steels, either as cast, or as rolled, or heat-treated.

Purpose. There are many purposes for which alloying elements are added, among which may be mentioned increase of the following:

1. Strength, with little or no loss in ductility (*i.e.*, toughness).
2. Hardness.
3. Resistance to softening at elevated temperatures after hardening.
4. Ease of hardening.
5. Depth of hardening (hardenability).
6. Properties at high or low temperature.
7. Wear resistance.
8. Electromagnetic properties.
9. Resistance to oxidation or corrosion.
10. Expansion with heat, or lack of it.
11. Electrical conductivity or resistivity.

Except during times when ordnance demands a large tonnage, about three-quarters of all American alloy steels go into the manufacture of automobiles. Most alloy steels are valued because of their combination of strength and ductility and go into structural uses in vehicles, ships, buildings, bridges, springs, and machines. Alloy steels are more costly than carbon steels, not only on account of their ingredients, but also frequently because of higher cost of melting, fabrication, heat-treatment, etc. The choice of which alloy steel to use must be based on technical factors and also, when possible, on cost factors. It is wasteful to use a steel having qualities beyond those needed in service if its cost is greater. A rough idea of the cost of alloy steels is given in Table 20.

TABLE 20. COMPARATIVE PRICES OF CARBON AND ALLOY STEELS, 1950[1]

	Cents per pound
Carbon steel ingots	2.50
Alloy steel ingots (depending on the alloying elements)	2.55–5.10
Carbon steel bars	3.45
Alloy steel bars (depending on the alloying elements)	3.95–6.00
Carbon steel plates	3.50
Alloy steel plates (depending on the alloying elements)	4.50–6.50
Wrought-iron plates	7.85
Silicon-steel transformer sheets	9.80
Stainless-steel sheets, 18 and 8	39.50
Stainless-steel clad sheets (20 per cent)	22.50
High-strength low-alloy sheets	5.00–6.00
Carbon tool steel	21.00
High-speed tool steel (18-4-1)	100.00

[1] Compiled from *Iron Age* and *Steel*.

History. No doubt the ancients used alloy irons and steels, because meteoric iron frequently contains 8 per cent nickel, and fortuitous mixtures of ores produced alloys with tungsten, nickel, and manganese; but scientific investigation began about the beginning of the nineteenth century, and at the end of that century, the manufacture of alloy steels for engineering had its beginnings. In 1865 Julius Baur patented chrome steel and, in 1869, established his Chrome Steel Works in Brooklyn, N.Y. In 1868 the first bridge in which (carbon) steel was used in its main arch members was built at Kuilenberg, Holland. It seems to be established now that in 1872 some of Baur's chrome steel was used in members of the Eads Bridge across the Mississippi River at St. Louis.[1] At the Philadelphia Centennial Exposition in 1876, a number of commercial alloy steels were exhibited, and alloy steel for armament was commonly used at that time. The rapid rise of the automobile industry created a demand for steel of higher quality, which was reinforced by demand for armament, projectiles, and the like. In 1951, 10 per cent (10,000,000 tons) of the steel produced in the United States was alloy steel, of which about 30 per cent was made in the electric furnace and the balance in the open hearth.

Low-alloy steels are especially amenable to toughening by heat-treatment, and the hardenability test has proved to be particularly beneficial in choosing steels for service uses. The classic paper by M. A. Grossman[2] throws a wealth of light on this subject and has established the following concepts:

[1] For this and some other data in this paragraph, the authors are indebted to C. A. Zapffe's monograph "A Brief History of Alloy Steel," American Society for Metals, 1948.

[2] "Hardenability Calculated from Chemical Composition," *Trans. Am. Inst. Mining Met. Eng.*, vol. 150, pp. 227–255 (1942).

1. Maximum hardness of annealed steels is a function of carbon content and grain size.

2. Depth of hardness (hardenability) is a function of the carbon and alloying element contents.

3. A multiplicity of elements in small quantities is more effective than a similar (total) quantity of one element.

4. In their effects, the alloying elements are to a large extent interchangeable.

During the Second World War, owing at first to a shortage of alloying elements, there arose a class of low-alloy heat-treatable steels, known as National Emergency (N.E.) steels, containing small amounts of manganese, silicon, and/or nickel, chromium, and molybdenum, some of which could be recovered from "residual" metals in the scrap. On heat-treatment, these produced tough steels which accounted for much of the United States tonnage of the early 1940's. Many of these have proved their usefulness in industry and have survived to the present time, without now being designated as "N.E."

Classification of Carbon and Alloy Steels by Composition. Some years ago the Society of Automotive Engineers adopted a classification designating by numerals the approximate analysis of steels for various purposes. The American Iron and Steel Institute later adopted the same classification as far as constructional steels, low-carbon, general-purpose, and high-ductility steels were concerned, adding a prefix indicating the process of manufacture, *e.g.*, B = bessemer; C = open hearth; E = electric. This system of numbers has been widely adopted and is given in Table 21 for reference.

A four-numeral series designates steels specified to chemical composition ranges. Five numerals are used to designate certain types of alloy steels.

The last two digits of the four-numeral series indicate the approximate middle of the carbon range, *i.e.*, 20 represents a range of 0.18 to 0.23 per cent. It is necessary, however, to deviate from this rule and to interpolate numbers in the case of some carbon ranges and for variations in manganese, sulfur, chromium, or other elements.

The first two digits of the four-numeral series are used for the various grades of alloy steel.

Constitution of Steel and the Effect of Alloying Elements. Annealed carbon steel containing less than 0.80 per cent carbon is composed at atmospheric temperature of crystals of ferrite and cementite. Above the critical range it consists of crystals of austenite. The austenite normally breaks down into intermediate products of which the ultimate result is ferrite and cementite. Alloying elements have an effect on these constituents and changes. As will become evident, some of them

PROPERTIES AND USES OF IRON AND STEEL

TABLE 21. AISI CLASSIFICATION OF STEELS

Series designation	Types
10xx	Plain carbon steel
11xx	Resulfurized (free-cutting)
13xx	Manganese 1.75 per cent
23xx	Nickel 3.50 per cent
25xx	Nickel 5.00 per cent
31xx	Nickel 1.25 per cent—chromium 0.65 or 0.80 per cent
33xx	Nickel 3.50 per cent—chromium 1.55 per cent
40xx	Molybdenum 0.25 per cent
41xx	Chromium 0.95 per cent—molybdenum 0.20 per cent
43xx	Nickel 1.80 per cent—chromium 0.50 or 0.80 per cent—molybdenum 0.25 per cent
46xx	Nickel 1.80 per cent—molybdenum 0.25 per cent
48xx	Nickel 3.50 per cent—molybdenum 0.25 per cent
50xx	Chromium 0.30 or 0.60 per cent
51xx	Chromium 0.80 per cent, 0.95 per cent, or 1.05 per cent
5xxxx	Carbon 1.00 per cent—chromium 0.50, 1.00, or 1.45 per cent
61xx	Chromium 0.80 or 0.95 per cent—vanadium 0.10 per cent or 0.15 per cent minimum
86xx	Nickel 0.55 per cent—chromium 0.50 per cent—molybdenum 0.20 per cent
87xx	Nickel 0.55 per cent—chromium 0.50 per cent—molybdenum 0.25 per cent
92xx	Manganese 0.85 per cent—silicon 2.00 per cent
93xx	Nickel 3.25 per cent—chromium 1.20 per cent—molybdenum 0.12 per cent
94xx	Manganese 1.00 per cent—nickel 0.45 per cent—chromium 0.40 per cent—molybdenum 0.12 per cent
97xx	Nickel 0.55 per cent—chromium 0.17 per cent—molybdenum 0.20 per cent
98xx	Nickel 1.00 per cent—chromium 0.80 per cent—molybdenum 0.25 per cent
	Stainless Steels
3xx	Austenitic (the predominant alloying elements are chromium and nickel)
4xx	Ferritic and martensitic (the predominant alloying element is chromium)

affect more than one constituent or change. The principal effects are given in the following paragraphs.

Strengthen Ferrite. According to the last edition of "Steel and Its Heat Treatment" (D. K. Bullens, Vol. II, 1949, as modified by E. C. Bain) the elements which strengthen ferrite are as follows: P, very strong (although it must be remembered in this connection that, when phosphorus plus carbon equals or exceeds 0.25 per cent, the steel may be brittle); Si and Mn, strong; Ni, Cu, Cr, Mo, W, fairly strong. Since most engineering annealed steels contain more than 90 per cent by weight of ferrite crystals, the importance of these elements is obvious, but nickel is the one most often used, when the price permits, because it strengthens ferrite without greatly decreasing ductility, whereas the cheaper elements, like silicon, manganese, and copper, strengthen and also harden.

Decrease Carbon Content of the Eutectoid. Some alloying elements bring the eutectoid point nearer to the ferrite ordinate, for example: Mn, Cr, V, considerably; Ni, Mo, W, Si, somewhat; Cu, Al, negligibly. With 1 per cent chromium, the eutectoid composition is about 0.70 per cent carbon, say 90 per cent ferrite instead of 88. With 15 per cent chromium, the eutectoid contains less than 0.30 per cent carbon, say 95 per cent ferrite.

Form Carbides. In some cases it is desirable to form a harder or more wear-resistant carbide than Fe_3C. In other cases it is desirable to form a carbide which does not precipitate on tempering so easily as does Fe_3C. In still other cases, it is desirable to prevent a carbide from forming; for example, chromium confers stainlessness when a maximum proportion of it is dissolved in the steel, but not when it forms a carbide chemically separated. Thus, in the welding of stainless steel, chromium carbides may form and separate along the grain boundaries, impoverishing the neighboring localities below the stainless limit. To prevent this, a welding rod is used containing some strong carbide former, such as columbium, which prevents chromium carbides from forming. The carbide formers are Ti, Cb, Zr, V, very strong; Cr, Mo, W, strong; Mn, fairly strong; P, Ni, Cu, Si, do not form carbides in steel.

Restrain Austenite Grain Growth. The following elements will restrain austenite grain growth: Al, very strong; V, Cb, Ti, Zr, fairly strong; Mo, medium; Cr, Si, weak; Mn, Ni, very weak.

Confer Depth Hardening. These elements increase the sluggishness of austenite transformation and thus increase hardenability: Si, medium; Cu, Ni, weak; V, very weak. Traces of boron (*i.e.*, not more than 0.003 per cent) increase hardenability to an astonishing extent, but larger proportions are not effective. It has already been mentioned that steel of a large grain size hardens deeper than the same steel of a small grain size.

Stabilize Hardened Structures on Tempering. If martensite is formed by rapid cooling of austenite in carbon steel, it loses its effective cutting hardness on heating to about 300°C (570°F). But some alloying elements stabilize the hardened structures in rapidly cooled steel and result in their retaining their cutting hardness up to a low red heat. In this connection Mo and W are strong; V, fairly strong; Cr, weak; Mn, very weak. But chromium in combination with tungsten and/or molybdenum causes a very strong resistance to softening by tempering.

Other Specific Effects of Alloying Elements. Molybdenum makes all changes in steel more sluggish, but especially minimizes temper brittleness. Copper above about 0.08 per cent produces precipitation hardening. Silicon above about 2 per cent increases the resistance to oxidation at high temperatures (scaling). Copper, and copper plus phosphorus, even in small amounts, confers improved resistance to atmospheric corrosion.

Nickel Steels. Nickel confers toughness without brittleness, and especially confers subzero impact toughness, and greatly lessens notch sensitivity at atmospheric and lower temperatures. It increases hardness slightly and decreases rusting. It decreases grain size, especially the size of the ferrite crystals, and lessens the "hot-shortness" due to copper. Most nickel constructional steels contain at least 90 per cent by weight of ferrite and are heat-treated by raising to the temperature where austenite is formed, cooling rapidly, and then tempering at temperatures between 370 and 590°C (700 and 1100°F). Many case-hardening steels contain 2 to 7 per cent nickel, because this causes the grain size of the core to be small without the necessity of the double heat-treatment (see page 183). It gives better properties to both core and case and usually permits oil quenching instead of water quenching.

Invar is an alloy of iron with 36 per cent nickel, which has an extremely low coefficient of expansion within a limited range of temperature change near atmospheric temperature, and alloys of 39, 42, 46, and 50.5 per cent nickel have coefficients which permit them to be rolled in glass to form "armored glass." They also form surface oxides which permit metal-to-glass seals. A recent addition to the series is an alloy containing 42 per cent nickel, 6 per cent chromium, and 52 per cent iron. Other nickel-iron alloys have magnetic qualities which will be discussed later.

Nickel-chromium Steels. If nickel and chromium are used together, with about 2½ times as much nickel as chromium, and the steel is then heat-treated as described previously, the result is a tough structural steel. A steel of 1.25 per cent nickel and 0.60 per cent chromium, quenched (preferably in oil) and tempered, has more strength and almost as much ductility as a steel of 3.5 per cent nickel, and costs less. In many low-alloy heat-treated steels, small proportions of nickel and chromium are used. Indeed, the tonnage of alloy steels containing chromium and/or nickel (including stainless steels) is greater than that of all other alloy steels together.

The commonest stainless steel contains 18 per cent chromium and 8 per cent nickel, and is known as "18 and 8." It is austenitic on ordinary cooling. For high creep strength and resistance to oxidation at high temperatures, steels up to 28 per cent chromium and up to 37 per cent nickel are used. The addition of silicon decreases oxidation at high temperatures.

Chromium Steels. Chromium is added to steels, either alone or in combination with other elements, all the way from a fraction of 1 per cent up to over 30 per cent. It increases the effectiveness of rapid cooling (*i.e.*, toughening) and is used for this purpose, and for wear resistance either alone or in combination, in amounts from 0.40 per cent or less up to 2.50 per cent or more. In this amount it does not seem to lessen ductility, but ductility of such steels depends greatly upon the carbon content. Its second most important use is for decreasing corrosion and oxidation, especially oxidation at high temperatures. These functions increase with increasing chromium, but have critical changes at about 3 to 4 per cent chromium and at 12 per cent, above which are the stainless steels and irons. Chromium improves the structure and hardness of nitrided steels. Nitrogen counteracts the tendency of chromium steels to be large in grain size.

Manganese in Alloy Steels. Because manganese strengthens ferrite, and because it shifts the eutectoid point to the left, it is an important and a rather inexpensive strengthener which is much used to the extent of 1 to 1.75 per cent in steels of about 0.40 per cent carbon, or less, either with or without silicon. These steels are normalized or rapidly cooled from well above the upper critical temperature and then drawn at a high tempering temperature (see Table 22). This is known as "medium manganese steel," or "pearlitic manganese steel." When used in combination with silicon, it is known as "silicomanganese steel." Over 1 per cent of manganese increases the resistance of steel to shock.

Manganese lowers the critical temperature—line *PSK* in Fig. 98, page 171—about 55°C (100°F) for each per cent of manganese. Therefore, steel with 7 per cent and higher of manganese is austenitic at atmospheric temperature, and analyses of 7 to 14 per cent manganese (usually 10 to 14 per cent manganese and about 1 per cent carbon) are often used to secure the high tensile, high ductility, and almost nonmagnetic qualities of austenite. As this steel is hypereutectoid, Fe_3C will separate on slow cooling; it is therefore heated to above the line *SE* in Fig. 98 and rapidly cooled. Austenite is not very hard, but it becomes martensitic on cold working; therefore, for jaws of crushing machinery, for railroad frogs, and the like, where resistance to abrasion is important, it has no superior, and for parts of electrical machinery which should be nonmagnetic, austenitic manganese steel is used. It has about one-sixth to one-seventh the thermal or electrical conductivity of iron. It is machined with difficulty. Austenitic manganese steel, usually with carbon below 0.15 per cent, and especially when associated with chromium or nickel in small proportions, has a high impact resistance at subzero temperatures.

TABLE 22. MECHANICAL PROPERTIES OF SOME CONSTRUCTIONAL ALLOY STEELS

AISI or SAE No.	Steel	C	Mn	Si	Ni	S	Cr	V	Mo	Ultimate strength, psi	Yield strength, psi	Elongation in 2 in., per cent	Reduction of area, per cent	Izod value	Quenching medium and temperature, °F	Drawing temperature, °F
	Silicon structural	0.10	0.60	1.00						72,000	52,000	27[1]	59		As rolled	
	Silicon-manganese	0.40[2]	1.00[2]	0.40[2]						93,000	55,000	18[1]	>35		As rolled	
9255	Silicomanganese	0.55	0.90	1.80						242,000	230,500	4[1]	21		Oil, 1742	842
										162,400	142,200	13[1]	31		Oil, 1742	1112
1330	Medium manganese	0.29	1.60							93,000	40,500[3]	31	68	4.5	Normalized	
1137	Medium manganese	0.38	1.75			0.103				209,000	158,700[3]	11	45	56	Water, 1475	625
2335	Nickel	0.35			3.50					245,000	220,000	11	38		Oil, 1450	400
										202,000	180,000	13	46		Oil, 1450	600
										160,000	138,000	16	53		Oil, 1450	800
										126,000	103,000	21	59		Oil, 1450	1000
										104,000	71,000	25	64		Oil, 1450	1200
										95,000	65,000	27	65		Oil, 1450	1300
3135	Chrome-nickel	0.35			1.25		0.60			240,000	214,000	8	28		Oil, 1500	400
										220,000	195,000	9	30		Oil, 1500	600
										180,000	151,000	12	49		Oil, 1500	800
										135,000	110,000	17	58		Oil, 1500	1000
										108,000	86,000	21	63		Oil, 1500	1200
										96,000	74,000	22	65		Oil, 1500	1300
6125	Chrome-vanadium	0.26					0.92	0.20		132,000	110,000	19	52		As rolled	
										83,700	61,100	35	66		Normalized	
										173,100	149,800	13	57		Oil, 1560	750
										171,100	147,150	15	61		Oil, 1560	840
										137,500	112,750	21	65		Oil, 1560	1020
										131,000	100,000	28	67		Oil, 1560	1155
Approx.	Vanadium steel casting	0.34						0.25		90,750	67,500	17	28	10.88[4]	Water, 1650	1200
4135	Chrome-molybdenum	0.35					1.06		0.36	205,000	189,000	14	50		Oil, 1550	600
										176,000	153,000	15	53		Oil, 1550	800
										152,000	132,000	15	61		Oil, 1550	1000
										127,000	112,000	23	66		Oil, 1550	1200
410	Stainless steel	0.11					12.5			202,000	157,000	18	57	49	Oil, 1800	500
										193,000	94,000	18	62	60	Oil, 1800	700
										186,000	114,000	18	63	60	Oil, 1800	900
										186,000	112,000	20	62	49	Oil, 1800	1100
										155,000	82,500	20	67	31	Oil, 1800	1300
										103,000	63,000	26	70	102	Oil, 1800	1500
										143,000	115,000	18	55	31	Oil, 1800	
										81,000	31,500	36	75	118	Annealed 1600	

[1] In 8 in.
[2] Maximum.
[3] Proportional limit.
[4] Charpy.

Vanadium in Alloy Steels. Vanadium forms a hard carbide that dissolves in austenite only at high temperatures; therefore, more than about 0.15 per cent of vanadium makes steel brittle, because of plates of vanadium carbide (probably V_4C_3). But vanadium is also a great scavenger of nitrogen and oxygen, and if about 0.30 per cent of vanadium is added to liquid steel after other deoxidizers have done their work, only about 0.15 to 0.20 per cent of residual vanadium will be left in the solid metal. It is frequently added to other alloy steels to increase strength (especially endurance limit and creep), and especially to promote fine grain size, which is one of its outstanding functions. For steel castings, which, of course, cannot have the benefit of mechanical work, it is especially advantageous. It increases hardenability (when dissolved) and resistance to tempering and decreases the tendency to age-harden. It improves impact resistance at all temperatures.

Heat-treatment. Alloy steels are frequently rapidly cooled from well above the upper critical temperature and then tempered at a relatively high temperature to restore ductility, but always, of course, below the lower critical temperature. Some typical examples are given in Table 22.

Tool Steels. Steel of about 1 per cent carbon, heat-treated to produce martensite and then tempered to reduce its brittleness, has been used for centuries for cutting purposes. Sometimes its hardness is increased by chromium, or similar hardening elements, or chromium is added to make hardening easier, so that it can be quenched in oil and hardened with less distortion. The limitation of this steel is that it will soften below the cutting hardness at a relatively low tempering temperature.

High-speed Steel. An alloy steel was developed at the beginning of the present century which was heat-treated by quenching from near the melting point, tempered at 565°C (1050°F), and then cooled with moderate rapidity. This could be heated by the friction of cutting to a temperature of almost red heat without losing its cutting hardness, and very fast cutting speeds were employed. As Howe, the famous metallurgist, said, "It was the only substance then known which would get hot without losing its temper." After some experimenting, an analysis was developed known as "18-4-1," that is, 18 per cent tungsten, 4 chromium, and 1 vanadium. Molybdenum could replace some, or all, of the tungsten, in the ratio of 1 molybdenum to 2 tungsten (equal atomic proportions), and tungsten and molybdenum are now often used together, in various proportions, of which a common example is 6 tungsten, 6 molybdenum, 4 chromium, and 1 to 2 vanadium. Vanadium is used to increase hardness, and 5 to 12 per cent cobalt is sometimes added to increase red-hardness. The carbides of tungsten and molybdenum will dissolve in austenite only at very high temperature, and the grain coarsening which would result is kept as small as possible by having the steel at the high temperature for the shortest possible time, and by the use of chromium and vanadium.

High-speed cutting alloys of nonferrous materials are discussed in Chap. 10.

STAINLESS STEELS AND IRONS

The stainless steels embrace a considerable group of highly alloyed iron-base alloys, of which many are not "steels" and some are not "stainless." In spite of the efforts of the technically minded to classify and define them, common usage has broadened the term to include all steely colored ferrous metals that do not tarnish or rust readily. This general definition includes alloys which contain 12 per cent or more chromium, while the heat-resisting steels include the stainless steels plus a number of alloys of lower chromium content which are resistant to scaling but which rust rather quickly.

No one investigator can claim credit for originating stainless steel; heat-resistant nickel-chrome alloys were made in 1903 and the first nickel-cobalt-chromium alloys in 1905, to be revived again to make possible the gas turbine and jet engine in the 1940's.

In 1915 the first fifty tons of stainless cutlery steel made in the United States was poured. Not long afterward appeared the first commercial nonhardenable stainless alloys, but it was not until 1926 that the first large heat made in the United States of the now familiar alloy "18-8" came from the furnaces of the Allegheny Steel Company.

The outstanding characteristic of the stainless steels is their ability to form an oxide film, usually invisible, which acts as a constant protection against further corrosion of the underlying metal. At ordinary temperatures this oxide film is extremely thin—so thin as to be practically transparent. In contrast to the films on ordinary steel, the film is quite stable, extremely tough and continuous, and very adherent. If this film, basically composed of chromium oxide, is broken by scratching, abrasion, or chemical action, it re-forms quickly and continues its protective action. Resistance to scaling at high temperature is based on the same phenomenon, most particularly the fact that the alloy oxide "skin" does not crack and fall off, which would expose the metal to further oxidation.

These alloys are divided into two basic groups: the austenitic alloys, which contain as the principal alloying elements combinations of chromium and nickel to the extent of at least 23 per cent (AISI type numbers in the three-hundred series); and the ferritic alloys in which the principal alloying element is chromium alone (AISI type numbers in the four-hundred series). When annealed the chromium-nickel stainless alloys contain sufficient nickel to be austenitic (nonmagnetic) at room temperature, while the straight chromium alloys are ferritic (magnetic). The straight chromium alloys are magnetic in all conditions of heat-treatment.

The straight chromium alloys can be further classified on the basis of their hardenability by heat-treatment. These hardenable stainless alloys are true steels and are said to be martensitic because they transform from a soft structure to a hard one upon rapid cooling from a high temperature. They include such types as 403, 410, 420, and others. The chromium-iron alloys of the four-hundred series, which cannot be hardened to a useful or commercial degree, are predominantly ferritic at both elevated and room temperatures, and are more properly classified as chromium irons rather than steels. These include such types as 405, 430, and 446.

The protective surface film on the austenitic alloys contains nickel, which makes the film tougher and more resistant to the more severe corrosives. The austenitic alloys offer more resistance to staining and discoloration than the ferritic alloys, which, however, offer adequate resistance to mild corrosives.

In comparison with carbon steels, the stainless alloys have higher tensile strength, yield strength, and hardness, and the austenitic alloys also show higher ductility. The austenitic alloys also work-harden much more rapidly. In certain temperature ranges some of the nickel-chromium austenitic stainless alloys are subject to chromium carbide precipitation, and the effects of this on service performance must be carefully considered. All the stainless types are resistant to oxidation and scaling as well as to acid attack. In general they have low thermal conductivity and high electrical resistance. The austenitic alloys have a very high coefficient of thermal expansion, while the ferritic and martensitic alloys show thermal expansion characteristics similar to ordinary steel.

In order to meet the various requirements for applications of stainless and heat-resisting steels, more than 30 separate and distinct types of analyses have been developed and adopted as standard by the various technical societies. Each of these alloys has distinctive characteristics which govern its application. The chemical composition ranges shown in Table 23 are based on ladle analyses, and small variations outside the limits shown may occasionally be encountered on individual pieces. The type numbers refer to the AISI and SAE standard numbering system for these steels and alloys.

MAGNETIC ALLOY STEELS

Alloy Steels for Magnetic Permeability. The purest possible iron is in many respects the ideal ferromagnetic material, but it has certain

TABLE 23. STAINLESS AND HEAT-RESISTING STEELS, STANDARD TYPE NUMBERS AND CHEMICAL-COMPOSITION RANGES

Type number	C	Mn max	Si max	Cr	Ni	Other elements[1]
301	Over 0.08–0.20	2.00	1.00	16.00–18.00	6.00–8.00	
302	Over 0.08–0.20	2.00	1.00	17.00–19.00	8.00–10.00	
302B	Over 0.08–0.20	2.00	2.00–3.00	17.00–19.00	8.00–10.00	
303	0.15 max	2.00	1.00	17.00–19.00	8.00–10.00	[2]
304[3]	0.08 max	2.00	1.00	18.00–20.00	8.00–11.00	
305	0.12 max	2.00	1.00	17.00–19.00	10.00–13.00	
308	0.08 max	2.00	1.00	19.00–21.00	10.00–12.00	
309	0.20 max	2.00	1.00	22.00–24.00	12.00–15.00	
310	0.25 max	2.00	1.50	24.00–26.00	19.00–22.00	
314	0.25 max	2.00	1.50–3.00	23.00–26.00	19.00–22.00	
316	0.10 max	2.00	1.00	16.00–18.00	10.00–14.00	Mo 2.00–3.00
317	0.10 max	2.00	1.00	18.00–20.00	11.00–14.00	Mo 3.00–4.00
321	0.08 max	2.00	1.00	17.00–19.00	8.00–11.00	Ti 5 × C min
347[4]	0.08 max	2.00	1.00	17.00–19.00	9.00–12.00	Cb 10 × C min
403	0.15 max	1.00	0.50	11.50–13.00		
405	0.08 max	1.00	1.00	11.50–13.50	....	Al 0.10–0.30
410	0.15 max	1.00	1.00	11.50–13.50		
414	0.15 max	1.00	1.00	11.50–13.50	1.25–2.50	
416	0.15 max	1.25	1.00	12.00–14.00	....	[2]
420	Over 0.15	1.00	1.00	12.00–14.00		
430	0.12 max	1.00	1.00	14.00–18.00		
430F	0.12 max	1.25	1.00	14.00–18.00	....	[2]
431	0.20 max	1.00	1.00	15.00–17.00	1.25–2.50	
440A	0.60–0.75	1.00	1.00	16.00–18.00	....	Mo 0.75 max
440B	0.75–0.95	1.00	1.00	16.00–18.00	....	Mo 0.75 max
440C	0.95–1.20	1.00	1.00	16.00–18.00	....	Mo 0.75 max
446	0.35 max	1.50	1.00	23.00–27.00	....	N 0.25 max
501	Over 0.10	1.00	1.00	4.00–6.00		
502	0.10 max	1.00	1.00	4.00–6.00		

[1] Phosphorus is 0.04 max and sulfur is 0.03 max for all grades except 416 and 430F, which are free-machining types.

[2] Phosphorus or sulfur or selenium, 0.07 min; zirconium or molybdenum, 0.60 max.

[3] Type 304L is the same as 304 except that carbon is 0.03 max.

[4] Type TS347A is the same as 347 except that columbium is partly replaced by tantalum.

drawbacks which make it unsuitable for alternating-current machinery, which represents about 75 per cent of all magnetic materials. Therefore, silicon is added to increase electrical resistivity and consequently to decrease core losses. Silicon is added in proportions of 0.5 to 4.5 per cent, more rarely 6 per cent, but above 4 per cent it causes brittleness which limits the use of the steel in practice.

TABLE 24. COMMERCIAL TYPES OF PERMANENT MAGNET STEELS

Type of steel	Nominal composition,[1] per cent							Nominal magnetic properties[2]		Hardening temperature, °F	Quenching medium
	C	Mn	Cr	W	Co	Mo	B_r, gausses	H_c, oersteds		
C-Mn	0.60	0.80	....	....	....	....	10,000	43	1450	Water
Cr	0.60	0.40	0.90	....	....	....	10,000	50	1450	Oil
Cr	0.90	0.35	2.25	....	....	....	9,000	58	1500	Water, oil
Cr	0.95	0.20–0.60	3.00–4.00	....	....	....	9,500	63	1525	Oil
Cr	1.00	0.35	6.00	....	....	....	9,000	72	1550	Oil
Cr-Mo	1.00	0.35	4.00	....	....	0.35	9,000	65	1500	Oil
W	0.70	0.30	0.20	5.50	....	....	10,000	65	1550	Water
W-Cr	0.70	0.50	0.50	6.00	....	....	9,000	70	1525	Oil
Co	0.90	0.35	4.75	1.25	8.50	....	7,500	120	1650	Oil
Co	0.90	0.30–0.85	3.50–5.75	3.75–7.00	35.00–41.00	....	9,700	235	1700	Oil
Co-Cr	0.95	0.30	9.00	....	16.00	1.30	8,000	180	[3]	Air
Co-W	0.85	0.50	2.00–5.00	8.75	17.00	....	9,000	165	1750	Oil

[1] Limits usually 0.30 per cent Si max, 0.03 per cent P and S max, 0.50 per cent Ni max.
[2] Values for previously annealed materials usually 5 to 10 per cent lower in H_c.
[3] Heat-treatment: 2100°F, cool in air; 1850°F, cool in air.

Nickel-iron alloys of 30 to 90 per cent nickel have very high magnetic permeability for low magnetizing forces. Those having the trade names Permalloy and Hipernik are described under nickel alloys, Chap. 10.

Permanent Magnets. The qualities and compositions of permanent-magnet steels are shown in Table 24, taken from K. L. Scott, "Metals Handbook," 1948. All permanent magnets require rapid, or moderately rapid, cooling from the austenitizing temperature and then magnetizing in a magnetic field.

WROUGHT IRON

Wrought iron is a tough, ductile iron, containing less than 0.10 per cent carbon, and usually not more than 0.05, but having, as a mechanical mixture among its crystals, webs and strings of slag, which make it break under certain conditions with a fibrous fracture. The properties of wrought iron are due to its being composed of almost pure iron crystals, mechanically mixed with slag. The most important properties are that it often rusts less than does steel and its ductility, magnetic permeability, and electrical conductivity are better. Due to the drawn-out fibers of slag, it has strong directional properties: for example, it is stronger if tested in the direction of the slag fibers than if tested transversely to them. Compared with steel, it is very little used today, especially in the United States.

Bibliography

See also references following Chaps. 2, 4, 11, and 13.

ALLOYS OF IRON RESEARCH MONOGRAPHS, McGraw-Hill Book Company, Inc., New York:

"The Metal—Iron," H. E. Cleaves and J. G. Thompson, 1935.
"The Alloys of Iron and Carbon": Vol. I, "Constitution," Samuel Epstein, 1936; Vol. II, "Properties," F. T. Sisco, 1937.
"The Alloys of Iron and Silicon," E. S. Greiner, J. S. Marsh, and Bradley Stoughton, 1933.
"The Alloys of Iron and Molybdenum," J. L. Gregg, 1932.
"The Alloys of Iron and Tungsten," J. L. Gregg, 1934.
"The Alloys of Iron and Copper," J. L. Gregg and B. N. Daniloff, 1934.
"Principles of Phase Diagrams," J. S. Marsh, 1935.
"The Alloys of Iron and Chromium": Vol. I, "Low-chromium Alloys," A. B. Kinzel and Walter Crafts, 1937; Vol. II, "High-chromium Alloys," A. B. Kinzel and Russell Franks, 1940.
"The Alloys of Iron and Nickel": Vol. I, "Special-purpose Alloys," J. S. Marsh, 1938.

AMERICAN FOUNDRYMEN'S ASSOCIATION: "Alloy Cast Irons," 2d ed., Chicago, 1944.
AMERICAN SOCIETY FOR METALS: "Properties of Materials in Materials Engineering," Cleveland, Ohio, 1949.
———: "Fundamental Relations in Fracturing of Metals," Cleveland, Ohio, 1949.
AMERICAN SOCIETY FOR TESTING MATERIALS: "Symposium on High-strength Constructional Materials," Philadelphia, 1936.

Archer, R. S., J. Z. Briggs, and C. M. Loeb, Jr.; "Molybdenum Steels, Irons, Alloys," Climax Molybdenum Company, New York, 1948.

Bain, E. C.: "Functions of Alloying Elements in Steel," American Society for Metals, Cleveland, Ohio, 1939.

Battelle Memorial Institute: "The Engineering Properties of Gray Cast Iron, a Critical Bibliography of the Technical Literature," Lakeside Printing Company, Cleveland, Ohio, 1939.

Boyles, Alfred: "The Structure of Cast Iron," American Society for Metals, Cleveland, Ohio, 1947.

Crafts, W., and J. L. Lamont: "Hardenability and Steel Selection," Pitman Publishing Corp., New York, 1949.

Fielding, John: "The Ferrous Metals," Burgess Publishing Co., Minneapolis, 1938.

French, Herbert J.: "Alloy Constructional Steels," American Society for Metals, Cleveland, Ohio, 1942.

Gillett, H. W.: "Report on Behavior of Ferritic Steels at Low Temperatures," 2 vols., American Society for Testing Materials, Philadelphia, 1945.

Heindlhofer, K.: "Evaluation of Residual Stress," McGraw-Hill Book Company, Inc., New York, 1948.

Institute of Metals: "Symposium on Internal Stresses in Metals and Alloys," London, 1947.

Malleable Founders' Society: "American Malleable Iron, A Handbook," Cleveland, Ohio, 1944.

McCombs, L. F., and M. Schero: "Bibliography of Non-Metallic Inclusions in Iron and Steel," Mining & Metallurgical Advisory Boards, Carnegie Institute of Technology, Pittsburgh, 1935.

Piwowarsky, Eugen: "Hochwertiges Gusseisen," Verlag Julius Springer, Berlin, 1942.

Robinson, W. J., and associates: "Alloys for Use at High Temperatures," Mapleton House, Brooklyn, 1948.

Sauveur, Albert: "The Metallography and Heat-treatment of Iron and Steel," 4th ed., McGraw-Hill Book Company, Inc., New York, 1935.

Simons, E. N., and Edwin Gregory: "The Structure of Steel Simply Explained," Prentice-Hall, Inc., New York, 1938.

Tapsell, H. J.: "Creep of Metals," Oxford University Press, New York, 1931.

Thum, E.: "The Book of Stainless Steels," 2d ed., American Society for Metals, Cleveland, Ohio, 1935.

Timken Roller Bearing Company: "Timken's Digest of Steels," Canton, Ohio, 1946.

Zapffe, C. A.: "A Brief History of Alloy Steel," American Society for Metals, Cleveland, Ohio, 1948.

———: "Stainless Steels," American Society for Metals, Cleveland, Ohio, 1949.

CHAPTER 10

PROPERTIES AND USES OF NONFERROUS METALS

The nonferrous metals and their alloys embrace all the metallic materials except iron and the alloys in which iron is the principal component. The aggregate annual tonnage of all the nonferrous metals combined is only about 5 per cent of the production of steel, but their total value is about half that of steel. The nonferrous metals and alloys exhibit a variety of properties and applications far beyond the scope of iron and the ferrous alloys. They offer the engineer a selection of materials that greatly increases his ability to design and build for the advancement of civilization.

The most important instances in which the properties of one or more of the nonferrous metals excel those of plain carbon steel are those of corrosion resistance, electrical and thermal conductivity, lightness in weight, fusibility and infusibility, and range of chemical activity; to these are added a variety of qualities of lesser importance. Cost varies greatly among the different nonferrous metals; it is in every case considerably greater than that of plain carbon steel, but in many cases it is less than for some of the alloy steels.

A complete cataloguing of the properties of each known metal would be of interest from the scientific standpoint and useful in developing applications for some of the metals. For the purposes of this book, however, the treatment must be confined to discussion of those properties which are factors in the present commercial uses; to include others would detract attention from those important to the engineer. The discussion will indicate how the uses of the metals are dependent on their properties. It is not possible to mention all applications; space will be given chiefly to the important engineering uses.

The details found in this chapter concerning properties, fabrication, treatment, and applications are given with two objects in view. One is to acquaint the student with the principal facts of importance to users of the metals, and the other is to reinforce his knowledge of metallurgical principles by numerous examples and illustrations. The wide scope of physical, mechanical, and chemical properties found among the nonferrous metals affords an excellent opportunity for a broader understanding of metallurgy. Except for this latter purpose, inclusion of many of the details would hardly be justified in a textbook.

It is not expected that the information given in these pages will take the place of reference to more extended treatments in instances where the user of metals is confronted in practice with problems of metal selection, service, or design. Reference to the "Metals Handbook" and to literature issued by metal producers is recommended in such cases; this may need to be followed by wider search of technical literature or by consultation with technical representatives of metallurgical companies.

PART I. COPPER AND COPPER ALLOYS

Copper ranks next to iron and steel as a metal of commercial importance. It is of particular interest to the electrical engineer, since it is the material of which transmission wires and other forms of electrical conductors, including parts of dynamos, switchboards, etc., are most often made. It has the highest electrical conductivity, volume for volume, of any metal or substance except silver, and in addition it has sufficient strength for many structural purposes, is easily rolled into sheet and drawn into wire, and has great resistance to weathering.

Copper may be rated as intermediate with respect to strength and cost. Two respects in which pure copper is unsatisfactory are in casting qualities and in welding qualities; these deficiencies, however, do not apply to the principal alloys, which in general have excellent casting properties and are more readily welded than copper.

Copper

Electrical Conductivity. The electrical conductivity of copper on the volume basis is 94 per cent of that of silver, while that of the next highest metal, gold, is only 66 per cent of that of silver; the conductivity of aluminum is 57 per cent and that of iron only 16 per cent of that of silver.

These figures refer to conductivity as usually expressed, *viz.*, the conducting power of a unit length per unit of cross-sectional area; they do not take into consideration the specific gravity, which is a factor in the conducting power of a given weight of metal. Since conductors are sold by the pound, a useful measure of conductivity from the engineering standpoint is the conducting power of a unit weight drawn to unit length. On this basis, with the lengths being equal, a pound of light metal will make a conductor of greater cross section—and therefore of relatively greater conductance—than a pound of heavy metal. This sort of conductivity is called "mass conductivity," to distinguish it from the more commonly stated volumetric conductivity. Actual figures may make the distinction more clear:

The standard[1] volumetric resistivity of copper is 0.017241 ohm for a length of 1 m with a cross section of 1 sq mm at 20°C (68°F) (or 0.00000-17241 ohm per cm³).[2]

The standard mass resistivity of copper is 0.15328 ohm for a length of 1 m weighing 1 g, at 20°C. This unit of resistivity is commonly stated as the "ohm (meter, gram)."

Another way of expressing volumetric resistivity frequently used in engineering practice is in "ohms (mil, foot)," meaning the resistance of a wire of circular cross section 1 ft in length and 1 mil in diameter (1 mil = 0.001 in.). The resistivity of copper in this unit is 9.529 ohms (mil, foot) at 0°C.[3]

Here the *conductivity* of copper has been discussed, but the *resistivity* has been stated. This is following the usual custom. Direct measurements are made of resistance and are recorded in ohms; the conductance is simply the reciprocal of the resistance, and the conductivity (or specific conductance) is the reciprocal of the resistivity (or specific resistance). The total resistance R is the resistivity r multiplied by the length l and divided by the cross-sectional area s: $R = r(l/s)$.

The resistivity of metals varies appreciably with the temperature, increasing with rise of temperature. The average increase of resistance for copper between 0 and 100°C (32 and 212°F) is 0.42 per cent of itself for each rise of 1°C. It is close to this figure for nearly all pure metals.

The mass conductivity of copper is surpassed by that of some of the light metals, notably aluminum, the mass conductivity of which is twice that of copper, though its volumetric conductivity is only three-fifths as great. The practical bearing of this fact is discussed under Aluminum, where aluminum and copper are compared as conductors (see page 283).

The standard mass conductivity quoted above is used as a basis for the commercial rating of copper as to conductivity, a value of 100 being assigned to the above standard and other conductivities designated in percentage thereof. The standard is often referred to as the IACS (International Annealed Copper Standard). The purest commercial electrolytic copper made today has a conductivity of about 102 on this basis, and most of the copper sold averages between 100 and 101.

---

[1] As adopted by the International Electrotechnical Commission, 1913; also standard specifications of the American Standards Association and the American Society for Testing Materials. Commercial copper surpasses this standard.

[2] By centimeter cube is meant a cubic section measuring 1 cm in each dimension (1 by 1 by 1 cm). It must not be confused with a "cubic centimeter," of which only the *product* of the three dimensions is equal to 1 cc. A section 1,000 cm long by 0.001 cm wide by 1 cm high would be a cubic centimeter, but its resistance would be 1,000,000 times that of a centimeter cube.

[3] 10.371 ohms (mil, foot) at 20°C.

The conductivity standards which have just been given apply to copper in the unstrained (annealed) condition. Cold work increases strength and decreases conductivity, the difference between the hard and soft conditions being about 3 per cent in the case of copper, as shown in Fig. 139.

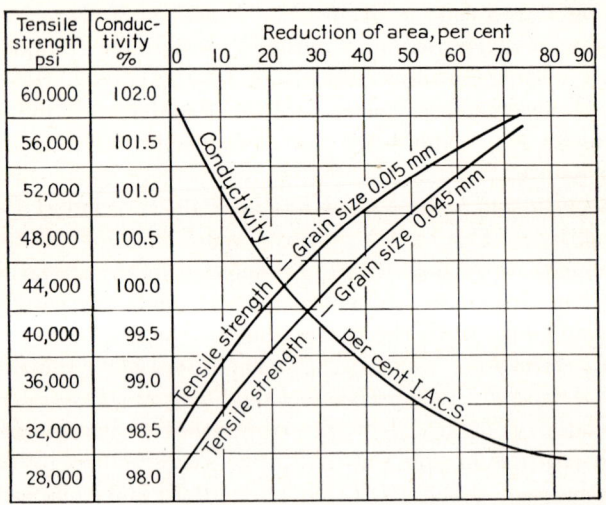

Tensile strength psi	Conductivity %
60,000	102.0
56,000	101.5
52,000	101.0
48,000	100.5
44,000	100.0
40,000	99.5
36,000	99.0
32,000	98.5
28,000	98.0

FIG. 139. Effect of cold work on the conductivity of tough-pitch copper [data of D. K. Crampton, H. L. Burghoff, and J. T. Stacy, *Trans. Am. Inst. Mining Met. Engrs.*, vol. 143, p. 228 (1941)] and on the tensile strength of tough-pitch copper annealed to two different grain sizes (figures of R. A. Wilkins and E. S. Bunn, "Copper and Copper Base Alloys," McGraw-Hill Book Company, Inc., 1943). Conductivity specimens, wire of 0.204 in. diameter annealed and then drawn to several reductions of area. Tensile specimens, strip 0.040 in. thick annealed and then rolled to several reductions of area.

Color and Corrosion. Copper and gold are the only two pure metals having a distinctively characteristic color. The color of copper is of some importance from an artistic standpoint in its uses for building and ornamental purposes. The surface of copper, unless it is kept polished, varies in color owing to the presence of a thin coating of some copper compound, usually one of the following or a mixture thereof:

1. Cuprous oxide (Cu_2O), a red substance, a thin film of which imparts a vivid coloring to the surface of ingots and castings when cooled in water from a red heat.

2. Cupric oxide (CuO), the black oxide, which forms when hot copper cools slowly in air, so that there is opportunity for the full degree of oxidation.

3. Hydrated copper carbonate and basic copper sulfate. The green substance which forms on copper exposed to weathering usually contains both of these. Its formation is analogous to the "rusting" of iron, but

there is an important difference: rusting may continue indefinitely, eating in toward the center of the iron or steel object until the whole may be converted into a crumbling mass of hydrated oxide, whereas with copper the action does not progress, but the surface coating protects the copper underneath from further attack. The resistance of copper to corrosion is one of its most valuable characteristics.

The color of copper may be altered by alloying with other metals. As zinc is added, forming different grades of brass, the color varies through shades of red to yellow. Only 25 per cent of nickel added to copper causes the salmon tint to disappear completely. Bronzes of various colors result from alloying copper with tin and other metals.

Malleability and Ductility. In malleability, copper is definitely surpassed only by gold and silver, among the common metals, and in ductility copper also ranks high. As a result copper wire and sheets may be made without trouble from cracking, and at relatively small expenditure for power and wear and tear of machinery.

Tensile Properties. Copper ranks high among pure unalloyed metals in tensile strength. It falls far short of the position of steel, however, and in general, copper in common with other pure metals—as distinct from alloys—is not sufficiently strong for structural purposes where considerable loads must be borne. Like most other metals, copper is strengthened by cold working, and in copper the change which is possible is great. The use of pure copper which probably calls for the maximum service in respect to strength is for electric transmission wires. Here the wire must support the weight of considerable lengths of itself—the length between poles spaced at suitable intervals—together with a liberal allowance for wind pressure and weight of ice and snow that may cling to it. Soft-drawn (or fully annealed) copper wire would not be equal to the demand so placed upon it unless the distances between supports were made very short. Hard-drawn copper wire, however, is suitably strong for this purpose, and in fact, it is common to use partially annealed (medium-drawn) wire for such conductors.

For large conductors used for distance transmission the requisite current-carrying capacity and also the requisite mechanical strength are obtained by stranding the wires into a cable. A $1\frac{1}{2}$-in. cable, for example, would commonly be made up of 127 stranded wires. When greater strength is necessary than can be obtained from copper alone, copper-clad steel wire is used, particularly for high voltages, where most of the conduction is in the outer section of the wire. Copper-clad steel wire commonly has a conductivity of 30 to 40 per cent of that of pure copper wire.

Actual figures will show the extent of the possible increase of strength of copper through working. The ultimate strength of cast copper is about 24,000 psi, while that of hard-drawn copper wire may be at least 67,000 psi. Hot-rolled sheet and annealed copper have tensile strengths of 30,000 to 38,000 psi, with a yield strength of 10,000 psi, elongation of 45 per cent in 2 in., and reduction of area of 50 to 70 per cent.

This effect of cold working is shown in Fig. 139. Copper can also be strengthened and hardened by the addition of other elements. This question is discussed under the effect of impurities on copper (page 249) and under copper alloys (page 254).

Hardness. The Brinell hardness of cast copper is about 35; it may be raised to 100 by cold working. Some of the ancient copper tools which have been unearthed are very hard because of the presence of impurities together with the cold working that was practiced in their making. This fact has given rise to speculation as to a "lost art of tempering copper," but it is safe to say that no such art ever existed beyond the possibilities that are known today. Copper is little hardened by quenching or other heat-treatment, but some heat-treated copper alloys are now used. Copper tools are often made of beryllium copper (see page 266).

Toughness. Copper is known as an exceedingly tough metal. Large pieces of copper cannot be shattered by blast, and heavy plates of the metal are sometimes used for protection against possible explosions, as in safes, for example. The fact that the elastic limit of copper is only about 50 per cent of its ultimate strength indicates its toughness.

Marketed Forms. Copper marketed in the United States is of three grades, electrolytic, lake, and fire-refined, about 90 per cent being electrolytic. Lake copper is discussed on page 389. Fire-refined copper is made mostly from remelted scrap and may be sold as "casting copper"; the total amount sold in this form is small because of its lower purity. Electrolytically refined copper is obtained from the refining tanks as cathodes having a purity of 99.98 per cent. Because of their inconvenient shape, only a small percentage of the cathodes are sold directly. Most are melted and cast into shapes suitable for fabrication. More than half is cast into wirebars for manufacture of copper wire. After casting the purity is about 99.94 per cent. Other shapes are cakes for rolling into sheet, billets for manufacture of tubing, and ingots and ingot bars for remelting to make copper alloys.

Formerly all shapes except round billets were cast in open horizontal molds, the upper surface assuming a characteristic wrinkled appearance. Vertical casting is now frequently used, especially for cakes and billets. Continuous casting of oxygen-free copper is a more recent development. In one process of this kind, a small stream of molten copper flows continuously into the top of a bottomless columnar mold, in which it solidifies and slowly descends. Sticking to the sides of the mold is prevented by rapid cooling and vibration of the mold. The billet is sawed into lengths suitable for fabrication as it emerges below the bottom of the mold.

Besides the cathode form, there are three different varieties of electrolytic copper. When melted the cathodes absorb oxygen; the variety marketed is dependent on the extent to which this oxygen is removed and the manner of removing it. The varieties are known in the industry as tough-pitch, oxygen-free, and deoxidized copper. Tough-pitch copper is so called because it is purposely cast with a small content of oxygen (about 0.03 per cent), which results in maximum density. Tough-pitch copper is the commonest variety, and market quotations for "electrolytic copper" apply to this type. If the consumer calls for oxygen-free or deoxidized copper, a slightly higher price must be paid. These two varieties will be discussed after considering the effect of impurities in copper.

Impurities and Their Effects. Conductivity, strength, ductility, and other properties of copper are greatly affected by the presence of small amounts of other elements. While the steel metallurgist commonly considers impurities in tenths or hundredths of a per cent, the copper metallurgist is concerned with thousandths or ten-thousandths of a per cent. Sulfur in electrolytic copper should be as low as 0.002 per cent; this result must be reached with sulfide copper ores containing often as much as 40 per cent sulfur, and in spite of the fact that the affinity of sulfur for copper is greater than it is for iron.

Impurities in copper may be divided into two main classes with respect to their mode of occurrence in the copper:

1. Elements which are dissolved in the copper in solid solution. When an element of this kind is present, the metal is no longer made up of crystals of pure copper, but is composed of crystals of a solid solution differing from pure copper. Such elements usually have a bad effect in lowering conductivity, but have a beneficial effect on hardness and strength. The most important impurities found in this class are arsenic, antimony, nickel, iron, phosphorus, aluminum, and silicon. Silver also is in this class, but its effect is small; only a slight lowering of conductivity becomes detectable when the content of silver approaches 0.03 per cent. Each 0.001 per cent antimony (as an example) lowers the conductivity of oxygen-free copper by 0.16 per cent IACS. For tough-pitch copper the effect of antimony is somewhat less than half as great, because some of the oxygen combines with antimony to form insoluble antimony oxide.

The solid-solution elements also raise the recrystallization or "softening" temperature of copper. Small percentages of silver or arsenic may be added to copper to cause it to retain its hardness and strength at elevated temperature. Addition of 0.03 per cent silver causes the softening temperature of copper to rise by 140 to 300°C (250 to 540°F).

2. Elements that are insoluble in solid copper. These separate as the copper solidifies and form between the crystals of copper. They have relatively little effect on conductivity; the metal is still composed of

crystals of pure copper, and the small amount of foreign matter between the crystals does not reduce the conductivity greatly, but it does weaken the metal, often to an important degree. The chief impurities in this class are lead, bismuth, selenium, tellurium, and sulfur, the last three being combined as Cu_2Se, Cu_2Te, and Cu_2S; also oxides or nonmetallic impurities may be found.

Oxygen is present in tough-pitch copper in much larger percentage than any other foreign element, and its effects are important. Oxygen combines with copper to form Cu_2O, which, as shown in the micrograph, Fig. 140, is found in the grain boundaries. This tends to weaken the metal, though not appreciably unless too much is present. Its effect

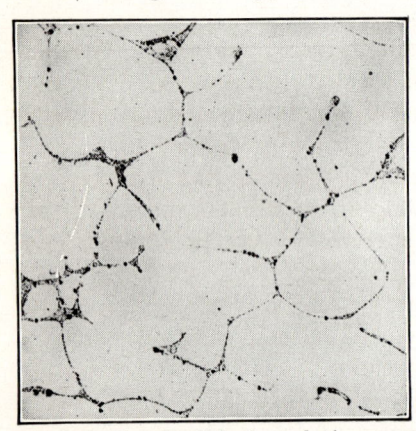

Fig. 140. Tough-pitch electrolytic copper as cast, showing oxygen occurring in the form of Cu_2O-Cu eutectic between grains of virtually pure copper.

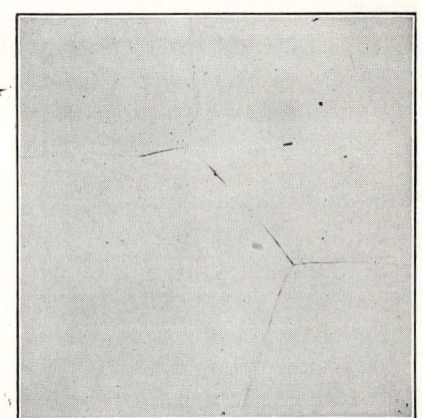

Fig. 141. Oxygen-free copper as cast (OFHC). Both magnifications 100 ×.

on conductivity depends on the other elements present, and usually oxygen up to a certain point has a beneficial effect on the conductivity, as noted above with respect to antimony. Of itself, the presence of Cu_2O, which would account for most of the oxygen in commercial copper, slightly decreases the conductivity in the manner of the elements in class 2.

The effect of various elements on the conductivity of copper is greatly complicated by the effect of one impurity on another.

A typical analysis of wirebar copper is shown in the accompanying list.

	Per cent		Per cent
Copper	99.94	Lead	0.001
Oxygen	0.035	Antimony	0.001
Iron	0.003	Silver	0.001
Nickel	0.002	Arsenic	0.001
Sulfur	0.002	Selenium, tellurium, gold, bismuth	Trace

Oxygen-free and Deoxidized Copper. Copper can be deoxidized by addition of small amounts of an element having a higher affinity for oxygen, such as phosphorus, silicon, manganese, or boron, after the manner of deoxidizing steel with ferroalloys or aluminum. When this is done, a small residue of the deoxidizing element is usually retained in the copper, and unless the residue is very low, a pronounced drop in conductivity results, so that the metal cannot meet electrical specifications.

Oxygen can also be eliminated from copper by means of carbon or reducing gases that are not absorbed by copper. This method produces oxygen-free copper as low in other impurities as is tough-pitch copper and, consequently, suitable for electrical uses.

While either method of removing oxygen results in copper that is free from oxygen, the industry commonly uses the term "deoxidized copper" for metal made by adding a deoxidizing element and the term "oxygen-free copper" for high-conductivity material made by deoxidation with carbon or a reducing gas.

Another kind of oxygen-free copper, called "coalesced copper," is made by compressing particles of a special cathode copper into briquettes, followed by sintering in a reducing atmosphere and extruding into a bar having the normal density of copper.

In making deoxidized copper, phosphorus is most often employed, and the product may be called "phosphorized copper." The phosphorus is added in the form of an alloy called "phosphor copper," containing about 10 or 15 per cent phosphorus. Similarly, manganese copper, silicon copper, etc., analogous to ferroalloys, may be used either as deoxidizers or to incorporate certain elements in making copper alloys.

The conductivity of oxygen-free copper may slightly surpass that of tough-pitch copper; more often it is slightly lower, but easily meets electrical specifications. Because it has no regular advantage in conductivity, and is of slightly higher cost, it is not often used for ordinary electrical purposes.

The principal advantages of oxygen-free or of deoxidized copper as compared with tough-pitch are (1) even greater ductility, so that it is better for operations requiring severe cold work, and (2) the ability to be annealed in a reducing atmosphere without becoming porous through reduction of copper oxide. This type of annealing is often desired in order to preserve a bright, unoxidized surface. Its effect on tough-pitch copper is shown in Fig. 142.

Shaping and Fabrication. Because of its poor casting qualities, and especially porosity due to release of gases from the metal when it solidifies, pure copper is not often used for castings. It is used for castings requiring high thermal conductivity, such as blast-furnace tuyères, and for motor rotors and other centrifugal castings. The various copper casting alloys have excellent casting qualities. Most of the pure copper used is cast into regular shapes which then go through the rolling mill. Extrusion, forging and pressing, piercing of billets for drawing into seamless tubes, and other working operations are also used. Both hot and cold working are extensively employed on tough-pitch, oxygen-free, and deoxidized copper. Hot-working temperatures are 700 to 900°C (1290 to 1650°F), the most suitable temperatures varying somewhat with the type of operation.

Rolling. Before rolling, the cakes or wirebars must be carefully inspected and imperfections in the surface chipped out. The copper

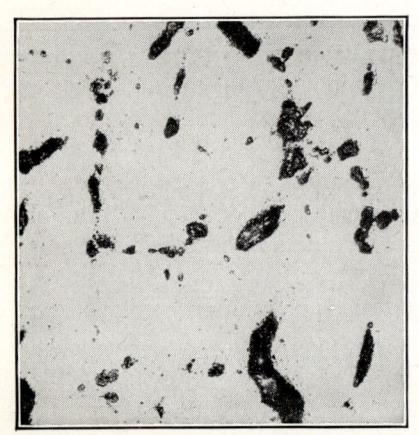

FIG. 142. Tough-pitch copper after working and heating in hydrogen. Shows porosity due to reduction of Cu_2O.

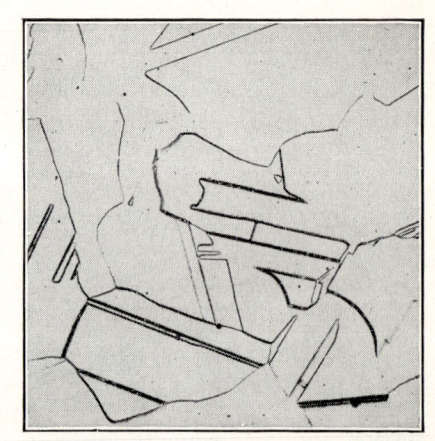

FIG. 143. Oxygen-free copper (OFHC) after working and heating in hydrogen. The above magnifications 100 ×.

Figures 140 and 141 etched with ammoniacal hydrogen peroxide. Figure 143 etched with potassium dichromate plus sulfuric acid. Figure 142 etched successively with each reagent. (*Courtesy of American Metal Company, Ltd.*)

is then heated and goes to the roughing mill, where it receives six or more passes. It then goes to the intermediate and finally to a train of finishing rolls. If the product is copper rod, this passes from the finishing mill to a machine which winds it into a coil. The rod is black from a surface coating of CuO, and this is removed by pickling, *i.e.*, placing the coils in dilute sulfuric acid.

Copper sheets are commonly rolled in five degrees of temper ranging from "hard" to "soft," with the intermediate tempers designated as ¾H, ½H, and ¼H. The required temper is obtained from a proportioned amount of reduction in cold rolling or by annealing.

Wire Drawing. For making wire, copper wirebars are first rolled to rod, which is then drawn through a series of dies, decreasing its diameter in successive steps. The dies are usually made of chromium-plated steel or sintered tungsten carbide containing tapered holes ground to exact size. Diamond dies may be used for fine wire. The larger sizes of rods may be taken through one die in a single drawing, but with smaller sizes the wire may pass through several dies in one drawing. All the drawing is done cold. The cold work so affects the metal, however, that for most purposes the wire must be annealed. When annealed at the end of the drawing operation, the wire has the maximum electrical conductivity but the lowest tensile strength and is termed *soft-drawn* wire. *Medium-drawn* wire is made by annealing after reduction to a certain point and then drawing to final size, the size at which the annealing is done being proportioned to the degree of hardness desired in the finished wire. Wire that is not annealed at all is termed *hard-drawn;* it has the maximum strength and the lowest conductivity.

Wire desired in extra long lengths is drawn from rods joined together, before drawing, by welding or by brazing with a silver solder.

Machinability. Owing to the relative toughness of copper, it is difficult to machine. By the addition of about 0.5 per cent tellurium, the machinability is improved to an extent approaching that of free-machining brass. The electrical conductivity is reduced by the tellurium addition to about 10 per cent less than that of pure copper. Tellurium copper may be extensively hot- and cold-worked, although at ordinary temperatures it is somewhat less plastic than pure copper.

Specifications. Many specifications for copper and copper-alloy products have been written and published by the American Society for Testing Materials. All these are periodically reviewed and are revised as may be required from time to time so that they reflect currently available material.[1] Specifications are given for wirebars and other shapes, and also for hard-drawn, medium-drawn, and soft copper wire. The latter include resistivity, departure from nominal dimensions, and a table of tensile strength and elongation for wire of different diameters, which shows the marked effects of mechanical work and annealing on the strength and ductility of copper.

Uses of Copper. The largest use of copper is for electrical purposes, and next is its use in making brass. Its use as a building material for roofing, water spouts, store fronts, screens, etc., is increasing, due to its permanency and appearance. An association of American companies[2] is actively engaged in promoting the use of copper and its alloys, particularly stressing the advantages for building purposes. Much copper tube is used in electric refrigerators, in air conditioning, and for water

---

[1] See "A.S.T.M. Standards," 1952, Part 2, and other volumes, issued triennially, with supplements in the intervening years.

[2] The Copper & Brass Research Association, New York.

pipe. In time of war the demand for copper grows enormously. It is required especially for making cartridge brass and shell bands, and great tonnages are used also in parts of naval vessels, automobiles, trucks, and tanks, and in wire and radios for field communication.

The ability to improve the properties and service characteristics of metals by combining or alloying them has led to a constantly growing number and variety of alloys, and many of the metals are used to larger extent in alloyed than in unalloyed form. Because of the predominance of electrical uses, copper is used more as the pure metal than in the form of alloys. Electrical conductivity is at a maximum in the pure metal. Corrosion resistance may be either improved or lowered by alloying. Of the copper used in the United States at present, about two-thirds is used in the form of pure copper and one-third in brass and other alloys.

The automobile industry is one of the largest consumers of copper, normally taking about 10 per cent of the total amount used. Electrical uses include motors and generators, switchboards, electric locomotives, telephones and telegraphs, light and power lines, in alloys such as brass for light bulbs and sockets, and many others.

Copper Alloys

Brass and bronze, probably the first alloys intentionally made by man, constitute one of the principal branches of the metal industry. The varieties of these, as well as of other copper alloys, are many and are still increasing.

The principal classes of copper alloys with respect to composition are the following:

Copper-zinc (binary brasses)
Copper-tin (binary bronzes)
Copper-zinc-tin (special brasses and bronzes)
Copper-zinc-lead and copper-tin-zinc-lead (leaded brasses and bronzes)
Copper-zinc-nickel (nickel silvers)
Copper-zinc-manganese plus tin, iron, aluminum (manganese bronzes)
Copper-tin-phosphorus (phosphor bronze)
Copper-aluminum and copper-aluminum plus iron, nickel, or manganese (aluminum bronzes)
Copper-silicon plus manganese, tin, iron, or zinc (silicon bronzes)
Copper-nickel (cupronickel)
Copper-beryllium and copper-cobalt-beryllium (beryllium copper)

Other elements may be added to some of the above combinations to form other alloy brasses and bronzes.

The properties of some of the alloys are such that they are used chiefly or exclusively for castings, while others are used chiefly or exclusively in wrought form. Table 25 gives the compositions of the more important alloys. Some of the names cover a group of varying compositions within

TABLE 25. PRINCIPAL COPPER-BASE ALLOYS
(Composition, per cent)

Wrought alloys

Name or designation	Cu	Sn	Pb	Zn	Ni	Fe	Mn	Al	Others
Gilding metal	95			5					
Commercial bronze[1]	90			10					
Red brass	85			15					
Low brass	80			20					
Cartridge brass	70			30					
High brass[1]	66			34					
Yellow brass[1]	65			35					
Muntz metal	60			40					
Forging brass	60		2	38					
Free-cutting brass	62		3	35					
Admiralty metal	71	1		28					
Naval brass[1]	60	0.75		39					
Manganese bronze	58	1		39		1.4	0.1		
Aluminum brass	76			22				2	
Phosphor bronze[1]	90–98.7	1.25–10							P 0.03–0.35
Nickel silver, 18%	55–65			17–27	16–20	0–1.6	0–1.5		Si 1.5–3.75
Silicon bronze	95–98	0–0.75		0–1.75	0–0.6	0–4	0–1		Si 0–2.25
Aluminum bronze	78–92	0–0.4		0–1.4	0–0.7			4–13.5	
Beryllium copper	97–98				0–0.35				Be 1.60–2.00, Co 0–0.25
Cupronickel	70–80				20–30				
Constantan	55				45				

Casting alloys

Name or designation	Cu	Sn	Pb	Zn	Ni	Fe	Mn	Al	Others
Leaded tin bronze	86–88	6–8	1.5	4.5					
High-leaded tin bronze	70–85	5–10	7–25	0–3					
88–10–2 or "G" bronze	88	10		2					
88–8–4 or modified "G" bronze	88	8		4					
85–5–5–5 (ounce metal or composition metal)	85	5	5	5					
Commercial red brass	83	4	6	7					
Valve composition	81	3	7	9					
Leaded yellow brass	62–72	0–2	0.75–3.75	24–37					
High-strength yellow brass or high-strength manganese bronze	58–62	2–5		26–39	12–25	2–4	2.5–5	3–7.5	
Nickel silver	57–66		1–11	2–20	0–5	0–1	0–1.25		
Silicon bronze	89–94	0–1		0–5		1–5			Si 3.5–5
Aluminum bronze	79–89							9–11	

[1] Also leaded varieties, with various percentages of lead. Some are used for casting as well as wrought alloys.

limits as indicated in the table. In addition to the essential components, as listed, all the alloys may contain small percentages of impurities, limits for which are given in standard specifications.

Brass. Binary brasses may be classified as follows:

1. According to zinc content: "low brass" and "high brass." These terms, as well as the terms "red" and "yellow" noted below, may be used in a general sense covering ranges of composition, but in American industry they have also come to be applied specifically to certain alloys. Thus, specifically in the trade the term "low brass" is applied to brass containing 20 per cent zinc and "high brass" to brass containing approximately 34 per cent zinc. The last-named is used more than any other one composition and is often called "common high brass."

2. According to color: "red brass," "yellow brass," and "white brass." As zinc is added to copper, the characteristic copper color is progressively lost. The red color predominates up to about 20 per cent zinc. The term "red brass" is applied to the same alloys as the term "low brass," but in the trade is applied more specifically to the 85:15 copper-zinc alloy. When additions of tin and lead have been made to these alloys, they are on the border line between brass and bronze, but are nevertheless often referred to as "red brass."

When the zinc content has reached 30 per cent, the reddish tinge has given way to a full yellow. The term "yellow brass" is applied especially to brass of 35 per cent zinc. At 40 per cent zinc, however, a reddish tinge is again found, the beta constituent being reddish. The term "white brass" refers rather indefinitely to brasses of very high zinc contents, 45 per cent or higher, but since such brasses are very brittle, they are rarely used. "White brass" may scarcely be regarded as a commercial alloy, and the material is not often encountered.

3. According to metallographic constituents: alpha, alpha plus beta, and beta brass. From the copper-zinc constitution diagram, Fig. 144, it is seen that all copper-zinc alloys up to 39 per cent zinc, under conditions of equilibrium at 453°C (847°F), are composed entirely of alpha solid solution. At lower temperatures the solubility of zinc in solid copper decreases, perhaps to as low as 35 per cent at room temperature. These solid solutions are called "alpha brass," and they include most of the industrial brasses. Above 39 per cent zinc at 453°C some of the beta constituent begins to appear, the alpha-plus-beta range extending from 39 to about 46 per cent zinc. From 46 to 50 per cent zinc, the brass may be composed wholly of beta; such brasses, as noted above, are outside the range of commercial alloys.

The percentages just stated apply to conditions of equilibrium. Actually equilibrium in the copper-zinc alloys is not reached under ordinary heating and cooling, and the beta constituent, which, as shown in Fig.

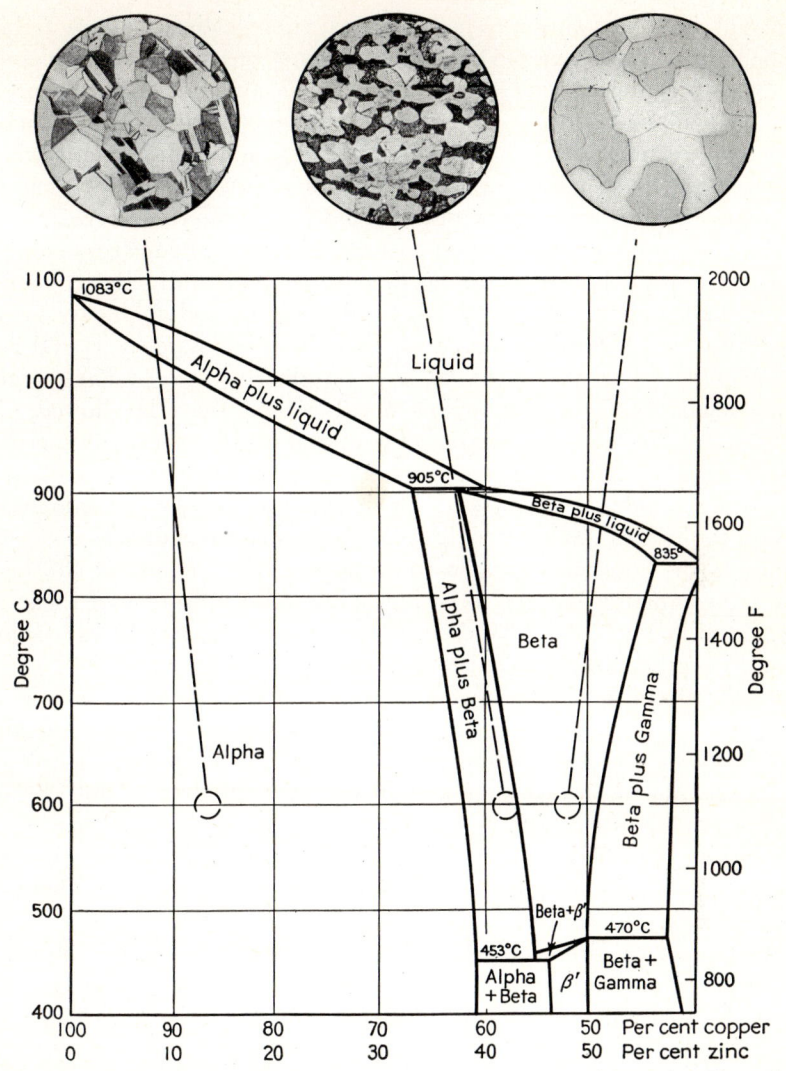

FIG. 144. Copper-zinc constitution diagram at the copper-rich end. The alloys below 45 per cent zinc are commercial brasses. The micrographs show the characteristic structures of the three types, alpha, alpha plus beta, and beta. Magnification 75 ×. (*Courtesy of Bridgeport Brass Company.*)

144, begins to form at 905°C (1661°F), in the alloys of 32.5 per cent zinc, is often found at room temperature in alloys of 35 per cent zinc, and sometimes at lower percentages, after ordinary rates of cooling. These stated percentages may also be altered somewhat by the presence of added elements or impurities. Beta is usually not present in common high brass, especially after cold working and annealing.

The alpha solid solution (a face-centered cubic lattice) is characterized by being readily cold-worked. The beta constituent is also a solid solution (body centered); it is harder than alpha and can only be worked hot. The alpha-beta brasses of the lower zinc contents may be worked cold but are more often hot-worked. The gamma constituent, which begins to appear above 49 per cent zinc, is very hard and brittle; it cannot be worked hot or cold, and is not present in commercial alloys.

The normal boiling point of zinc (905°C) is below the melting point of copper (1083°C, 1981°F). In making brass industrially the copper is melted first and the zinc is added, causing it to dissolve quickly before much of it can volatilize. Even so, there is some loss of zinc, and it is not possible to arrive exactly at a given zinc content. Consequently some departure from nominal chemical compositions is allowed. In specifications for copper-zinc alloys the copper content is usually specified over a range of 2 to 3 per cent; then after specifying the percentages of any other added elements and maximum permissible percentages of certain impurities, the zinc content is specified as "remainder."

Effects of Additions of Zinc to Copper. The important effects of zinc are summarized in the following paragraphs, and some of them are illustrated in Fig. 145. The exact shape of such graphs will vary somewhat with grain size, impurities, etc.

Tensile strength increases with increasing zinc content up to a maximum at about 40 per cent zinc. The amount of possible work-hardening also increases with zinc content, so that the gain in hardness and strength due to zinc is considerably greater in cold-worked than in hot-worked, cast, or annealed material.

Ductility (which in many metals varies inversely with tensile strength) also increases with zinc content, but reaches a maximum at about 30 per cent zinc.

The casting qualities are greatly improved; these are further improved by addition of other elements, and the plain binary brasses are not generally used for castings. Welding qualities also become satisfactory. Corrosion resistance, excellent in pure copper, is little affected up to 20 per cent zinc. Thereafter it begins to fall off, and declines sharply when the beta constituent appears.

Copper is difficult to machine because of its toughness. Machinability improves with increasing zinc content, but lead is added to brass to secure good machinability.

Cost becomes lower, since the price of zinc is less than that of copper.

Electrical conductivity falls rapidly and is seriously lowered even by small amounts of zinc.

Fabrication and Uses of Brass. Brass is shaped by nearly all methods. All the binary and most of the alloy brasses are readily cold-worked

PROPERTIES AND USES OF NONFERROUS METALS 259

except those of very high zinc contents. The common brasses of intermediate to low zinc, however, are less easily hot-worked, but hot working is now used on some compositions for which the method was formerly regarded as unsuitable. Hot working of such brasses is made possible by using zinc of the highest purity in their manufacture and employing close temperature control. Casting is done by all methods, including some die casting. Rolling, pressing, forging, extrusion, wire drawing,

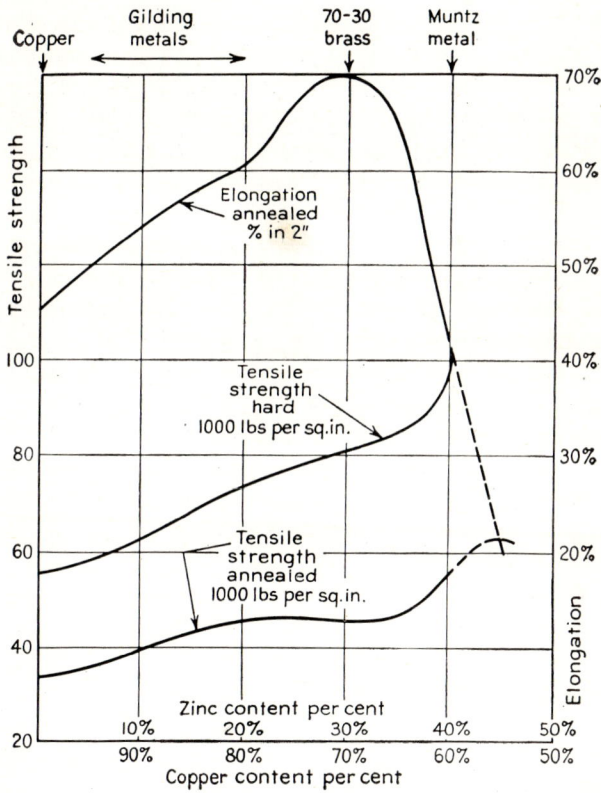

Fig. 145. Effect of increasing zinc content on the mechanical properties of copper-zinc alloys. (*Courtesy of Revere Copper and Brass, Inc.*)

deep drawing, and stamping are employed. Seamless tubes are made by hot piercing cylindrical billets longitudinally, followed by cold drawing through a die and over a mandrel. They are also made by casting, extrusion, and cupping processes.

Grain size is an important consideration in wrought brasses. Large grain size results in higher ductility, but causes the surface to roughen during working and makes it difficult to polish. The initial size of the grain before fabricating operations is controlled by the temperature and time of annealing after partial reduction. Material having average grain diameters of 0.010 to 0.150 mm is regularly supplied by the brass mills. Grain sizes below 0.030 mm are used for operations requiring relatively little forming and in which a high surface finish is desired. Sizes from 0.030 to 0.050 mm permit more severe cold work, and a

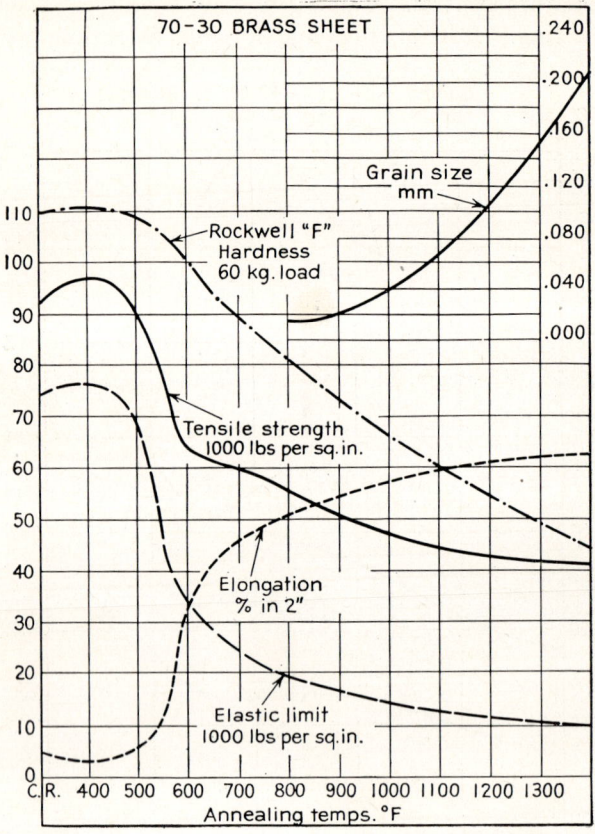

Fig. 146. Annealing curves of 70:30 brass sheet. (*Courtesy of Revere Copper and Brass, Inc.*)

satisfactory polish can be obtained; these are most commonly used. Sizes above 0.050 mm are used for heavy drawing and spinning when the surface finish is not important. Deep drawing of material having too large a grain results in an "orange-peel" effect on the surface.

Different grain sizes in the 70:30 copper-zinc alloy are shown in Fig. 147.[1]

The important uses of brass include gears, propellers, steam fittings, tubing, noncorroding castings, valves and valve stems, engine parts,

[1] "ASTM Standards," 1949, Part 2, p. 1088.

FIG. 147. Micrographs of annealed 70:30 copper-zinc alloy of different grain sizes. Magnification 75 ×. Etched with ammoniacal hydrogen peroxide. These micrographs are selected from a set of 10 ranging from average grain diameters of 0.010 to 0.200 mm used as grain-size standards for the estimation of average grain of annealed materials, particularly nonferrous alloys such as brass, bronze, and nickel silver. D = diameter of average grain. (*By permission of American Society for Testing Materials.*)

pump castings, cartridges, hardware, ornaments, screws, plumbing, condenser tubes, chain, musical instruments, and numerous others.

Season Cracking and Dezincification. Some brasses are subject to two special forms of corrosion. *Season cracking* is a form of stress-corrosion, probably the first manifestation of this troublesome occurrence to come to the attention of metallurgists. It is chiefly intergranular, resulting when cold-worked yellow brass is left with internal stress and subjected to even very mildly corroding conditions, especially atmospheres containing traces of ammonia. It develops slowly, and stress, time, moisture, and the presence of ammonia are the controlling factors. It is usually preventable by a proper stress-relieving anneal at a temperature sufficient to permit crystalline readjustment but too low to cause undue softening. Annealing 30 min at 300°C (570°F) is often recommended. Although all copper alloys appear to be susceptible to season cracking, the liability increases with increasing zinc content. It often occurs in cartridge brass, but rarely in red brass and other alloys of less than 15 per cent zinc.

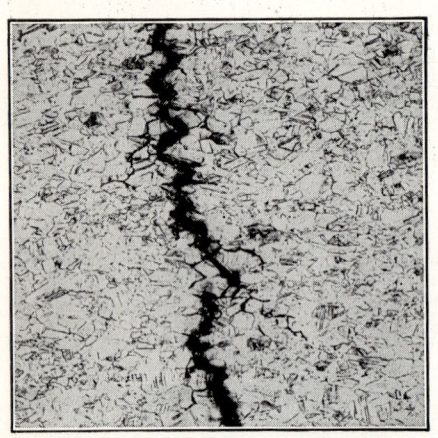

FIG. 148. Micrograph of stress-corrosion cracking (season cracking) in a brass cup. Magnification 75 ×. (*Courtesy of Bridgeport Brass Company.*)

Figure 148, a micrograph of season cracking in a brass cup, shows how the crack has occurred between the grains rather than through them.

Dezincification is a type of corrosion in brass where zinc atoms are dissolved from the solid solution preferentially to the copper atoms. It is manifested in a surface deposit of copper, underlain by porous and weakened metal. It is believed that both copper and zinc dissolve initially, the copper then being deposited as it is replaced in solution by additional zinc. Dezincification occurs in acids, acidic or salt water, and some impure or hard waters. It does not occur in low or red brass, but may be rapid in high brass.

Another kind of dezincification, especially troublesome in processing thin sections, may occur during annealing through vaporization of zinc from the surface because of its relatively high vapor pressure as compared with copper. It may be combatted by using a furnace atmosphere that will form a surface skin through which zinc does not easily diffuse.

Varieties of Brass. *Cartridge brass* is the nominal 70:30 composition when made from high-grade copper and zinc, so as to meet the ductility requirements necessary for severe cold-working operations such as used in the manufacture of cartridge cases. This composition has the maximum ductility and not far from the maximum strength for binary brass. The steps in the cold-drawing process for cartridge manufacture are shown in Fig. 24, page 80.

Admiralty brass or *admiralty metal* approximates the 70:30 alloy with the addition of 1 per cent tin. The tin increases soundness in casting and enhances corrosion resistance, particularly in salt water.

Muntz metal is the nominal 60:40 composition. It has the maximum strength for binary brass. It contains some of the beta constituent, which lowers its ductility and resistance to corrosion, but it retains sufficient ductility to be readily cold-workable, and it has excellent hot-working qualities.

Naval brass is the 60:39 alloy plus 0.75 per cent tin.

Leaded brass. Although lead is partly soluble in liquid copper, it is almost entirely insoluble in solid copper. The particles of free lead in the solidified alloy render it both hot short and cold short, so that it is workable only with care. At the same time the machinability is markedly improved, and addition of 0.75 up to several per cent of lead is often made to various cast brasses (and bronzes) to confer "free-cutting" qualities. Up to 2 per cent lead is sometimes used in wrought brasses.

Nickel Silver. Addition of nickel to brass results in complete discharge of the yellow color, forming a white alloy capable of taking a brilliant polish. These nickel brasses are called "nickel silver" because they resemble silver in appearance. They were formerly called "German silver." Ordinary nickel silver does not contain silver. The copper content is usually 55 to 66 per cent; the nickel content varies from 5 to 30 per cent, with 18 per cent being most common. The balance is zinc, except that in some cases 1 per cent lead is added for machinability. Besides the qualities of whiteness and luster, nickel silver is notable for superior corrosion resistance. Hardness and strength are also increased, and while there is some loss of ductility, the alloys are readily cold-worked. They are used for many purposes where the slightly higher cost is justified, especially architectural and ornamental applications, as a base for silver-plated tableware, jewelry, marine fittings, soda-fountain equipment, keys, and parts of instruments or other apparatus.

Manganese Bronze. Manganese bronze is a copper alloy of considerable variability in composition and properties. Of the three principal varieties, the one used in wrought form is in reality a 60:40 brass with small additions of tin and iron (not over 2 per cent of each) and just enough manganese thoroughly to deoxidize the melt, leaving only 0.10 to 0.50 per cent in the metal.

The original manganese bronze was a true bronze in that it contained tin, together with some iron and manganese.

A third type is now generally used for castings. It is called "high-tensile manganese bronze," "manganese-aluminum bronze," or "high-strength yellow brass." It usually contains no tin, but has 2.5 to 5 per cent manganese, 2 to 4 per cent iron, and 3 to 7.5 per cent aluminum. This variety exhibits very high tensile strength (90,000 to 110,000 psi) without heat-treatment.

In general, manganese bronzes are characterized by strength with lowered ductility and fair to good corrosion resistance. Some types are subject to season cracking. The cast varieties have high shrinkage. The wrought variety is usually hot-worked. Uses include propeller blades, pumps, valves, worms, gears, and high-strength cast engine parts and frames.

Bronze. The term *bronze* without other qualifications denotes a copper-tin alloy. Special bronzes may be made either (1) by addition of one or more other elements to the copper-tin system (phosphor bronze, nickel bronze, ternary tin-zinc bronzes) or (2) by substitution of a different element or elements for tin (aluminum bronze, silicon bronze).

Binary Tin Bronze. Copper dissolves tin to form alpha solid solution up to a maximum of 16 per cent at elevated temperatures. On cooling, there is separation of a compound Cu_3Sn, or of a similar compound called the delta constituent, leaving about 10 per cent tin in the alpha solid solution with ordinary cooling rates or as little as 5 per cent with chill casting. Tin has effects generally similar to but more pronounced than zinc, except as to color change. Hardness and strength increase more rapidly, resistance to corrosion is excellent, and casting qualities are of the highest. The alpha phase is readily worked, but beyond 10 per cent tin brittleness is increasingly evident. The alloys of more than 10 per cent tin are used only in cast form.

Ternary Tin-zinc Bronzes. The binary bronzes are used much less commonly than formerly. They have been superseded to a large extent by the ternary alloy known as "88-10-2" and especially by "88-8-4," in which the figures represent the Cu-Sn-Zn percentages. These bronzes are also given the names *gun metal, composition G,* and others. In general they provide even better qualities than the binary alloys at slightly lower cost. They are used in cast form.

Other compositions of Cu-Sn-Zn and Cu-Sn-Pb-Zn alloys are much used for castings. Perhaps the most useful of these is 85-5-5-5, a high-grade "red brass" that is easily machined. It is often called *ounce metal* or *composition metal*.

The United States "copper" cent is of bronze containing 95 per cent copper, 5 per cent tin and zinc.

Because of the high price of tin, bronze is much more expensive than brass. It is used for bearings and bushings, pumps, gears, and applications where a combination of resistance to wear and corrosion is necessary, and also for statuary and ornamental purposes.

Phosphor Bronze. Phosphor bronze is made by adding a little phosphorus (in the form of phosphor-copper) to a copper-tin melt. The phosphorus acts as a powerful deoxidizer, and the small residual phosphorus content in the alloy increases the hardness and strength. This is commonly about 0.15 per cent, but varies from 0.03 to 0.35. Different grades of phosphor bronze are designated not according to phosphorus content but according to tin percentage; the commonest grades are the 5, 8, and 10 per cent. Lead may also be added.

Phosphor bronze is one of the older copper alloys, and has maintained a high reputation for high-strength alloys, either in wrought or cast form. Tensile strength varies from 40,000 to over 120,000 psi, depending on the tin content and amount of cold work. This material is often used for springs because of resilience and fatigue resistance. Many other applications result from wear resistance, toughness, and strength. The leaded alloys make excellent bearing metals.

Aluminum Bronze. Two principal varieties of aluminum bronze are in use, together with a large number of compositions of lesser importance. Those most used are the binary copper-aluminum alloy containing 4 to 7 per cent aluminum and a complex alloy containing 7 to 11 per cent aluminum with additions of various percentages and combinations of the elements iron, nickel, and manganese. The former are wrought alloys, and the latter are used in both wrought and cast form. The binary alloys are composed of alpha solid solution up to 9.5 per cent aluminum. Above 11 per cent aluminum, increasing brittleness occurs. The 10 per cent alloy, with or without 1 per cent iron, is one of the few copper alloys heat-treated to increase hardness and strength. It may be quenched in water and then tempered by reheating. Varieties lower in aluminum and containing nickel are sometimes treated by precipitation hardening.

The aluminum bronzes are notable for high strength (comparable with manganese bronze) combined with great corrosion resistance (superior to manganese bronze), including resistance to salt-water corrosion. They are somewhat difficult to cast and machine unless proper techniques are followed. Color is also an important attribute from the decorative standpoint. This varies from pale yellow to gold, some compositions having the same appearance as pure gold.

Silicon Bronze. The silicon bronzes also are made in a variety of compositions. They usually contain about 3 per cent silicon, though larger amounts up to 5 per cent are used for added strength with sacrifice of ductility. Except for one 97:3 binary alloy, they have one or more of the additional components manganese, tin, iron, or zinc. These alloys were developed originally for the chemical industry because of their exceptional corrosion resistance in many liquids. Their applications have now extended far beyond this field. Their conductivities are exceptionally low for copper alloys, and they are notable for ease of welding. They have moderately high strength and hardness and good casting qualities. The varieties higher in copper are used as wrought alloys and those lower in copper as casting alloys. Most varieties are readily cold-worked, and nearly all can be hot-worked. They are sold under various trade names such as Everdur, Herculoy, Olympic Bronze, Duronze, P.M.G., and others.

Other Copper Alloys. *Beryllium Copper.* The addition of small amounts of beryllium to copper produces alloys remarkably responsive to heat-treatment by precipitation hardening. The percentage of beryllium contained is usually 1.60 to 2.25, this content imparting the maximum desirable properties without causing undue brittleness or difficulty in manufacture. About 0.4 per cent nickel or, more often, 0.25 per cent cobalt may be added to inhibit grain growth and improve hardening qualities. The smallness of the percentage of beryllium brings the cost within bounds, though high price is still an objection.

These alloys have outstanding hardness and strength, especially as regards resistance to wear and to fatigue (in which properties they surpass all other copper alloys), while retaining the corrosion resistance of copper and having good ductility and fair conductivity. They are especially valuable for making hard corrosion-resistant tools and parts of apparatus, also for springs, especially in instruments where a nonmagnetic spring is needed.

Typical procedure in heat-treatment is as follows: The alloy is first heated to about 775°C (1425°F) and then quenched in cold water. Quenching prevents decomposition of the alpha solid solution and yields a cold-workable material which is then rolled, drawn, etc., as desired. Before working, the 2.00 per cent alloy has a tensile strength of 70,000 psi, compared with 33,000 for pure copper. A 38 per cent reduction by rolling will raise this to 118,000 psi for 0.05-in. gage sheet. After the forming operations are finished, the alloy is heated to 315 to 400°C (600 to 750°F), causing partial precipitation of another crystalline phase. This increases the tensile strength to 193,000 psi. The particles causing the precipitation hardening are probably too small to be resolvable by the microscope. Figure 149 is a micrograph of fully heat-treated beryllium-copper tube at 500 diameters. The particles may be precipitated both in the grain boundaries and in slip planes. In these alloys the reheating is essential; the desired age hardening will not occur at room temperature.

Cupronickel. Copper and nickel are mutually soluble in all proportions in both liquid and solid states. The binary alloys are used industrially with nickel contents from 2.5 to 45 per cent. Except at the lower percentages, the alloys have the same appearance as nickel, small amounts of that element discharging the copper color completely. The United States 5-cent piece is 75 per cent copper, 25 per cent nickel. Although higher in cost than most other copper alloys, the cupronickels are extensively used for their combination of strength, ductility, and corrosion resistance. They are used in both cast and wrought form,

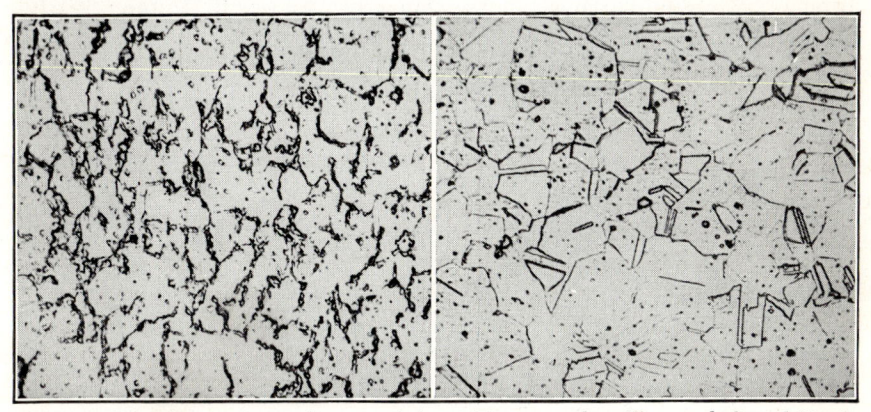

Fig. 149. Beryllium-copper tube, containing 1.85 per cent beryllium, cobalt stabilized. Magnification 500 ×. Left micrograph, solution treated; hardness Rockwell B-60. Right micrograph, precipitation treated at 330°C (626°F) for 40 min; hardness Rockwell C-38; a beryllium-copper component is precipitated as small round particles in the grain boundaries. (*Author's laboratory.*)

but especially for severely wrought material. The 70:30 alloy is the most common, and is widely used for condenser tubes.

Another copper-nickel alloy (more correctly a nickel-copper alloy since nickel predominates) of much industrial importance is monel; it is discussed on page 313.

PART II. ZINC AND LEAD

Zinc now ranks as the second most important nonferrous metal as regards tonnage produced, both in the world and in the United States. Lead was first surpassed by zinc as to world tonnage in 1940, and in 1952 it was passed by aluminum. Though the present outlook is for further relative increase in production of zinc as compared with lead, this trend may be reversed at some later time. Although these metals are discussed in the same section and they occur together in nature to a great extent, their metallurgy, both chemical and physical, and most of their properties and uses are widely different.

Zinc

The four largest outlets for use of zinc are for coating iron and steel to protect them against corrosion (galvanizing), manufacture of brass, die castings, and rolled zinc (mainly sheet and strip). In the United States, 45 to 50 per cent of all the zinc is used for galvanizing. Die castings have been the fastest growing use in recent years; more die castings are made of zinc-base alloy than of any other metal. In the United States in the past few years nearly 30 per cent of the zinc has been used for die castings, more than twice as much as was used for brass. In Great Britain brassmaking constitutes the largest use of zinc.

Mechanical Properties. In a brief discussion of the mechanical properties of zinc, it should first be pointed out that, although the strength and ductility of zinc and zinc alloys are satisfactory for many structural applications, the extent to which these materials can be used under constant load is limited by the fact that they are subject to relatively high creep. Creep strength is considered of far greater importance than static tensile strength in most design problems involving zinc. It is recommended that creep data which are now available for zinc and zinc alloys be used when designing structures for continuously applied stresses.

The strength and ductility of zinc depend, to a somewhat greater extent than with other common metals, on the purity of the metal and whether cast or hot-rolled. If rolled, the values for tensile strength depend on whether measured parallel with or perpendicular to the direction of rolling, the latter being 20 to 25 per cent greater than the former in the case of commercial hot-rolled zinc, and as much as 30 per cent greater in the case of cold-rolled strip alloyed with 1 per cent copper and 0.01 per cent magnesium. The tensile strength of hot-rolled zinc strip of purity conforming approximately to that of "high grade" (see Table 26) is about 17,000 to 20,000 psi (depending on the direction of rolling), while that of purity corresponding to that of "intermediate" is about 23,000 to 29,000 psi. The latter figures indicate that zinc has a strength about double that of commercial aluminum in comparable form, and about three-quarters that of copper. High ductility for rolled zinc is shown by elongation values of 63 per cent for material of 20,000 psi to 30 per cent for material of 29,000 psi.

Zinc is one of the few metals whose crystal lattice is in the hexagonal system. Unlike aluminum and copper, cast zinc crystallizes normally in very large grains; these tend to grow in columnar form from the walls of the mold. As a result of these factors, zinc cannot be directly cold-rolled without cracking. If the slabs are heated to the proper rolling temperature, usually about 200°C (390°F), they are readily hot-rolled, and after the grain has been broken down and refined by hot rolling, the metal becomes highly ductile and reduction may be finished by cold rolling.

The results of rolling are dependent on purity of the metal. Pure zinc undergoes "annealing" or softening at room temperature; its recrystallization temperature may be below 0°C. Small amounts of the common impurities and alloying elements raise this temperature considerably. Thus pure zinc cannot be permanently hardened by cold work. When a certain amount of work hardening is desired, as is usually the case, zinc of lesser purity is used, or small amounts of cadmium may be added. For higher strength and greater work hardening, copper may be added, usually in the amount of 1 per cent, and the effect may be further enhanced by addition of 0.01 per cent magnesium. Lead, a principal impurity, does not affect work hardening.

Resistance to Corrosion. The durability of zinc against weathering, so important in galvanized products as well as in those of solid zinc, is due to its becoming coated with a thin film of hydrated zinc oxide or carbonate, which retards the penetration of oxygen, just as in the case of copper. The color of the coating is a dull gray. Zinc is resistant to corrosion by water, but reacts with many chemicals; nearly all the common acids dissolve it rapidly.

Zinc Coating. *Hot Galvanizing.* Galvanizing is most often done by the dip or hot-galvanizing process. The iron or steel surface must first be thoroughly cleaned and freed from oxide, for which acid pickling (generally by dipping in hot dilute sulfuric acid) is most commonly employed. The clean material is then dipped for a few seconds in molten zinc at a temperature between 425 and 460°C (800 and 860°F). Usually the zinc bath is covered with a layer of flux—molten sal ammoniac (NH_4Cl). Dipping is now done by automatic machines.

The hot-galvanized coating is not simply a layer of zinc on iron. Molten zinc alloys readily with iron. By diffusion of iron into the zinc coating, different alloy layers grow outward from the steel base. Micrographs of galvanized material (except electrogalvanized) show an outer zone of zinc, an inner one of iron or steel, and in between these, several zones of zinc-iron alloys rich in zinc (see Fig. 150). Recent studies[1] show that all the phases of the iron-zinc constitution diagram are normally present in the coating, with the zeta phase, represented by the composition $FeZn_{13}$, constituting the major portion of the usual alloy layer.

[1] Rowland, D. H., *Trans. Am. Soc. Metals*, **40**, 983 (1948).

The usual weight of the hot-dip coating is 1.25 to 2.75 oz per sq ft in the case of galvanized sheet; this weight includes the coating on both surfaces and is equivalent to an average thickness of 0.001 to 0.0024 in. on each side if the coating is considered as pure zinc. Greater thicknesses are usually required for other types of material. The American Society for Testing Materials has published specifications for all the important classifications of galvanized materials.

The protection afforded by zinc to galvanized iron or steel is of two kinds: one, that naturally due to covering with a rustproof metal, and the other arising from the fact that zinc is above iron in the electropotential series of metals, so that even where there is a break or pit in the coat-

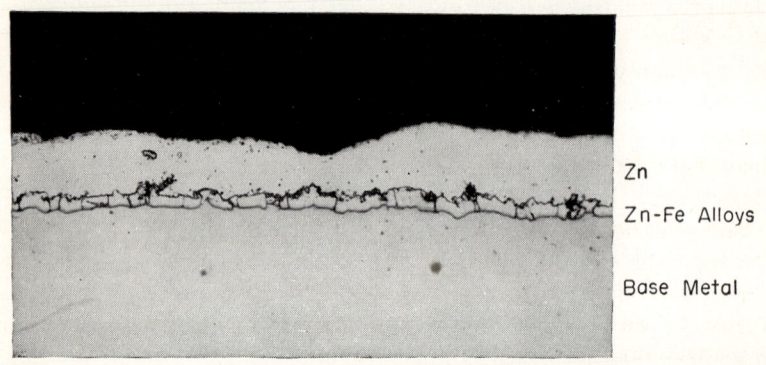

FIG. 150. Micrograph of section of galvanized iron at surface. Magnification 1,000 ×. (*Courtesy of American Steel & Wire Company, Cleveland.*)

ing, the exposed iron is protected electrochemically. The zinc and iron form a galvanic couple in which minute currents flow from the zinc (anode) to the iron (cathode), relegating oxidation to the zinc surface and maintaining a reducing condition at the iron surface. Since the zinc itself is gradually oxidized, and since the electrochemical action may not be sufficiently strong to overcome severely corrosive conditions, the time and amount of protection afforded by galvanized coatings is approximately proportional to their thickness. Manufacturers are practicing false economy if they make the zinc coating too thin, and consumers should be aware of the thickness provided.

Galvanized iron and steel are used in vast amounts for roofing and side walls of factory and farm buildings, for wire fencing, pipes, wire screens, chains, buckets, and a host of other purposes. More than a million tons of galvanized sheets are consumed annually in the United States alone. An idea of the relative amounts of other forms of galvanized material may be obtained from Table 27, page 275.

Electrogalvanizing. The coating of zinc may be applied by electrolytic deposition instead of dipping in molten zinc. This method is growing in use for certain fields of application and where relatively thin coatings are sufficient. The thickness range of these coatings is usually between 0.00015 and 0.001 in. Electroplating with zinc is usually done with a bath of zinc sulfate, but zinc cyanide is used at low current density on fabricated parts, and recently zinc chloride is being used in the intermediate range of current density. The particular advantages of the electrolytic method are the high purity and the greater uniformity in thickness of the coating. Thin uniform coatings permit holding close dimensional tolerances. Fabricated parts can be coated without subjecting them to heat. Greater uniformity permits the use of thinner coatings for the same degree of protection. Especially in galvanizing wire, modern methods use sulfate solutions at very high current density, made possible by strong solutions with the wire moving continuously through them.

In electrogalvanizing no alloying occurs between the zinc and the iron. Absence of the brittle intermetallic compounds between zinc and iron cause the coating to be less liable to crack or flake off when subjected to bending. Ductility is promoted also by the greater purity of the coating.

Anodes of high-purity zinc are used in electrogalvanizing. However, in the Bethanizing process, developed by the Bethlehem Steel Company, insoluble anodes are used and the zinc is obtained from a solution made by direct leaching of zinc ore, or zinc-bearing wastes, with sulfuric acid, then carefully purifying the solution in the manner used in production of zinc by leaching and electrodeposition. Bethanizing has thus far been used chiefly for wire; the surface of the wire is thoroughly cleaned and deoxidized by making it the cathode in molten caustic soda (NaOH) before plating.

Other Coating Methods. In the *Schoop metallizing process*, a spray of atomized molten zinc is directed by means of a special apparatus against a heated iron or steel surface. This process is not confined to zinc, but is also used for coating with other metals of low melting point.

In *sherardizing*, the objects to be coated are put into a tight rotating drum with zinc and heated for several hours to a temperature of 300 to 420°C (570 to 790°F). A coating of zinc-iron alloy is formed on the iron, giving an efficient penetration even into objects of irregular shape and rough surface.

Zinc Alloys. The most important alloys in which zinc is the major constituent are the die-casting alloys (some of which are used to a lesser extent for sand castings) and certain rolled zinc alloys. Some zinc-base bearing alloys and the slush-casting alloys (used also for permanent-mold castings) are of importance. Slush castings are hollow castings made by filling the mold with molten metal, allowing a certain amount of it to freeze on the walls of the mold, then inverting the mold and pouring out the still-liquid metal from the center. Brass lighting fixtures are frequently made in this way. The principal alloys of this type are the 5.5 per cent aluminum, balance special high-grade zinc, and the 4.75 per cent aluminum, 0.25 per cent copper, balance special high-grade zinc.

Zinc is also used as an essential component of many alloys in which it is present in a minor percentage.

Uses of Zinc and Zinc Alloys. *Zinc-base Alloy Die Castings.* Representing less than 2 per cent of the zinc consumed in the United States in 1925, this use of zinc has grown to a consumption of 30 per cent of American zinc in 1951. This development has been made possible by improvement in the die-casting alloys. Early zinc die castings gave trouble because of corrosion which caused swelling, warping, and cracking in service, with sticking and lack of fit in movable parts and assemblies. Research carried on by the New Jersey Zinc Company proved that these troubles disappear when minute amounts of certain impurities formerly present are avoided and proper alloy compositions are used. It was found essential to use zinc of a purity not less than 99.99 per cent (so-called 4-9 zinc, specified as Special High Grade), in which the sum of cadmium, iron, and lead is not over 0.01 per cent and tin is limited to 0.003 per cent. Intergranular corrosion in the die castings is prevented by addition of a small amount of magnesium to the alloys.

The two alloys most used are one containing 4 per cent aluminum and 0.04 per cent magnesium, and one containing 4 per cent aluminum, 1 per cent copper and 0.04 per cent magnesium. From these alloys are die-cast a large variety of articles ranging from large automobile-radiator grilles and many other parts of automobiles to the most intricate parts of machines such as cash registers and automatic vending machines, also office and household equipment, padlocks, cameras, and many small articles. The castings are often finished by nickel or chromium plating.

These two alloys have tensile strengths of 41,000 and 47,600 psi as cast, respectively, with elongations of 10 and 7 per cent, and Charpy impact values of 43 and 48 ft-lb. Other compositions are even stronger, but less desirable in some other respects. As noted previously, creep resistance is a primary consideration in zinc die castings subjected to continuous stress.

Rolled Zinc. Zinc is usually rolled from one of the commercial grades, or a mixture of grades, using high grade for maximum ductility and lower grades for greater strength and hardness. The use of zinc alloys for rolling is increasing. If small controlled amounts of lead and cadmium are regarded as impurities rather than alloy constituents, then the principal rolled zinc alloys are those containing 1 per cent copper and the same with addition of 0.01 per cent magnesium. Cadmium to 0.3

per cent and magnesium to 0.10 per cent are also used to provide work-hardening qualities. Copper gives stiffness and creep resistance with good ductility. Alloys containing up to 3.5 per cent copper are used in the aircraft industry for dies of rolled plate used in blanking aluminum and steel sheet. Manufacturers of rolled zinc often adjust compositions as well as details of rolling procedure to meet special purposes as required by customers.

The largest single use of rolled zinc, including zinc deep-drawn from plate punchings, is in the manufacture of dry cells, in which the zinc serves the double purpose of container and negative electrode. Other important uses include metal linings and containers, fruit-jar caps, weather stripping, moldings, eyelets, name plates in addressing machines, and sheets for photoengraving. Sheet zinc is used as a roofing material, especially in Europe, and for other purposes normally employing galvanized iron where the longer life and superior corrosion resistance of solid zinc justify its higher cost.

Other Uses. Certain other uses of zinc may be mentioned because of special features of interest. The ability of zinc to act as anode in galvanic couples with other elements, because of its high position in the electropotential series of metals, accounts for its use in dry cells and most forms of primary cells. The same principle is applied in using zinc for cathodic protection of steel, as in pipe lines, ship plates, and boilers. For a discussion of this principle, see page 351.

Zinc is essential in the common method of refining lead. When added to molten lead bullion, it forms an alloy with the silver and gold which rises to the top of the melt, permitting recovery of the precious metals. In the principal method of producing gold and silver from ore, the ore is leached with a cyanide solution and the metals are precipitated from the solution with zinc, usually in the form of zinc dust. Zinc dust is also used in metal paints and for other purposes. Some zinc oxide is made from metallic zinc, but most of the oxide and other compounds are produced directly from the ore.

Zinc oxide, which is usually made in the same plants making slab zinc, is used in large tonnages. Among its many uses the two largest are in paints and in rubber tires. Other industrial zinc compounds are the chloride, the sulfide, the sulfate, and lithopone (ZnS plus $BaSO_4$).

Commercial Zinc and the Effects of Impurities. Zinc metal is sold by the producers chiefly in the form of slabs. Slab zinc is often called spelter, but the use of that term is being discouraged. It is marketed in six commercial grades. These are listed and their relative purities shown in Table 26.

The principal impurities are lead, cadmium, and iron. Lead up to 1.0 to 1.25 per cent, in zinc for ordinary rolling, is not injurious and may even be desirable, but brass made from lead-bearing zinc will crack under severe mechanical treatment, as in cartridge manufacture; in zinc to be used for this purpose, the lead should not exceed 0.07 per cent. Ordinary (alpha) brass, which is commonly cold-rolled, can be hot-rolled if the lead content is kept very low by using Special High Grade zinc.

Iron increases the hardness and brittleness of zinc. It should be below 0.05 per cent in zinc intended for brass manufacture.

Cadmium is usually present in zinc ores, and being more volatile than zinc it distills over with the zinc. The effect of cadmium in zinc for various purposes has been the subject of much discussion; for most uses it is agreed that cadmium is deleterious, but in only a few cases is its harmfulness sufficient to be clearly evident. In zinc for galvanizing it causes a slight brittleness, enough to cause cracking or flaking of the coating if it is subjected to severe bending, as in some uses of wire. In zinc for brass, trouble is not experienced because cadmium vaporizes in the melting and does not actually enter the brass. In some rolled zinc, cadmium is desired for hardening.

The lowest grade, Prime Western, accounts for the greater part of the slab zinc sold, the galvanizing trade using this grade principally. Special High-grade and High-grade zinc are used for die-casting alloys, deep-drawing rolled zinc, hot-galvanizing wire, anodes for electrogalvanizing, and deep-drawing brass. Intermediate and Brass Special are used for brasses that do not require high ductility. Prime Western is used for some brass castings.

TABLE 26. ASTM SPECIFICATIONS FOR SLAB ZINC[1]
(Maximum allowable percentages)

Impurity	Special high grade	High grade	Intermediate	Brass special	Selected	Prime western
Lead................	0.006	0.07	0.20	0.60	0.80	1.60
Iron................	0.005	0.02	0.03	0.03	0.04	0.08
Cadmium............	0.004	0.07	0.50	0.50	0.75	
Total cadmium, iron, and lead............	0.010	0.10	0.50	1.00	1.25	
Aluminum............	None	None	None	None	None	
Tin.................	[2]					

[1] "ASTM Standards," 1949, Part 2, p. 323. (Specification B6-37.)
[2] Not regularly determined, but when used for die castings purchaser may reject metal if it contains over 0.003 per cent tin.

Distribution of the Uses of Zinc. The total consumption of zinc in the United States is divided among its principal uses as shown in Table 27, which shows also changes that have taken place since 1939.

Table 27. Distribution of Zinc Consumed As Metal in the United States[1]

Use	Percentage of total consumed	
	1939	1951
Galvanizing:		
Sheets	24	16
Tubes	7	9
Wire	5	6
Shapes and other[2]	8	13
Total galvanizing	44	44
Brass making	28	16
Die castings[3]	13	30
Rolled zinc	10	7
Other purposes[4]	5	3
Total	100	100

[1] From data of the American Bureau of Metal Statistics.
[2] Includes hardware, chains, wire cloth, and all articles not mentioned elsewhere.
[3] Includes a small amount of other zinc alloys.
[4] Includes zinc converted from metal into chemicals, zinc used for light alloys, and for desilverization of lead.

Lead

The amount of lead used in industry at the present time places it fourth among the nonferrous metals, closely following aluminum. It occupies a rather special position with respect to types of application. Depending in some cases on resistance to corrosion and in others on certain chemical reactions, the uses of lead involving the largest tonnages may be regarded as chemical in nature. Much of it is used in the form of compounds instead of the metal itself. Its lack of strength prohibits its use for structures subjected to stress, but its plasticity, which enables it to be bent and deformed without rupture, makes it valuable for sheathing electric cables and for pipes and traps used in building construction. These applications make use also of its high corrosion resistance, especially underground and under water. Its use in paints, as compounds, also demands corrosion resistance, as do many of the applications of metallic lead, but it is not so extensively used as a coating for iron and steel as is the case with zinc, tin, and nickel. By far its largest use is in storage batteries, where a high-lead alloy constitutes the framework of the plates and lead and lead compounds make up the active material. Thus lead is of greatest importance to the automobile industry, the electric power industry, and the building industry, besides having many other uses.

Resistance to Corrosion. Lead is practically unaffected by atmosphere, moisture, or water under any ordinary conditions or in any length of time. It does not stand up well under live steam, however. Freshly fractured or solidified lead has a bright metallic surface, which turns a dull dark gray in a few days, due to a thin film of oxide, but no further action takes place. Lead is soluble in nitric acid, but not in hydrochloric, and it is the cheapest metal that will successfully withstand sulfuric acid under most conditions. Accordingly, it is used for the construction and lining of tanks and apparatus in which sulfuric acid solutions are to be used, and the chambers and other parts of the apparatus in which sulfuric acid is made are built of lead. Boiling sulfuric acid, however, attacks lead.

Tensile Properties. Lead is a very weak metal, having a tensile strength of only about 2,000 psi. This fact is partially made up for, however, by the complete absence of brittleness, so that lead makes a good construction material when it is not to be subjected to any great amount of stress, as in lining, pipes, etc.

Malleability and Ductility, Softness, and Pliability. The ease with which lead is worked and shaped is an important advantage which it possesses over other metals. A growing development is the use of lead wool as a calking material, the lead in the form of fibers, or shreds the size of thread, being pressed by hand into openings for joining pipe, repairing leaks, etc. Lead is also a valuable constituent of some bearing metals. For cable covering, lead a little below the melting point is extruded continuously through an annular die through the center of which the cable passes at the same rate that the lead is extruded around it, thus forming a continuous moistureproof casing.

Lead foil is also easily made and is valuable for wrapping material and for other uses. Lead foil, however, cannot be used in contact with food products or for other purposes where harm might result because of the poisonous character of lead.

For many uses it is desired to give lead more rigidity or increase its resistance to abrasion. For this purpose it is hardened by the addition of antimony, producing what is called *hard lead* or *antimonial lead*. Storage-battery plates and tank linings are largely made of antimonial lead, using 1 to 12 per cent antimony. Such material containing 4 to 8 per cent antimony has about twice the tensile strength of pure lead and may be heat-treated to yield a tensile strength of about 12,000 psi.

For cable sheathing and thin sheet, lead is often hardened with cadmium (0.25 per cent plus 0.5 per cent antimony), calcium (0.03 per cent), or tellurium (0.07); these alloys have superior fatigue resistance. Transverse cracks sometimes occur in cable sheathing as a result of stresses arising from alternate heating and cooling.

Lead cannot be hardened except by alloying. Cold working has no appreciable effect because the recrystallization temperature is below room temperature.

Melting Point. The low melting point of lead, 327°C (621°F), also contributes to the ease of using it, and makes it valuable as a constituent of solders. This is discussed under Tin (page 309) and on page 162. The commonly used method of employing lead as a calking material, which is one of its important uses, is by melting and pouring it into the opening.

Another advantage of its low melting point is the ease of autogenous welding with lead. This work is of such importance that it forms a trade in itself, called lead burning. Acid-tank linings must be joined in this way, since solder would be corroded.

Weight. Lead is the heaviest of the base metals, having a specific gravity of 11.3 compared with 8.9 for copper, 7.85 for iron, and 7.15 for zinc. Much lead is used for counterweights and sinkers.

Lead Poisoning. Lead is one of the three common industrial metals that are highly poisonous, the others being mercury and arsenic. Lead is particularly troublesome because when absorbed gradually in minute amounts it is not ordinarily entirely eliminated by the system, but gradually builds up until it causes ill health. There is little danger from the solid metal, but working where there is exposure to lead vapor, dust, or fume and the handling of lead compounds require the use of respirators and other precautions. Great progress in minimizing lead poisoning has been made in both the producing and consuming ends of the industry through precautions and regulations, cleanliness, and periodic health examinations of workers. Proper care would be a complete remedy if it were not human nature to be careless.

The large use of arsenate of lead as an insecticide for fruits and vegetables and its imperfect removal from the marketed products are matters which should be given further study and subjected to proper regulation.

Uses. The framework of storage-battery plates is composed of antimonial lead, and the active materials are sponge lead, lead peroxide, and lead sulfate. The electrochemical action of the battery is as follows:

$$Pb + PbO_2 + 2H_2SO_4 \rightleftarrows 2PbSO_4 + 2H_2O$$

Traps and bends of lead pipe are made and sold in standard forms and sizes. Lead-lined iron pipe for use with acidic water and solutions is widely employed.

Lead used for making white lead is called "corroding lead," and must be exceptionally pure. White lead is basic lead carbonate, approximating the composition $2PbCO_3.Pb(OH)_2$. Other lead pigments or compounds used in paints and ceramics include litharge (PbO), red lead (Pb_3O_4), and certain others of lesser importance. Lead oxides are used also in the manufacture of rubber, glass, and oil.

Lead is most effective in absorbing short-wave radiations. Accordingly it has been much used in the form of heavy sheet as a shield around X-ray equipment, for protecting against radium and other radioactive material, and for containers of such material. This use promises to become of great importance in the future, and it has already played an important part in equipment for atomic-energy research.

The damping qualities of lead in absorbing vibrations also provide interesting applications, such as in cushioning the foundations of tall buildings. One of the most important uses of lead, now accounting for about 12 per cent of its total consumption in the United States, is in the form of the compound tetraethyl lead used as an antiknock component in gasoline.

Lead Alloys. Antimonial lead and its chief applications have been mentioned. Perhaps an equally important alloy is type metal, used exclusively for casting printer's type on account of its sharp castings combined with ease of melting. It is composed of 60 to 94 per cent lead with the balance antimony and tin. These alloys contract only slightly in freezing. The usual composition of linotype metal is approximately 84 per cent lead, 12 per cent antimony, and 4 per cent tin; this melts at 246°C (475°F).

White bearing metals contain 10 to 80 per cent lead. The lead-base bearing metals, *i.e.*, those containing over 50 per cent lead, are called "antifriction metal"; these contain antimony and tin as alloying elements. Common solder is 50 per cent lead, and some compositions contain more. Some lead is used as a protective coating for steel sheet, fence wire, etc.; this use may employ pure lead or "terneplate," in which the lead is alloyed commonly with about 18 per cent tin (see page 308). Shotgun shot is made of lead containing up to 1 per cent arsenic. Shrapnel employs lead hardened with antimony, and this is also used in the cores of bullets.

Lead is also a constituent of many alloys in which the major constituent is another metal. It is added to many brasses and bronzes in amounts up to 5 per cent to give them better machining qualities and is sometimes used in larger amounts. Copper-lead bearing metals and lead-bearing bronzes are used for bearings. Pewter and other tin alloys often contain lead, and lead is a large component of Wood's metal and other very low-melting ("fusible") alloys.

Distribution of Lead among Its Uses. Table 28, from data published by the Lead Industries Association, shows the percentage of total lead consumption accounted for by each of its major uses.

TABLE 28. DISTRIBUTION OF LEAD CONSUMPTION IN THE UNITED STATES, 1951

Use	Per cent of total
Storage batteries	31
Cable covering	12
Tetraethyl lead	11
Solder	6
Red lead and litharge, exclusive of use in storage batteries	7
Building and chemical construction	5
Calking	4
Bearing metal	3
Type metal	2
White lead	2
Ammunition	3
Other uses	14
Total	100

Marketed Grades. Four principal grades of lead are sold in the United States, as follows:

Grade I. Corroding lead.
Grade II. Chemical lead.
Grade III. Common lead:
  1. Desilverized lead.
  2. Soft Missouri lead.

Corroding lead is the highest grade, containing 99.94 to 99.99 per cent lead and not more than 0.05 per cent bismuth, which is the chief impurity.

Chemical lead is the name given to high-grade lead made in the Southeast Missouri district. It runs from 99.9 to 99.95 per cent lead with 0.04 to 0.08 per cent copper. It is much used for storage-battery lead, cable covering, and sheet lead.

Soft Missouri lead is lead from the Joplin district (Missouri-Oklahoma-Kansas). It is the best grade of common lead and is practically equal to chemical lead.

Desilverized common lead may contain up to 0.25 per cent bismuth, but is low in other impurities. Its lead content runs usually from 99.8 to 99.9 per cent. It is frequently used for the same purposes as chemical lead, as well as for solder, shot, pipe, and all uses not requiring great purity.

Specifications. Standard specifications for pig lead as to chemical composition were adopted by the American Society of Testing Materials in 1943. In these, common desilverized lead is divided in two classifications, A and B, and two other classifications are added to the four principal grades described above. These are acid lead and copper lead, both made by adding copper to fully refined lead, making a total copper content of 0.04 to 0.08 per cent, the same as in chemical lead.[1]

PART III. ALUMINUM, MAGNESIUM, AND LIGHT ALLOYS

Demand for aluminum and magnesium underwent a phenomenal growth during the Second World War. Nothing approaching the rate of expansion in production and use of these metals has ever been seen in the metallurgical industry. From 1938 to 1943, production of aluminum in the United States increased nearly sevenfold. Production of magnesium at the peak was multiplied more than eighty times, having increased from an average of 270 tons per month in 1938 to 22,300 tons in the peak month of March, 1944. The chief factor in demand for aluminum was aircraft manufacture; magnesium was required in large amounts for incendiary bombs as well as for aircraft; and in both cases numerous other uses contributed.

Although the use of both these metals naturally declined after the close of the war, nonwar uses continued to expand, and by 1950 consumption was again about six times as high as in 1939 in the case of aluminum, with a similar percentage gain in use of magnesium.

A large factor in the increased importance of aluminum, and also of magnesium, is the new situation as regards comparative prices of the principal metals. Larger-scale production and greater plant capacity have permitted and to some extent necessitated lower relative prices for the light metals. Just before the war, aluminum cost 20 cents per pound and copper about 10 cents per pound. During the war, the price of copper was fixed just under 12 cents, while that of aluminum was reduced to 15 cents. After removal of government price control, the price of copper rose rapidly to 24.5 cents per pound, while the price of aluminum advanced only to 19 cents. Aluminum is now for the first time cheaper than copper by the pound, and per unit volume it costs less than one-quarter as much. The competitive position of aluminum with respect to other metals, such as steel and especially zinc, has been similarly improved.

At its present price of 24.5 cents per pound, magnesium has now the lowest cost of any of the nonferrous metals on the volume basis. A metal part or object of fixed dimensions can be made more cheaply of magnesium than of any other nonferrous metal, and will cost only twice as much as if made of plain carbon steel (see Table 36, page 329).

Aluminum

Before the Second World War, aluminum ranked fifth among the metals in production and use, surpassed by iron, copper, zinc, and lead. In the

[1] Cf. "ASTM Standards," 1949, Part 2, p. 327. (Specification B29-43.)

United States, production of aluminum passed that of lead in 1942 and by 1951 was not far below that of zinc. In world production it overtook lead in 1952, but was still considerably below copper and zinc. This comparison refers to tonnages; on the volume basis, because of its lightness, aluminum is the leading nonferrous metal, both in the United States and in the world.

Properties. In discussing the properties of aluminum, it should first be pointed out that the best grade of aluminum that is sold in large quantities has a purity of only about 99.3 per cent aluminum, and that some of the properties of aluminum containing over 99.85 per cent aluminum are considerably different from those of the commercially pure material. "Pure" aluminum in the ordinary commercial sense refers to the 99+ per cent grade, and as the engineer is concerned with the properties of this material, the discussion given here will refer to them.

Probably three-fourths of the aluminum now being consumed is in the form of light alloys, and only one-fourth as the commercially pure metal. The proportion used in alloy form has been increasing.

Specific Gravity. The lightness in weight of aluminum may be regarded as its most important property, since this distinguishing feature of the metal—taken, of course, in conjunction with suitable properties in other respects—is the leading factor in its largest uses. The specific gravity of aluminum is 2.70. Thus it is only three-tenths as heavy as copper (sp gr 8.9), and about one-third as heavy as iron (sp gr 7.8), its two chief competitors in the electrical and structural fields, respectively. It is, however, 50 per cent heavier than magnesium.

Light aluminum alloys have specific gravities ranging from 2.6 to 2.9. Aluminum-magnesium and aluminum-silicon alloys are lighter than aluminum; other alloying metals increase the weight.

Tensile Properties. The lightness of aluminum would be of little use were it not accompanied by suitable strength. The tensile strength of the metal in the fully annealed condition is 12,000 to 13,000 psi. Hard-drawn transmission wire will run about 24,000 psi, which compares with 50,000 psi for copper in a similar condition and about 180,000 for hard-drawn steel spring wire (0.60 per cent carbon, 0.12 in. diameter). Cold working increases the strength markedly. Cold-rolled aluminum sheet may test as high as 25,000 psi or even higher.

On account of the relatively low melting point of aluminum the tensile strength decreases rapidly at elevated temperatures.

Practically, the tensile strength per square inch should not be considered alone, and it is here that the lightness of aluminum becomes important. A pound of aluminum has a volume 7.8/2.70, or 2.9, times that of a pound of steel. Consequently, a pound of aluminum drawn to a given length will have a cross-sectional area 2.9 times that of a pound of steel of the same length. In comparing the strength of equal weights of steel and aluminum at the same length, the strength of aluminum per square inch should therefore be multiplied by the factor 2.9. This argument, of course, does not apply in considering pieces of fixed dimensions; then it is the size that counts, not the weight, and the lightness of aluminum may be of no advantage. Even then, however, its lightness may be of great advantage in certain cases, *viz.:* (1) when the piece is to be transported or is part of an automobile, airplane, etc.; (2) when the piece is of large size and must support its own weight, as in transmission wires suspended from pole to pole. Thus copper wires of a given diameter must be supported at shorter intervals than aluminum wires of the same diameter, since the tensile strength of copper *in proportion to its weight* is less than that of aluminum. For copper, using the values already given, the ratio is 50,000/8.9, or 5,600; for aluminum, 24,000/2.7, or 8,900.[1]

For uses requiring high strength, aluminum alloys are more suitable than pure aluminum. By alloying alone much higher tensile properties may be obtained, and many of the alloys can be further strengthened by heat-treatment as well as by cold-working operations. The ultimate strength of different casting alloys ranges from 17,000 to 32,000 psi for sand castings not heat-treated, and up to 46,000 for die castings and 48,000 for heat-treated castings. Heat-treated wrought alloys are still stronger. The alloy now used in the largest tonnages (24S), employed especially for aircraft construction, is also one of the strongest; in its usual heat-treated form (24S-T4), it has a tensile strength of 68,000 psi. Higher values are obtained by cold working.

The above figures are quoted for illustration and comparison. The tensile strengths of heat-treated wrought aluminum alloys fall in the same range as those of plain-carbon structural steels. In proportion to their weight they are about three times as strong as the latter, and on this basis are stronger than most of the alloy steels, though somewhat below the strongest.

In designing aluminum structures, yield strengths are usually considered more significant than tensile strengths. Details on these and other mechanical properties for the different alloys will be found in handbooks and producers' literature. The yield strength of pure aluminum (2S-O) is about 5,000 psi, and the elongation is about 45 per cent.

The advantage indicated for aluminum over steel because of its lightness cannot always be fully realized in design because of its lower modulus of elasticity. This is 10,000,000 to 11,000,000 psi for aluminum and its alloys compared with 29,000,000 for steel.

[1] For further discussion of strength-weight ratios, see p. 330.

Electrical Conductivity. Aluminum is being increasingly used for electric power applications. Measured on the ordinary basis of conductivity per unit of cross-sectional area, its electrical conductivity is 61 per cent of that of copper and 3.5 times that of iron. Measured on the mass basis, however, the conductivity of aluminum is twice that of copper. The manner in which the weight factor enters will be evident from the discussion of the effect of weight in relation to tensile strength, and also from the discussion of the electrical conductivity of copper, page 244. This gives aluminum one advantage over copper for conductors, and a further factor is its lower cost. The question of choice of conductors is to a considerable extent one of comparing the value of the power loss due to resistance with the interest charge on the cost of the metal used. For long-distance transmission, however, comparison cannot be made on the basis of the pure metals alone. Aluminum is used in the form of cables reinforced with steel. This gives suitable strength with smaller cables, offsetting the factor of greater wind resistance and ice accumulation if cables of larger diameter were used. Similarly, steel-cored cables are used for copper transmission lines.

The alloying of other metals—even copper—with aluminum considerably reduces the electrical conductivity, so that aluminum alloys have not been extensively used as conductors.

Thermal Properties. The conductivity of aluminum for heat is of importance in its use for cooking utensils and other applications. Its thermal conductivity is nearly five times that of cast iron, but only 55 per cent of that of copper.

Aluminum in flaky powder form is used as a paint for ornamental and protective purposes. Aluminum paint has been applied to the outsides of industrial furnaces and other surfaces with the object of reducing the loss of heat by radiation. Aluminum paint is excellent for this purpose, since it tarnishes but little, retaining a bright metallic luster indefinitely if kept free from dirt. A bright metallic surface radiates comparatively little heat. The emissivity of aluminum-painted surfaces is probably between 0.30 and 0.50, which means that they radiate only 30 to 50 per cent as much heat as a dull carbon-black surface, and probably about half as much as a rusty iron surface. Also, the rule works both ways, and absorption of radiated heat can be cut down with aluminum paint. The paint is applied to oil tanks, transformers, the roofs of cars and buses, etc., serving the double purpose of protection against heat and against corrosion.

The relatively low melting point of aluminum—660°C (1220°F)—is a disadvantage for some uses.

Corrosion. The resistance of aluminum to corrosion or weathering is an important point of superiority for this metal over iron and steel for structural uses, cooking utensils, etc., as well as making it useful as a metal paint.

The resistance of aluminum to weathering is due to the protective action of the superficial film of oxide (Al_2O_3) which forms and prevents the action from penetrating deeper and progressing into the metal. A film so thin as to be invisible is sufficient to arrest further oxidation under ordinary conditions. In the presence of chlorine or salt water, however, the film may be broken down and corrosion may result. Most acids attack aluminum either slowly or not at all; hydrochloric and hydrofluoric acids, however, dissolve it rapidly. Alkalies, especially strong alkalies such as caustic soda and lye, also attack it. These dissolve aluminum oxide as well as the metal, so that the protective film is removed.

Of the aluminum alloys, those in which the primary alloying constituents are manganese, magnesium, chromium, or magnesium plus silicon in the proportions to form Mg_2Si resist corrosion practically as well as commercially pure aluminum. The aluminum-silicon alloys have a resistance ample for most atmospheric conditions. The high-strength aluminum-copper alloys have a somewhat lower resistance to corrosion but give satisfactory service when protected by commercial methods as used for aircraft, trucks, busses, railroad cars, and bridges. These alloys require less frequent maintenance than structural steel.

Alclad. The resistance to corrosion of the strong duralumin-type alloys is lower than that of commercially pure aluminum, and under some conditions of heat-treatment these alloys are susceptible to intergranular corrosion instead of the pitting type. The high strength of these alloys may be maintained under corrosive conditions by making them in alclad form. Alclad materials, originally developed by the Aluminum Company of America, provide a solution of this once troublesome problem. They are made by applying thin coatings of commercially pure aluminum, or sometimes of a corrosion-resistant aluminum alloy, by rolling them onto the surface of an ingot, usually of a strong but less corrosion-resistant alloy requiring protection. The pure aluminum coating is applied in considerable thickness to both sides of the alloy ingot in the early stages of rolling, and ingot and coating become reduced in thickness together as rolling progresses. Under the combined effect of heat and pressure, some of the alloying elements, particularly copper, diffuse from the alloy into the lower part of the coating, resulting in perfect adherence and a gradual transition from the properties of the alloy to those of pure aluminum at the surface. Thickness of the coating, and the temperature and time of heat-treatment, must be so proportioned as to prevent excessive diffusion of the alloying elements into the coating. The protection afforded by the alclad coating is electrolytic as well as mechanical, just as iron or steel is protected by galvanizing (see pages 270 and 352).

Anodic Oxidation. The corrosion resistance of aluminum and some other metals can be enhanced by the formation of thick oxide films by electrolytic oxidation, the metal being used as anode in a special electrolyte. The process is usually called *anodizing*. One method for doing this with aluminum is known as the *Alumilite process*. Coloring of the oxide coating when desired has been incorporated in this process by subsequent dipping in a dye or mineral pigment, which is readily absorbed. As the film is integral with the metal, a firmly bound colored coating may be obtained. Whether colored or uncolored, the pores of the coating are sealed by immersion for several minutes in boiling water or dichromate solution.

Hardness. Aluminum is a comparatively soft metal, ranking between tin and zinc in hardness. Cold working increases the hardness to a marked degree. The addition of other metals also hardens aluminum, and all the commercial light alloys are much harder than the pure metal. Though soft, aluminum takes a beautiful high polish, which is not dulled by tarnishing under ordinary conditions but is retained indefinitely when not abraded.

Malleability and Ductility. Aluminum ranks high in these properties, so that it is readily rolled into sheet or drawn into wire. In general, this is also true of aluminum alloys, with the proviso that the temperature be properly controlled, since some aluminum alloys are both hot-short (due to weakness at high temperatures) and cold-short (due to tendency toward brittleness). Duralumin and other light alloys can be used for forgings with good results.

Casting Aluminum. Pure aluminum exhibits high shrinkage, poor fluidity, porosity, and other bad casting qualities; consequently, castings are not made of aluminum alone. These deficiencies are overcome when certain alloying elements are added to aluminum. Many aluminum alloys have excellent casting properties; most of them contain over 90 per cent aluminum, and the castings are termed "aluminum" castings.

Most of the castings made are ordinary sand castings, but where conditions justify the expense of permanent metallic molds, these are employed, since they yield stronger and sounder castings. Certain aluminum alloys are excellent for die casting, yielding strong castings of intricate design at a rapid rate.

Owing to the affinity of aluminum for oxygen, a good deal of dross is made in melting the alloys for casting. Some of the dross may sink in the melt since the specific gravity of aluminum oxide is considerably greater than that of the metal—an unusual condition among metals. Most of the dross, however, floats on top, because of surface tension.

Rolling and Wire Drawing. For rolling, aluminum and aluminum alloys are melted and cast into ingots, which are then preheated to about 350 to 500°C (660 to 930°F). The ingots are broken down into slabs, which then go to roughing and finishing mills. With some of the harder alloys, the slabs are scalped (machined) to remove surface cracks which develop in the initial passes through the rolls. Finishing of sheet and strip is by cold rolling, with or without annealing. Wire rods are hot-rolled and then cold-drawn to wire of the desired diameter, with annealing at the end of the operation, at an intermediate stage, or omitted, depending on the final temper desired.

Fig. 151. Rolling aluminum or aluminum-alloy sheet. (*Courtesy of Aluminum Company of America.*)

Other Shaping Methods. Aluminum and its alloys are also shaped by forging, extrusion, impact extrusion, deep drawing, spinning, stamping, etc. Adaptability to all methods of shaping and fabrication is one of the most important advantages of aluminum. Shaping operations are shown in Figs. 151 to 154.

Welding and Soldering Aluminum. The film of oxide inherent to an aluminum surface must be removed in soldering or welding the metal, but both can be accomplished if suitable means are adopted. Any of the usual welding processes can be used, usually necessitating the employment of a proper flux for the oxide. The heliarc and other inert arc processes are useful. Soldering is not reliable when the joint is to be exposed to the atmosphere without protection, but there are several aluminum solders on the market. Brazing is often used for joining aluminum, with far better results than soldering.

Both pure aluminum and aluminum alloys are welded, but in welding heat-treated alloys, account must be taken of the fact that heat spreading from the weld may heat the metal to an annealing temperature for some distance from the joint, thus destroying the effect of the heat-treatment. Strength due to work-hardening is likewise removed. Heat-treated alloys are successfully welded by spot, seam, and flash welding, but other methods are limited in their application.

Aluminum Alloys. Aluminum alloys are divided into two groups, the *casting alloys* and the *wrought alloys*. Each of these groups is also divided into *heat-treated alloys* and *non-heat-treated alloys*.

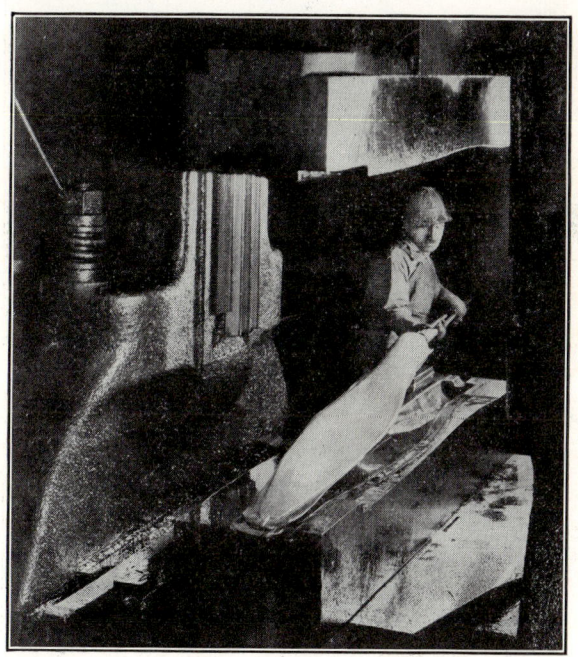

Fig. 152. Forging a propeller blade of aluminum alloy. The aircraft manufacturer will finish by machining and balancing. (*Courtesy of Aluminum Company of America.*)

In the earlier days of the industry many of the alloys were named, but the principal producers in the United States and Great Britain have adopted different systems of designating the alloys by letters and numbers. As the number of useful alloys has continued to grow and as many of the earlier compositions have been superseded by better ones, the letter and number designation has continued, and in the United States and Canada it has become more or less standard, so that today names are seldom applied to aluminum alloys.

In America, casting alloys are designated by a number; and if the original or principal alloy of this type is made in a variant composition, the number is preceded by a

Fig. 153. Extruding an aluminum structural member in a hydraulic press. The member is a side post for a railway passenger car; airplane fuselage and wing parts are often produced in this way. (*Courtesy of Aluminum Company of America.*)

Fig. 154. Spinning an aluminum cooking utensil. (*Courtesy of Aluminum Company of America.*)

letter to denote the variation. If the casting alloy is heat-treated, the number is followed by the letter T, which is in turn followed by a number to designate the kind of heat-treatment given.

The wrought alloys are designated by a number followed by the letter S. The letter O following S denotes that the alloy is in the fully annealed or soft condition. The wrought alloys that are not heat-treated can be hardened by working ("strain hardened"). In this case the letter S is followed by the letter H, which in turn is followed by a number to denote the strain-hardened temper.

In the case of the wrought alloys that are heat-treated, the fully heat-treated condition is denoted by the letter T, as with the casting alloys. The letter may be followed by a number to show what heat-treatment has been given. The letter W, used with alloys that must be hardened by accelerated aging, indicates that the alloy has been quenched but not reheated. In the case of heat-treated wrought alloys, the letter R has sometimes been inserted before T to denote that the alloy has been rolled before heat-treatment, a step which produces greater strength and hardness.

The letter F, applied especially to extruded alloys, denotes "as fabricated," or "as cast" in the case of some casting alloys.

The above terminology, developed by the Aluminum Company of America, has been generally adopted in America. The Reynolds Metals Company uses the same designations for the older standard alloys, but has its own numbers preceded by the letter R for some of the alloys developed by that company.

Alloying Elements. The seven principal elements added to commercial aluminum to make aluminum alloys are the following, divided into three groups: (*a*) copper, magnesium, and zinc; (*b*) silicon; (*c*) iron, manganese, and nickel. In addition to these, chromium up to 0.3 per cent is now a constituent of several alloys, titanium is sometimes used as a grain-refining agent, and certain alloys of lesser importance contain tin, lead, or bismuth.

Group *a* comprises the elements which form solid solutions with aluminum up to certain limits of several per cent, excess amounts separating in the form of an intermetallic compound or as constituent particles of zinc when this element is the addition. Each of these three elements is soluble in solid aluminum to a considerably greater percentage at elevated temperature than at room temperature, and because of this fact is able to bring about hardening and strengthening through heat-treatment.

Group *b* consists only of silicon, which forms a eutectic between silicon and aluminum containing a small amount of silicon in solid solution. It does not form an intermetallic compound with aluminum, and has a much lower solid solubility than the elements in group *a*.

Group *c* comprises the elements which are relatively insoluble in solid aluminum, but form definite intermetallic compounds which have a pronounced effect in small quantities.

All the seven principal alloying elements have some effects in common, although to widely varying degrees, and all have certain special effects. In general, all the elements increase hardness and strength and all, as previously noted, improve the casting qualities as compared with pure aluminum. All reduce conductivity greatly, and all tend to reduce ductility, though in some cases this effect is not large. Pure aluminum has the best resistance to corrosion, but the alloys with manganese and with magnesium are virtually as good in this respect, and silicon lowers it only slightly. The addition of chromium in some alloys improves resistance to corrosion and stress-corrosion cracking.

The most important aluminum casting alloys are made by adding copper or silicon, or both, with or without other elements. Silicon produces the best casting qualities with good corrosion resistance. Copper produces high strength but lowers the resistance of the alloy to corrosion. The aluminum-silicon alloys have high ductility, but are somewhat difficult to machine. This deficiency may be counteracted by using both silicon and copper as the alloying agents.

The elements of group c add hardness and strength without taking part in the effects of heat-treatment. In particular they produce greater strength at elevated temperatures than other elements, tending to counteract this drawback of aluminum alloys. Nickel is especially good for this purpose. Manganese is especially valuable for high corrosion resistance, while this property suffers from the presence of iron or nickel. These elements are powerful in small amounts and if too much is added will cause brittleness; this is especially true of iron. While alloys in which iron is added as a component are no longer much used, iron is nearly always present in alloys in an amount of the order of 0.5 per cent because it is in the commercial aluminum from which the alloys are made.

Important Alloys. In Table 29 the compositions of some of the more important casting alloys and the more important wrought alloys are indicated.

The eutectic between aluminum and silicon occurs at 11.6 per cent silicon, freezing at a temperature of 577°C (1070°F). The most important aluminum-silicon alloys are the binary alloys containing either 5 per cent silicon or 10 to 13 per cent silicon. At the higher percentages the eutectic structure tends to be accompanied by plates or flakes of silicon which would cause weakness and brittleness in the resulting alloy. This is avoided by the process of "modifying," which alters slightly the eutectic composition and temperature, at the same time causing the silicon to separate in very fine dispersed particles which produce hardness and strength with little loss of ductility. Modification may be accomplished in several ways, the usual method now being addition of about 0.05 per cent sodium to the melt. However, the 5 per cent silicon alloy (No. 43) is now used more than the higher silicon alloys. Number 43 is recommended for die castings as well as for permanent-mold and sand castings.

TABLE 29. NOMINAL COMPOSITIONS OF SOME ALUMINUM ALLOYS
(Per cent)

Casting alloys[1]

Alloy	Cu	Si	Mn	Mg	Zn	Ni	Cr	Pb	Bi
43	....	5.0							
108	4.0	3.0							
A108	4.5	5.5							
112	7.0	....	...	....	1.7				
113	7.0	2.0	...	....	1.7				
142	4.0	....	...	1.5	....	2.0			
195	4.5	0.8							
B195	4.5	2.5							
212	8.0	1.2							
214	....	....	...	3.8					
220	....	....	...	10.0					
355	1.3	5.0	...	0.5					
356	....	7.0	...	0.3					

Wrought alloys

Alloy	Cu	Si	Mn	Mg	Zn	Ni	Cr	Pb	Bi
3S	....	....	1.2						
11S	5.5	....	...	....		...	....	0.5	0.5
14S	4.4	0.8	0.8	0.4					
17S	4.0	....	0.5	0.5					
18S	4.0	....	...	0.6	....	2.0			
24S	4.5	....	0.6	1.5					
25S	4.5	0.8	0.8						
32S	0.9	12.2	...	1.1	....	0.9			
A51S	....	1.0	...	0.6	....	...	0.25		
52S	....	....	...	2.5	....	...	0.25		
61S	0.25	0.6	...	1.0	....	...	0.25		
75S	1.6	....	...	2.5	5.6	...	0.3		
E	2.5	....	0.5	0.5	20.0				
Y	4.0	....	...	1.5	....	2.0			
R303	1.2	....	...	2.5	6.5	0.1	0.25		
R317	4.0	1.0[2]	0.7	0.5	....	...	0.25[2]	0.5	0.5
R353	....	0.6	...	1.2	....	...	0.25		

[1] No. 43 is recommended for sand, permanent-mold, and die casting; Nos. 113, 142, 355, and 356 are recommended for sand and permanent-mold casting; all others are for sand casting only.

[2] Maximum.

The original No. 12 alloy (Al:Cu 92:8), which at one time accounted for about 90 per cent of all aluminum castings made, has given way to improved compositions such as Nos. 112 and 212.

The first heat-treated wrought alloy to attain great importance was duralumin; it was manufactured originally in Germany about 1911. It contains about 4 per cent copper and 0.5 to 1 per cent each of magnesium and manganese. Although no silicon is added, the small percentage of silicon present in the commercial aluminum used in making most aluminum alloys plays a part in the heat-treatment. It combines with magnesium to form Mg_2Si, which brings about some precipitation hardening. The American counterpart of duralumin is 17S. The alloy 24S, developed just prior to the Second World War especially for aircraft manufacture, is a modification of 17S in which the copper is increased from 4.0 to 4.5 per cent and the magnesium is increased to 1.5 per cent. This yields slightly higher mechanical properties with a slight loss in working qualities. It has largely superseded 17S. A number of other wrought alloys, each with one or more special features which make then superior in some respects, and usually inferior in other respects, may also be regarded as modifications or outgrowths of the original duralumin.

A different type of wrought alloy, developed more recently, is Alcoa alloy 75S, in which zinc, magnesium, and copper are the principal alloying elements. The Reynolds Metals Company alloy R303 is also of this type. Zinc was formerly used chiefly in certain casting alloys now of lesser importance; in these it was notable for the fact that two or three times as much zinc is necessary to bring about effects similar to the smaller percentages of copper.

A well-known British alloy is "Y" alloy, developed at the National Physical Laboratory. It is the only alloy used in large amounts in both cast and wrought forms. It is similar to duralumin with addition of 2 per cent nickel. It is stronger than duralumin at elevated temperatures, but more difficult to fabricate. Alloys 14S and 18S are similar. "E" alloy, another British alloy, is a duralumin type with addition of 20 per cent zinc.

Commercially pure aluminum has the alloy designation 2S. 3S is an important alloy, especially used for wrought cooking utensils as well as for aircraft and other purposes where a combination of corrosion resistance with ductility and moderate strength are needed. It is made by adding 1.2 per cent manganese to 2S. Alloys 2S and 3S are not heat-treatable.

Heat-treatment of Aluminum Alloys. Heat-treatment for improvement of hardness and strength is as important to many aluminum alloys as to steel. The nature of the process is different, however, and it is on the whole simpler because fewer structural variations are involved. This type of heat-treatment, which includes precipitation hardening, will be discussed first. Thermal treatments for softening and stress relieving will be noted later.

Heat-treatment is largely applied both to castings and to wrought material. Only certain types of alloys are heat-treatable, but these include most of the important wrought alloys and a number of the casting alloys. Copper is the element which plays the largest part in the hardening of aluminum alloys by heat-treatment; but magnesium (especially in combination with silicon as magnesium silicide, Mg_2Si) and zinc as $MgZn_2$ are likewise important. The behavior of the latter elements is essentially the same as that of copper except that different percentages and different temperatures are involved. The heat-treating process will be discussed with reference to the aluminum-copper equilibrium diagram, shown in Fig. 155; the theory of precipitation hardening in general has been taken up on page 192, and reference should be made thereto.

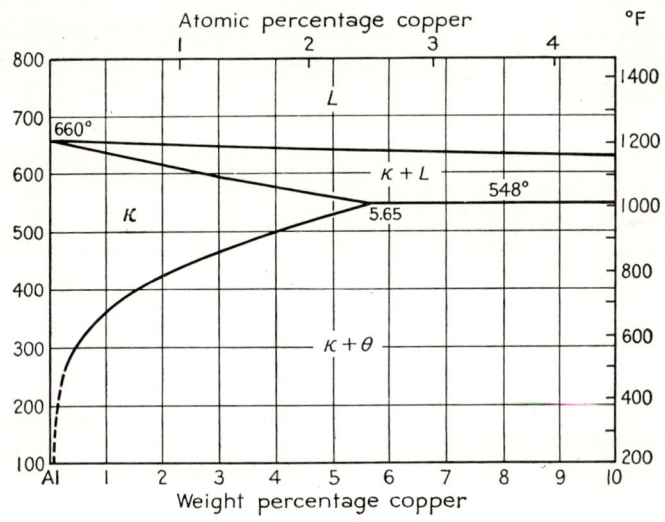

Fig. 155. Aluminum-copper constitution diagram at the aluminum-rich end. A eutectic occurs at 33 per cent copper. (*From W. L. Fink, L. A. Willey, and C. S. Smith, "The Metals Handbook," 1948.*)

From Fig. 155 it is seen that copper dissolves in aluminum in solid solution to a maximum of 5.65 per cent and that as the solid solution cools slowly it breaks down with precipitation of $CuAl_2$ from it, owing to the fact that at room temperature the maximum solubility of copper in aluminum is only 0.50 per cent or less. The exact nature of the precipitated particles is uncertain. They were formerly regarded as being the definite compound $CuAl_2$, and although this is now known to be untrue, the difference is of little practical consequence and it is convenient to refer to the precipitate as $CuAl_2$. The change in solid solubility with temperature, together with the ability to control the precipitation, is the key to the heat-treatment of aluminum alloys.

Even without heat-treatment, the presence of copper and other elements increases the hardness and strength of aluminum. With heat-treatment the increase is greatly augmented by copper in amounts between 2.5 and 5.65 per cent. If the alloy is allowed to cool slowly so that equilibrium is approached, the precipitate forms in large particles which have a minimum effect. If, however, the alloy is quenched, precipitation is arrested and a supersaturated solid solution is formed. This is somewhat stronger and harder than the slowly cooled alloy would have been. If the quenched solid solution is allowed to stand at room temperature, or is reheated to about 150°C (300°F) precipitation will occur because of the tendency to restore equilibrium. At these low temperatures, however, the precipitation will take place only slowly and in the form of very fine dispersed particles, probably colloidal, and not visible under a microscope. Precipitation in this form causes hardening of the alloy progressively as it occurs (see page 192). At room temperature most of the hardening takes place in a few days and is essentially complete in a matter of several days. The rate of precipitation and the particle size depend on the temperature from which the alloy is quenched and on the composition of the alloy. Number 24S alloy age-hardens much more rapidly than 17S. About 50 per cent of the gain in hardness occurs in the first two hours with 24S, and hardening is practically complete in 4 days. Most of the hardening of 17S occurs in the first four days and is practically complete in 10 days.

After quenching, the rate of hardening may be accelerated by reheating and holding at a temperature above room temperature. The treatment at elevated temperature necessary to cause accelerated aging is called a *precipitation treatment*. Whether or not an alloy age-hardens sufficiently at room temperature depends on its composition; for a number of alloys, accelerated aging is required.

The steps in heat-treatment of aluminum alloys may be summarized as follows:

A. Solution treatment. Heating in the solid-solution range until the copper or other soluble elements are completely dissolved (a few minutes to several hours, depending on the size of the piece).

B. Quenching. Quickly immersing in a cooling medium, usually cold water.

C. 1. Aging at room temperature.

or 2. Precipitation treatment. Reheating, usually for 2 to 18 hr at 140 to 180°C (285 to 360°F)

The precipitation treatment is not generally employed on alloys which will age-harden substantially at room temperature, since too rapid precipitation will result in a loss of corrosion resistance. Corrosion resistance is also impaired by quenching too slowly, so that cold water is usually employed instead of oil, hot water, or air. The milder quench may be necessary in some cases, however, to minimize warping. Heating is most often done in ovens or muffles provided with circulation of air

PROPERTIES AND USES OF NONFERROUS METALS 295

("air furnaces") and heated by electricity, oil, or gas. Wrought alloys, however, are often heated in fused salt baths of sodium nitrate or mixed sodium and potassium nitrate. This provides rapid heating with maximum uniformity of temperature and close control.

Heat-treated aluminum alloys are worked most easily immediately after quenching, and before age hardening has progressed. Precipitation is retarded at low temperatures just as it is accelerated at elevated temper-

TABLE 30. TYPICAL MECHANICAL PROPERTIES OF SOME ALUMINUM ALLOYS

Alloy and temper	Tension Ultimate strength, psi	Yield point, psi[1]	Elongation in 2 in., per cent[2]	Shearing strength, psi	Endurance limit, psi[3]	Brinell hardness[4]
\multicolumn{7}{c}{Sand-cast alloys}
43........	19,000	9,000	6.0	14,000	6,500	40
112.......	24,000	15,000	1.5	20,000	9,000	70
195-T4....	32,000	16,000	8.5	24,000	6,000	60
195-T62...	40,000	30,000	2.0	31,000	7,000	95
212.......	23,000	14,000	2.0	20,000	8,000	65
214.......	25,000	12,000	9.0	20,000	5,500	50
220-T4....	46,000	25,000	14.0	33,000	7,000	75
\multicolumn{7}{c}{Wrought alloys}
2S-O......	13,000	5,000	45	9,500	5,000	23
3S-O......	16,000	6,000	40	11,000	7,000	28
3S-H12....	19,000	17,000	20	12,000	8,000	35
3S-H14....	21,500	19,000	16	14,000	9,000	40
3S-H18....	29,000	26,000	10	16,000	10,000	55
17S-O.....	26,000	10,000	22	18,000	13,000	45
17S-T4....	62,000	40,000	22	38,000	18,000	105
24S-O.....	27,000	11,000	22	18,000	13,000	47
24S-T4....	68,000	48,000	19	41,000	18,000	120
25S-W.....	48,000	25,000	18	30,000	14,500	80
25S-T6....	58,000	37,000	19	35,000	18,000	110
A51S-T6...	48,000	43,000	17	32,000	11,000	100
61S-T6....	45,000	40,000	17	30,000	13,500	95
75S-T6....	82,000	72,000	11	49,000	21,000	150
Y.........	54,000	34,500	23			
R317......	55,000	30,000	16	......	......	100
R353-T....	35,000	28,000	16	......	......	80

[1] For 0.2 per cent offset.
[2] Round specimen, 0.5 in. diameter.
[3] R. R. Moore rotating beam machine, 500 million cycles.
[4] 500-kg load, 10-mm ball.

atures. Frequently in manufacturing operations the material is kept in dry ice until ready for fabrication; at temperatures below 0°F hardening is retarded for several weeks or longer. If too high a temperature is used in precipitation treatment, the particles of $CuAl_2$ tend to agglomerate, maximum strength is not attained, and corrosion resistance is lowered. Such material is said to be "overaged."

Annealing of aluminum alloys is done chiefly for elimination of strain hardening in wrought alloys or stress relief in castings. The metal is heated to the recrystallization temperature, the effect occurring almost instantly at 350 to 400°C (660 to 750°F). In some cases lower temperatures may be employed for longer times.

Table 30 gives typical mechanical properties of important aluminum alloys, and the effect of strain hardening or of heat-treatment is shown for some of them. For explanation of the alloy designations, see page 287.

Uses. The important uses of aluminum have for the most part been covered in the discussion of properties, which has touched on its use for electrical conductors, for structural purposes in the automotive and other industries, for cooking utensils, as a metal paint, and for castings. Other leading uses include architectural, especially for decorative trim, window frames, doors, and panels; also furniture and numerous household articles. Another important use is as a deoxidizer and grain-refining agent in pouring steel ingots and castings. Since its action is more powerful than that of ferromanganese and ferrosilicon, it is common practice to use some of it after using the other deoxidizers.

The percentage division of aluminum among the principal types of industrial consumption is indicated in Table 31. Although the figures are shipments of the Aluminum Company of America only, and for a single year, they give an idea of the relative importance of different applications at the present time.

TABLE 31. USE OF ALUMINUM BY INDUSTRIES
(Shipments of Aluminum Company of America only, in 1950)

Use or industry	Per cent
Building products	19
Transportation (land, sea, air)	18
Power transmission	8
Household appliances	8
Cooking utensils	6
Machinery (general and electric)	4
To fabricators for further processing	23
All other uses	14
Total	100

Purity and Marketed Forms of Aluminum. Aluminum in the form obtained directly from the electrolytic cells is commonly cast in pigs weighing about 50 lb. Pig aluminum is not uniform in composition and contains included dross and solidified electrolyte. This is remelted to obtain clean metal which is cast in notched ingots of various weights; the greater part of the metal is sold in this form. Ingot aluminum is marketed chiefly in the grade designated as 99+ per cent aluminum, but its actual purity is 99.3 per cent or more. A special grade carrying 99.45+ per cent aluminum is also sold, especially for electrical conductors. Electrolytically refined aluminum can be bought in purities over 99.85 per cent, but there is little demand for aluminum of such high purity. Secondary aluminum, made by remelting of scrap, etc., is also regularly marketed. Such material is of about the same average purity

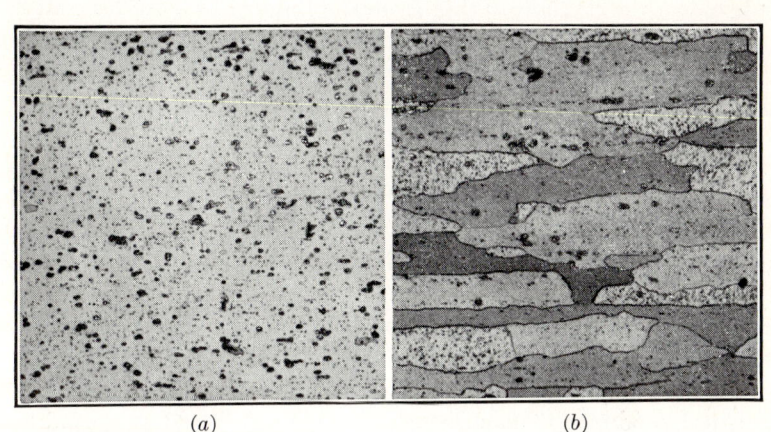

FIG. 156. Microstructure of 24S alloy in the form of 0.064-in. sheet. Both magnifications 250 ×. (a) Annealed (24S-O). Much fine precipitate has resulted from annealing. (b) Solution-treated, quenched, and aged (24S-T3). The grain contrast is due to copper in solid solution. The large black areas in both a and b are chiefly an Al-Cu-Fe-Mn constituent. (*Courtesy of Kaiser Aluminum and Chemical Corporation.*)

as the lower-grade primary metal, but its composition is more uncertain and unreliable. It is an important factor in the market, the annual secondary production in the United States being 20 or 25 per cent of the primary production.

Ingots of various aluminum alloys are also marketed, the alloying elements being added when the pig aluminum is remelted for casting into ingots.

Specifications. Specifications covering aluminum ingots were adopted by the American Society for Testing Materials in 1944 and revised in 1946.[1] The ingot specifications cover two grades containing a minimum of 99.3 and 99.75 per cent aluminum. In these, copper is an allowable impurity to the amounts of 0.10 and 0.05 per cent, respectively; iron, 0.50 and 0.20 per cent; silicon, 0.30 and 0.10 per cent; magnesium, 0.05

[1] "ASTM Standards," 1949, Part 2, p. 470. (Spec. B24-44.)

and 0.03 per cent; and unspecified impurities, a maximum of 0.05 and 0.03 per cent each.

Microstructure of Aluminum and Aluminum Alloys. The presence of impurities in commercial aluminum—chiefly iron and silicon—render it metallographically an alloy. Under the microscope there appears a matrix of aluminum crystals containing some iron and silicon in solid solution, together with some crystals of several Al-Fe-Si constituents and perhaps some of the compound $FeAl_3$.

The microstructure of most aluminum alloys is somewhat more complex. Copper occurs in an Al-Cu solid solution plus $Al\text{-}CuAl_2$ eutectic in addition to crystals resulting from the impurities. Alloys containing manganese and magnesium have crystals of the compounds $MnAl_6$ and an Al-Mg solid solution or compound. The microstructure of the duralumin type is shown in the micrographs of 24S alloy, Fig. 156.

MAGNESIUM

Magnesium is the lightest in weight of all the metals that are stable under atmospheric conditions. It is a little lighter than beryllium and only two-thirds as heavy as aluminum. Its lightness, combined with attractive mechanical properties and the ability to form strong alloys, has aroused much interest and stimulated a growing development, but its present importance in industry is still far below that of tin or nickel. It was not produced in quantity until the First World War, and subsequently its progress was retarded by high cost. Its structural applications in aircraft, portable equipment, etc., besides its use for incendiary bomb casings, expanded greatly during the Second World War. Its price has been progressively lowered until it is now a relatively low-cost metal, and this together with metallurgical improvements point to a more rapid future growth of the magnesium industry.

Properties. A comparison of the principal properties of magnesium with those of aluminum shows some points of advantage and some of disadvantage. With reference to the ordinary commercial grades of the two metals, unalloyed, magnesium is lighter than aluminum and also harder and stronger. On the other hand, because it crystallizes in the hexagonal system, it is less readily workable than aluminum, tending toward brittleness when cold in the cast condition. It is inferior to aluminum in corrosion resistance and has much lower conductivity. It costs a little more than aluminum per pound, but at present is cheaper than aluminum per unit volume.

The specific gravity of magnesium is 1.74, compared with 2.70 for aluminum and 7.8 for steel. The lightness of the metal and its alloys is advantageous in the same manner and to an even greater degree than has been explained for aluminum in discussing conductivity and mechanical properties. For electrical conductors, little consideration need be given to magnesium, since its conductivity, section for section, is only 63 per cent of that of aluminum and slightly less than that of aluminum even on the mass basis. The tensile strength of annealed magnesium sheet (99.8 Mg) is 27,000 psi and its yield strength 14,000 psi, the comparable figures for aluminum being 13,000 and 5,000 psi; but the aluminum sheet has much greater ductility. Despite its lower modulus of elasticity

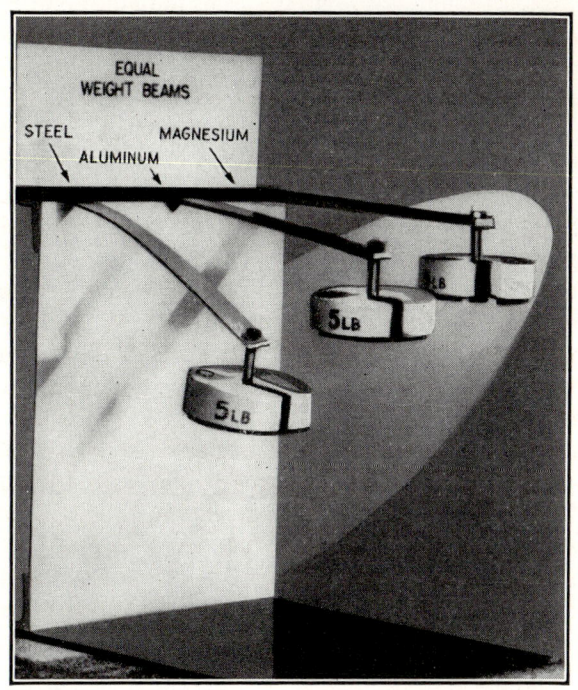

Fig. 157. Comparison of stiffness in beams of equal width and weight. Despite its lower modulus of elasticity, the greater thickness of the magnesium produces greater stiffness as compared with aluminum or steel. (*Courtesy of Dow Chemical Company.*)

(6,500,000 psi), magnesium provides greater stiffness than aluminum or steel in beams of equal width and weight; this is shown in Fig. 157.

The melting point of magnesium is close to that of aluminum—651 and 660°C (1204 to 1220°F), respectively. The boiling points, however, are far apart, magnesium vaporizing at atmospheric pressure at the relatively low temperature of 1110°C (2030°F) compared with 2060°C (3740°F) for aluminum.

The strength and hardness of magnesium is greatly increased by alloying, just as in the case of aluminum. But whereas with aluminum the pure metal offers advantages over the alloys as regards ductility and corrosion resistance, this is not true of magnesium. Consequently, whereas pure aluminum has many structural applications, in the case of magnesium this field is taken over almost entirely by the alloys, because of their generally superior properties. As with aluminum, castings are not made of the pure metal, because the alloys have better casting qualities as well as properties. A notable advantage of magnesium alloys for castings is their excellent machinability, in which quality they are even better than cast iron and probably the best of all the metals.

Fabrication. Although not so workable as aluminum, magnesium and its alloys are shaped and fabricated by all the principal methods, except that cold working is limited to small reductions. Sand casting, permanent-mold casting, and die casting are all widely practiced. Extrusion, rolling, and forging are commonly used, extrusion more often than with most metals. While hammer forging is often done, the relative hardness of magnesium makes press forging more desirable, especially for large sections. Huge presses were built during the recent war, including a 30,000-ton press for airplane parts at Bitterfeld, Germany. After the war the latter was brought to the United States, and even larger presses are now being constructed in this country.

Most forming operations must be done hot, but sheet is finished by cold rolling. The amount of reduction possible under cold rolling without cracking is less than with other metals, but up to 50 per cent can be used for thin sheet. Frequent anneals are necessary because of rapid work-hardening. In hot rolling, the metal temperature is 300 to 450°C (570 to 840°F). The rolls are often heated to assist in maintaining the temperature. Much attention has been given to casting ingots for rolling with a sufficiently fine grain structure for optimum results; several methods of doing this have been developed, including elaborate methods of securing uniform cooling and the addition of grain-refining agents. One of the latter frequently used in alloys is calcium, in amounts up to 0.3 per cent. Zirconium is also used for this purpose.

In the foundry, gases are removed from the molten metal by bubbling chlorine through it prior to casting. This yields denser castings and avoids microshrinkage due to hydrogen; the stirring action also promotes separation of nonmetallic inclusions. Grain refinement in foundry practice is accomplished by superheating the melt to 900°C (1650°F), after which it is cooled in air to the proper casting temperature, which usually ranges from 730 to 870°C (1350 to 1600°F). Another method of grain refinement is addition of carbonaceous material such as lampblack or a carbide to the melt.

Deep drawing of magnesium is also extensively practiced, and because this is done hot, it is possible to perform in one operation very deep draws that in other materials would require several cold draws with intermediate anneals. Thus economies in fabrication may be achieved. The great extent to which magnesium can be deep drawn in one operation is illustrated in Fig. 158.

It is necessary to protect the surface of molten magnesium and its alloys to prevent oxidation and possible burning. The inflammability of magnesium ribbon and powder is well known. Masses of solid magnesium, however, will not burn, and even unprotected molten metal does not ignite unless superheated or poured in a thin stream. Protection of the surface of a melt is usually by means of fluxes, largely chloride mixtures. In some cases sulfur is burned in a hood or around a pouring lip, forming a protecting gas envelope of SO_2. In heat-treatment it is advisable to introduce a small percentage of SO_2 (about 0.5 to 1.0 per cent) in the furnace atmosphere to prevent burning. Fine magnesium turnings and dust are a fire hazard unless covered with oil; these should not be allowed to accumulate, and proper precautions should be observed in machining.

Although beryllium does not alloy with magnesium in appreciable quantity, introduction of a very small amount of beryllium, 0.002 per cent or less, greatly reduces the inflammability of magnesium by raising the ignition temperature. This method of protection is not favored in cast alloys because it interferes with grain refinement, but it is sometimes used in wrought alloys and in furnace brazing.

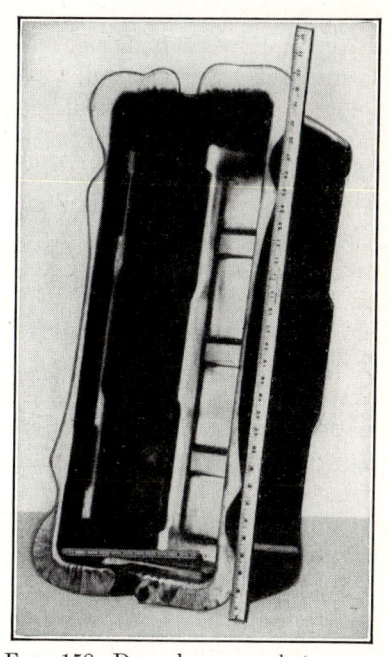

FIG. 158. Deep-drawn rocket-carrying box of magnesium. The box was drawn hot in one operation. (*Courtesy of Dow Chemical Company.*)

Magnesium and most of the alloys can be welded by several methods, but are not successfully welded to other metals. Gas welding is done with suitable fluxes, the lower-temperature gases being preferred to oxyacetylene. Arc welding was done with difficulty until the development of the heliarc process, using helium or argon as a shielding gas; no flux is then required. Spot welding and flash welding are often used. Brazing has also been successfully introduced recently, but thus far is limited to joining parts made of alloy M1. Alloy AZ92 is a good brazing alloy for furnace and flux dip brazing, while another is used for torch brazing; suitable fluxes must be used. Magnesium can be soldered, but this method of joining is not recommended for conditions of stress or corrosion. Any fluxes used in joining by any method must be removed by effective washing since they will cause the joints to corrode.

Corrosion and Surface Treatment. The oxide corrosion product that forms on magnesium is not so adherent and protective as in the case of aluminum. Untreated magnesium surfaces soon become gray and powdery, although penetration into the metal is far less serious than in the case of steel. Methods of preventing corrosion of magnesium and its alloys have now been developed to a very successful state, and except in the case of actual salt-water contact, the corrosion resistance of magnesium alloys is good. The chief concern in design is insulating the joints where the metal would come in contact with dissimilar metals, since the high position of magnesium in the electropotential series makes it able to cause high potential differences if such contact occurs.

The first requisite for minimizing corrosion of magnesium is to eliminate as much as possible of the salt (electrolyte) that was included in the production of the original ingots. This is done by remelting. There must be thorough removal of fluxes used in casting or in welding. The presence of even very small amounts of iron promotes salt-water corrosion, and in casting ingots for rolling, forging, or extrusion the iron content is often reduced to less than 0.005 per cent by using a flux of manganese chloride or zirconium chloride. Nearly all magnesium alloys have a small percentage of manganese as a component, its chief purpose being to reduce corrodibility. The amount of manganese contained is usually 0.1 to 0.3 per cent, the higher the aluminum content of the alloy, the less manganese being retained when the alloy solidifies.

Surface treatments of magnesium alloys have been partly standardized, with adoption of two principal types, although a number of others are sometimes used. These treatments have the primary purpose of providing a suitable base for painting or lacquering. They cause a passivation of the surface and also promote good adherence. The treatment alone without the subsequent painting is not sufficiently protective for long service, although it is satisfactory during transportation and storage. The "chrome pickle" treatment is the most used. The metal is dipped for about one minute at room temperature in a solution of 180 g per liter of sodium dichromate ($Na_2Cr_2O_7.2H_2O$) and 187 ml per liter of concentrated nitric acid. The second type, called the "dichromate treatment," is used for more severe conditions and especially for salt-water exposure. It consists of two steps, first a dip in 15 to 20 per cent hydrofluoric acid for 5 min at room temperature, followed by boiling for 30 to 45 min in sodium dichromate solution containing 100 to 150 g of the salt per liter. This treatment does not remove metal, as does the chrome pickle, and therefore can be used on parts machined to close dimensions.

Such surface treatments are commonly applied both to castings and to wrought products by the producers themselves.

Magnesium alloys are sometimes clad with other materials in the manner of Alclad. Anodizing treatments are also employed, and electroplating magnesium with other metals has been developed recently.

Any corrosive attack of magnesium alloys is not ordinarily of the intergranular type met with in some aluminum alloys. It is of the surface variety and usually rather uniformly distributed.

TABLE 32. PRINCIPAL MAGNESIUM ALLOYS

ASTM number	Nominal composition, per cent				Principal application
	Al	Zn	Mn	Sn	
Casting alloys:					
A10............	10.0	...	0.10	...	Sand and permanent-mold castings
AZ92...........	9.0	2.0	0.10	...	Sand and permanent-mold castings
AZ63...........	6.0	3.0	0.20	...	Sand castings
AZ91...........	9.0	0.7	0.20	...	Die castings
Wrought alloys:					
M1.............	....	...	1.50	...	Sheet and extrusions
AZ31...........	3.0	1.0	0.30	...	Sheet and extrusions
AZ61...........	6.5	1.0	0.20	...	Extrusions and forgings
AZ80...........	8.5	0.5	0.15	...	Extrusions and forgings
TA54...........	3.5	...	0.50	5.0	Hammer forgings

Magnesium Alloys. The Dow Chemical Company uses the name "Dowmetal" for the series of magnesium alloys produced by that company; the American Magnesium Corporation (subsidiary of the Aluminum Company of America) uses the name "Mazlo alloys"; and the German and British producers have called their series "Elektron alloys." In each case individual alloys in each series are designated by letters, numbers, or combinations thereof. Table 32 gives the ASTM designation of the more important alloys, together with their compositions and chief types of application.

The principal alloying elements for magnesium are aluminum, zinc, and manganese. Minor use is made of tin, silicon, cadmium, cerium, zirconium, and lithium. Cast alloys have tensile strengths of 14,000 to 40,000 psi, with yield strengths of 4,500 to 24,000 psi. Rolled alloy sheets have tensile strengths of 32,000 to 40,000 psi in the annealed condition and up to 50,000 psi when hard-rolled. Extrusions and forgings vary from 35,000 to 48,000 psi when untreated, with one heat-treated composition reaching 53,000 psi. All these figures yield very high strength-weight ratios.

304　　　　　　　　　ENGINEERING METALLURGY

It is noteworthy for purposes of design that, whereas magnesium alloy castings have yield strengths in compression equal to those in tension, most of the wrought magnesium alloys have much lower yield strengths in compression. The ratio of compressive to tensile yield strength is less than 0.5 for alloy M1, ranging up to 1.0 for other wrought magnesium alloys and averaging about 0.7.

Aluminum forms with magnesium solid solutions to a maximum solubility of 12.1 per cent at 436°C (817°F), falling to about 2 per cent at

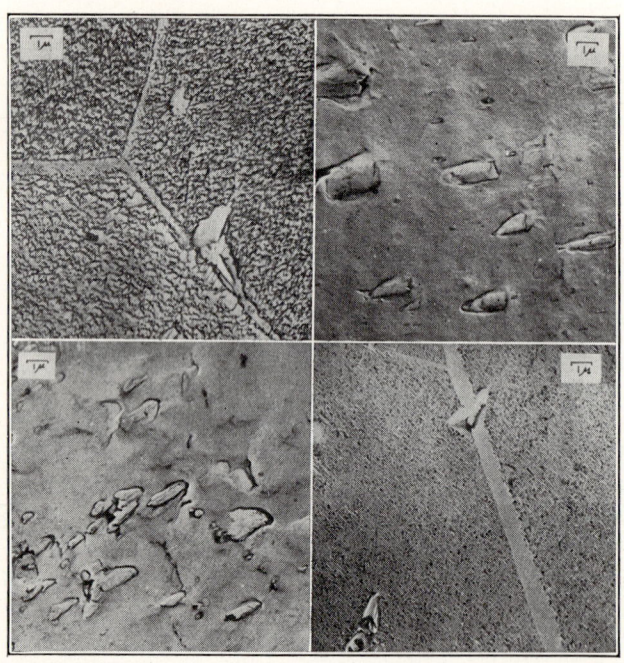

Fig. 159. Electron micrographs of magnesium alloy containing 0.50 per cent aluminum or more. Magnification 6,000 ×. The fine structure in the upper left-hand corner is obtained by solution heat-treatment at relatively high temperature. Aging at lower temperature causes disappearance of this structure with precipitation of a Mg-Al compound as shown in the upper right-hand corner. In the lower right the fine structure has been restored by a subsequent heat-treatment, and in the lower left reaging has caused reprecipitation. (*Courtesy of J. C. McDonald, Dow Chemical Company.*)

room temperature. This indicates the possibility of precipitation hardening; actually heat-treatment improves strength and hardness only of alloys containing more than 6 per cent aluminum. The heat-treatment is in some cases a simple solution treatment, in others, a solution treatment followed by accelerated aging. Only a limited amount of age hardening occurs at room temperature with magnesium alloys. The magnesium-zinc equilibrium diagram is similar in form to the magnesium-aluminum diagram at the magnesium end.

The alloy containing only manganese (1.5 per cent) as an alloying element is used because of its better corrosion resistance, especially in salt water.

Two recently developed alloys are worthy of mention. One containing 6 per cent zinc with 0.8 per cent zirconium (No. ZK60) can be worked at higher temperature without hot-shortness; it is especially used for extrusions. Zirconium produces a fine grain size, and also reduces the iron content. The other is a cast alloy in which magnesium is alloyed with cerium, commonly 6 per cent; it has outstanding resistance to creep.

Uses and Commercial Forms. The uses of magnesium which are developing most rapidly are those in which lightness combined with strength are most needed. Use in the form of alloys, both cast and wrought, is required for these purposes, while the older uses more commonly employ the pure metal. The largest users now are the aircraft industry and manufacturers of portable tools and movable equipment. In aircraft, magnesium alloys are used for landing wheels, crankcases, intake manifolds, oil pumps, instrument panels, and to some extent for frames. About half of the wartime production in the United States went into structural uses, and half was used for the casings of incendiary bombs, partly because of the high-temperature combustibility and partly because larger bomb loads were made possible. The older uses in powder form include fireworks, military flares, marine signals, flashlight powders, and synthesis of organic chemicals. Magnesium is used as a deoxidizer for certain metals, particularly for nickel, in which it removes nickel sulfide as well as oxide. It is also used to produce some of the rarer metals by reduction from their salts, notably titanium from titanium chloride and beryllium from beryllium fluoride. Magnesium anodes are used for cathodic protection against corrosion in the same manner as described under Zinc.

The standard purity of commercial magnesium is 99.8 per cent, although other grades can be obtained, including purity as high as 99.99 per cent. Standard specifications have been adopted by the American Society for Testing Materials for 99.8 per cent ingot and stick and for ingots of several alloy compositions. Producers also supply the various fabricated forms in different conditions of treatment.

PART IV. TIN, NICKEL, AND COBALT

Tin

The outstanding properties of tin are its resistance to corrosion, its fusibility, and its softness and pliability. It is also a constituent of numerous alloys.

The chief uses of tin are in the same categories as those of zinc. Just as the largest application of zinc is in coating steel to make galvanized iron, the largest use of tin is in coating steel to make tin plate. Both metals have principal uses as alloying agents for copper in brasses and bronzes. Zinc has higher mechanical properties and hence is used in die castings and in rolled form more than tin, while the greater malleability and workability of tin cause it to be used in the form of tubing and tin foil to a greater extent. In competing against zinc, tin carries the handicap of a price usually six to eight times as high as that of zinc. The specific gravities of the two metals are about the same.

Resistance to Corrosion. Tin is silver white in color and retains a bright finish satisfactorily, although it receives a slightly yellowish tarnish on long exposure. It has an intermediate position in the electropotential series of metals; its resistance to corrosion is enhanced by the presence of a thin surface film of stannic oxide (SnO_2), normally invisible. Under atmospheric conditions tin does not protect iron electrochemically as does zinc, so that tin plate soon becomes spotted with iron rust under outdoor exposure as the iron corrodes through the pores of the tin coating (see page 352). In the interior of a "tin can," however, where conditions are altered by the partial exhaustion of air and the presence of the contents of the can, the relative potentials of the iron and tin may be reversed so that galvanic protection can exist.

Tin is readily attacked by both strong acids and strong alkalies, but has high resistance to corrosion by weak acids and alkalies such as those in food products. It is virtually unattacked by water and resists salt-water corrosion well.

One of the applications of tin is in coating copper to avoid corrosion under certain conditions. Copper wire that is to be insulated with rubber is first tinned, since there is a chemical action between copper and rubber but none between tin and rubber. This is probably due to the fact that tin has only slight affinity for the sulfur which is used to vulcanize rubber as compared with the strong affinity of copper for sulfur.

Tin is nonpoisonous, a property which supplements its resistance to corrosion as a reason for its use in contact with foods. A large use for tin is in the form of tubing used in making or dispensing beverages. Tin is used because it is easy to form into cooling coils and because it causes no detectable effect on flavor.

Fusibility. The melting point of tin is 232°C (449°F), which is lower than that of any of the common low-melting metals such as lead, cadmium, or bismuth, though not so low as some of the rarer metals. Since its boiling point is high, 2270°C (4120°F), it exists in the liquid state over an unusually long temperature range.

When tin is alloyed wth other metals, the melting temperature is reduced still further, giving rise to such useful alloys as the tin solders (see below) and the "fusible alloys" (see page 162).

Mechanical Properties and Shaping. Like lead, tin is structurally weak but highly plastic. It is readily cold-rolled to thin foil. Tin foil may be of pure tin, or it may contain several per cent of zinc, lead, or antimony, or a little copper, for greater hardness and strength. It has been widely used for wrapping food products and is also used for electric condenser foil. Tin foil has now been replaced in large degree by the lower-cost aluminum foil, which resembles it greatly in appearance.

Besides rolling, tin and its alloys are commonly shaped by other methods, especially casting, die casting, extrusion, and spinning. The die-casting alloys contain 60 to 92 per cent tin, together with antimony, copper, and often lead. Collapsible tubes, used for tooth paste, shaving cream, etc., are made by impact extrusion, just as with the competing aluminum tubes.

Allotropy. At temperatures below 13°C (55°F) tin may undergo an allotropic transformation to a form called "gray tin." This form has a specific gravity of only 5.3, and the transformation is accompanied by disintegration with formation of powder. The rate of transformation is inappreciable at temperatures above 0°C and is slow even at temperatures as low as minus 40. It is restrained by the presence of impurities and accelerated by stress, as in sheet tin. It has not caused any serious difficulty in the practical use of tin.

Uses. Over one-third of the American consumption of tin goes into tin plate. In 1951, 32,500 long tons of tin was used for this purpose, making 4,030,000 tons of tin plate and terneplate, of which about 92 per cent was tin plate.

TABLE 33. DISTRIBUTION OF THE USE OF TIN IN THE UNITED STATES AND IN THE UNITED KINGDOM

Use	Per cent of total consumed United States, 1950	Per cent of total consumed United Kingdom, 1949
Tin plate (including terneplate)	37	45
Other tinning	4	6
Solder	26	8
Bronze, brass, bearing metals and other alloys	20	27
Babbitt	6	1
Collapsible tubes and tin foil	1.5	7
Type metal	1.5	1
Tin compounds and salts	1	3
Miscellaneous	4	4
Total	100	100
Total consumption, tons of 2,240 lb	103,600	21,000

[1] Included in other items.

Table 33 gives recent figures showing the present distribution of tin among its various uses in the United States and in the United Kingdom, as reported by the U.S. Department of Commerce and the British Ministry of Supply, respectively.

Tin is considerably more expensive than copper, nickel, and other common metals. Its present price is about four times that of copper.

Commercial Tin. Tin is marketed chiefly in ingots or small bars, sometimes in large blocks. The purity of the metal is high. "Standard" tin as designated by the marketing center in London must contain over 99.75 per cent tin. Most brands are about 99.9, some are over 99.99, and only a few are as low as 99.2 per cent.

Tin Plate. This product, from which "tin cans" are made, and which is used also for other containers, kitchen ware, roofing, and many other purposes, consists of low-carbon steel (usually 0.1 per cent carbon or less) coated with pure tin. The steel base may be rolled hot or cold, but all American steel for tinning is now cold-rolled. Two methods of coating are used, dipping in molten tin, called "hot tinning," and electroplating, called "electrotinning."

In hot tinning, the sheets are first cleaned by pickling in sulfuric acid and are then fed into automatic machines, passing first through a flux of zinc chloride, then into molten tin, and emerging through a compartment containing palm oil. In both the tin and the oil compartments, the sheets pass between steel rolls which squeeze off excess tin. The oil serves to give a better distribution of tin and protects it from oxidation while hot.

Electrotinning gives a more uniform coating with close control of the thickness of the deposit. A thinner coating may be made of no greater porosity than a considerably thicker hot-dip coating. Tin plate suitable for most, though not all, conditions of use may thus be made with about two-fifths as much tin as commonly used in hot tinning. Comparative thicknesses for ordinary use are 0.0002 to 0.00025 in. with hot tinning and 0.00007 to 0.0001 in. with electrotinning. The proportion of United States tin plate made electrolytically grew rapidly from 18 per cent in 1943 to 64 per cent in 1951. Electrotinning of copper and brass has been practiced on a smaller scale for many years.

Two types of plating baths are widely used for electrotinning, the alkaline bath of sodium stannate (Na_2SnO_3) with other additions, and the acid bath of stannous sulfate ($SnSO_4$) with other additions. A chloride bath and a fluoborate bath also have some use.

Terneplate. This product, a substitute for tin plate, employs a lead-tin alloy coating. It is made by the hot-dip method in the same manner as hot tinning. It is made in several grades containing 10 to 25 per cent tin. It may be hardened by addition of a little antimony. Its cost, made lower because of the relatively low tin content and the lower cost of lead, is intermediate between that of galvanized sheet and tin plate. Among its uses are spouting and roofing, hardware, and automobile gasoline tanks.

Tin Alloys. The principal classes of alloys in which tin is the major component are the babbitts, solders, and pewters. Tin is also a minor component of many alloys, notably bronzes and some special brasses. Tin is also an essential constituent of type metal.

Babbitt is a name for various compositions of so-called "white" or low-melting bearing alloys. The original babbitt metal, the invention of Isaac Babbitt in 1839, was composed of 88.9 per cent tin, 7.4 per cent antimony, and 3.7 per cent copper. There are now many kinds of babbitt, the principal tin babbitts containing 65 to 91 per cent tin with varying amounts of antimony and copper and sometimes lead. There are also lead-base babbitts containing only 5 or 10 per cent tin. It is preferable to call these lead-base alloys "antifriction" metal or "bearing metal," reserving the term babbitt for the tin-base alloys.

There are also numerous kinds of solder. The common low-melting solders are tin-lead alloys, often called "soft solders" to distinguish them from other kinds. The word solder without other designation usually signifies a tin-lead alloy containing 50 to 70 per cent tin. The 50:50 grade, called "half-and-half," is most used, especially by plumbers and sheetmetal workers. "Eutectic solder," containing 63 per cent tin with 37 per cent lead, has the lowest melting point of the series; it is used in electrical work. Some of the soft solders are mostly lead. Solder may be used to join most metals, but is limited by its low tenacity, its low melting point, and its corrosion by such acids as attack either tin or lead.

Pewter is an old alloy of tin used for tableware, trays, vases, cups, and other containers, and Britannia metal is a similar alloy in the same range of composition. Modern pewter is usually composed of 90 to 95 per cent tin, 1 to 3 per cent copper, and the remainder antimony. Older compositions frequently contained lead up to 20 per cent. The different compositions of pewter and Britannia metal fall in the same range as the high-tin bearing metals, but they are usually free from lead or contain relatively little, because crystals of lead may cause lead poisoning.

Several tin compounds are used industrially, but none is of major importance. Tin oxide is used in enamels, and the chloride in textile dyes and bleaches. Use of the chloride for weighting silk is now considerably diminished.

Nickel

The use of nickel has grown more than that of most of the common metals during the past 25 years. Its production, below that of tin prior to the second World War, is now greater than that of tin.

Nearly half of the nickel consumed is used in alloy steels and cast irons, and over a third in other alloys; less than one-sixth is used as commercially pure nickel. Table 34 shows the distribution of nickel in its different forms in the United States.

TABLE 34. DISTRIBUTION OF NICKEL BY USES
(Based on nickel consumed in the United States in 1950)

Use	Per cent
Ferrous:	
Stainless steels	17
Other steels	22
Cast irons	5
Nonferrous (copper-nickel alloys, nickel silver, brass, bronze, beryllium, magnesium, and aluminum alloys, and monel, Inconel, and malleable nickel)	28
High-temperature and electrical resistance alloys	6
Electroplating:	
Anodes	18
Solutions	1
Catalysts	1
Other uses	2
Total	100

Marketed Forms. Metallic nickel is regularly sold in several different forms, chiefly the following: cathode sheets, cut in various sizes; cast blocks; shot, made by pouring molten nickel into water; round pellets, formed by decomposition of gaseous nickel carbonyl (Mond process); malleable ingots; and cubes or rondelles, reduced from the oxide without fusion. Various alloys are also marketed by the primary producers, and also nickel oxide and nickel salts.

Electrolytically refined nickel contains a small fraction of a per cent of cobalt, which is not deleterious and is commonly counted with nickel in all stated percentage compositions. On this basis the purity of electrolytic nickel is 99.95 per cent before melting the cathodes and about 99.6 per cent after melting. The impurities of principal importance as shown in the specifications of the American Society for Testing Materials for the different grades of nickel are iron, carbon, and sulfur.[1]

The form of nickel designated as "A" nickel by the International Nickel Company is nearly pure deoxidized nickel; it is used especially for wrought products. Its nominal composition is 99.4 per cent nickel (plus cobalt), 0.25 manganese, 0.20 iron, 0.10 copper, 0.07 carbon, 0.03 silicon, and less than 0.005 per cent sulfur; it may contain slightly higher

[1] Specifications for nickel, nickel alloys, electrodeposited nickel coatings, etc., are given in "A.S.T.M. Standards," 1949, Part 2, p. 330. (Spec. B39-22, and others.)

percentages of impurities, but not to exceed 1 per cent total. "A" nickel is commonly deoxidized with magnesium.

Nickel refined by the carbonyl or Mond process is over 99.8 per cent nickel, and is practically free from both cobalt and copper.

Properties and Uses of Commercial Nickel. The properties of nickel resemble those of iron in many respects, but it is far more resistant to corrosion. Like iron, nickel is a heavy metal of high melting point (1455°C or 2651°F).

Mechanical Properties. Nickel is the hardest and strongest of the common metals, unalloyed. "A" nickel is as strong as mild steel. When hot-rolled, or when cold-drawn and then annealed, its tensile strength is 50,000 to 80,000 psi, its yield strength 20,000 to 30,000 psi, and its Brinell hardness 90 to 120. Cold-drawn wire of spring temper has a tensile strength of 135,000 to 165,000 psi. Elongation of the annealed material is 35 to 50 per cent in 2 in. The high ductility and malleability of pure nickel, however, may be markedly lowered by oxygen and certain impurities.

Magnetism. Nickel, like iron and cobalt, is ferromagnetic at ordinary temperatures. Its magnetism is lost on heating to 352°C (666°F).

Resistance to Corrosion. Nickel is chemically a rather inactive metal, and freedom from oxidation or tarnishing is one of its important properties. It is not attacked even in the presence of salt water. Sulfuric and hydrochloric acids attack it very slowly, but nitric acid dissolves it readily. Certain nickel alloys are among the foremost materials for resistance to oxidation (scaling) combined with strength at high temperatures.

Cost. Nickel costs two to three times as much as copper. Its price is well stabilized. For many years it was 35 cents per pound in the United States, and unlike prices of most metals, it did not vary during periods of active business or depression. Recently, however, it has risen to 63 cents, largely because of the necessity of mining and treating ores of lower grade, as well as generally increased production costs.

Uses of Pure Nickel. The principal applications of unalloyed nickel are in rolled form (sheet, rods, wire, tube, etc.), for nickel-clad steel, and for electroplating. These and other forms are used in food processing, in the chemical industry, in the nickel-iron storage battery, for coinage, electronic tubes, and as a catalyst in the hydrogenation of organic compounds, such as the production of edible fats from vegetable oils.

Nickel Plating. The hardness of nickel, its nonrusting qualities, moderate cost, and ability either to take a high polish or to be deposited directly as "bright nickel" make it an excellent metal for coating steel, brass, and other base metals. Electroplating constitutes the largest use of the commercially pure metal. The full extent of this use is not apparent because a deposit of chromium is usually superimposed on the nickel plating. The nickel layer, however, is typically 100 times as thick as the chromium layer, and the present tendency is to make it even thicker. The thickness of nickel is often 0.0003 in. for plating on brass and 0.001 in. for plating on steel. Without undercoating, chromium would afford little protection to steel against corrosion.

Nickel plating on steel is usually underlain by a plating of copper. This minimizes exposure of iron through pores in the plating. If such exposure exists, the presence of nickel, which is below iron in the electropotential series of metals, will accelerate corrosion of the iron, with formation of scattered spots of rust (see page 352). Nickel sulfate is the basis of most nickel-plating solutions, various other substances being added. The properties of the plating may be varied by variations in composition of the solution, together with appropriate variations in the conditions of electrolysis.

Nickel Alloys. A listing of properties conferred by nickel when used as an alloying element in different alloys indicates strikingly the variety of benefits that may be obtained by use of this element. Its effects vary, of course, in different alloys, and any one item from the following list may apply in only a few cases, but the list serves to emphasize the usefulness and versatility of nickel as an alloy component. The properties it may confer include (1) fineness of grain structure, (2) greater strength without brittleness, (3) improved fatigue resistance, (4) improved corrosion resistance, (5) improved strength at high temperatures, (6) resistance to oxidation at high temperatures, (7) high electrical resistance, (8) special magnetic properties, (9) lower coefficient of expansion, (10) discharge of color in alloys of copper and gold. Nickel has high strength at subzero temperatures, and it may be added to steel to confer strength at these temperatures.

There are over 3,000 alloys in present use containing nickel in varying proportions.

Nickel-iron Alloys. Although nickel steels constitute the largest single use for nickel, they contain relatively small percentages of nickel and therefore are nickel-bearing rather than nickel-base alloys. Nickel steel for constructional purposes commonly contains 2 to 3.5 per cent nickel. Nickel is a component of many alloy steels in conjunction with chromium, molybdenum, and other elements. These include many varieties of stainless steels, of which "18-8" (18 per cent chromium, 8 per cent nickel) is the best known. The nickel-bearing alloy steels and cast irons have been discussed in Chap. 9. The cast irons include the special alloys Ni-tensyliron, Ni-hard, and Ni-resist, and also the recently developed family of "ductile irons," in which nickel is commonly introduced along with magnesium.

Nickel-iron alloys containing 9 to 80 per cent nickel are made for a number of special purposes. Those having 25 to 40 per cent nickel are used for applications involving low thermal coefficients of expansion; nickel causes the coefficient of expansion to decrease progressively to practically zero at 36 per cent nickel, at which point it begins to rise again. Such alloys are used for reinforcement wire imbedded in glass, for glass seals in radio and television tubes, for gas engines, boiler tubes, valve stems on sea-water pumps, etc. The alloy of 36 per cent nickel is called *invar*, and is used for surveyor's tapes, clock pendulums, and such purposes where it is desired to have length invariable with temperature.

A number of nickel-iron alloys have special magnetic properties. A group extremely useful in telegraph and telephone cables is termed Permalloy, the principal one containing 78.5 per cent nickel, the balance iron. The most important property of Permalloy, brought out by a special heat-treatment, is a very high magnetic permeability at low magnetizing forces. In some samples tested a permeability 200 times as great as that of pure iron has been attained. Small percentages of chromium or molybdenum are sometimes added in Permalloy to give higher electrical resistance or for other purposes.

The 50 Ni:50 Fe alloy, called Hipernik, has about one-half the permeability of the 78.5 per cent nickel alloy, but is less sensitive to heat-treatment.

The nickel and cobalt alloys for permanent magnets have attained wide use; they have exceptionally high coercive force. Magnets more powerful than any previously known can be made with some of them. The one best known is Alnico, which contains typically 20 per cent nickel, 5 cobalt, 12 aluminum, and 63 iron. These alloys may be heated to 315°C (600°F) without loss of magnetism.

Nickel-copper Alloys. The nickel-copper alloy of greatest usefulness to the engineer is monel. It is called a "natural" alloy, in that the combination of the two metals exists in the ore and they remain together all through the process of extraction. Nickel and copper form with each other a continuous series of solid solutions in all proportions. Monel is sometimes made also by melting nickel and copper together.

Monel contains, on the average, about 67 per cent nickel, 30 per cent copper, the balance chiefly iron and manganese. It is even harder and stronger than pure nickel and, being also of somewhat lower cost, it can be applied for certain high-grade constructional purposes to better advantage than the pure metal, particularly in place of steel where resistance to corrosion is a prime requisite. It resembles nickel very much in appearance and in most of its properties.

Several varieties of monel have been introduced. In one, a heat-treatable variety named "K" monel, about 2.75 per cent of aluminum is incorporated, together with a little titanium. After quenching from 790°C (1450°F), it is reheated to about 580°C (1075°F); precipitation hardening takes place, resulting in one of the strongest precipitation-hardening alloys. Spring wire of "K" monel is furnished with tensile strengths of 175,000 to 200,000 psi. "R" monel, a free-machining grade, carries 0.025 to 0.06 per cent sulfur, compared with 0.01 per cent in regular monel.

Some nickel-bearing copper alloys, including nickel silver and others, were mentioned under Copper (page 263). Nickel in bronze increases its fluidity for casting and results in a better surface. It also lowers the cost through saving of tin.

Constantan, an alloy of 45 per cent nickel, 55 per cent copper, has the highest electrical resistivity of the nickel-copper alloys. It is used for resistors and also as a thermocouple wire in couples of low temperature range.

Nickel-chromium Alloys. These alloys are used chiefly for their heat-resisting qualities; they have high melting points, and they resist oxidation at high temperatures to an unusual degree. Also they have very high electrical resistivity. They are used for casehardening boxes and other apparatus that is to be heated to a red heat or above; also for electrical purposes, and especially for wire which must stand up under high temperatures, such as resistance wire in wire-wound electric furnaces, rheostats, and high-range thermocouple wire. They contain 7 to 22 per cent chromium, and may or may not contain considerable iron and some manganese, the balance being nickel. One of the best known is Nichrome, which is made in several grades. One grade for wire is 80 per cent nickel, 20 per cent chromium, while one much used for castings carries 60 per cent nickel, 12 chromium, 26 iron, and 2 manganese. Nichrome resistance wire has a resistivity of about 700 ohms per mil-ft, nearly 70 times that of copper.

Inconel is a nickel-chromium-iron alloy, commonly in the proportions 72:14–17:10. It has a large and growing use for purposes requiring high strength combined with high resistance to corrosion, and especially for resistance to oxidation at high temperatures. The oxide scale formed at high temperature is tightly adherent. Inconel X is a wrought, non-magnetic, age-hardenable variation of Inconel developed primarily for gas turbines and jet engines when high rupture strength and low creep rates under high stress at temperatures up to about 815°C (1500°F) are essential. Inconel X has the added components titanium (2.25 to 2.75 per cent), columbium (0.70 to 1.20), and aluminum (0.4 to 1.0).

Ni-span C is an age-hardenable nickel-chromium-titanium-iron alloy which has a nearly constant modulus of elasticity over the range −18 to 93°C (0 to 200°F). Its thermoelastic coefficient can be adjusted by suitable heat-treatment and prior cold work so that small negative, zero, or small positive coefficients can be obtained. It is useful for springs in accurate weighing systems and in vibrating systems such as those in watches and clocks.

Other Nickel Alloys. Two types of nickel alloys important in the field of corrosion resistance are Hastelloy and Illium. Each is made in several modifications. The principal varieties of Hastelloy are nickel-molybdenum-iron alloys; they are especially valuable for resistance to hydrochloric acid and chlorides. Other varieties contain chromium, tungsten, silicon, or copper. Illium is a complex nickel alloy containing typically 22 per cent chromium with 6 per cent each of copper, molybdenum, and iron.

Cobalt

Cobalt is a metal of relatively small production, less than 10,000 tons annually, yet has several important engineering uses. It is very scarce in relation to the demand for it.

The commercial use of cobalt as pure metal is practically negligible. Its properties, both physical and chemical, are in most respects very similar to those of nickel, but it commonly costs about four times as much as nickel. The alloys in which cobalt is an important constituent, on the other hand, have grown in number and in use in recent years. The principal types are listed in Table 35.

Cobalt is one of the three common metals that are ferromagnetic at ordinary temperatures. It is more magnetic than nickel, but considerably less so than iron. Its Curie point is the highest of the three, being 1115°C (2039°F). As noted below, one of the principal uses of cobalt is in magnetic alloys.

Cobalt Alloys. Most of the cobalt alloys are multicomponent. The oldest and the one usually containing the highest percentage of cobalt is stellite. This alloy, or rather group of alloys, since it is made in several compositions for different applications, contains 50 to 90 per cent cobalt, 10 to 35 per cent chromium, and up to 2.75 per cent carbon. Most varieties also contain tungsten, usually 5 to 17 per cent. Other elements sometimes added are molybdenum, nickel, and iron. Cobalt and chromium form solid solutions in all proportions, and tungsten has a solid solubility in cobalt beyond the percentage used. The presence of tungsten and carbon is of great importance in stellite used for cutting tools, since it results in particles of tungsten carbide of extreme hardness which retain their hardness at red heat. Thus stellite exhibits similar behavior in this respect to high-speed steel.

The cobalt-base alloys work-harden rapidly and can be machined only with great difficulty if at all. Most of the varieties of stellite can be forged with difficulty at 750 to 1200°C (1380 to 2190°F), but some are not workable at any temperature and must therefore be cast. Stellite is readily welded to steel, and steel tools are often tipped or clad with stellite, an operation called "␣stelliting." Hard wearing surfaces and heat-resisting surfaces are applied in this manner; this is called "hard facing." Another valuable property of stellite is that it is not subject to rust or tarnishing. This makes it valuable for surgical and dental instruments, with the added advantage over steel that they can be sterilized by heating without loss of hardness through a tempering or annealing effect of the heat. Resistance to corrosion and to high temperatures is combined in stellite searchlight reflectors, much used in the Navy. These resist shattering from shock of gunfire, corrosion by salt air and water, the effect of powder fumes, the heat of the arc light, and pitting by hot particles of copper or carbon from the electrodes.

Cobalt is used as the "cementing" or supporting material in the cutting tools, dies, etc., of cemented tungsten carbide, as exemplified by Carboloy and others. The proportion of cobalt in these tools, which are discussed under Tungsten, is commonly 3 to 13 per cent. Although applied as pure cobalt, the metal absorbs some tungsten and carbon during the cementing or sintering operation, becoming an alloy of increased hardness and heat resistance.

Another use of cobalt which has grown to large proportions is in the newer types of permanent-magnet alloys, capable of exerting exceptionally high magnetic force. Alnico (see page 313) contains 5 per cent cobalt, while Vicalloy, developed at the Bell Telephone Laboratories, is 36 to 62 per cent cobalt. A high-cobalt steel, containing 35 per cent cobalt, has been used for some time for permanent magnets of lower magnetic strength.

Cobalt is also used as a component of some high-speed steels, of the cobalt-chromium-tungsten type, containing 5 to 12 per cent cobalt, and of some razor-blade steels.

A number of the stellite compositions are included in the high-temperature resistant and creep-resistant alloys, brought out during the Second World War, which have played so important a part in making possible the development of gas turbines and jet engines. These and other cobalt-base alloys are used for the blades in gas turbines and for the buckets in turbosuperchargers operating under stress at temperatures as high as 815°C (1500°F). While some of these alloys may be wrought, they are usually fabricated by precision casting. Stellite 21 (63 per cent Co, 27 Cr, 6 Mo, 2 Ni, 1 Fe, 0.25 C) has the same composition, except for the carbon content, as Vitallium, an alloy originally used in dentistry, and still important in that field and in surgery.

Marketed Forms. Cobalt is most commonly sold in the form of rondelles. These are small slugs made by briquetting the black oxide, Co_3O_4, with carbon and heating, thus reducing the oxide to metal without fusion. Some cobalt is also sold in the form of shot, made by reducing in the molten state and pouring into water. A good deal of cobalt is also sold directly in the form of the oxide, the steel industry using it either in this form or as metal. The oxide is also used in making blue glass and blue enamels.

TABLE 35. DISTRIBUTION OF THE USE OF COBALT IN THE UNITED STATES[1]
(Per cent)

Use	1950	1952
Permanent-magnet alloys	38	15
Cast Co-Cr-W-Mo alloys	24	59
High-speed and other steels	6	3
Cemented carbides	2	6
Hard-facing alloys	2	5
Other uses in metallic form	3	1
Cobalt in salts and compounds	25	11
Total	100	100

[1] U.S. Bureau of Mines.

PART V. OTHER METALS

Tungsten (Wolfram)

The properties of tungsten are unique in several respects. It has the highest melting point of any of the metals—3390°C (6134°F). When properly wrought it becomes one of the most ductile metals, and while a rod of large diameter is not exceptionally strong, the tensile strength increases rapidly with reduction of size through drawing, until at a diameter of 0.0014 in. it attains a strength of 590,000 psi, greater than that of any other material. In other words, while tungsten is not the most ductile metal and cannot broadly be called the strongest, it combines ductility with strength to a greater degree than any other substance. Tungsten also has the highest recrystallizing temperature following strain of any metal, and it exhibits a peculiar structural property, *viz.*, that when it exists in small equiaxed grains it is very brittle at room temperature, but when it has a fibrous structure it may be very ductile and pliable at room temperature; in exhibiting ductility with respect to grain structure in this way, its behavior is in direct opposition to that of the common ductile metals.

The 1.14-mil wire fractures with a reduction of area of about 65 per cent. Yet tungsten is one of the hardest metals. It is also extremely heavy, its specific gravity of about 19.3 being almost the same as that of gold.

Uses. The use of tungsten for electric-light filaments is known to all, but this use consumes less than 10 per cent of all the tungsten produced. The reason lies in the extreme fineness of the wire filament. It is said that a single ton of tungsten oxide (WO_3) will yield enough metal to make 18,000,000 electric lamps.

About 90 per cent of the tungsten is used in making tungsten steels. For this purpose the tungsten is used in a less pure form or in the form of the iron alloy, ferrotungsten. The leading tungsten steel is high-speed

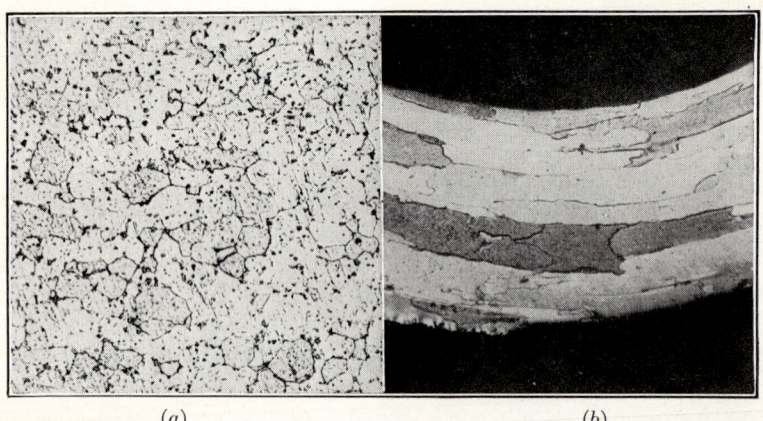

(a) (b)

FIG. 160. (a) Structure of a tungsten filament which resists vibration, obtained by adding a small percentage of thorium nitrate to the tungstic oxide before reduction. The small black specks are particles of thoria (ThO_2). Original magnification 200 ×, enlarged to 500 ×. (b) Nonsag structure of a coiled tungsten filament after being used in a lamp. The nonsag properties are obtained by adding a small percentage of foreign material such as KCl and SiO_2. Original magnification 200 ×, enlarged to 500 ×. (*Courtesy of Westinghouse Electric Corporation, Lamp Division. Photomicrographs by G. R. Moritz.*)

steel containing 14 to 25 per cent tungsten, together with other elements. This material has been discussed on page 236; its outstanding property is that of retaining its hardness when cutting at such speed that it becomes red hot. Tungsten is also used in other special steels and alloys in smaller percentages and in conjunction with other elements. Finally, the tungsten steel containing about 5 per cent tungsten is the material most commonly used for large permanent magnets.

Tungsten as first reduced to metal and sintered to ingot form is very fragile and brittle. The process of making it ductile is described on page 411. Tungsten wire can be coiled on mandrels with diameters almost as small as the wire itself. In order to achieve this result it is necessary to control the amount and direction of grain growth in the wire. Without such control large grains would form with smooth grain boundaries normal to the axis of the wire. Obstruction to grain growth was first accomplished by addition of 0.75 per cent thoria, a method which is still used for certain purposes. Strong, nonsag wire is now made by addition of potassium silicate. At high temperature this becomes silica in a plastic fibrous form which retards growth normal to the axis. Elongated grains with interlocking irregular boundaries result (see Fig. 160).

The development of radio brought other uses for tungsten. Tungsten wire is used as the filamentary body of vacuum tubes both for broadcasting and receiving. Wrought tungsten is also used for electrodes in certain rectifiers, as well as for cathodes and anodes in x-ray tubes, and for electrical contact points, where it has been substituted for platinum. Phonograph needles are sometimes made of tungsten. Tungsten wire and rod are sometimes used for high-temperature electric-resistance furnaces; such resistors must be operated in a neutral or hydrogen atmosphere. In addition to its use as filaments of incandescent lamps and vacuum tubes, tungsten wire is used for lamp and vacuum-tube support and anchor wires.

Tungsten Carbide. Tungsten carbide is one of the hardest substances known, its hardness approaching that of diamond. It retains its hardness at high temperatures to an exceptional degree. The carbide is made by heating tungsten powder with carbon powder at very high temperature; the resulting composition is largely WC, with a little W_2C. The extremely fine carbide particles are cemented with a hard, tough, and ductile metal, usually cobalt. This is accomplished by first grinding the carbide in a ball mill with a few per cent of the metal, pressing, partly sintering, machining to final shape, and finally sintering at white heat in an atmosphere of hydrogen. Dies, especially for hot and cold drawing, deep drawing, and extrusion, are made in this way; also cutting tools which are attached to shanks of alloy steel or high-strength cast iron by brazing. The cemented carbide has a modulus of elasticity sometimes as high as 69,000,000 psi, higher than that of any other material. The Brinell hardness may be over 1300. A typical percentage composition of such a cutting tool is about 82 per cent tungsten, 13 cobalt, 5 carbon. It has been said that 1 lb of tungsten used in this manner can cut fifty times as much steel as 1 lb used in high-speed steel. The tools tend to be brittle and must be used only according to recommended practice.

The performance of such cutting tools, especially in cutting steel, has been found to be improved by addition of other carbides to the tungsten carbide. Titanium and tantalum carbides are often used. One type, called "Kennametal," employs a double carbide of the composition $W_2Ti_2C_4$, formed by dissolving the components in molten nickel, from which it crystallizes on freezing.

Molybdenum

The properties of molybdenum are similar to those of tungsten, and its uses have developed along much the same lines. It is a strong metal of very high melting point, and when used as an alloying element it confers the property of strength and hardness at high temperature. It has assumed a position of importance among the metals comparatively recently. Beginning with the development of a large deposit of molybdenum ore in Colorado by the Climax Molybdenum Company, at the time of the First World War, its use has grown steadily. It has been found possible to use it instead of tungsten both in the form of the pure metal and as a constituent of high-speed steel. A number of other steels as well as nonferrous alloys containing molybdenum have also been developed. Molybdenum filled a special need during the Second World War as a constituent of several "national-emergency" steels, replacing "strategic" elements that were scarce and hard to obtain. About 90 per cent of the world's molybdenum is mined in the United States, whereas we are dependent on other countries for most of our tungsten.

The growing use of molybdenum is by no means due to enforced substitution. As an alloying element in steel it is more diversified than tungsten in its effects and therefore in its applications. As a pure metal it is more easily wrought and fabricated than tungsten. It is also lower in cost. Both metals are also frequently sold in the form of the ferroalloy for use in making alloy steels.

While molybdenum is a heavy metal (specific gravity 10.2), it is much lighter than tungsten, so that less of it is required to make a part of given size.

Properties and Uses. The melting point of molybdenum is 2620°C (4750°F). Whereas the filaments in electric-light bulbs are of tungsten, the supports are of molybdenum wire. In electronic tubes molybdenum is used for the grid wires, the requirements of which include strength at high temperature, good ductility, uniform spring back, low thermal expansion, and freedom from secondary emission of electrons. The grid wires may also be made of an alloy containing molybdenum, iron, and manganese. The hooks or supports in electronic vacuum tubes are also of molybdenum. Resistance wire in electric furnaces suitable for temperatures of 1200 to 2000°C (2190 to 3630°F) is an important application of molybdenum. For this purpose the heating element must be kept in a nonoxidizing atmosphere (usually hydrogen). Molybdenum should not be used at temperatures over 500°C (930°F) under oxidizing conditions. At lower temperatures, however, it has good corrosion resistance in air and in the presence of some chemicals.

Because of its hardness molybdenum is often used for electrical contacts. However, its conductivity is low, and this objection is sometimes overcome by making the contacts from a sintered compact of molybdenum and silver powders.

Like tungsten, molybdenum is commonly made by the methods of powder metallurgy, without fusion, making a dense metal that is readily fabricated into wire, sheet, and tube. However, a growing demand for molybdenum in larger bars and shapes has led to the manufacture of small ingots for forging, by means of a new process of melting with an electric arc in a vacuum.

Molybdenum does not undergo recrystallization below 870°C (1600°F).

Molybdenum Steels. The largest use of molybdenum is for alloy steels. These include molybdenum high-speed steels, creep-resisting steels, nitriding steels, 18-8 stainless steels with addition of 2 to 4 per cent molybdenum, other high-alloy corrosion-resistant steels, chromium-molybdenum steels for heavy springs, and others. Molybdenum is often added for hardenability, especially in steel castings, since it is the only element contributing largely to hardenability that is not partly lost by oxidation when the steel is melted. Molybdenum steels are discussed in Chap. 9.

Other Ferrous and Nonferrous Alloys. Important nonferrous alloys of molybdenum include the nickel-molybdenum-iron alloys of the Hastelloy type. Molybdenum above 15 per cent exerts a marked passivating effect on nickel. Several high-temperature alloys, such as Vitallium and other modifications of stellite, contain molybdenum. Tungsten-molybdenum alloys containing 20 to 90 per cent molybdenum are often used instead of pure molybdenum or tungsten for supports in electric-light bulbs, radio tubes, etc., and for resistance wire.

Molybdenum-iron alloys are used for metal-to-glass seals because of their low coefficients of expansion. Molybdenum is used in a number of special alloys for magnetic purposes.

This incomplete list indicates the increasing number of alloys of this metal.

Beryllium

Beryllium is a light metal having a specific gravity of 1.83, only a little more than that of magnesium. Unlike aluminum and magnesium it has a high melting point, 1287°C (2348°F). It is very brittle, and for this reason as well as because of its high cost, only minor uses have been found for the pure metal. It can be hot-rolled to a very limited extent, and there is a small use of the sheet for x-ray windows because of its transparency to X rays. At the present time larger amounts are being used in atomic-energy research, because of its desirable nuclear properties. In its use as a "moderator" to slow down the passage of neutrons, it is said to be several times as effective as graphite.

In the handling of finely divided beryllium metal, oxides, and other chemical compounds, extreme precautions must be taken to avoid beryllium poisoning.

Several useful beryllium alloys have been developed, but the only one of major importance is beryllium copper. This contains 1.60 to 2.25 per cent beryllium, usually with smaller amounts of cobalt or nickel. Beryllium copper has been discussed on page 266.

Titanium

The properties of titanium are so attractive that it would be one of the most widely used metals if it were not for the high cost of producing it in metallic form of sufficient purity. Production of the oxide, TiO_2, in pure form for use in the paint industry was begun at Niagara Falls in 1918 and has grown so greatly that it is now the leading white pigment, surpassing both zinc oxide and the lead-pigment compounds in tonnage. Titanium ferroalloys have also been used for a long time, but only in small amounts. Production of titanium as a pure ductile metal for industrial use was started by the du Pont company in a small pilot plant in 1948. There are now several producers, and use of titanium is growing rapidly for purposes that justify the present high cost ($7.50 per pound in ingot form). Production is expected to expand greatly as costs are lowered.

The interest in and growth of titanium are rooted in three factors: discovery of large new sources of ore, research and development in production and fabrication methods, and wider realization of the possibilities of titanium as shown in its properties, perhaps inspired by recent rapid development in aluminum and magnesium.

Titanium is a light metal, its specific gravity of 4.5 being nearer to that of aluminum (2.7) than to that of iron (7.9). But unlike aluminum and magnesium, it has a high melting point and it is much stronger. It melts at 1725°C (3137°F), considerably above iron and almost as high as platinum. Its tensile strength when annealed is about 80,000 psi, and after 50 per cent cold reduction it is 115,000 to 130,000 psi. Thus it is stronger than steel used for ordinary construction, and per unit weight it is much stronger.

The strength of titanium can also be raised by alloying. Development of titanium alloys is just beginning, but future use of the metal is likely to be greater in alloyed compositions than unalloyed.

When of proper purity, titanium is highly ductile. Elongation of the annealed metal is stated as 25 per cent in 2 in. However, it is more readily worked hot than cold.

The modulus of elasticity is 16,000,000 psi, between that of aluminum and steel.

The corrosion resistance of titanium under atmospheric and many other conditions is excellent, and it competes with stainless steel or aluminum in special applications. It is particularly good for resistance to salt-water corrosion. Some of the common acids attack it at boiling temperatures.

When heated to red heat, titanium begins to combine with both oxygen and nitrogen. Although it is annealed in air for most purposes, for maximum ductility it should be annealed in a vacuum. For casting, it must be melted in a protective atmosphere. It is inferior both in casting qualities and in machinability. Despite good elongation when pure, it is not easily drawn into wire or tubing because of galling or seizing. It is readily fabricated by hot rolling, forging, and welding. For rolling and forging, large ingots are being made by melting in arc or induction furnaces either in a vacuum or in an argon atmosphere.

Gold and Silver

The so-called precious metals have relatively few engineering applications, but they are of great economic importance, and some of their properties are particularly interesting.

Gold is said to rank first and silver second in malleability and ductility, and gold ranks with tungsten as the heaviest common metal. Both gold and silver are very resistant to corrosion.

The tensile strengths of these metals are good, that of annealed wrought gold being 19,000 psi and that of annealed silver wire 22,500 psi. When hardened by alloying or by working they become considerably stronger. After 60 per cent reduction gold has a tensile strength of 32,000 psi, and that of cold-rolled silver may be 54,000 psi or more. Gold is a soft metal, though it is harder than aluminum, tin, and lead. Silver, while considerably harder than gold, ranks next in order above it among the common metals. Both gold and silver must be hardened by alloying when used for such purposes as coinage and jewelry.

The electrical conductivity of silver is the highest of all the metals on the usual volumetric basis, being about 8 per cent greater than that of copper; the conductivity of gold is only two-thirds as much. In thermal conductivity silver is still more distinctive, being one-third above copper in this property.

Uses for Gold. The two large uses for gold are for monetary purposes and for jewelry. The former is much the larger; though gold coins are now rarely circulated as money, large stocks of gold bars are held as reserves by the treasuries of the leading nations, and paper money is issued against the reserves. Watches, rings, and jewelry in other forms are large uses. A smaller use is gold leaf, which consists of nearly pure gold beaten into very thin sheets, used largely for lettering on signs and other ornamental purposes. Other uses of gold are in dentistry, photography, electroplating, gilding, and in scientific instruments.

Uses of Silver. Coinage was formerly the largest use for silver as well as for gold, but a great change has taken place during the past ten years in the ratio of silver used by industry to that used for monetary purposes. Use of silver for coinage has declined greatly in some countries, notably China and India, and while the amount so used in the United States has increased, the amount used by industry has increased much more. This amount was about 110,000,000 troy ounces (3,800 tons) in the United States in 1951, about three times the amount used for coinage and more than three times the industrial consumption in 1939.

The largest industrial use of silver in the United States is for sterling silverware. Although silver-plated ware is made in greater amounts, the amount of silver in it is relatively small because of the thinness of the plating. Another important use of silver is in photography, especially because of the vast motion-picture industry. The largest engineering use, and the one that has grown most rapidly in recent years, is in silver brazing alloys, often called silver solders. These are mainly silver-copper-zinc alloys containing 10 to 80 per cent silver. The proportions of the metals vary, yielding different properties for different applications. The melting points are usually between 680 and 820°C (1255 and 1510°F), but occasionally lower melting alloys are used and also higher melting ones, including pure silver. Excellent joining qualities and high-strength joints are obtained with the silver brazing alloys, without using excessively high temperatures.

Other engineering uses include lining and coating of chemical and photographic manufacturing equipment, coils and evaporating equipment, other corrosion-resistant apparatus, bearing alloys, and electrical alloys and conductors. Other nonengineering uses include jewelry, dentistry, surgery, as a backing for mirrors, and in pharmaceutical compounds.

Designation of Purity. Instead of the percentage basis as commonly used for other metals, the purity of gold and silver and the content of these metals in their common alloys is usually stated in another way. Silver is commonly designated by its fineness, in which pure silver is 1,000 fine; 900 fine means 90.0 per cent silver; etc. The grade of silver known as *sterling silver* is 925 fine, while United States coin silver, known as *standard silver*, is 900 fine. In both cases the alloying metal is copper.

Gold is frequently also designated by fineness, but more commonly on the carat basis, in which pure gold is 24 carat; 18 carat means 75 per cent gold; etc. Gold is usually hardened by addition of both silver and copper, except that "coin gold" contains copper only. "White gold" is usually 18-carat gold, the remainder being nickel plus zinc. An alloy of 90 gold plus 10 palladium makes a superior kind of white gold.

Bibliography

See also chapters in books listed at the end of Chap. 14.

ADDICKS, L. (editor): "Silver in Industry," Reinhold Publishing Corporation, New York, 1940.

AITCHISON, L., and W. R. BARCLAY: "Engineering Nonferrous Metals and Alloys," Frowde and Hodder and Stoughton, London, 1923.

ALUMINUM COMPANY OF AMERICA: Booklets (revised at intervals): (1) "Alcoa Structural Handbook," (2) "Alcoa Aluminum and Its Alloys," (3) "Aluminum Casting Alloys and Alloys for Other Purposes," (4) "Casting Aluminum Alloys," (5) "Aluminum in Aircraft," (6) "Alcoa Aluminum Impact Extrusions," (7) "Forming Aluminum," (8) "Machining Alcoa Aluminum and Its Alloys," (9) "Riveting Alcoa Aluminum," (10) "Welding and Brazing Alcoa Aluminum," (11) "Alcoa Aluminum in Automatic Screw Machines," (12) "Finishes for Aluminum," (13) "Aluminum Paint Manual," (14) "Aluminum in the Chemical Industry," (15) "Finishes for Alcoa Aluminum," Pittsburgh.

AMERICAN FOUNDRYMEN'S ASSOCIATION: "Cast Metals Handbook," 3d ed., Chicago, 1944.

AMERICAN INSTITUTE OF MINING AND METALLURGICAL ENGINEERS: "Nonferrous Melting Practice," New York, 1948.

———: "Nonferrous Rolling Practice," New York, 1948.

AMERICAN MAGNESIUM CORPORATION: Booklets (revised at intervals): (1) "Properties of Magnesium Products," (2) "Designing with Magnesium," Cleveland, Ohio.

AMERICAN SOCIETY FOR METALS: "The Metals Handbook," Cleveland, Ohio, 1948.

AMERICAN SOCIETY FOR TESTING MATERIALS: "A.S.T.M. Standards," Part I, Metals, Philadelphia (annual).

ARCHBUTT, S. L., and W. E. PRYTHERCH: "Effect of Impurities in Copper," British Non-ferrous Metals Research Association, London, 1937.

ARCHER, R. S., J. Z. BRIGGS, and C. M. LOEB, JR.: "Molybdenum: Steels, Irons, Alloys," Climax Molybdenum Company, New York, 1948.

BASSETT, H. N.: "Bearing Metals and Alloys," Edward Arnold & Company, London, 1937.

BECK, A. (editor): "Technology of Magnesium and Its Alloys," F. A. Hughes & Co., London, 1940.

BROWN, H.: "Aluminum and Its Applications," Pitman Publishing Corp., New York, 1948.

BUDGEN, N. F.: "Aluminum and Its Alloys," 2d ed., Sir Isaac Pitman & Sons, Ltd., London, 1947.

BULIAN, W., and E. FAHRENHORST: "Metallography of Magnesium and Its Alloys" (translation from the German), F. A. Hughes & Company, Ltd., London, 1944.

COPPER DEVELOPMENT ASSOCIATION: Booklets: (1) "Copper Data," (2) "Copper for Bus-Bar Purposes," (3) "Copper for Earthing," (4) "Copper in Chemical Plant," (5) "Machining of Copper and Its Alloys," (6) "Copper Flashings and Weatherings," (7) "Brasses," (8) "Bearing Bronzes," (9) "Brass, Bronze, and Other Copper Alloy Wire and Wire Products," (10) "Aluminum Bronze," (11) "Copper and Its Alloys in Engineering and Technology," (12) "Equilibrium Diagrams of Binary Copper Alloys," (13) "The Welding, Brazing, and Soldering of Copper and Its Alloys," London, 1936–1952.

DAESEN, J. R.: "Galvanizing Handbook," Reinhold Publishing Corporation, New York, 1946.
DEAN, R. S.: "Electrolytic Manganese and Its Alloys," The Ronald Press Company, New York, 1952.
DOW CHEMICAL COMPANY: "Dowmetal: Magnesium Alloys," rev. ed., Midland, Mich., 1943.
EASTWOOD, L. W.: "Gas in Light Alloys," John Wiley & Sons, Inc., New York, 1946.
EDWARDS, J. D., F. C. FRARY, and ZAY JEFFRIES: "The Aluminum Industry," Vol. II, Aluminum Products and Their Fabrication," McGraw-Hill Book Company, Inc., New York, 1930.
ELLIS, O. W.: "Copper and Copper Alloys," American Society for Metals, Cleveland, Ohio, 1948.
FINK, W. L., F. KELLER, W. E. SICHA, J. A. NOCK, JR., and E. H. DIX, JR.: "Physical Metallurgy of Aluminum Alloys," American Society for Metals, Cleveland, Ohio, 1949.
FUSS, V.: "Metallography of Aluminum and Its Alloys" (translation from the German by R. J. Anderson), The Sherwood Press, Cleveland, Ohio, 1936.
GIBBS, L. E.: "Cold Working of Brass," American Society for Metals, Cleveland, Ohio, 1946.
GREGG, J. L.: "Arsenical and Argentiferous Copper," Reinhold Publishing Corporation, New York, 1934.
GREGORY, E., and E. N. SIMONS: "Non-Ferrous Metals and Alloys," Paul Elek Publishers, Ltd., London, 1948.
HAUGHTON, J. L., and W. E. PRYTHERCH: "Magnesium and Its Alloys," His Majesty's Stationery Office, London, 1937.
HUGHES, F. A.: "Magnesium Alloy Handbook," Magnesium Elektron, Ltd., London, 1947.
HULL, D. R.: "Casting of Brass and Bronze," American Society for Metals, Cleveland, Ohio, 1950.
INTERNATIONAL NICKEL COMPANY: "Nickel and Nickel Alloys," rev. ed., New York, 1946.
JENNY, A.: "The Anodic Oxidation of Aluminium and Its Alloys" (translation by W. Lewis), Chemical Publishing Company, Inc., Brooklyn, 1940.
MATHEWSON, C. H. (editor): "Modern Uses of Nonferrous Metals," American Institute of Mining & Metallurgical Engineers, New York, 1935.
MONDOLFO, L. F.: "Metallography of Aluminum Alloys," John Wiley & Sons, Inc., New York, 1943.
PIDGEON, L. M., J. C. MATHES, N. E. WOLDMAN, J. V. WINKLER, and W. S. LOOSE: "Magnesium," American Society for Metals, Cleveland, Ohio, 1946.
REYNOLDS METALS COMPANY: "Aluminum Alloys and Mill Products," also booklets on forming, extrusions, finishes, welding, machining, heat-treatment, etc., Louisville, Ky., 1948–1952.
ROAST, H. J.: "Cast Bronze," American Society for Metals, Cleveland, Ohio, 1953.
SAMANS, C. H.: "Engineering Metals and Their Alloys," The Macmillan Company, New York, 1949.
SMITHELLS, C. J.: "Impurities in Metals," 2d ed., John Wiley & Sons, Inc., New York, 1930.
SPOWERS, W. H., JR.: "Hot Dip Galvanizing Practice," 2d ed., Penton Publishing Company, Cleveland, Ohio, 1947.
TITANIUM ALLOY MANUFACTURING COMPANY: "Titanium and Its Use in Steel," New York, 1940.

VENABLE, F. P.: "Zirconium and Its Compounds," Reinhold Publishing Corporation, New York, 1922.
VINES, R. F.: "The Platinum Metals and Their Alloys," International Nickel Company, Inc., New York, 1941.
VON ZEERLEDER, A.: "The Technology of Aluminium and Its Light Alloys" (translated by Field, A. J.), Gustav Fock, New York, 1936.
WILKINS, R. A., and E. S. BUNN: "Copper and Copper-base Alloys," McGraw-Hill Book Company, Inc., New York, 1943.

CHAPTER 11

EXAMPLES OF APPLICATION OF METALS IN ENGINEERING SERVICE

The principal uses of the various metals have been discussed in the two preceding chapters. In this chapter several fields of their application will be discussed briefly as illustrations of how the properties of metals determine their selection as materials for specific uses.

Preliminary to this consideration, it will be of interest to have information as to the distribution of steel among various industries in the United States. Since the tonnage of steel used is about seventy times that of any other single metal, the figures give one an idea of the relative importance on a tonnage basis of the different forms of metal consumption. The distribution of many of the nonferrous metals among industries has been given in Chap. 10.

Up to about 35 years ago, the railroads were the largest users of steel, but the enormous increase in automotive manufacture has caused this industry to be the chief consumer of steel in America, almost without exception from 1927 to date, and it now uses about one-fifth of the steel produced, while the railroads consume only about one-fourteenth. Automobiles consume about three-quarters of the tonnage of alloy steels, while automobiles plus airplanes use approximately four-fifths. The consumption of steel for construction and maintenance is only slightly below that of the automotive industry. The oil, gas, water, and mining industries together use about one-tenth, and the use of steel for containers—tin cans, barrels, tanks, gas containers, and the like—accounts for nearly as much. Machinery, including tools and electrical equipment, takes about one-twelfth, and appliances, including utensils, cutlery, and other domestic and commercial equipment, take a little less. Exports are now about 5 per cent of American production.

Looking at consumption of steel from another angle, we find that, in the United States in 1950, sheet and strip, including galvanized sheet and tin plate, accounted for about 28 million tons; hot-rolled bars, 10 million; pipes and tubes, 9 million; plates, 5 million; wire and wire rods, 5 million; heavy structural shapes and piling, 4 million; cold-finished bars, 2 million; and rails, 2 million. Production of electric-furnace steel, which in 1939 was 1 million tons, in 1950 was 6 million tons.

Inexperienced users of metals may often use a metal or alloy which, though appropriate for the required service, is unnecessarily costly.

They sometimes also think of design from the standpoint of static strength only, without taking into consideration ductility, fatigue resistance, impact strength, resistance to corrosion, machinability, etc. The strength-weight factor is of great importance in connection with the dead load of bridges, aircraft, trucks, automobiles, locomotives, etc. This is exemplified by the use of lightweight and high-strength aluminum alloys for structural purposes and the strong competition between aluminum alloys and strong alloy steel for the construction of aircraft and high-speed trains.

In any particular case, the factors which determine the selection of the material to be used will depend on the purpose in view. In general there may be two or three major factors and several minor ones, the nature of which has been indicated in the preceding paragraph. Though it will not be advisable to attempt to discuss here each of the properties which may need to be considered, it may be useful to discuss further a few of those which are oftenest of major importance, particularly with a view to show how different factors may be interrelated.

Table 36. Prices of Metals by Weight and by Volume
(June, 1952)

Metal	Cents per pound	Dollars per cubic foot
Aluminum, ingot	19	32
Brass, yellow, ingot	23.3	121
Copper, electrolytic, wirebar	24.5	137
Iron, pig	2.35	11
Lead, pig	15.5	109
Magnesium, ingot	24.5	27
Nickel, electrolytic, ingot	59.6	331
Steel, carbon, forging ingots	2.60	13
Steel, low alloy, ingots	2.7	14
Steel, stainless (18 Cr, 8 Ni), ingots, No. 302	15.2	75
Tin, ingot	121.5	554
Zinc, slab	15.8	70

Cost. Though cost is always a primary consideration in engineering work, the relative importance of the cost of the material is variable. In large structures, it is usually the determining factor, while in some cases, as with airplane engines, for example, an expensive material may be used because the demands are rigid and because other costs greatly outweigh the materials cost.

Metals are sold by the pound or ton, yet the cost per unit volume is more likely to be the point directly at issue. The engineer may begin by calculating the stresses for a structure, and then figure the dimensions of members necessary for those stresses with materials of given strengths per unit area. Obviously when the dimensions of a member—or of any object—are fixed, the comparative costs of materials *per unit volume* are then determining factors. The specific gravities of metals differ widely, and the light metals and alloys actually become less costly than their prices per pound would indicate. A comparison of the prices of the principal metals on both the weight and the volume bases is given in Table 36. The data will, of course, change from time to time.

Strength-weight Factors. A light material will in most cases be preferred to a heavy material of the same strength; or if the light material is of lower strength, a larger section may be used and perhaps still save weight. Conversely, a strong material, though heavy, may be made of small section for a given load and weight saved in this way. Obviously neither strength alone nor weight alone is of most significance, but often the ratio between these properties. A study of these factors was made by H. C. Knerr (see Table 37), who drew attention to the high strength-

TABLE 37. TYPICAL STRENGTH-WEIGHT FACTORS[1]

Material	Tensile strength, psi	Average specific gravity	Strength-weight ratio ÷ 1,000
Steel, piano wire, cold drawn very fine	400,000	7.84	51.0
Titanium alloy	150,000	4.50	33.3
Steel, high alloy, heat-treated	250,000	7.85	31.8
Tungsten filament	590,000	19.30	30.6
Steel, stainless, 18-8, heavily cold-rolled	200,000	7.93	25.2
Aluminum alloy, 24S-T4	68,000	2.77	24.5
Magnesium alloy, AZ61X, extruded bar	45,000	1.85	24.3
Steel, low alloy, heat-treated	190,000	7.85	24.2
Beryllium copper, HT, rod	200,000	8.35	24.0
Spruce, for aircraft	10,000	0.435	23.0
Aluminum alloy, 17S-T4 (duralumin)	62,000	2.79	22.2
Plastic, laminated phenol, paper base	17,000	1.35	12.6
Steel, stainless, 18-8, annealed	90,000	7.86	11.5
Aluminum, 2S, cold-rolled	24,000	2.71	8.9
Plastic, molded polystyrene	9,000	1.07	8.4
Steel, cold-rolled	65,000	7.84	8.3
Brass, forging	70,000	8.47	8.3
Copper, hard-drawn wire	67,000	8.94	7.5
Zinc die casting	48,000	6.70	7.2
Iron, ingot	40,000	7.87	5.1
Cast iron, gray	30,000	7.20	4.2

[1] Mostly from H. C. Knerr, *Metal Progress*, January, 1937; and D. Masson, *Mining & Metallurgy*, August, 1944.

weight factors of heat-treated alloy steels. These steels are relatively low in cost and are easily fabricated, but are subject to corrosion. Stainless steel, on the other hand, is costly and more difficult to fabricate. Pure aluminum, while easily shaped and fabricated, and having excellent corrosion resistance, has a very low strength-weight ratio. Some heat-treated aluminum alloys have high strength-weight ratios, but may lose strength in welding so that often they must be joined by riveting. Stiffness is often an important factor in light structures, and this may be a handicap to aluminum alloys, as indicated by their low modulus of elasticity. Stiffness increases rapidly with dimensional increase, and when large sections can be used may be obtained to good advantage with light alloys. Much depends, however, with this factor as with others on the design of the member, whether, for example, it is plain or webbed, solid or hollow, rod or tubing. Round tubing is often used in light framework, such as for aircraft, busses, etc., because of both good strength-weight ratio and a high ratio of rigidity to weight.

Automobile Manufacture. Without heat-treated alloy steel, the modern high-powered, high-speed, safe, and efficient automobile could not be manufactured. A representative illustration of this principle is in gears, which used to be of large size, with some backlash, poor in meshing, and often broken. The modern gear must be small, silent, shift smoothly and evenly, remain in gear, and stand up for the life of the car. For toughness, it must have a low-carbon core, with strength to resist impact and fatigue; for hardness, it must have a highly carburized tooth surface; it must not be distorted from accurate design by heat-treatment; it must contain alloying elements in order to be very hard after oil quenching. The grain size must be small. Most gear steels consist of heat-treated nickel-chromium or nickel-molybdenum steels, although straight nickel, straight chromium, or chrome-vanadium are used sometimes. The banding at the root of the teeth must be roughly parallel to the surface and the fillet; it must be relatively free from inclusions, and the best types are made of electric steel. The shafts and transmission mechanism of automobiles must be designed to withstand high stresses and yet be tough and ductile.

In some cars high-strength cast iron for crankshafts has been adopted, because of high damping capacity, cheapness, and ease of machining. At least 10 per cent of the weight of an automobile is in cast iron. This is due to the alloy cast-iron engine blocks, which are especially used because of their ease of machining, and to the piston rings, pistons, and the like.

Obviously all parts running in bearings are made hard by carburizing on the surface. Bearings must resist abrasion in order not to knock. Modern bearings are frequently alloys of copper and lead, or cadmium and nickel, or cadmium, silver, and copper. Only the finest grades of steel are used for steering parts and front axles. They are usually of chrome-nickel or chrome-molybdenum steels, with about 0.30 to 0.40 per cent carbon. Balls and rollers in bearings have to withstand extremely high stresses and corrosion from lubricants containing acids. They are made of heat-treated chromium or chrome-vanadium steels high in carbon throughout. They are especially characterized by extreme hardness. Ball races are of the same high character. Plain carbon steel is used for bodies, frames, bumper bars, valve springs, and other parts which are not highly stressed. However, body springs, coil springs, and the like must be of high-grade heat-treated alloy steel, silicomanganese being used commonly for this purpose and sometimes chrome-vanadium steel. Nickel steel is commonly used for structural support parts and for some transmission gearing, although transmission gearing having the highest combination of strength and toughness is frequently heat-treated nickel-chrome or chrome-vanadium steel.

Cost does not permit much aluminum to be used for the low- and medium-priced cars, but aluminum alloys are commonly used for many parts of trucks in order to decrease the dead load and correspondingly increase the pay load, in which way their extra cost is usually paid for in the first year.

Automobile inlet valves are exposed to a temperature in the neighborhood of 620°C (1150°F), and exhaust gases subject the exhaust valves to temperatures of 900°C (1650°F). Valves and valve seats therefore have to resist scaling and distortion by heating and pounding. Silchrome is often used for valves. The discussion of heat-resisting alloys is taken up later in this chapter.

Railroad Rolling Stock. There has been a strong trend toward the use of aluminum alloys to decrease the weight of railroad cars and locomotives. American railroads now use diesel engines in locomotives and these make extensive use of heat-treated and alloy steels, but steam locomotives are made by American companies for export. The aluminum parts comprise sheets for the sides of gondolas, cabs, etc. Heat-treated aluminum-alloy connecting rods are sometimes used. Axles can be made smaller when of heat-treated alloy steel, and this is practically universal. If, for example, they are made of 2 per cent nickel steel, they are both smaller for the same loads and harder and therefore save friction because of both less frictional surface and lower coefficient of friction. Many diesel- and steam-locomotive forgings are made of nickel steels or vanadium steels, heat-treated.

Machine Design. Because of economy and ease of machining, cast iron is commonly used for cylinders—steam, gas, and diesel. In many cases it is customary to use cylinder linings, which can be replaced when worn out of round. Pistons and piston rings are also commonly made of cast iron. This material has low frictional qualities, and the service does not subject it to great stress. Steel castings are commonly used for parts of intricate shape, but castings lack the strength and toughness of forgings, and engine frames are often built up of fabricated material assembled by welding. Bronze is used for bearings and bushings, since it is stronger than brass. Cast iron is a good bearing metal because of the hard carbides and the graphite flakes which act as lubricant. Compacted metal powders with a porous structure into which oil is impregnated, as described on page 93, make efficient bearings. Machinery transmission shafting has to withstand fatigue and torsional stresses. It is usually cold-drawn, so that it requires no machining, and contains about 0.40 to 0.50 per cent carbon for strength with reasonable ductility, which combination gives good fatigue resistance. If this or other machinery parts are exposed to corrosion as well as fatigue stresses, they must be made of stainless steel or else must be designed with unit stress in no case more than 24,000 psi.

An outstanding example of fatigue stress is the structural parts and machinery of a ship, which vibrate and change shape with almost every passing wave. The breaking of propeller shafts was a common occurrence until this matter was understood. Now propeller shafts are made of hollow nickel-steel forgings designed to withstand a heavy fatigue stress. Obviously the structural and power-transmission parts of airplanes are subject to vibration and/or fatigue. The transmission mechanism is built of heat-treated high-strength alloy steel, and it should be frequently examined for the start of fatigue cracks, for which purpose the engine must be disassembled, and some method like Magnaflux used. Strict attention to this liability has almost eliminated failures of machine parts in airplanes, even though the factor of safety is as low as 1½.

Static Structures. Suspension bridges have the longest span possibilities because high-strength carbon-steel wire containing about 0.80 per cent carbon can be cold-drawn to a tensile strength of 235,000 psi, with elongation in 2 in. of 6 to 12 per cent. Other materials and heat-treated products for making suspension cables have failed. Acid open-hearth steel should be used for long suspension cables on account of vibration and fatigue stresses. The other parts of bridges are commonly made of basic open-hearth steel because of greater toughness on account of lower phosphorus and sulfur. Nickel and silicon structural steels have been used with success, except for cables, and result in decreasing the dead weight of the structure. The heat-treatment of bridge members is usually not justified because their mass is so great. Structural steel usually contains about 0.22 per cent carbon and is therefore composed of pearlite with a goodly amount of excess ferrite. This is in order that the steel may have high ductility, not entirely because of stresses in service, but more particularly because of deformations or abuse during fabrication. Buildings are commonly made of basic open-hearth, and more rarely bessemer, steel structural shapes, because of economy.

Heat-resisting Applications. Development of alloys for high-temperature service has long been an important field for the metallurgist, and it has assumed new importance with the advent of superchargers, gas turbines, and jet engines.

Among the older applications are high-pressure steam boilers, valves and cylinder heads and walls in internal-combustion engines, exhaust manifolds and other ducts for hot gases, rheostats and resistors for electric furnaces, electric-light filaments, case-carburizing boxes, parts of furnaces and burners, grate bars, machine guns, chemical laboratory ware, retorts for high-temperature reactions, etc. High-speed cutting tools, too, require that the softening effect of high temperatures must be minimized.

In some of these applications, the parts are unstressed or lightly stressed. These generally present the easier problems; the combination of high temperature with high stress is being given the greatest amount of study, and on the results of such study depends the limitation of future aircraft engines, power generation, and many other engineering needs. In the older applications frequent use was made of heat-resisting alloy steels and cast irons, nickel-chromium alloys such as Nichrome, and heat-resistant pure metals, especially platinum for oxidizing atmospheres and tungsten and molybdenum in protective atmospheres. Among the newer uses, the turbosupercharger wheel must operate under very high loads at temperatures up to 700°C (1300°F), while the buckets may be heated to 925°C (1700°F) with somewhat lower stresses. Gas turbines as used in jet engines are much larger in size; they operate at lower speeds and lower temperatures but higher stresses. Bucket temperatures may be 730°C (1350°F).

The special requirements of metals for high-temperature service have been discussed by Rebecca H. Smith.[1] They are chiefly the following:

1. High melting point.
2. Maintenance of strength and hardness at high temperature.
3. Maintenance of ductility at high temperature.
4. Resistance to oxidation, scaling, and intergranular corrosion.
5. Resistance to creep.
6. Lack of excessive grain growth.
7. Resistance to changes in alloy structure, especially those which result in embrittlement, or in dimensional changes which occur on aging.

[1] *Iron Age*, vol. 161, Jan. 22, 1948.

In addition, the cost of the material is a most important consideration in many cases, especially because in the heat-resisting alloys relatively scarce and expensive metals are employed. The availability of the necessary quantities of some of the elements is important, especially in wartime.

Welding is apt to be difficult with many of the high-temperature alloys, yet may be essential for fabrication. Resistance to oxidation at high temperature is a prime requisite, and many of those corrosion-resistant metals and alloys that also have high melting and softening points are suitable for high-temperature service.

Shaping of alloys capable of withstanding high stresses at high temperatures presents special problems. Forging is a common method and is

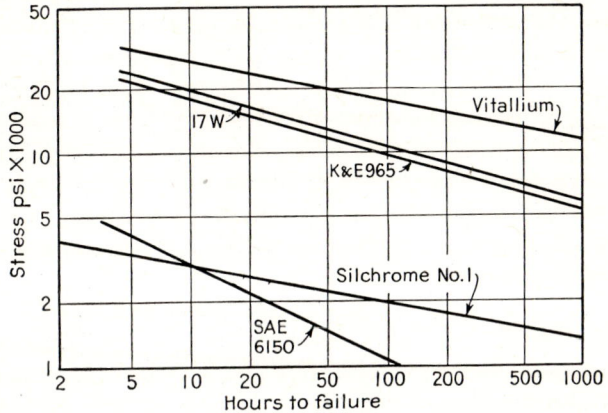

FIG. 161. Average stress-rupture curves of supercharger bucket alloys at 815°C (1500°F). (*Courtesy of General Electric Company.*)

desirable when possible. But forgeability declines as ability to resist stress when hot increases, so that a number of the strong alloys must be cast. Machining may be difficult or impossible. With forging and machining so difficult, turbine rotor blades and buckets are often manufactured by precision investment casting.

In some cases temperatures may be kept lower and the heat-resistance problem therefore lessened by providing for rapid heat conduction away from the part. Most of the heat-resisting alloys have low thermal conductivity, and when this is the case, hollow parts containing metallic sodium or a salt mixture that will fuse at the operating temperature may sometimes be used for better conduction of heat away from the hottest portion of the piece.

The ordinary tensile test at elevated temperature has not been found satisfactory for this type of service. It has been largely replaced by the rupture test, in which a series of loads are suspended on test bars in a furnace, determining the time in hours before failure occurs at different loads. The results are usually plotted on log-log paper, as in Fig. 161, which compares the stress-rupture curves of several alloys at 815°C (1500°F), and in Fig. 162, which shows the effect of temperature on the rupture time of the alloy Vitallium (stellite 21). The rupture test is supplemented by corrosion tests in gases at high temperatures and by creep tests.

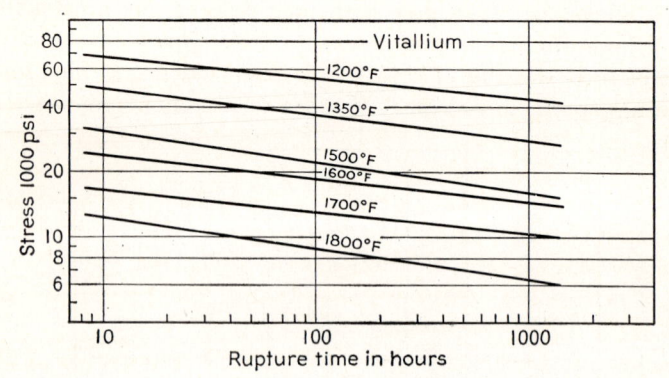

Fig. 162. Stress-rupture curves for Vitallium, showing effect of temperature. (*Courtesy of Iron Age*.)

The principal heat-resisting alloys fall into the following types:

1. Stainless steels, especially those of very high alloy content. These are essentially Fe-Cr-Ni alloys.
2. Modified stainless steels containing cobalt.
3. Stellite alloys, basically Co-Cr-W or Co-Cr-Mo.
4. Modified stellite alloys, employing such additions as nickel, tantalum, columbium, tungsten, and carbon.
5. Nickel-chromium alloys, such as Nichrome, Chromel, Inconel, and Nimonic. These may also contain iron, titanium, columbium, and a little aluminum.

The heat-resisting steels have been discussed on page 238. The high-cobalt alloys appear to afford the best combination of high-temperature and high-stress resistance. The alloys compared in Fig. 161 represent those in principal use for supercharger buckets in different periods, as follows, showing the improvement which has taken place:[1]

SAE 6150...............	1918–1922
Silchrome No. 1.........	1922–1928
K & E—965..............	1928–1933
17W....................	1933–1942
Vitallium...............	1942–1945

[1] Badger. W. L., *Iron Age*, July 25, Aug. 1, 1946; General Electric Company publication.

The first four are alloy steels, while Vitallium is a Co-Cr-Mo alloy. Since 1945 a number of other cast Co-Cr-Mo alloys having higher stress-rupture curves than Vitallium have been developed. The highest to date appears to be 73J, having the composition Co 60 per cent, Cr 23, Mo 6, Ni 6, Ta 2, Mn 1, C 0.73. All the high-temperature alloys are notable for their complexity.

A comprehensive summary of heat-resistant alloys from 650 to 960°C (1200 to 1800°F), based on Research Memorandum No. 3-47 of the U.S. Navy Bureau of Ships, has been published by N. J. Grant, A. F. Frederickson, and M. E. Taylor.[1] Recent developments in "Metals for High Temperature Service" have been reviewed by W. F. Simmons and A. B. Westerman.[2] New types of material for this purpose are the "ceramals" or "cermets." These combine nonmetallic (ceramic) materials with metals, using methods adopted from powder metallurgy, similar to the manufacture of Carboloy. Several carbides are used, also oxides, borides, silicides, and other compounds. The binding metal is usually cobalt alloyed with molybdenum or tungsten, but others may be used. The strength of the ceramal at high temperature is greater than that of the alloy constituent.

Development of Atomic Energy. Although the application of nuclear energy in engineering service belongs largely to the future, the tremendous importance of its development calls for a brief account of the part played by metallurgy.

Many metallurgists were engaged in the Manhattan Project,[3] which produced the atomic bomb, and many are now employed in working toward utilization of atomic power. Metallurgical divisions were established early in the Second World War at the University of Chicago and other universities, and at the Clinton (Oak Ridge), Los Alamos, and other atomic-energy plants and research institutions. During 1947-1948 a metallurgical laboratory costing more than a million dollars was built as a unit of the Oak Ridge National Laboratory, at Oak Ridge, Tenn.

Early work (1942-1943) centered on the metallurgy of uranium, extraction of the fissionable uranium isotope 235 from uranium 238 (in which the former exists in the proportion of one atom in 140), and the production of plutonium from uranium 238. Although much of this work conforms to the definition of metallurgy, actually the operations were not those ordinarily carried on by metallurgists, and the necessary techniques have been due largely to physicists and chemists. Develop-

---

[1] *Iron Age*, vol. 161, Mar. 18, Apr. 8, Apr. 15, 1948.

[2] *Metals Rev.*, June, 1949.

[3] One who took an important part was John Chipman, Massachusetts Institute of Technology. Much of the information given here is from an unpublished lecture given by Dr. Chipman in 1946.

ment of nuclear energy is an outstanding example of scientific teamwork, the essential theory stemming from nuclear physics and the ramifications extending into all branches of science and engineering. It is not our intention to magnify the contribution of metallurgy, which may be described as vital yet relatively small. Metallurgy promises to play a much larger part in the production of atomic power for peaceful uses.

Metallic uranium of satisfactory purity had been produced in small amounts before the war, but was not regularly used or sold as a commercial product. Little was known of its properties. Besides the problems of large-scale production of both uranium and plutonium, and study of the properties of these metals, the more strictly metallurgical aspects such as casting, extrusion, and other methods of shaping, applied to tonnage quantities, as well as corrosion, alloying, and other problems have now been successfully attacked. Microstructures of the metals and their alloys, and the effects thereon of working and heat-treatment, have been studied. The constitution diagrams of uranium with over thirty other elements have been established in whole or in part.

Uranium for the atomic pile must be protected against corrosion, and at the same time must be effectively sealed against escape of dangerous radioactive fission products. The coating must permit the passage of neutrons without excessive loss and must readily transmit heat to a coolant. After much experimental development these requirements were obtained by the sealing of each slug of uranium in an aluminum can.

Beryllium has been found to have exceptional transparency to passage of neutrons, and also to be superior to graphite for use in the pile as a moderator of neutron velocity. These applications require fabrication, and though beryllium is a brittle metal, it has been found possible to shape it fairly well by extrusion and less readily by other methods. Considerable amounts of beryllium are now being used in the development of nuclear energy.

Zirconium also does not absorb neutrons, and its resistance to corrosion and to high temperature makes it an excellent material for building reactor equipment. It can be forged at red heat.

Possibilities in the field of metallurgy have been enhanced by production of new metals such as neptunium (atomic number 93) and plutonium (atomic number 94). The metallurgy of thorium, another fissionable metal, is being intensively studied. Heat-resistant alloys, too, are needed for atomic power, and there is a need to develop new alloys of this kind which will not require large quantities of metals that are relatively scarce and may be very difficult to obtain in time of war. Fabrication of parts made from molybdenum, titanium, and zirconium is a challenging problem, as is the shaping of alloys that must remain hard and strong at yellow or white heat. Metallurgical research, as with research in many other fields, has also benefited by the production of radioactive elements as by-products of nuclear fission. Some applications of such elements used as tracers have been in the study of corrosion mechanisms and films, of metal-slag transfer of impurities in refining processes, of rates of diffusion in metals, and of segregation of impurities in casting. These radioactive elements have also been applied as substitutes for radium in radiographic work. Many other uses have been tried or suggested.

Bibliography

AMERICAN SOCIETY FOR TESTING MATERIALS: "Symposium on High-Strength Constructional Metals," Philadelphia, 1936.
———: "Symposium on Materials for Gas Turbines," Philadelphia, 1946.
———: "Symposium on New Materials in Transportation," Philadelphia, 1940.
ESHBACH, O. W.: "Handbook of Engineering Fundamentals," 2d ed., John Wiley & Sons, Inc., New York, 1952.
GILLETT, H. W.: "The Behavior of Engineering Metals," John Wiley & Sons, Inc., New York, 1951.
———: "Engineering Approach to the Selection, Evaluation, and Specification of Metallic Materials," Penton Publishing Company, Cleveland, Ohio, 1944.
HILL, F. T.: "The Materials of Aircraft Construction," 4th ed., Sir Isaac Pitman & Sons, Ltd., London, 1940.
HOLLOMON, J. H., and L. D. JAFFE: "Ferrous Metallurgical Design," John Wiley & Sons, Inc., New York, 1947.
HOYT, S. L.: "Metals and Alloys Data Book," 2d ed., Reinhold Publishing Corporation, New York, 1953.
SMITH, G. V.: "Properties of Metals at Elevated Temperatures," McGraw-Hill Book Company, Inc., New York, 1950.
TEED, P. L.: "The Properties of Metallic Materials at Low Temperatures," John Wiley & Sons, Inc., New York, 1950.
YOUNG, J. F. (editor): "Materials and Processes," John Wiley & Sons, Inc., New York, 1944.
ZUCROW, M. J.: "Principles of Jet Propulsion and Gas Turbines," John Wiley & Sons, Inc., New York, 1948.

CHAPTER 12

CORROSION AND ITS PREVENTION

Metals in the service of mankind are plagued by a kind of chemical deterioration, largely at the surface, fundamentally due to chemical activity and energy change. Its most common and therefore most destructive manifestation is familiar to everyone in the "rusting" of iron and steel; in its broader aspects this chemical action is known as *corrosion*, and every metal is subject to it in some degree when certain factors or conditions exist. The degree varies greatly among the different metals and for the same metal under different conditions and surroundings. Metallic corrosion is essentially a wastage of metal occurring when the metal combines chemically with a nonmetal, forming a compound in which the valuable metallic characteristics no longer exist. Often mechanical failure ensues when the metal object or structure has been weakened by corrosion.

The importance and also the complexity of the corrosion problem is evidenced by the enormous amount of work devoted to it, the existence of numerous corrosion laboratories, the corrosion divisions of technical societies, corrosion conferences and symposia, and the great volume of corrosion literature. The importance can also be judged by the estimate made some years ago that 25 to 30 million tons of steel is lost annually by rusting, an amount equal to about one-quarter of the average annual world production of steel at that time; or by the calculation of J. C. Hudson that the annual cost of corrosion in the United Kingdom alone is of the order of 40 million pounds sterling. U. R. Evans has expressed the opinion that possibly half of this waste could be avoided by application of scientific methods of prevention. The growing attack on the problem is both one of research in underlying theory and practical case studies. In this chapter the theory of corrosion and means of combatting it in practice will both be outlined, subject to limitations of space for so large a subject. The present discussion must also be limited by the fact that the theory of corrosion depends so largely and fundamentally on electrochemical principles, full explanation of which cannot be given in the space available.

Corroding Agents. The agents of corrosion, the surrounding substances with which the metal affected by corrosion may combine or react, may be classified as follows:

1. The atmosphere. This includes not only oxygen in the air, but also moisture, CO_2, and gases such as SO_2 present in small amounts especially in industrial localities. Atmospheric corrosion includes also the action of condensed moisture such as rain, fog, and dew, of salt-bearing mist or any other source of chlorine ions contained in moisture in marine and coastal localities, and air-borne dust or smoke.

2. Liquid chemicals. These include any manufactured liquids in contact with metals during manufacture, transportation, storage, or use.

3. Water. This embraces water of varying degrees of purity, pH, and aeration contained in water pipes, boilers, hot-water tanks, etc.; also natural bodies of water in which metal structures are placed, sea water, mine waters, etc.

4. Soil. This includes besides the soil itself any contained material such as cinders or wastes, together with moisture.

5. Foods and beverages. Similar to class 2 above, but where an effect on odor, taste, or toxicity of the agent itself is an added consideration.

Theory of Corrosion. In most cases corrosion cannot be explained in terms of simple chemical reaction between the metal and surrounding substances. Usually the driving force that causes the reaction to take place is electrochemical, a difference of potential between different points on the metal surface which produces a flow of current from one point to the other. At the point from which the current flows (anode), metal dissolves or corrodes; at the point to which the current flows (cathode), no corrosion occurs. The metal surface is thus divided into anodic and cathodic areas, but these pairs may exist in large number per unit area, with correspondingly small spatial separation. Some separation, however, is essential, and it is also essential that an electrolyte be present to conduct the current; this requires moisture or other liquid. In dry climates corrosion is minimized; in perfectly dry surroundings it cannot take place except at high temperature. The electrochemical nature of corrosion has been shown by measuring the current flow and showing that its relation to the weight of metal corroded is that of Faraday's laws. It is important to note that, as in any electrolytic circuit, the amount of current flow will depend not only on the basic potential difference but also on polarization and resistance.

Of equal importance is the fact that the progress of corrosion is often retarded, and in some cases completely prevented, by formation of the product of corrosion on the surface. Since corrosion is the combination of a metal with a nonmetal, a corrosion product must exist as a compound of the metal being corroded. If the corrosion product forms as an impervious adherent film, further reaction with the metal surface immediately ceases; no appreciable amount of corrosion can occur. Metals whose oxides spontaneously form such protective films become highly resistant to corrosion under ordinary conditions. Common examples are aluminum and stainless steel; the films that form on these metals are so thin as to be transparent and virtually invisible in place, yet are effective in preventing corrosion. These films have been isolated experimentally, their thicknesses measured, and their properties studied. If broken they quickly form again, exhibiting rapid "self-healing" qualities.

If the corrosion product does not form a continuous adherent film, as in the case of iron and plain carbon steel, and even with aluminum and other metals when in contact with certain liquids or in the presence of certain ions, the progress of corrosion may be only partly retarded, and in some cases it may actually be accelerated by the establishment of electrolytic couples between the metal and the corrosion product. It is evident that there are two factors to be considered here, one that of mechanical covering or insulation from contact with surroundings, the other that of establishment of potential differences.

Potential differences on metal surfaces may be set up by any kind of chemical or physical inhomogeneity, either in the metal itself or in the electrolyte in contact with it. They are especially large and capable of causing rapid corrosion when two metals having positions far apart in the electropotential series are connected or allowed to be in contact. Thus the joining of copper and iron, or similar pairs of metals, is bad design from the standpoint of corrosion resistance. Impurities in metals, if not in homogeneous solid solution, have the same effect, which may be increased by segregation of the impurities. Other causes of potential difference are (1) in the metal, locked-up stresses or any difference of stress in different parts of the metal, grain-size differences, temperature differences in different parts of the metal, nonmetallic inclusions and dissolved gases, particles of dust and dirt on the surface; and (2) in the electrolyte, differences in aeration or content of dissolved oxygen or other gases, differences in concentration, differences in temperature, suspended solids.

Polarization reduces the normal potential difference and thus reduces the flow of current. Since polarization increases rapidly with small rise of current density, a given current flowing over a large surface may result in continuing rapid corrosion while the same current flowing over a small surface may result in a diminishing rate of corrosion. Thus the relative size of anodic and cathodic areas is an important factor.

Potential differences may also arise from external sources, as in the vicinity of electric railroads and power lines. Some cases of extreme corrosion damage have occurred where stray currents or leakage currents have flowed through the soil from a pipe line or the structural steel of a building. A survey of conditions should precede the placing of metal in any location where external differences of potential may exist. This same principle is utilized in reverse in cathodic protection (see page 351), where small currents are caused by external means to flow continuously *to* a metal structure in contact with soil, water, or conducting liquid.

The acceleration of corrosion by sea water and coastal atmospheres is well known. This is due to two causes: (1) Through the chemical action of salt or of chlorine ions, protective oxides are converted to soluble chlorides, the protective film is pierced or destroyed, passivity is overcome. (2) Salt solutions provide a more effective, more highly conducting electrolyte.

Chemical equilibrium may be an important factor in corrosion. In still liquids the rate of corrosion may diminish through accumulation of the reaction products, while in moving liquids this cannot occur. While corrosion is usually more rapid in moving liquids, especially when they dissolve or erode the corrosion products, it is sometimes retarded by the supplying of oxygen by the liquid, resulting in the formation of a protective film. Corrosion may be especially rapid at certain points in badly designed structures containing pockets or recesses, such as in riveted lap joints. These also give rise to electrolytic concentration cells due to difference in dissolved oxygen content.

Types of Corrosion Reactions. Oliver P. Watts divided corrosion reactions into four types, as follows[1]:

I. Corrosion without displacement from the solution. Example: $Fe + 2Fe^{+++} = 3Fe^{++}$. This can occur only when the corroding compound exists in a higher valence that may be reduced to a lower valence in solution.

II. Corrosion with displacement of a metal from solution. Example: $Fe + Cu^{++} = Fe^{++} + Cu$. This occurs when the corroding solution contains a metal lower in the electropotential series which will be replaced by the one higher in this series.

III. Corrosion with visible displacement of hydrogen. Example: $Fe + 2H^+ = Fe^{++} + H_2$. This may occur when the corroding agent is an acid, alkali, a salt of a chemically strong metal, or in some cases water. The potential difference existing must be great enough to liberate hydrogen, overcoming the hydrogen gas polarization.

IV. Corrosion with invisible displacement of hydrogen. Example: $Fe + 2H^+ + O = Fe^{++} + H_2O$. The displaced hydrogen is rapidly oxidized to water, which may or may not be combined in the corrosion product. This is by far the most common type of corrosion.

The composition of ordinary iron rust varies. Basically it is composed of one or both of the compounds $Fe(OH)_2$ and $Fe(OH)_3$, often with some Fe_3O_4. In addition to the primary reactions given in III and IV, the

[1] *Trans. Electrochem. Soc.*, **64**, 135 (1933).

following are known to occur:

$$Fe + H_2O + O = Fe(OH)_2 \quad (\Delta F = -58{,}840 \text{ cal})$$
$$Fe(OH)_2 + H_2O = Fe(OH)_3 + H$$
$$Fe(OH)_2 + 2Fe(OH)_3 = Fe_3O_4 + 4H_2O$$

The last two take place without free oxygen.

While it was at one time thought that the main role of oxygen in corrosion was to combine with the metal being corroded, it is now known that this is but one of four roles, a most important one being that illustrated in IV above. Here oxygen removes the displaced hydrogen, making it unnecessary for hydrogen to be evolved as a gas and thus reducing the potential difference required. It thus acts as a depolarizer. It prevents accumulation of H_2 at the cathode and allows the corrosion reaction to proceed. Oxygen also promotes corrosion by causing concentration cells. Finally, it may have a preventive role, often retarding corrosion by forming an oxide protective film or by polarizing the anodic areas.

Corrosion-resistant Metals. In concordance with what has been said above, it will be evident that there are two types of corrosion-resistant metals:

1. The chemically weak metals, *i.e.*, those low in the electropotential series (see page 46), which are corrosion-resistant because of low chemical activity, and because when present in electrolytic couples they will be cathodic. Metals that possess this type of corrosion resistance to a high degree are gold, silver, and the platinum group.

2. Some chemically strong metals (and alloys), namely, those which form oxide films that are continuous, nonporous, and adherent. These include aluminum, titanium, silicon, zinc, chromium, tin, cadmium, tungsten, molybdenum, tantalum, and others; also stainless steel and other alloys. Some metals of intermediate chemical strength also are protected by film formation, notably nickel, lead, and copper. In the case of the last two, and also in the case of zinc, the film is clearly visible, being of a different color, usually thicker, and sometimes becoming somewhat powdery or porous at the outer surface while affording good protection at the metal-film junction.

With metals on which protective films of oxide or other compounds do not form naturally, it is possible to produce them by artificial oxidation or chemical treatment. These methods vary a great deal in their effectiveness.

Tarnishing is discoloration of a surface due to incipient corrosion. The tarnish film has little tendency to penetrate, and can usually be removed without appreciable damage or loss of metal underneath.

Prevention of Corrosion. *Passivity and Passivators.* Metal surfaces that lose all or part of their normal chemical activity are said to become *passive*. This may be the result of a definite film formation as discussed above, or it may be caused by entrance of oxygen atoms into the metal lattices at the surface or by the adsorption of oxygen or oxidized molecules. The effect is to render the potential of the surface more uniform and more noble (cathodic). *Passivators* are substances used to produce passivity. Their ions adsorb strongly on the metal surface and satisfy secondary valence forces. Examples of substances widely used as passivators in paints are red lead (Pb_3O_4) and zinc chromate, and in solutions sodium dichromate, chromic acid, and nitric acid of proper concentration.

Inhibitors. Inhibitors are substances added to solutions or otherwise applied to minimize normal chemical effects; corrosion inhibitors reduce the effects of corroding agents. They include the passivators just described and also other types, chief of which are the organic inhibitors. These adsorb on metal surfaces in the form of monomolecular or monoionic films, acting as a barrier that retards or prevents access of hydroxyl and other ions to the surface. They possess large and complex molecular patterns which account for this property.

Forms of Corrosion. Combatting corrosion requires an understanding not only of its causes, but also of the different ways in which it is manifested. Chemically, corrosion has been classified above into four types of reaction. It may be also classified according to the various ways in which it occurs. M. G. Fontana has divided these into eight forms and has discussed and illustrated them.[1] These are:

1. Uniform attack or general corrosion.
2. Pitting.
3. Galvanic or two-metal corrosion.
4. Concentration-cell corrosion.
5. Dezincification.
6. Erosion-corrosion.
7. Intergranular corrosion.
8. Stress-corrosion.

Uniform attack or over-all corrosion is the commonest form and represents the greatest destruction of metal on a tonnage basis. Most of the foregoing discussion applies to it. It is not entirely uniform, but is roughly or generally so on a macroscopic scale.

Pitting occurs when corrosion is localized, either because of localized differences in composition or because a small spot is continuously anodic with current flowing from it at a relatively high density. It is especially destructive in containers, which may become perforated in a relatively

---

[1] *Metal Progress*, vol. 53, February, March, May, June, 1948.

short time. It is insidious because it may be overlooked when the pits, though deep, are small in area or few in number. Chlorides are great pitting agents. Normally corrosion-resistant materials such as stainless steel are subject to pitting under certain conditions. Figure 163 is a micrograph of pitting that occurred in the salt-spray test on an aluminum alloy.

As previously pointed out, most corrosion is essentially electrolytic or galvanic. The severe form denoted in 3, above, refers to definite contact between two dissimilar metals. Although rapid corrosion may result from a design involving this condition, it may be permissible in some

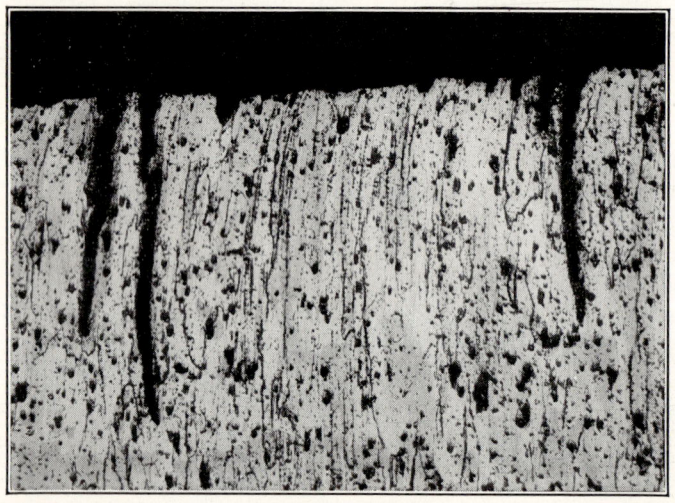

Fig. 163. Micrograph of transverse section of aluminum alloy 75S-T6 exposed to standard salt spray for 6 weeks. Magnification 100 ×. Etched with Keller's reagent. (*D. D. Pollock, author's laboratory.*)

instances if the anodic part is made of heavy section of low-cost metal, such as steel, while the cathodic part can be a thin piece of high-cost metal such as bronze, provided that a tight fit or close contact between the parts need not be maintained. In most designs involving two or more different metals, it is better to insulate them so that they do not come in contact.

Concentration-cell corrosion has been discussed above. Dezincification is discussed under Brass, page 262. While the term refers specifically to selective removal of zinc from brass, it may include more broadly any similar selective leaching of one component from an alloy. In this sense there are numerous other, if less important, examples of this action. Dezincification in a brass water pipe is shown in Fig. 164.

In erosion-corrosion, the destructive effects of erosion and corrosion supplement each other. A surface weakened or made porous by corrosion

CORROSION AND ITS PREVENTION 347

is quickly eroded, and the abrasive effect removes corrosion products and may prevent the presence of a protective film, resulting in corrosion even of such material as stainless steel. This is shown in Fig. 165. Erosion-corrosion occurs in the presence of rapidly moving liquids, turbulence,

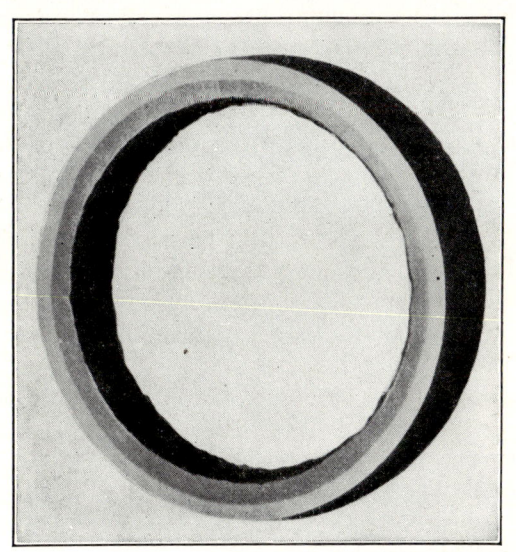

Fig. 164. Uniform dezincification halfway through a brass water pipe. (*Courtesy of M. G. Fontana.*)

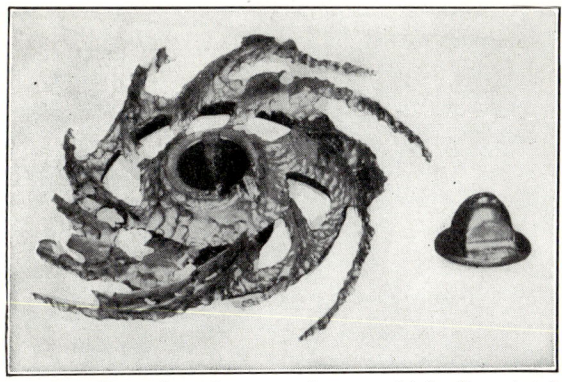

Fig. 165. Destructive effect of erosion-corrosion on a high-alloy stainless-steel pump impeller after a few weeks in service. (*Courtesy of M. G. Fontana.*)

and impingement of fluid streams; it is increased by the presence of suspended solids. Pumps, valves, ship propellers, agitators, centrifugal apparatus, and pipe lines, especially at elbows and tees, are examples of equipment subject to erosion-corrosion. This form of corrosion is often associated with cavitation erosion, in which cavities in an eroding liquid moving at high velocity periodically form and collapse with resulting impact sufficient to cause deformation and breakdown of the metal surface.

Intergranular Corrosion. Selective attack between the grains of metals and alloys may occur because of potential differences set up when there is precipitation in the grain boundaries, or even because of different grain orientation. While it usually begins at the surface where there can be contact with an electrolyte, it may rapidly progress inward, so that the damage may be largely internal and incipient disintegration of the metal part may occur. Under applied stress, separation of the grains and consequent failure may take place. High-strength aluminum alloys containing copper may be especially susceptible, but the trouble here has been largely overcome by proper heat-treatment and by Alcladding or painting. Failures in the framework of some early "dirigibles" were due to this cause. Intergranular corrosion occurs in stainless steel when chromium carbide is caused to precipitate through overheating (see page 232).

Intergranular corrosion is often related to stress-corrosion, and internal stress is one of its principal causes. However, stress-corrosion cracking may be either intercrystalline or transcrystalline.

Stress-corrosion. The ability of stresses to cause potential differences which in turn cause corrosion has been noted. The term "stress-corrosion" is applied more broadly to the effects of stress and corrosion acting to supplement each other. Not only may differential stress produce corrosion, but corrosion from any cause may produce a weakening or embrittlement in a part which may then crack under a stress which would not otherwise have affected it. The stress may be either internal or applied. The cracking is largely internal, but may originate on the surface. The stress is nearly always tensile; the cracking usually occurs in parts under tension at the surface. It appears that tensile stress may either pull the grains apart from each other or cause a fracture through the grains when selective corrosion is present. According to J. T. Waber and H. J. McDonald, precipitation in grain boundaries or in slip planes within crystals may be induced by stress, and the precipitate then sets up electrolytic corrosion.

Season cracking in brass (see page 262) is a form of stress-corrosion cracking, as is also "caustic embrittlement" in steam boilers. The latter can take place only where conditions have permitted a concentration of NaOH to occur in the presence of high stress, and usually occurs along rows of rivets.

While stress-corrosion cracking is more prevalent in some metals and alloys than in others, it apparently may occur in almost any, including those normally corrosion-resistant, provided that certain environmental conditions are present. These vary with the material. It is apt to occur in welds because of locked-in stresses. Warm surroundings assist it, and considerable time is required for it to develop. It is of frequent occurrence, but exhibits vagaries that have not yet been fully explained. An example is shown in Fig. 166.

Corrosion Fatigue. Corrosion fatigue is basically fatigue intensified by the effects of corrosion. It is discussed on page 19.

Practical Protection Against Corrosion. Means of combatting corrosion include both internal and external measures. The former deal with the composition and condition of the metal or alloy. Pure metals and homogeneous solid solutions are least corrodible. Avoiding of impurities, of segregation, and of two-phase alloys is therefore desirable. Addition of certain elements in solid solution may be used to make corrosion-

Fig. 166. Stress-corrosion cracking in a yellow brass valve body used on liquid chlorine tanks. The chlorine contained traces of moisture. (*Author's laboratory.*)

resistant alloys. These operate in either of two ways: they may make the potential of the alloy more noble, as in a number of nickel alloys for example, or they may cause formation of a protective film on the surface, as in stainless steel. Annealing is often necessary to remove stresses and avoid stress-corrosion. In precipitation hardening of aluminum-copper alloys it is desirable to employ a rapid quench, so that the precipitate which forms on subsequent aging will be so finely dispersed that the alloy behaves like a single phase; otherwise the alloy may be susceptible to intergranular attack. In artificial aging of such alloys, too, it is desirable to avoid too large a particle size or to heat long enough to bring about approximate uniformity of composition in the region of the grain boundaries.

External measures consist of various forms of surface treatments and coatings, and also of cathodic protection. Electroplating a corrodible metal with one less corrodible for surface protection has been discussed in Chap. 3. Coating by dipping in molten metal is a most important means of protection, especially with zinc and tin. Zinc coating (galvanizing) and tinning are discussed on pages 269 and 308. Other useful methods for protection against corrosion include cladding, which is bonding one sheet metal to another by hot rolling. Steel is thus clad with stainless steel and with copper, nickel and nickel alloys, and silver. Aluminum alloys are clad with pure aluminum (Alclad), and recently a similar process is being applied to magnesium alloys. Spraying with molten metal (metallizing) is practiced with a number of metals, chiefly those of lower melting points such as zinc, and especially for coating large structures in place of painting. Metallic paints employing aluminum, bronze, and other powders are used as with other types of paint. There are a number of processes in which steel is coated by heating it in a metal powder, usually with addition of other substances ("cementation" processes); these include sherardizing (zinc), calorizing or aluminizing (aluminum), chromizing (chromium), and Ihrigizing or siliconizing (silicon). The last three provide resistance to oxidation at high temperature as well as ordinary corrosion resistance, and the last two also provide a hard case for wear resistance. Metal coatings are occasionally applied by condensation of metal vapor on a surface.

Coating metals with nonmetallic materials includes painting, lacquering, and plastic coatings; also vitreous enameling, in which a thick coating of a fused silicate or glass is baked on to a steel or cast-iron surface. Application of greases, called "slushing compounds," is also used, especially for protecting machinery, ordnance, and other manufactured steel articles during transportation and storage. The greases are first treated for removal of any acid that would attack the metal; ordinary oil and grease are not satisfactory. Inhibitors are now often added to slushing compounds.

Another means of protection is artificial building up of an oxide film or production of a protective film of some other composition. *Anodizing* is a method of developing an oxide film by using the metal as anode in an electrolytic bath of suitable composition. It was first used for aluminum (see page 285), but is now being applied to some other metals as well. On iron and steel an oxide film is readily formed by simple heating; these films give only a partial protection, but may be satisfactory for considerable periods indoors. The blue color on some razor blades is an example of such a film; black films are also produced on steel plate, usually by immersion in a fused salt mixture. Bronze and other metals are also sometimes given oxide coatings by heating. Coatings made in this way are often called *patinas*.

Other protective films are made by chemical surface treatments or dips. Phosphate coatings are produced on steel, and magnesium alloys are regularly given surface treatments for improving corrosion resistance (see page 302). Treatments of this kind are often used as a means of preparing a metal surface for painting, giving a base that is somewhat corrosion-resistant and at the same time promoting good adherence of paint, lacquer, oil, or wax. In chemical surface treatments the principal object sometimes is to produce a surface of pleasing appearance or color, as in the case of some brass articles.

Protective surface treatments, particularly when of an oxidizing character, are a form of passivating treatment. In the case of iron and steel surfaces, they may be used, because of simplicity and low cost, to retard corrosion rather than to afford a more complete protection under prolonged outdoor exposure. When the latter is necessary, coating with another metal is probably the most common and satisfactory method; however, in the case of bridges and other large structures, such coating is often not practicable, and frequent painting must be relied on.

The use of inhibitors in liquids is growing as a practical means of combatting corrosion arising from contact with various liquids.

Still another means of reducing corrosion is by removal of oxygen from water. Water in boiler plants is now commonly deaerated to an oxygen content of less than 0.005 part per million.

Phosphating of Iron and Steel. In this method of surface treatment, of which *Bonderizing, Parkerizing,* and *Coslettizing* are examples, the surface is first thoroughly cleaned and then exposed to a hot phosphate solution for several minutes. The solution usually contains one or more metal phosphates, such as those of iron, manganese, or zinc, some free phosphoric acid, and an accelerator. The acid forms some primary ferrous phosphate, which reacts further to form insoluble secondary or tertiary phosphates. The phosphate coating has two valuable effects: it affords directly some protection against corrosion, and usually more important, it constitutes a porous blanket for holding an application of oil, paint, or shellac. It may be used alone in some cases, but the full protective value is obtained from the added application. An additional property of the coating is that of preventing galling and seizing when a part so treated is drawn and formed. Use of phosphating has increased greatly in recent years.

Cathodic Protection. A wholly different kind of protection against corrosion makes direct use of electrochemical principles. If a surface of steel or other metal requiring protection is made a cathode, current will flow through an electrolyte only to it and not from it. It will be subject only to a reducing, not an oxidizing, influence. Local galvanic cells on its surface will be obliterated by a higher external potential. For these reasons it cannot corrode, and this method affords a means of complete protection if properly installed. Even iron and steel may have unlimited life. Cost of maintenance is a drawback to this method, which nevertheless is being increasingly used. According to H. H. Uhlig, the order of magnitude of required current flow for each square foot of iron surface is

0.005 amp when exposed to flowing fresh water, 0.015 amp for flowing sea water, and 0.05 amp for a corrosive soil. The current is maintained by means of a potential higher than the surface to be protected, with a contact for completing the circuit. The external potential may be obtained from an electrical source, or it may be generated by means of a piece of metal higher in the electropotential series than iron, which is fixed nearby and serves as a natural anode. The metal used in this way is termed a "sacrificial anode," since it will itself be slowly corroded. Zinc or magnesium is usually employed.

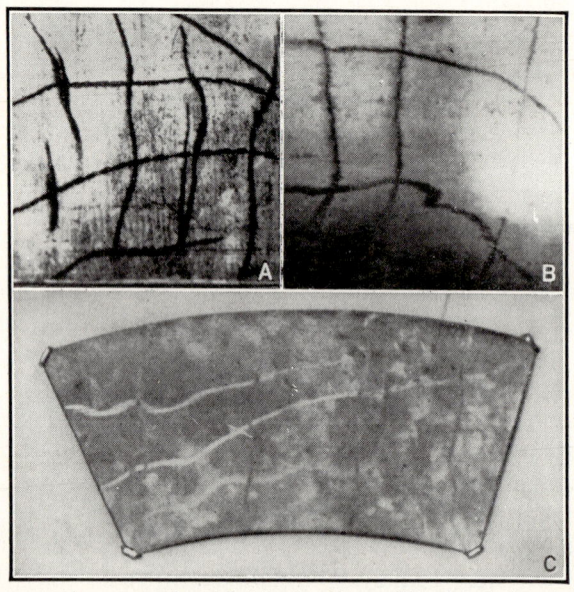

Fig. 167. Comparative corrosion of (a) tin plate, (b) nickel-plated iron, and (c) galvanized iron after scratching through the coating. (*Author's laboratory.*)

Comparison of Coatings; Galvanic Protection and Discontinuity. The service given by a metal protective coating depends on a number of factors, chief among which are the corrodibility of the metal used for the coating, the continuity or porosity of the coating, and the relative positions of the metals in the electropotential series. Chromium makes an excellent plating because, in addition to its extreme hardness, it is practically unaffected by corrosion or tarnishing under any ordinary conditions. But chromium platings contain microscopic cracks or holes, and in order to minimize trouble from this cause, undercoatings of other metals are used beneath the chromium. For example, the steel body is usually given a thin plating with copper, then a heavier one of nickel, and finally a thin plating of chromium.

In making coatings not only by electroplating but also by hot dipping, it is difficult to make a continuous coating free from pinholes or porosity extending to the basic metal. Where the metal is exposed even microscopically to the atmosphere or other corroding agent, the insulating effect of the coating is broken. Galvanic protection, which depends on the relative positions of the basis metal and the coating in the electropotential series, may then come into play. If the coating is chemically stronger (*i.e.*, anodic), the basis metal is galvanically protected and will not corrode even though some exposure exists. If the coating is the more noble (*i.e.*, cathodic), corrosion of the basis metal not only may occur, but is actually accelerated.

This is illustrated in Fig. 167, which shows three pieces of iron sheet coated with tin, nickel, and zinc, respectively, then deeply scratched to expose the iron, and then hung out of doors side by side for 6 weeks in warm damp weather. Tin and nickel are both below iron in the electropotential series, so that, where the iron base has been exposed, current flows from the iron to the tin or nickel and corrosion of the iron is not prevented but is accelerated, as shown in the heavily rusted scratches. Coatings of these metals on iron must be unbroken if they are to be effective out of doors. Zinc, on the other hand, is above iron in the series and protects it electrochemically as well as mechanically. The iron exposed by the scratches shown in the figure has remained bright and entirely free from rust.

Relative Corrosion of Wrought Iron, Steel, and Cast Iron. Wrought iron would be expected to have better corrosion resistance because of its relative purity as regards other metallic elements; but this advantage seems to be largely overcome by its content of slag. Comparative tests of wrought iron versus steel pipe lines have given conflicting results, and it is evident that improper manufacture may cause either to be inferior. What evidence there is seems to indicate that well-made wrought iron is better than steel in industrial air, but that there is little difference underground.

The coating or glaze acquired by cast-iron pipe when the liquid metal is poured into a sand mold is a protection against corrosion. The greater thickness of cast-iron pipe also makes it last longer under corrosive conditions. If the outer glaze of cast iron is removed before exposure, then it appears that cast iron has no superiority over steel and wrought iron. However, the comparatively rough surface of a glazed cast-iron pipe makes it much better for the retention of such preservative coatings as tar, paint, etc. This often applies also to wrought iron in comparison with steel.

Graphite in cast iron and iron carbide in steel, like slag in wrought iron, cause potential differences which promote corrosion. Instances are known where the metallic part of cast iron has been corroded in acid waters to such an extent that the pipe was left as an almost pulpy mass of graphite through which one could thrust a finger.

Corrosion Testing. Because rates of corrosion depend on so many interrelated variables, it is difficult to devise a test that will satisfactorily predict resistance to corrosion in service. The time factor is especially important. Short-time tests often give misleading information as regards long-time service, yet are useful for comparative purposes if their limitations are recognized.

There are a number of field stations where different metals are continuously undergoing long-time exposures to corrosion and being reported on at intervals. These are located in various kinds of surroundings, and include atmospheric, sea-water, soil, and chemical-plant exposure. Service conditions, however, may not be the same, and the slowness of the test is objectionable.

Many short-time or accelerated tests are in use, some of which have been standardized. Space does not permit describing these. The one most used is the salt-spray test. Others include electrolytic tests, usually with the specimen as anode and with or without applied potential; potential-time measurements; current density-time measurements; continuous immersion, either total or partial, in the latter case with particular attention to corrosion at the metal-liquid-air or metal-liquid-vapor junction, under still conditions; continuous immersion, either total or partial, under conditions of flow or motion of the corroding liquid, including high-velocity tests for erosion-corrosion; cyclic immersion with alternate exposure to the liquid and the atmosphere above the liquid; and refluxing of boiling solutions. To permit simultaneous exposure of a number of specimens to the same set of conditions, the samples are often mounted on test "spools" which electrically separate them from each other. An electrochemical apparatus called the *polarograph* is used to determine the amounts of minute quantities of metals dissolved in corroding liquids.

Reproducibility of test results is likely to be poor, and the work of experienced investigators has led them to the conclusion that the results may be of relatively little value unless all the conditions of the tests are suitably controlled and reported. Initial attack may be very different from, often much greater than, the attack which ensues on further exposure; this is especially true when a film is formed. The best procedure in testing corrosion by chemicals is to divide the exposure into suitable initial and subsequent test periods.

High-temperature Corrosion. The combination of a metal with a nonmetal may occur at elevated temperature under dry conditions. This type of corrosion, a familiar example of which is the "scaling" of iron and steel when heated, is basically the same as tarnishing in air at room temperature but with heat playing an accelerating role and causing a much thicker layer of the corrosion product. It is believed to be essentially electrolytic, the surface of the metal being the anode and the air or other environment at the interface between the latter and the corrosion product being the cathode. Metal ions and electrons migrate outward from the anode through the corrosion product, which builds up at its outer surface. The process may be supplemented by inward diffusion of oxygen or other element.

As in other corrosion, the protective ability, or lack of it, of the film or scale determines whether corrosion continues undiminished, or is retarded, or ceases as soon as a thin film has formed. In air, the film is probably initially a monatomic layer of oxygen atoms; in some cases this may persist, while in others it may give way to formation of a chemical compound, usually an oxide, which may form a relatively thick layer. The protective ability of the film is determined in part by porosity, which in turn depends largely on the relative volume of the corrosion product compared with that of the metal from which it formed. When this ratio is high, the film usually has high protective ability, though there are some exceptions. In high-temperature corrosion there is an additional factor, namely, that a film which is protective within a certain temperature may break down at a critical higher temperature. The breakdown may be chemical or the result of fusion, or it may result from spalling due to unequal thermal expansion of the corrosion product compared with the metal. It is evident that the properties of the scale rather than those of the metal are of most importance. Films may be protective through forming a nonpermeable barrier or through poor conductivity for ions or electrons. Metals and alloys that resist atmospheric corrosion and attack by aqueous solutions do not necessarily possess good high-temperature corrosion resistance, and vice versa.

The rate of corrosion at high temperature is determined especially by the following factors: composition of the metal or alloy, composition of the environment, cleanliness of the surface, roughness, contact with other materials, temperature, and time of heating. Metals that resist high-temperature corrosion are the noble metals and the metals that form enduring protective films when heated to elevated temperature. Among the latter are cobalt, nickel, iron, and especially chromium. Chromium-iron alloys and stainless steels, nickel-chromium and nickel-chromium-iron alloys such as Nichrome and Inconel, cobalt-chromium base alloys such as stellite, and other heat-resisting alloys are valuable for high-temperature corrosion resistances. Additions of chromium, aluminum, or silicon are effective in reducing scaling of iron and steel through causing the formation of a protective film. Aluminum is especially good for this purpose as an addition to iron and other metals, but since aluminum often produces brittleness, the protection may be achieved by diffusion of aluminum only into the surface; this process is called *calorizing*.

The rate of growth in thickness of scale is an important consideration. It has been found to be governed by several types of thickness-time curves dependent on the conditions. A porous scale forms in accordance

with a linear equation
$$y = kt + c$$
while a parabolic equation
$$y^2 = kt + c$$
governs a nonporous type. A logarithmic equation
$$y = k_1 \log (k_2 t + c)$$
applies in some cases. In these equations y is the thickness of the film or the gain in weight equivalent to this thickness, t is the time, and k and c are constants. The values of k and c depend on the metal or alloy being corroded and the corroding medium, as well as the units employed. Values have been determined experimentally for a number of cases.

Steam is often a more active scaling agent than air at high temperatures. Mixtures of steam, CO_2, and SO_2 in air may increase the corrosion rate. While high-temperature corrosion is most often oxidation, some metals, such as nickel and copper, suffer high-temperature attack by sulfur. Hot metal surfaces may be attacked by oxides that are liquid at the operating temperature. Thus heated steel may be corroded by lead oxide paint. Molten metals often corrode solid metal surfaces rapidly. Exhaust gases from jet engines are corrosive to metals.

Bibliography

AMERICAN SOCIETY FOR METALS: "Corrosion of Metals," Cleveland, 1946.

AMERICAN SOCIETY FOR TESTING MATERIALS: "Symposium on Atmospheric Exposure Tests on Nonferrous Metals," Philadelphia, 1946.

———: "Symposium on Corrosion Testing Procedures," Philadelphia, 1937.

AMERICAN SOCIETY FOR TESTING MATERIALS, Philadelphia, and AMERICAN INSTITUTE OF MINING AND METALLURGICAL ENGINEERS, New York: "Symposium on Stress-Corrosion Cracking," 1945.

BURNS, R. M.: "Protective Coatings for Metals," Reinhold Publishing Corporation, New York, 1939.

EVANS, U. R.: "An Introduction to Metallic Corrosion," Edward Arnold & Co., London, 1948.

———: "Metallic Corrosion, Passivity, and Protection," 2d ed., Edward Arnold & Co., London, 1946.

HEDGES, E. S.: "Protective Films on Metals," 2d ed., Chapman & Hall, Ltd., London, 1937.

HUDSON, J. C.: "Corrosion of Iron and Steel," Chapman & Hall, Ltd., London, 1940.

MCKAY, R. J., and R. WORTHINGTON: "Corrosion Resistance of Metals and Alloys," Reinhold Publishing Corporation, New York, 1936.

SILMAN, H.: "Chemical and Electroplated Finishes; the Protective Treatment of Metals," Chapman & Hall, Ltd., London, 1948.

SPELLER, F. N.: "Corrosion: Causes and Prevention," 3d ed., McGraw-Hill Book Company, Inc., New York, 1951.

UHLIG, H. H. (editor): "The Corrosion Handbook," John Wiley & Sons, Inc., New York, 1948.

CHAPTER 13

PRODUCING AND REFINING IRON AND STEEL: EFFECTS ON PROPERTIES

The Commercial Forms of Iron. The term "iron" is used for two commercial products, *viz.*, wrought iron, which has been made and used since before the dawn of history; and pig iron, or cast iron, which has been made since about A.D. 1320. Cast iron is so called because it can be cast, but cannot be wrought. Pig iron is cast iron as it comes from the blast furnace. From the technical and chemical standpoint there is no difference between the two. They are impure substances containing about 94 per cent iron, 4 per cent carbon, and other impurities such as silicon, manganese, sulfur, and phosphorus. They break into pieces if rolled or hammered. Iron ore is first smelted to pig iron; about three-quarters of all the pig iron made is then purified into steel and one-quarter used for different forms of cast iron. Wrought iron is so named because it can be wrought to shape by means of rolls or hammers; it cannot be cast because it is drawn from the furnace in a pasty form. It is very low in carbon, and at one time steel was made by heating wrought iron in a bed of red-hot carbon, which caused the carbon to diffuse into the iron while both were in a solid state. This enabled the metal to be hardened, while wrought iron, on account of its low carbon, would not harden. The capacity to be hardened was the old distinction between iron and steel. Iron very low in carbon, produced in an open-hearth steel furnace and drawn therefrom in liquid form, is known as ingot iron. It exceeds wrought iron in tonnage in America, where wrought iron is now used in very small amount. Wrought iron is defined as iron very low in carbon and containing mechanically entangled slag.

Steel is defined as an alloy of iron and carbon containing not more than 2 per cent carbon; it does not contain mechanically entangled slag. In its commercial form it contains, usually, small amounts of manganese and silicon and traces of phosphorus and sulfur. It is purer than cast iron and superior to it in strength and ductility.

THE PRODUCTION OF PIG IRON

Pig iron is produced by smelting iron ore in a blast furnace with a porous fuel, usually coke. For each ton of pig iron produced 2 tons of iron ore, 1 ton of coke, ½ ton of flux, and 4½ tons of air are used. These are average figures, and vary with locality, kinds of ore used, and practice.

American Blast-furnace Smelting. The iron blast furnace is a shaft up to 110 ft high and 31 ft inside diameter at its largest point (see Figs. 168 and 169). From the bottom to the top of the bosh (see Fig. 170)

Fig. 168. Blast furnace, gas-cleaning apparatus, and stoves. (*Courtesy of Armco Steel Corporation.*)

it contains a column of coke, into which, at the tuyères, is blown air preheated to between 600 and 870°C (1110 and 1600°F) in the three or four accessory stoves. On top of this column of coke rest alternate layers of ore and coke with limestone flux. The ore contains more than 50 per cent iron, usually in the form of hematite (Fe_2O_3), but often magnetite (Fe_3O_4), and sometimes other compounds. The flux forms a fusible slag with the ash of the coke and the impurities of the ore when the fusion temperature is reached. The air blast from the tuyères unites with the carbon of the coke to form intensely hot carbon monoxide gas, which pours up through the layers of coke and ore, quickly reducing the ore to a spongy form of iron even before the ore is melted. The furnace is always kept full, and the solid materials are charged into the top. It takes

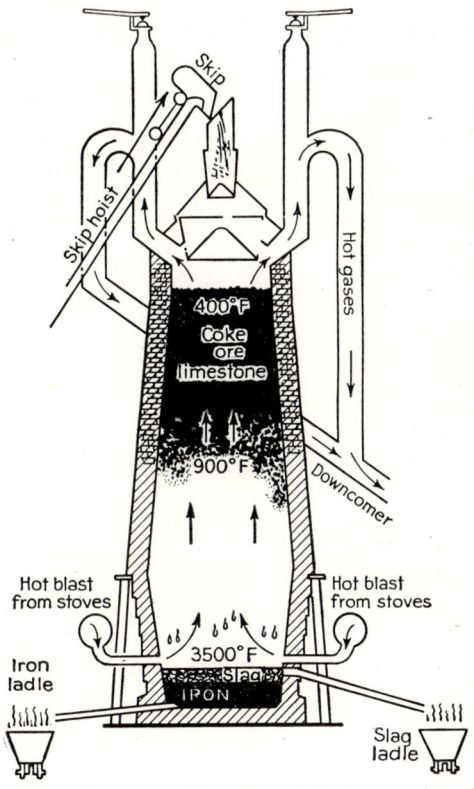

Fig. 169. Section of blast furnace. (*Courtesy of Steelways, American Iron and Steel Institute.*)

about 17 hr for the solid materials to descend to the bottom of the furnace, and about 20 sec for the gases to rise from the tuyères to the top. Before the ore has descended 40 ft from the stock line, the iron oxide should all be reduced to metallic iron (see Fig. 170).

At a point coinciding approximately with the top of the bosh, all the solid materials except the coke fuse and trickle down in liquid form to the crucible below the tuyères. Here they remain in a liquid pool, the slag because of its lower specific gravity floating on top of the iron. Every six hours 125 to 400 tons of iron (depending on the size of the furnace) is tapped from the furnace into transfer ladles, or else is cast into solid blocks called "pigs." The slag is tapped at more frequent intervals and is usually manufactured into cement, or used for road filling or similar purposes. The blast furnace must be considered as a piece of chemical apparatus, maintained at a white heat in the hottest part, for the purpose of deoxidizing those ingredients which do not separate from their oxides at lower temperatures. Thus the process is a chemically reducing one and goes on normally without interruption for many years until the brick lining is worn out. A modern furnace will produce

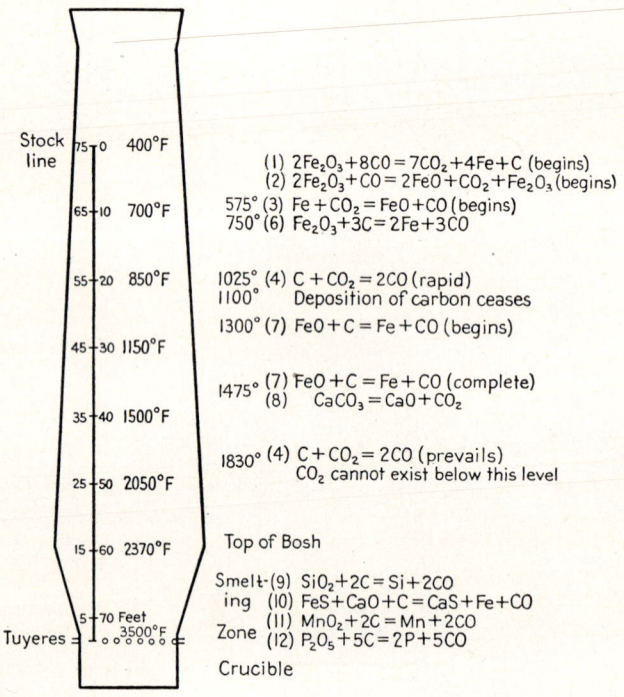

```
Stock line   75—0   400°F
             65—10  700°F        (1) 2Fe₂O₃+8CO = 7CO₂+4Fe+C (begins)
                                 (2) 2Fe₂O₃+CO = 2FeO+CO₂+Fe₂O₃ (begins)
                           575° (3) Fe+CO₂ = FeO+CO (begins)
                           750° (6) Fe₂O₃+3C = 2Fe+3CO
             55—20  850°F
                          1025° (4) C+CO₂ = 2CO (rapid)
                          1100°  Deposition of carbon ceases
             45—30 1150°F 1300° (7) FeO+C = Fe+CO (begins)

             35—40 1500°F 1475° (7) FeO+C = Fe+CO (complete)
                                (8)    CaCO₃ = CaO+CO₂

             25—50 2050°F 1830° (4) C+CO₂ = 2CO (prevails)
                                    CO₂ cannot exist below this level

             15—60 2370°F    Top of Bosh

                          Smelt- (9) SiO₂+2C = Si+2CO
                            ing (10) FeS+CaO+C = CaS+Fe+CO
              5—70 Feet       (11) MnO₂+2C = Mn+2CO
Tuyeres         3500°F   Zone (12) P₂O₅+5C = 2P+5CO
                                Crucible
```

FIG. 170. Chemical action in the iron blast furnace, showing reduction of iron oxide by CO, and reduction by solid carbon of the silicon, phosphorus, and manganese that go into the pig iron.

1,000 to 1,700 tons of pig iron in 24 hr, the amount depending upon the amount of coke which can be burned, which is directly related to the amount of air that can be forced into the furnace. In some plants, oxygen is mixed with the air blast, which increases the temperature in front of the tuyères (where temperature is most influential) and thereby increases the output and lessens the ratio of fuel used to pig iron produced.

Top-pressure Blast Furnace. If the top pressure is increased to about 10 psi, by throttling exhaust gases, the result is an increase in the average pressure in the furnace stack, with consequent increase in gas density, lessened resulting flue dust, slipping, channeling, and the like. By blowing large volumes of air at velocities lower than normal, a more uniform flow of gas results, with consequent longer time for contact between gas and ore and therefore lower coke ratio and lower ratio of CO to CO_2 in the top gases. The Republic Steel Corporation has thereby increased iron production by 11 to 20 per cent, decreased the coke ratio by about 13 per cent, and decreased flue-dust production by about 30 per cent.

Chemistry of Iron Smelting. The blast furnace reduces to metallic form almost all the iron oxide charged into it, and the reduced iron is fused and collects in the crucible. Extending all through this bath of iron is the column of coke, which reaches from the bottom of the furnace to the top of the bosh. The iron therefore is saturated with carbon. The saturation point of iron for carbon at the temperature of the furnace is about 5 per cent. However, as the iron comes out of the furnace, much carbon separates as graphite and, being very light and flocculent, rises to the surface and blows away, so that pig iron usually contains 3.50 to 4 per cent carbon when solidified.

The reducing action of the furnace is also sufficient to deoxidize over half of the manganese and all the phosphorus compounds charged into the furnace. This reduction takes place at the very high temperature in the hearth of the furnace, as shown in Fig. 170, whereas the iron was reduced in the stack by CO gas. The percentage of manganese and phosphorus in the pig iron is determined chiefly by the kind of ores charged into the top; some ores are high in manganese and phosphorus, and some are low. Lime (CaO) comes into the furnace in the limestone flux; alumina (Al_2O_3) is a common impurity in iron ores and is also a component of coke ash. It is therefore present in the furnace. But Ca and Al will not separate from oxygen through any reducing influence present in the iron blast furnace, because the temperature is not high enough. All the lime and alumina charged into the furnace come out as components of the slag.

Silicon in Iron Smelting. Silicon is always present in coke ash and in iron ores, in the form of SiO_2. The SiO_2 will go into the slag, unless it is deoxidized. It has been learned by experience that the temperature of the iron blast furnace is just in that range where carbon will deoxidize SiO_2 with greater or less efficiency; so that a hot furnace will reduce much silica, and a cold furnace will reduce little. This reduction takes place in the hearth, where the temperature is highest. Pig iron produced in a "hot" furnace, therefore, will be high in silicon, and that produced in a "cold" furnace will be low in silicon.

Sulfur in Iron Smelting. Sulfur comes into the furnace chiefly in the form of FeS in the coke. This FeS will dissolve in the iron, and to get it into the slag, it must be transformed into a compound insoluble in the iron. The chemical reaction by which this is accomplished is the following:

$$FeS + CaO + C \rightarrow CaS + Fe + CO$$

The reaction in question requires a strong reducing influence, since it involves separating calcium from oxygen through the combined attraction of carbon for oxygen and sulfur for calcium. The higher the temperature, the greater will be the reducing effect of carbon; therefore the more prevalent will be the reaction given above. This shows that a "hot" furnace results in less sulfur in the pig iron and more in the slag. Slags frequently carry more than 3 per cent CaS when the furnace temperature is high.

Quality of Pig Iron Produced. It is evident from the preceding that pig iron carries the following impurities: carbon, manganese, phosphorus, silicon, and sulfur. The carbon is present to its saturation point in the metal; the manganese and phosphorus vary according to what is put into the furnace in the charge. Manganese is often added to give better pig iron for steelmaking or for iron castings; phosphorus is sometimes wanted in iron castings because it makes the metal more fluid, but oftener phosphorus is present in ores as an undesirable impurity. Silicon and sulfur are under the direct control of the blast-furnace manager, through his regulation of the temperature of the furnace operation. Long before the theory of the process was understood, the term *hot iron* was used to indicate a blast-furnace metal high in silicon and low in sulfur, and *cold iron* was the reverse. It is found that pig iron high in silicon and low in sulfur makes castings which are easy to machine and not too brittle under shock. This is because they are low in combined carbon and, therefore, relatively high in separated flakes of graphite (say, 2.50 per cent by weight). On the other hand, iron castings low in silicon have a hard surface to resist abrasion and are, therefore, useful for railroad freight-car wheels, the tread and flange of which are liable to wear down in grinding against the track. The chilling of cast iron to make a white exterior with a gray interior and illustrations of gray and white cast iron are discussed on page 221 and shown in Figs. 131 and 132.

A recent method of taking sulfur out of pig iron is by adding soda ash (impure Na_2CO_3) to the iron in the ladle.

Gray Pig Iron. Gray pig iron is high in silicon and relatively low in sulfur. A sample containing about 4 per cent carbon, 1.50 per cent silicon, and 0.03 per cent sulfur is shown in Fig. 171. The gray color of the freshly broken surface is due to the fact that the carbon is precipitated in the form of graphite, which separates in thin, flat flakes. When the metal is broken, it fractures through these flakes of graphite, which easily split apart, leaving one part sticking to each side of the fracture.

Separation of graphite leaves the metal relatively low in combined carbon.

White Pig Iron. White pig iron is low in silicon and high in sulfur. It may contain about 0.5 per cent silicon and 0.10 per cent sulfur. There is no separated graphite, but the carbon is partly combined in the form of Fe_3C and partly dissolved in the iron. This metal is too hard to be machined, and it is brittle under shock. This comparison of properties and appearance shows what a great difference is made by a slight change in the content of silicon and sulfur in the pig iron.

Regulation of Blast-furnace Temperature. It is evident that the regulation of temperature is the most important feature of blast-furnace operation, as far as the properties of the pig iron are concerned. The

Fig. 171. Fracture of gray cast iron. Magnification approximately 2 ×. Compare this with a micrograph of gray cast iron, Fig. 131. (*Author's Laboratory.*)

temperature can be regulated most quickly by changing the temperature of the hot blast, which, in a modern furnace, will vary from 600 to 870°C (1110 to 1600°F). Another method is to change the ratio of coke to ore in the charge; and a third is to change the ores or flux in the charge so as to produce a less fusible slag. The less fusible the slag, the less quickly will it melt and drip through the smelting zone, which is the hottest part of the furnace; thus more heat will be absorbed there, and the temperature of the products will be hotter.

Disposal of Blast-furnace Gases. The gases which pass upward through the furnace are very large in volume. They have a slight combustible value by virtue of their content of some 25 per cent of CO. One-third of these gases is used to heat the stoves which preheat the blast going to the furnace; the other two-thirds is used to generate power. The modern method of doing this is to burn the gases in gas engines, but some plants burn all, or part, of the spare gas under boilers.

Cast Iron and Its Uses. Gray cast iron is the variety customarily employed in industry, although chilled cast iron has its uses, as already indicated. The making of gray-iron castings is easy and cheap; it requires no special skill or costly apparatus. As nearly as can be estimated, about 25 per cent of the pig iron made in the United States is consumed in industry in the form of iron castings. About 4,000 foundries are engaged in making such castings, and these are distributed throughout almost every part of the country. Cast iron is by far the cheapest metal that can be produced in useful form.

THE PRODUCTION OF STEEL

Wrought iron and steel are made by the purification of pig iron. Purification results in a material which can be wrought into shape. It is also

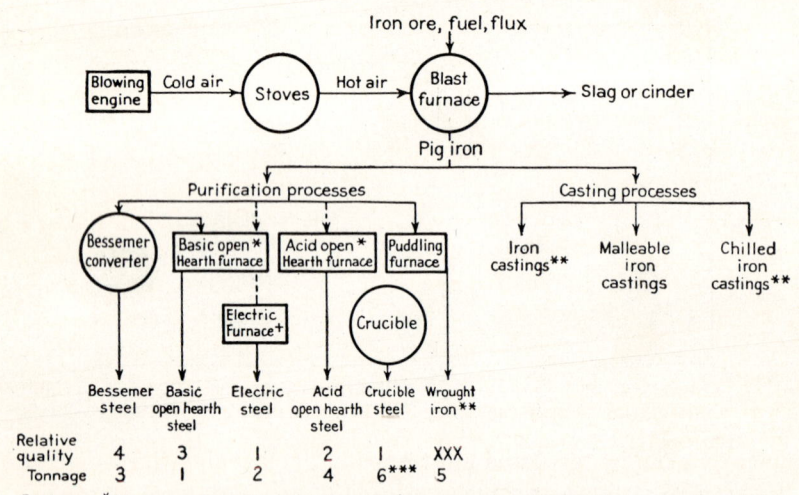

FIG. 172. General scheme or skeleton of iron and steel manufacture.

stronger than cast iron and is possessed of very important ductility. The purified metal will stretch considerably without breaking, and it can be bent, hammered, rolled, and drawn into wire at atmospheric temperature. It has already been learned that the impurities in pig iron consist of carbon, manganese, phosphorus, silicon, and sulfur. The ideal purification process is one which could remove at will any or all of these impurities without introducing new harmful elements. Unfortunately, there is no such ideal process, and therefore several different purification processes have developed, each of which has its points of advantage and disadvantage. The general summary of processes is shown in Fig. 172.

Chemistry of Purification Processes. The fundamental principles of fire metallurgy are employed in the blast furnace to reduce iron from its ore. The purification processes use the same rule in reverse: they leave the iron in reduced condition and oxidize the impurities in it. The oxidation may be effected either by the oxygen of the air or by adding some oxidizing agent, such as Fe_2O_3 or Fe_3O_4 as ore or as rust on the scrap. The oxidation must be effected in a liquid mass, which necessitates maintaining the metal in a molten condition. The carbon is oxidized to CO or CO_2, which passes out of the metal and escapes with the furnace gases; the manganese, phosphorus, and silicon are oxidized to compounds which unite with the slag; sulfur may be converted to MnS, which will separate from the iron if plenty of time is allowed, or to CaS. The removal of sulfur is imperfect, except in the electric refining process, which will be described in turn.

Basic Open-hearth Process. The basic open-hearth process is now predominant because it is the least expensive method of eliminating, or partly eliminating, all five of the different common impurities in pig iron. It is customary for a part of the charge to consist of steel scrap because this is not only lower in impurities than pig iron, but it can usually be bought at a lower price, and the "return scrap" from the finishing mills is utilized in amounts usually equal to the "bought scrap." Scrap makes the process shorter and less expensive. In normal times it averages about 50 per cent by weight of the charge, but this depends greatly on availability of both scrap and pig iron. Scrap cast iron can be used in place of a part of the pig iron. Whenever possible the pig iron is brought to the open-hearth furnace in a molten condition. The furnace is lined with magnesite (MgO) and repaired with dolomite (MgO + CaO). The average capacity of recent furnaces is 150 to 250 tons, and they are fired with preheated gas burned with preheated air, or else with oil or tar. Their general form and operation is shown in Fig. 173.

Chemistry of Basic Open-hearth Process. It is customary to put a weighed amount of Fe_3O_4 or Fe_2O_3 in with the other materials of the charge, in order to begin the oxidation of impurities as soon as the first melted metal collects. If the correct adjustment of materials has been made, the charge as soon as melted will be entirely purified of silicon and will contain only a small amount of phosphorus and a percentage of carbon only slightly higher than is desired in the finished product. It will be covered by a slag containing about 50 per cent CaO, formed by limestone introduced into the furnace with the charge. The slag will also contain 10 to 20 per cent iron oxide, which serves as an oxidizing agent in the process, and will contain silica and a small proportion of P_2O_5. The furnace gases are oxidizing and tend to maintain the slag in an oxidized condition. From the pig, the silicon, most of the phosphorus, and some of the manganese are removed early in the operation, partly because the temperature is low and partly because the reactions are exothermic (Si + 2FeO → SiO$_2$ + 2Fe + 72,400 cal), whereas the reaction between carbon and FeO absorbs heat. As soon as the bath and slag are fully melted, the carbon begins to bubble off in the form of CO gas, which produces a "boiling" which is more or less violent, depending upon the temperature and the rate of carbon oxidation. It is necessary to reduce carbon to the proper point and to get the metal and slag to the correct

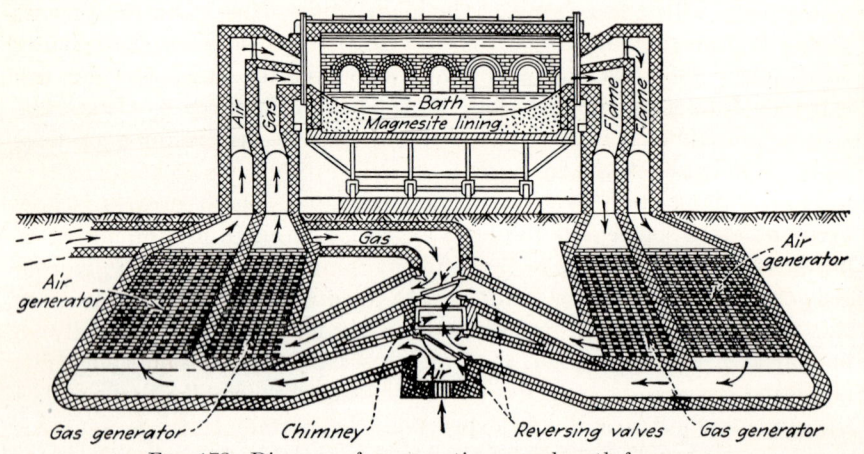

Fig. 173. Diagram of regenerative open-hearth furnace.

The four regenerative chambers below this furnace are filled with checkerwork of brick around which the gas and air may pass. Before the furnace is started, these bricks are heated by means of wood fires. The gas enters the furnace through the inner regenerative chamber on one side, and the air enters through the outer one on the same side. They meet and unite, passing through the furnace and thence passing to the chimney through the two regenerative chambers at the opposite end. In this way the brickwork in the outgoing chambers is heated still hotter by the waste heat of the furnace. The current of gas, air, and products of combustion is changed every 15 min, whereby all four regenerators are always kept hot. The gas and air enter the furnace in a highly preheated condition and thus give a higher temperature of combustion, while the products of combustion go to the chimney carrying relatively little heat, and thus fuel economy is secured. If oil or tar is used, it is introduced through a water-cooled burner which enters the furnace through the end wall.

temperature and desired degree of fluidity before opening a hole in the side of the furnace to allow the metal to drain out into a waiting ladle.

The total time used in America for the treatment of a charge is 6 to 14 hr, depending on the purity of the materials charged and the exact mode of operation. Thus the process is a very slow one as compared with the bessemer, but the slowness permits careful control. Toward the end of the heat, samples are taken and analyzed, and the results are reported to the operator so that he may adjust the bath to the proper composition before casting. The carbon is very quickly and accurately determined at the furnace by means of a magnetic analyzer known as a "carbometer."

If the original metallic charge contained about 1 per cent manganese, there will be a removal of a fair proportion of the sulfur in the form of

MnS, which slowly finds its way into the slag. When this happens, some sulfur is apt to be oxidized by the furnace gases and carried away through the flue. The removal of sulfur is assisted if the slag is made fluid by using fluorspar (CaF_2).

Function of Manganese in the Basic Open Hearth. Manganese helps to remove sulfur, but its principal function is to minimize dissolving of oxygen in the bath. One of the dangers of the basic open-hearth process is that it always operates with an oxidizing slag and therefore leaves the metal itself with some oxygen dissolved in it. This is harmful to its rolling and forging qualities, at a red heat, and also reduces its ductility when cold. The oxygen is probably present in more than one form, but it is known to form FeO, which is very soluble in the metal. If manganese is present, it combines with the oxygen more strongly than does iron and forms MnO, which does not so easily dissolve in the bath, and is less harmful than FeO to the mechanical properties of the steel, especially at a red heat. All modern open-hearth operations therefore maintain 0.2 to 0.4 per cent manganese in the bath at all times. This can be done only by having a fairly large amount of manganese in the original charge (say, 1.5 per cent or more) and by dissolving further manganese in the bath in case that originally charged becomes oxidized and transferred to the slag. After the carbon begins to oxidize, there is little danger of manganese being oxidized, because the carbon will tend to oxidize in preference to manganese at a high temperature. Another matter of prime importance in open-hearth furnace operation is that the slag should be as little oxidizing in character as possible during the last period of the heat. No flux of an oxidizing nature, therefore, such as iron ore, should be added to the slag or bath within 60 min of the time of tapping

Improving Practice and Quality of Open-hearth Steel. The work of C. H. Herty, Jr., and others has led to important progress in improving the practice and quality of basic (and later acid) open-hearth steel by such techniques as lessening the uncontrolled diffusion of oxygen from slag to bath, especially in the later stages of the process, by deoxidizing the bath with manganese 10 min before tapping, and by controlling the temperature and viscosity of the slag. At most American open-hearth plants slag "cakes" are now taken at intervals to indicate the viscosity and available oxygen content of the slag. For about 30 years open-hearth conferences have been held annually under the auspices of the American Institute of Mining and Metallurgical Engineers, for the first several years under the chairmanship of L. R. Reinartz, at which superintendents and others in attendance freely exchanged experiences on fuels, refractories, automatic control of operations, and other phases of practice and on slag control and physical chemistry of steelmaking. In recent years the Institute has published the proceedings of these conferences in special volumes.

Control of Austenitic Grain Size. By finishing the heat with a controlled proportion of oxygen in the metal and by deoxidizing the metal in the ladle with 2 to 4 lb of aluminum per ton, it is now common practice to control the grain size of the steel to Nos. 5 to 8 (see page 208). It is believed by some metallurgists that the result achieved is due to submicroscopic particles of Al_2O_3 well distributed in the boundaries of the austenite grains, which particles mechanically prevent the merging of the grains. This inhibition ceases when the temperature reaches the point where the tendency of the grains to absorb one another overcomes the resistance of the inhibiting particles present (see Fig. 120, page 206; also page 232).

Silicon is also used for deoxidizing steel. When the carbon is below 0.20 per cent, aluminum produces softer steel than does silicon, with better response to annealing at temperatures below the critical temperature (line *PSK* in Fig. 98) and better deep-drawing properties. Silicon gives better resistance to creep, less predictable and poorer cold-working properties, less response to annealing, and less control of grain size.

Use of Oxygen in the Open-hearth Furnace. For some years oxygen has been used in open-hearth furnaces in two ways: (1) to enrich the air blown in to burn the fuel, and (2) blown directly into the bath in order to hasten the carbon removal. In the first case it makes a hotter flame and increases the speed of melting, especially of steel scrap. In the second category it speeds the carbon elimination and supplements oxidation. Its use has increased the speed of the open-hearth process by about 20 per cent, and decreased the amount of fuel required.

Open-hearth Furnace Operation Controls. Automatically maintaining a predetermined ratio between fuel and combustion air obviously tends toward combustion efficiency. It is now commonly applied with economic advantage. The reversal of regenerators is effected when the temperature of the outgoing gases exceeds by a predetermined amount that of the air entering the furnace. This control either can be automatic, or it can give a signal to the operator. Furthermore, a pyrometer which constantly indicates the temperature of the roof and automatically reduces the fuel admitted to the furnace when a danger point is reached, or else warns the operator, is a safeguard commonly employed. Lastly, a device which keeps a slight pressure in the furnace through control of the flue valves and the fan forcing the air into the air regenerator is also common.

Acid Open-hearth Process. In the acid open-hearth process the slag contains 50 per cent, or more, of silica (SiO_2). The furnace lining must, therefore, be made of acid material, because an acid slag will attack and dissolve a basic lining, and vice versa. In other respects, the acid open-hearth furnace is like the basic open hearth, although it is commoner for acid furnaces to be smaller. Size is not an essential feature, however. The use of an acid instead of a basic slag introduces two differences in procedure: First, an acid slag is not so oxidizing in character as is a basic slag; therefore acid open-hearth steel comes out of the furnace less oxidized than the corresponding basic steel. It is therefore less liable to contain inclusions and is preferred for service requiring resistance to fatigue stresses. It is also less liable to contain blowholes, when the carbon is not high. For both reasons, it is preferred to basic steel for making steel castings. An acid slag will not hold P_2O_5, and the acid process will not remove sulfur, but manganese, silicon, and carbon are removed from the charge in an acid furnace. Therefore, pig iron and scrap low in phosphorus and sulfur, for which a premium price must be paid, must be used.

In the best acid open-hearth work it is customary to complete the process by a long "carbon boil" of 2 to 3 hr. This results in carrying away much of the oxygen which was dissolved in the metal. It is also customary to get the steel very hot before tapping, so that it may stand in the ladle for a half hour or so, in order to free itself from tiny inclusions, which are suspended in it like silt in muddy water. Unless a period is allowed for their separation by gravity, they will remain entrapped in the solid steel. All these precautions increase the superiority of acid over basic steel.

Bessemer Process. The bessemer process as operated in America is an acid process, and this is the reason that it is no longer the predominant purification process, for pig iron low in phosphorus is becoming yearly more costly on account of the exhaustion of our low-phosphorus iron ores. The bessemer furnace is a pear-shaped converter, lined with silica brick (see Fig. 174). It is not adapted to melting iron, but molten pig iron is brought to it and poured in, to the amount of about 25 tons per charge. Then the converter is turned into an upright position, and a blast of cold air (say 50,000 cu ft per min, at a pressure of 25 psi) is blown through it. In about 7 min the oxygen of the air has oxidized all the silicon and manganese in the iron. This produces a great deal of heat, which increases the temperature of the bath. Now the carbon begins to burn to CO, which escapes at the mouth of the converter and there burns to CO_2, with a long and brilliant flame. In a few minutes the carbon is also oxidized and removed, and all the impurities are now eliminated except phosphorus and sulfur (see Fig. 175).

Commercial oxygen has been used to enrich the blast blown into the bessemer converter, with resulting higher temperature and shorter time. This is not a new idea, but is becoming practical because oxygen can now

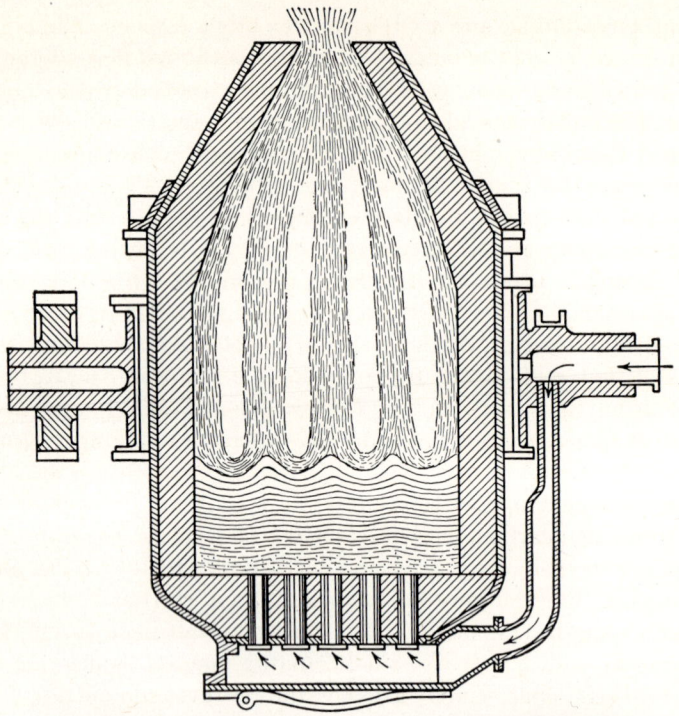

Fig. 174. Section through bessemer converter while blowing.

Fig. 175. A bessemer blow, Lorain Works, National Tube Company. In this converter the bath is deoxidized before pouring by adding a little molten pig iron containing 4 per cent carbon. (*Courtesy of Steel News, U.S. Steel Corporation.*)

be had at a reasonable price. The higher temperatures reached permit scrap to be used, if obtainable. This procedure, as that of the use of oxygen for blast-furnace, open-hearth, and cupola air enrichment, is limited at present by the limited amount of commercial oxygen available. It is hoped that the supply of "tonnage oxygen" at a commercial price will soon be greatly increased.

The rapid and simple bessemer purification process was the first to give large quantities of cheap steel to the world; it inaugurated the Age of Steel in civilization. Its disadvantages were that it left the metal with all its original phosphorus and sulfur and also with oxygen in it. It is also higher in nitrogen than are steels from the other processes. The chief use of bessemer steel is for free-machining screwstock, for which it is unexcelled. Sometimes sulfur is intentionally added to basic open-hearth steel to make it free-machining, and recent attempts have been made to add nitrogen also. Bessemer steel is also used for small structural shapes, small railroad rails, some wire, pipe, and uses where highest quality is not demanded. The process is also used as an adjunct to the basic open hearth in the so-called "duplex process," which probably produces about five million tons per year in America.

Duplex Process. Liquid pig iron from the blast furnace and liquid purified metal from a bessemer converter are poured into a basic open-hearth furnace. This eliminates the time and cost of melting in the open hearth, and requires only that the bath be purified of phosphorus and some sulfur and then brought to the requisite temperature for tapping.

Electric Process. Steel is often produced with the aid of electric energy. The electricity has no other function than to provide the necessary heat (Fig. 176). The use of electric heat in metallurgy is discussed in Chap. 15, but it will be well to point out here that, for melting furnaces, the two chief technical advantages are as follows:

1. The possibility of attaining any temperature in reason.
2. The possibility of working in a nonoxidizing atmosphere.

Heat from electric energy is costlier than that obtained from combustion of fuel, but the very high temperature obtainable makes it possible to perform certain operations which can be performed only in an unsatisfactory manner in combustion furnaces, such as the open hearth. The outstanding example of this is the possibility of desulfurizing metal through the use of a slag so rich in lime that it would not be fusible in other types of furnace. A slag containing calcium carbide (CaC_2) is one of the best desulfurizers and deoxidizers for steel that has been developed. Calcium carbide is formed at the temperature reached in the electric-arc furnace when lime and carbon are in contact. It can exist only in high-lime slags in a nonoxidizing atmosphere.

The induction principle is also used for the heating of electric melting furnaces (see page 423). A thorough stirring of the charge and the protection of the charge from the atmosphere are two outstanding characteristics of this type of furnace. The melting of alloy steel scrap with highly oxidizable components, such as tungsten, is satisfactorily accomplished. Vacuum melting is sometimes practiced in furnaces of less than 2 tons capacity. All induction furnaces are rather small in size, the maximum being about 15 tons capacity, and often only 2 or 3 tons, as compared with capacities of 10 to 120 tons for an arc furnace.

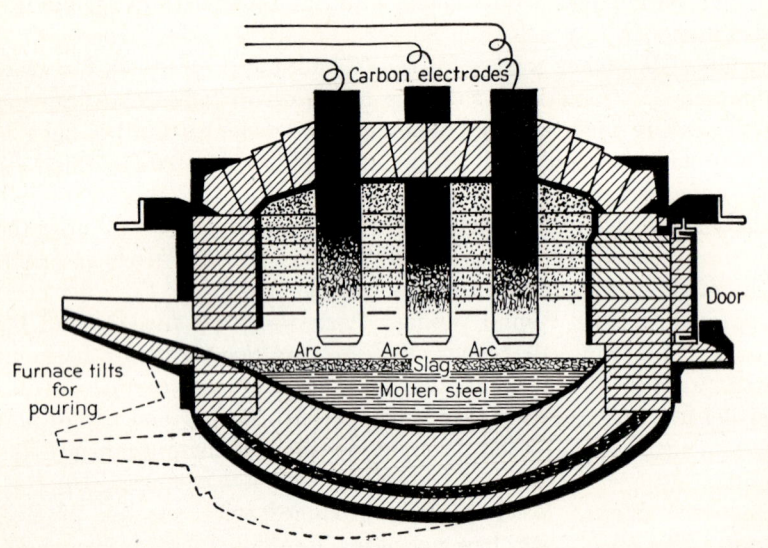

Fig. 176. Longitudinal section through electric arc furnace. (*Courtesy of Steelways, American Iron and Steel Institute.*)

Electric Superrefining. The cheapest electric process is the superrefining of basic open-hearth steel in an arc furnace. In this process the impurities are reduced to the lowest possible point in the basic open-hearth furnace, and then the melted metal is poured into the electric furnace, in which it is superrefined; *i.e.*, it is purified to any desired point in sulfur content and to almost any desired point in oxygen and solid inclusions. No oxidizing slag is used, but the metal is maintained in a fluid condition at a fairly high temperature under a slag rich in lime and reducing in character by virtue of its content of carbon, which is charged in the form of crushed coke. It is of importance that the metal should lie quietly in the furnace under deoxidizing conditions for a considerable length of time, in order that the suspended particles, which are often almost microscopic in size, can rise by gravity and clarify the bath. The stream of metal must be protected as much as possible from surface oxidation during the pouring from the furnace into the ladle and from the ladle into the mold in which it solidifies, and finally, the metal should be protected from subsequent entrainment of particles such as would occur if the slag were churned up with the metal, or if elements like silicon, manganese, etc., were added to the metal in the ladle. In the latter case particles of oxidized silicon, manganese, etc., are likely to be produced and then become entrapped in the solid metal.

Finishing Steel after Purification. When pig iron, or steel scrap, has been purified to the desired point by any one of the processes mentioned, there is still one step necessary before the steel is ready for casting into the desired form for solidification. This step is known as *recarburization*, and consists in adding the desired amount of carbon to produce the grade of steel that is needed. At the same time manganese is added, the addition of which to the liquid metal removes a good deal of the oxygen. It is customary to add a slight excess of manganese, so as to leave about 0.50 per cent in the steel. Silicon is also added at the end of the purification operation. The action of these elements, which are added in the form of the ferroalloys (ferromanganese and ferrosilicon) has been discussed on page 367.

In the basic open hearth the necessary ferromanganese is added in the furnace and the metal is tapped within 10 to 15 min thereafter. The silicon, carbon, and aluminum, when used, are added to the metal in the ladle. A basic slag is oxidizing and is also rich in phosphorus. If all the recarburizing were done in the furnace, there would be active "boiling," during which some P_2O_5 might be reduced and returned to the metal.

In the bessemer and in the acid open-hearth processes the necessary carbon, silicon, and manganese are added to the metal while it still remains in the furnace. It is possible to do this because the acid slag is not so oxidizing in character, and because it does not contain phosphorus, so that there is no danger of reducing phosphorus back into the metal.

In the electric process, either acid or basic, it is also possible to recarburize in the furnace because the slag is not oxidizing. Here it is customary to dissolve the added elements in the metal as soon as the deoxidation process is complete. Following this addition, the metal is held for an hour or so in order that any SiO_2 or MnO formed by the added elements shall have an opportunity to rise by gravity.

Crucible Steel. Crucible steel is not made by the purification of pig iron or scrap, but by melting wrought iron, together with the additions necessary to give the desired composition, in covered crucibles at a fairly high temperature, and then holding the bath in a quiescent state, under reducing conditions, to allow the metal to free itself from gases and solid particles. The crucible process is employed to a small extent in England

and Europe for high-grade steels, but has been practically superseded in America by the electric process.

Making the Ingot. After steel has been properly made, it is still in liquid form in a ladle or other receptacle. The next step is to pour it either into a casting, in which it may have a direct industrial use, or else into a large ingot, suitable for forging or rolling into a final product varying all the way in size and shape from a knife blade to a structural I beam or cannon tube. Defects in the steel may appear during this ingot-making stage. Some of these may be the direct result of errors during the purification or recarburizing process, while others may be caused during the ingot-making stage itself. The most important of the defects which may appear here are the following:

1. The inclusion in the solid steel of minute particles of slag or other oxidized substances. These occur often in so fine a form as to be like

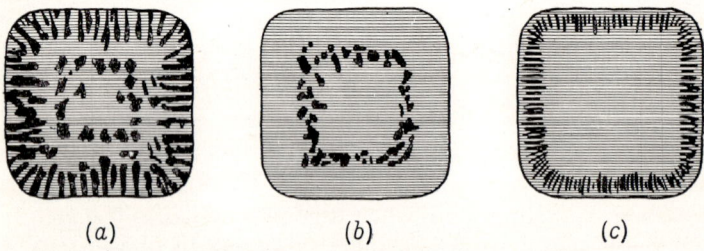

FIG. 177. Blowholes in steel ingots. (a) Deep-seated and skin blowholes. (b) Deep-seated blowholes only. (c) Skin blowholes only.

an emulsion, and it has been suggested that they might almost be considered as colloids. They separate from the steel very slowly, and their presence in the solid metal is a source of weakness or brittleness, or both. Their sources of origin are usually the following:

a. Nonmetallic inclusions of entrapped slag or sulfides and/or oxides, the result of deoxidation in which the products have failed to clear the bath either in the furnace or in the ladle.

b. Refractory inclusions, which are eroded bits of the spout runner, ladle assembly refractories, and the like.

2. Blowholes or gas bubbles entrapped in the metal (see Fig. 177). Blowholes are more harmful in castings than they are in ingots, because the rolling or forging to which the ingot is subjected at a high temperature often welds up the blowholes and thus eliminates them. It is evident, then, that blowholes located far in the interior of the ingot are less harmful than those on the exterior, because there the pressure put on the ingot will break the surface blowholes so that air will oxidize their interior. After the surface of the metal is once oxidized, it will not be welded up. Blowholes are most likely to occur in direct proportion to

PRODUCING AND REFINING IRON AND STEEL

the oxidized character of the steel. Blowholes are therefore more liable to occur in basic steel than in crucible, electric, or acid open-hearth steel; also in low-carbon than in high-carbon steel, because the lower the

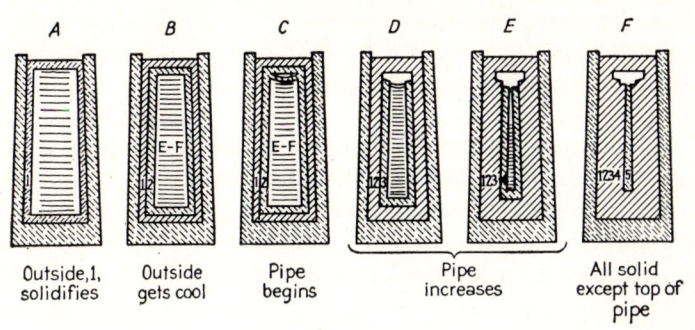

FIG. 178. Stages in the freezing of an ingot and the formation of a pipe.

carbon, the more oxygen is in the metal. Carbon protects steel from the formation of FeO and of oxygen dissolved in the metal.

3. A pipe or shrinkage cavity extending so far down into the ingot that it is not removed when the ingot top is cut off during the rolling operation (see Fig. 178). Various expedients are now employed to limit the shrinkage cavity to the upper part of the ingot and thus lessen the liability that a portion of it may remain in the rolled steel after an upper section has been sheared off. For example, ingots may contain hot tops; or they may be cast with the smaller end down and the big end up, which tends to draw the shrinkage cavity to the top; or they may have sinkhead coverings, which tend to keep the top molten.

4. Internal checks, or *flakes*, that is, minute cracks in the interior of the steel which weaken the structure. These cracks are caused by the uneven contraction of the steel during freezing in the ingot. Steel cools from the outside inward. At some period there is a liability that the interior may shrink away from the solidified walls. The larger the ingot, the more probability there is of serious pulls of this kind. And it will be evident from consideration of Fig. 178 that the central portion of the ingot will always be of a less dense character than the outside.

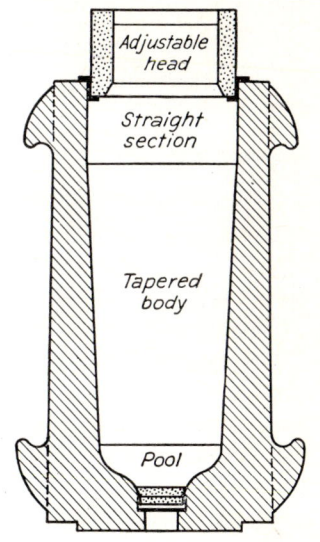

FIG. 179. Gathmann type of big-end-up ingot mold. (*From "Ingot Contour and Its Relation to Sound Steel," Gathmann Engineering Company.*)

5. External cracks due to straining the surface of the steel during solidification or when the ingot mold is removed in the "stripping" process. Very large ingots are always made in a fluted shape (see central illustration in Fig. 180), because this lessens the tendency to crack during the strains of cooling. Rounded flutes eliminate sharp planes of weakness caused by intersection of growing dendrites.

6. A weak crystalline structure formed during the solidification of the steel and having such forms as very large crystals, or "ingotism"; fir-tree crystals or dendrites; columnar crystallization. The crystals of steel grow from the cooling surface inward. The most rapid growth is at the highest temperature, with the result that when steel is poured into the mold at a high temperature there is an increased liability to large crystals.

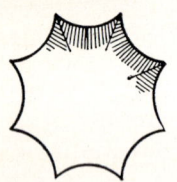

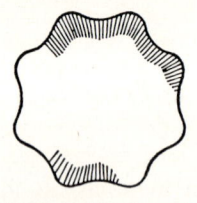

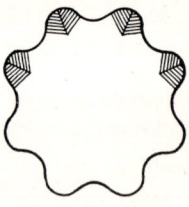

Deep plane of weakness and segregation of chill crystals   No plane of weakness or segregation of chill crystals   Plane of weakness in chill crystals

Fig. 180. Horizontal sections of ingots, showing different forms. Steel crystals grow from the cooling surface inward. The relation between the size of crystals and the radius of curvature of the cooling surface will determine the extent of weakness due to crystal junctions.

In square ingots, and those having sharp corners (see Fig. 180), the crystals form lines of junction planes. This makes planes of weakness along which cracks are especially liable to occur if the steel is put under stress, as, for example, when the ingot is rolled.

7. Segregation, or the concentration of impurities in certain localities. When excessive, this is almost invariably the result of oxidized or dirty steel, excessive impurities left from the furnace stage, or excessively slow cooling of the ingot, allowing the liquation of more fusible compounds to the late-freezing portions of the ingot or casting. All impurities lower the melting point of steel. The physicochemical result of this fact is that, when the crystals begin to form in the liquid mass, they are likely to be purer than the liquid from which they are born. This results in a general concentration of the impurities in the last part of the metal to freeze. It is therefore very common to find carbon, manganese, sulfur, and phosphorus two to four times as rich in the last-frozen part of the steel as in the outer portions. Fortunately, this last portion of the steel to freeze is the part most likely to be cut off and rejected as scrap when the steel is sheared to get rid of the pipe. The higher the phosphorus and sulfur, the more likely is segregation to occur.

Killed, Semikilled, and Rimming Steels. Modern practice in steel-making includes three main types of deoxidation: "Killed steel" is

Good rimming steel
Slight fall

Poor rimming steel
Rising steel

Killed steel
Central pipe

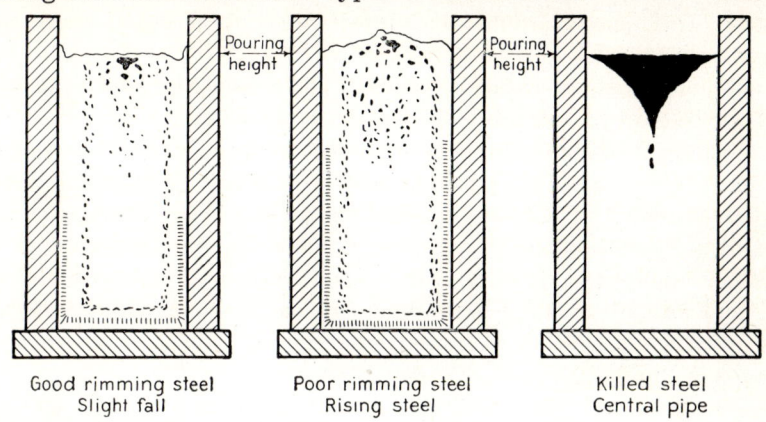

FIG. 181. Solidification of rimmed and fully killed steel. (*Courtesy of Samuel Epstein and J. W. Frame, Bethlehem Steel Company.*)

deoxidized to the extent that there is practically no action in the molds, so that the steel freezes quietly and contains no blowholes; the size of the "pipe" represents practically the difference in volume between that of the liquid steel and that of the solid ingot (see Fig. 181). In "semi-killed steel" the deoxidation is intentionally partial (see Fig. 182). "Rimming steel," or "rimmed steel," is always less than 0.30 per cent carbon, and may be much less. The commonest practice is to tap at less than 0.15 per cent carbon. The oxygen in the metal is intentionally high, and there is a vigorous reaction in the mold between oxygen and carbon in the metal, which causes an effervescence that forces the steel to flow up along the mold walls and then down the center. When experience tells the operator that "rimming" has progressed sufficiently, he "caps" the molds; *i.e.*, he places a heavy metal top on the ingot, which causes it to freeze, cuts off the escape of gas, and allows the metal to solidify with the remaining gas therein (see Fig. 181). The outside surface of the rimmed ingot is of very low carbon and therefore soft; it is also free from scum of oxides. Rimmed steel is especially advantageous for deep drawing and cold drawing, because the outside surface stretches readily without cracking. It cold-draws well into wire, plates, strip, skelp, and sheets. Its chief disadvantage

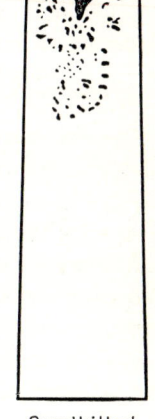

Semikilled
FIG. 182.
Semikilled steel. (*From "Basic Open Hearth Steelmaking," Am. Inst. Mining Met. Engrs., 1951.*)

is segregation on account of rejection of impurities from surface to center. The location of blowholes must be well controlled, so that they be deep-seated and not open up during heating and rolling. Alloying elements therein are limited to nickel, copper, molybdenum, and phosphorus; other elements, such as chromium, may interfere with the reaction between oxygen and carbon.

Continuous Casting of Steel Billets. The continuous casting of nonferrous metals and alloys has been practiced commercially for some years. The continuous casting of steel is more difficult on account of the higher melting temperature involved, but the process is being investigated on a commercial scale. The faster cooling results in lowered segregation and fine and uniform structure instead of the usual columnar structure. It offers less opportunity for dirt or other foreign material to enter the steel, and, of course, there is no pipe, so there is increased production. The capital equipment for making ingots, for soaking pits, and for blooming mills is eliminated.

Steel Ingots and Steel Castings. The imperfections arising in the ingot stage of manufacture are also liable to occur in steel castings. Of these the most important are blowholes, because if and when formed, they are never welded up by treatment. Sharp corners and weak crystalline structure are liable to result in cracks. Shrinkage cavities must be displaced from the casting by large risers or headers, which will also take care of the worst of the segregated metal.

General Skeleton of Iron and Steel Manufacture. Figure 172 summarizes the general scheme or skeleton of iron and steel manufacture, including the various processes mentioned in this chapter.

The first thought that will probably strike the student of iron and steel manufacture is that the processes are needlessly complicated: Iron ore is smelted to make an impure product containing carbon, silicon, manganese, etc.; then this is purified to get the carbon, silicon, and manganese out of it; and then some of these elements are put back. Why not smelt the ore in such a way as to get in one operation just the composition desired, without adding and taking away? Perhaps a process for economically doing this will some day be developed, but attempts so far have been failures, for commercial reasons. Strange as it may seem, the cheapest way to produce good iron and steel of different kinds is by the complicated processes summarized in Fig. 172. There are many different processes for purifying pig iron because the several kinds of steel vary in quality and in cost of production, which means also in price.

COMPARISON OF QUALITY OF THE DIFFERENT PURIFIED PRODUCTS

The relative quality of the different steels is indicated in figures under the names of the steels in Fig. 172.

Wrought Iron. Wrought iron is not directly comparable with the different steels, because properly made wrought iron is always very soft, tough, ductile, highly weldable, and rusts less readily than most of the other products. The steels do not have this invariability. They are purposely made sometimes soft and sometimes hard, sometimes ductile and sometimes brittle, sometimes highly weldable and sometimes the reverse. Wrought iron is not so strong as most steel, but it owes its usefulness to its ductility, weldability, and less liability to rusting. These characteristic properties are due to the fact that it always contains less than 0.10 per cent carbon. Since it is finished in a pasty condition, instead of the liquid form in which steel is poured from the furnace, it contains about 1 per cent slag mechanically mixed with the crystals of iron. Genuine wrought iron, made from pig iron by the puddling process, or else by pouring purified pig iron in a bath of liquid slag, may be identified by the content of slag, which can be determined by chemical analysis or microscopic examination, and also by the fact that the metal is low in both carbon and manganese. Wrought iron, because of its purity, is high in electrical conductivity and magnetic permeability; it breaks with a fibrous fracture, and has a rough surface which is more retentive of paint and other rust-resisting coatings than is the smoother surface of steel (see Fig. 55, page 127).

Relative Quality of Different Kinds of Steel. Crucible steel and electric steel stand at the top of the quality column of steels because of their relative freedom from oxygen and other gases, oxides, and solid oxidized inclusions, *e.g.*, microscopic particles of slag, dirt, FeO, MnO, SiO_2, MnS, Al_2O_3, etc. These two steels are finished in a nonoxidizing atmosphere; they also undergo a long quiescent period, so that they are clarified from suspended particles. They are used for the most exacting types of service, *e.g.*, tools, the finest cutlery, carbon steels and alloy steels for special magnets, parts of machines which have to undergo great stress or which must have unusual reliability, or for uses which require a high degree of some special quality, like magnetism or hardness. The prices of these steels are commensurate with their superiority.

Acid Open-hearth Steel. Acid open-hearth steel is of higher quality than basic open-hearth steel, because (1) acid slag is not so oxidizing as basic slag, and (2) a long quiescent period may be maintained in the acid open-hearth furnace, followed by a quiescent period in the ladle, during both of which the steel will tend to clarify itself from solid oxidized inclusions. The fact that the steel may be recarburized in the acid furnace is an added advantage over the necessity of at least partial recarburizing in the ladle following the basic purification. Acid open-hearth steel is more expensive than basic, because it uses raw materials low in phosphorus and sulfur. It is used especially for service involving fatigue stresses or vibrations. It is also preferred by many engineers for steel castings, because it is less subject to blowholes, although steel melted in electric furnaces is more often used for steel castings.

Basic Open-hearth Steel. The important characteristic of the basic open-hearth process is its ability to purify iron and scrap of phosphorus. Since iron ores from most of the world's available sources are too high in phosphorus to make a good steel without purification, the basic process is predominant in order of tonnage production. In the United States, about 90 per cent of all the steel produced is made by this process. Moreover, the basic process can remove some of the sulfur in the metal. From the standpoint of these two impurities, the basic steel is superior to any except the product of the electric process.

Bessemer Steel. Bessemer steel is inferior to basic open-hearth steel chiefly because it usually contains more phosphorus, more sulfur, and more nitrogen. Its greatest superiority over other steels is its ready machinability.

Identifying Different Kinds of Steel. A skilled metallurgist can usually distinguish by means of chemical analysis, the microscope, and physical tests between steels made by the different processes.

Bibliography

See also references following Chaps. 1, 5, and 9.

ALLISON, ARCHIBALD: "The Outline of Iron and Steel," H. F. & G. Witherby, Ltd., London, 1936.

AMERICAN FOUNDRYMEN'S ASSOCIATION: "The Cast Metals Handbook," 3d ed., Chicago, 1944.

———: "Handbook of Cupola Operation," Chicago, 1946.

———: "Symposium on Centrifugal Casting," Chicago, 1944.

AMERICAN INSTITUTE OF MINING AND METALLURGICAL ENGINEERS, Committee on Physical Chemistry of Steelmaking: "Basic Open Hearth Steel Making," revised ed., New York, 1951.

———: "Open Hearth Proceedings," several volumes at intervals.

BRAY, J. L.: "Ferrous Production Metallurgy," John Wiley & Sons, Inc., New York, 1946.

BREARLEY, HARRY: "Talks about Steelmaking," American Society for Metals, Cleveland, Ohio, 1946.

BRIGGS, C. W.: "The Metallurgy of Steel Castings," McGraw-Hill Book Company, Inc., New York, 1946.

———: "Steel Castings Handbook," Steel Founders' Society of America, Cleveland, Ohio, 1941.

BUELL, W. C., JR.: "The Open Hearth Furnace; Its Design, Construction, and Practice," 3 vols., Penton Publishing Company, Cleveland, Ohio, 1936–1939.

CAMP, J. M., and C. B. FRANCIS: "The Making, Shaping, and Treating of Steel," 6th ed., Carnegie-Illinois Steel Company, Pittsburgh, 1951.

CLEMENTS, FRED: "Blast Furnace Practice," 3 vols., Ernest Benn, Ltd., London, 1929.

GATHMANN, EMIL: "The Ingot Phase of Steel Production," Gathmann Engineering Company, Baltimore, Md., 1937.

GILL, JAMES P.: "Tool Steels," American Society for Metals, Cleveland, Ohio, 1944.

HOLBROOK, STEWART H.: "Iron Brew, A Century of American Ore and Steel," The Macmillan Company, New York, 1939.

HUDSON, R. P.: "The Blast Furnace, Its Raw Materials, Products, By-Products, and Their Chemical Analysis," Chemical Publishing Company, Inc., Brooklyn, 1942.

HURST, J. E.: "Melting Iron in the Cupola," Penton Publishing Company, Cleveland, Ohio, 1929.

PALMER, FRANK R., and GEORGE V. LUERSSEN: "Tool Steel Simplified," rev. ed., Carpenter Steel Company, Reading, Pa., 1948.

PARKER, CHARLES M.: "Steel in Action," Jacques Cattrell Press, Lancaster, Pa., 1943.

PAVLOV, M. A.: "Metallurgy of Cast Iron," Part II, "Blast Furnace Practice" (in Russian), Moscow, 1945.

STOUGHTON, BRADLEY: "The Metallurgy of Iron and Steel," 4th ed., McGraw-Hill Book Company, Inc., New York, 1934.

SWEETSER, RALPH H.: "Blast Furnace Practice," McGraw-Hill Book Company, Inc., New York, 1938.

TEICHERT, ERNEST J.: "Ferrous Metallurgy," Vol. I, "Introduction to Ferrous Metallurgy," Vol. II, "The Manufacture and Fabrication of Steel," Vol. III, "Metallography and Heat Treatment of Steel," McGraw-Hill Book Company, Inc., New York, 1944.

"Watkins' Cyclopedia of the Steel Industry," 4th ed., Steel Publications, Inc., Pittsburgh, Pa., 1953.

CHAPTER 14

PRODUCING AND REFINING NONFERROUS METALS

The various processes used for production and refining of metals have been outlined in Chap. 3. In the present chapter each of the more important nonferrous metals is taken up individually, and its production in the form marketed as a raw material is sketched briefly. A knowledge of the methods by which each metal is produced and refined will give a better appreciation of the important question of impurities in metals and of qualities and commercial grades.

The chemical metallurgy of the nonferrous metals is of very broad scope, embracing a variety of chemical principles. The present chapter will illustrate the use of these principles and make evident the breadth of metallurgical application.

The chief methods of extracting metals from their ores are the following:

1. Reducing smelting with carbon.
2. Smelting to matte, followed by converting.
3. Leaching (hydrometallurgy), often followed by electrolysis of the leaching solution.
4. Vaporization and condensation.
5. Chemical preparation of a pure salt, followed by extraction of the metal by electrolysis in a molten salt bath.
6. Chemical preparation of a pure compound, followed by reduction without fusion, either by hydrogen or by a chemically stronger metal such as sodium, calcium, or magnesium.

In the production of many of the metals, more than one of the above types of process is used for the same metal, and likewise more than one method of refining[1] may be used. In order to focus attention on metallurgical principles rather than details of processes, the metals are taken up in this chapter in sequence governed by the principal method of extraction used for each; at the same time the discussion of each metal will be made complete within itself by including any important application of other methods in its production. We shall begin with the metals obtained by smelting to matte, since copper, the nonferrous metal having the largest production, is one of this group.

Copper. Copper ores include a greater number and variety of minerals than the ores of any other metal. Likewise the metallurgy of copper embraces operations of great variety and considerable complexity.

---

[1] Methods of refining have been listed and outlined on p. 52.

Ores. Copper is one of the three leading metals occurring in important quantities in the native (metallic) state, the other two being gold and silver. The only important native copper mines, however, are those in Michigan, and these supply now only 4 per cent of the United States copper production. The leading copper ores are the sulfides; oxide ores also are fairly abundant, and carbonates, silicates, arsenides, and other combinations contribute large amounts of the metal. The average copper content of ore now mined in the United States is only 1 per cent. Most copper ores contain some gold and silver, and the recovery of the

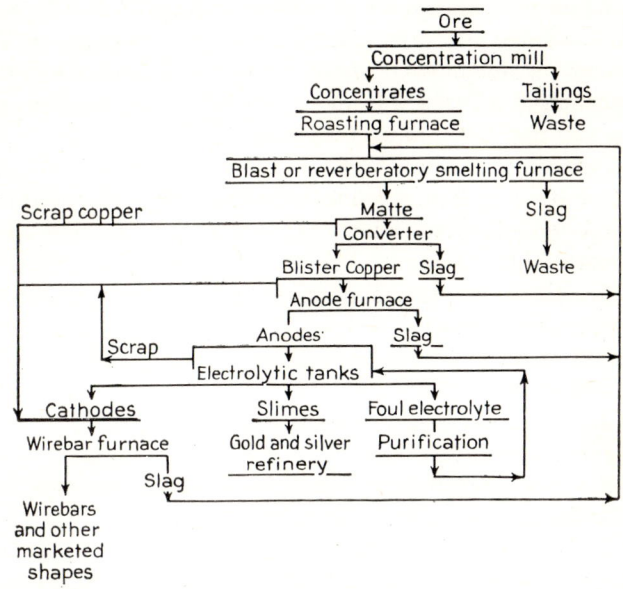

```
                        Ore
                         ↓
                   Concentration mill
                   ↓              ↓
             Concentrates      Tailings
                   ↓              ↓
             Roasting furnace   Waste
                   ↓
          Blast or reverberatory smelting furnace
                         ↓           ↓
Scrap copper          Matte         Slag
                         ↓            ↓
                      Converter     Waste
                         ↓
                  Blister Copper   Slag
                         ↓
                    Anode furnace
                         ↓
                      Anodes      Slag
             Scrap      ↓
                   Electrolytic tanks
                   ↓           ↓
             Cathodes      Slimes     Foul electrolyte
                ↓              ↓              ↓
          Wirebar furnace  Gold and silver  Purification
                ↓           refinery
              Slag
           Wirebars
           and other
           marketed
           shapes
```

FIG. 183. Flow sheet of common method of copper extraction and refining.

precious metals as by-products forms an important part of the copper industry.

Prior to smelting, the greater part of the gangue is separated by ore dressing, most often employing flotation, yielding concentrates averaging 20 to 40 per cent copper.

Secondary copper, which is copper derived from scrap, supplies a considerable part of our requirements. The amount varies a good deal from year to year; if the copper in remelted alloys, not actually separated as copper, is included in the total, secondary production in the United States usually amounts to more than half of the amount of copper produced from ore.

Pyrometallurgical Extraction. Most copper is extracted from its ores by smelting, though an important amount is produced by leaching. Smelting of copper ores differs basically from smelting of iron ores in that the ore, after concentration, is usually smelted to matte instead of directly to metal. Copper matte is an indefinite mixture of Cu_2S and FeS, together with smaller amounts of impurities, chiefly as sulfides. The components form a molten solution; all the gold and silver in the ore also dissolve in the matte, which thus acts as a collector of the precious metals as well as of the copper.

Matte having been obtained by the smelting operation, the next step is converting the matte to metal by oxidizing the sulfur and iron, the former passing off in the gases as SO_2 and the FeO being fluxed with SiO_2, forming an iron silicate slag. Metallic copper is left, in an impure form called *blister copper*, still containing the precious metals.

The next step is refining the impure copper. This is accomplished by a partial refining in a furnace from which the metal is cast into anodes, followed by electrolytic refining to a pure cathode copper deposit, with subsequent melting of the cathodes and casting into shapes for the market. In the electrolytic refining, the gold and the silver are insoluble in the electrolyte, falling to the bottom of the tanks in a *slime*, from which they are recovered.

Figure 183 gives an outline of a typical pyrometallurgical copper process in flow-sheet form.

Smelting. Copper smelting is usually done in reverberatory furnaces (Fig. 184).

The furnace is fired at one end with gas, oil, or pulverized coal. The air for combustion is not preheated. The furnaces are not regenerative, but waste-heat boilers are always used to recover heat from the gases, which leave the furnace at a high temperature. The charge consists of the ore and flux; no fuel is mixed with it. Thus, the action in the furnace is not essentially reduction, but a fusion of the charge as rapidly as possible, promoting chemical reactions which result in formation of the matte and slag. Charging is done in the part of the furnace toward the firing end, usually through holes in the roof, either near the side walls or at the center. The slag runs off at the opposite end (the flue end), while the matte settles in the furnace and is tapped from it at intervals when needed for the converters. These furnaces are built in very large sizes, the largest modern furnaces smelting over 2,000 tons of charge in 24 hr. Details of construction and operation vary greatly in different plants.

Converting. The matte obtained in the blast or reverberatory furnace is tapped into a ladle and poured immediately into a converter. The converting operation is the counterpart of the bessemer process for steel. Air is blown through the matte, oxidizing the iron to FeO and the sulfur to SO_2. No fuel is used, the heat of the oxidation being sufficient to carry on the process. The process is very slow as compared with the bessemer steel blow, owing to the great amount of material to be oxidized; 10 to 24 hr is required to blow charges of 120 to 300 tons of matte. The time depends on the amount of matte charged and also on its grade, *i.e.*, the percentage of copper it contains. Forty per cent is a common matte grade, but it varies considerably. Low-grade mattes require excessive blowing times; if the grade is too high, insufficient heat may be generated.

Copper converters are steel shells with a thick lining of magnesite brick. The most common type, the Peirce-Smith converter, is in the

Fig. 184. Interior of reverberatory copper smelting furnace. The roof and upper side walls are of silica brick; the side walls at and below the slag line are of magnesite brick; the hearth is of silica. (*Courtesy of General Refractories Company.*)

shape of a horizontal barrel (Fig. 185). There is no water or other cooling device; the temperature in the converter should be kept below 1200°C (2190°F) to avoid destruction of the lining, and this is accomplished by limiting the rate of air supply and by stopping the blow occasionally and adding cold scrap or other material. The copper converter differs from the steel converter in having the tuyères in the side instead of in the bottom, the purpose being to keep the blast passing through matte and allow the metallic copper to collect below, where the air will not oxidize it.

The pigs of blister copper usually carry 98 to 99+ per cent copper. Many elements are present as impurities, the chief ones being sulfur, nickel, arsenic, antimony, iron, lead, selenium, and tellurium, besides the gold and silver that were in the matte. The name *blister copper* is derived from the characteristic blistered appearance of the upper surface of the pigs, due to sulfur dioxide and other gases escaping from the copper while solidifying.

Anode Furnace. The purification of the blister copper consists of a furnace refining followed by electrolytic refining. The furnace refining is commonly carried out in a large reverberatory furnace, or sometimes in a horizontal cylindrical furnace, from which the partly refined copper is cast into anodes, *i.e.*, into heavy plates ready for hanging in the electrolytic tanks. The anodes carry only 99 to 99.6 per cent copper, so

Fig. 185. Peirce-Smith copper converter, 30 by 13 ft. (*Courtesy of Allis-Chalmers Mfg. Company.*)

that the increase of purity in the anode furnace is small. Nevertheless this refining is necessary, because it removes impurities that would cause excessive fouling of the electrolyte if present in too large an amount in the anodes and also adjusts the composition of the copper to the point where flat, smooth anodes may be cast. This adjustment involves reducing the sulfur to a low figure and putting about 1 to 2 per cent of Cu_2O in the copper. The action of the Cu_2O is to control the release of gases from the copper as it freezes so as to produce a level "set." Sulfur is commonly reduced below 0.005 per cent.

The furnace-refining process takes 24 hr. It includes the following operations, the time required for each in a 300-ton furnace being approximately as shown: (1) charging the furnace with the pigs of blister copper, 2 hr; (2) melting and skimming, 13 hr; (3) blowing air into the molten copper and skimming the slag from the surface of the bath, 3 hr; (4) reducing the resulting Cu_2O content and the sulfur content to the desired point by poling, 2 hr; (5) pouring or casting, 4 hr. In some plants the copper is transferred directly from the converters to the anode furnaces in the molten condition, thus eliminating remelting.

During the melting, some of the impurities are oxidized and the oxidation is furthered by the blowing, in which the air is introduced beneath the surface of the molten bath through small steel pipes. The oxidized elements rise to the top and form a thick slag, no flux being used. This

Fig. 186. Casting copper wirebars. (*Courtesy of Anaconda Copper Mining Company.*)

slag is tapped and raked off through a door at one end of the furnace. The copper is now saturated with Cu_2O, of which it will dissolve about 6 per cent, and reduction to the desired amount is accomplished by "poling," inserting poles of green wood into the bath. The gases evolved cause ebullition in the bath and a more effective reducing action than can be gained in any other known way. The poles are young trees stripped of their branches, each 15 or 20 ft in length, and 20 or 25 of these, weighing 300 to 500 lb each, are required for poling a single charge of 300 tons of copper.

Casting is done in casting machines, which revolve slowly under control of the operator, carrying the molds under a small pouring ladle into which molten copper flows from the furnace. Figure 186 shows a portion of one type of such a machine in use for casting copper wirebars.

Electrolytic Refining. The anodes are suspended in a solution of copper sulfate and sulfuric acid. Thin sheets of pure copper ("starting sheets") are hung in the tanks to serve as cathodes; these alternate with the anodes as shown in Fig. 187. A large number of electrodes, for example, 30 anodes and 31 cathodes, are placed in each tank. One lug of each anode rests on the positive bus bar, while the other lug rests on the nonconducting side of the tank. One end of each cathode rod rests on the negative bus bar, while the other end rests on the tank. Thus all the anodes are connected together and all the cathodes, making a parallel system of electrode connections. The tanks are built side by side, as seen in

Fig. 187. View in tank house, electrolytic copper refining. (*Courtesy of U.S. Metals Refining Company.*)

Fig. 187, with the negative bus bar of one tank serving as the positive bus bar of the next, so that the tanks are connected electrically in series. The current enters each anode, passes through the electrolyte from both sides of the anode and into the next cathodes, whence it leaves the tank and enters the anodes of the next tank.

As the current passes through the electrolyte, Cu^{++} ions travel to the cathode, there giving up their electric charges and depositing as pure copper in a somewhat rough but adherent plating. The SO_4^{--} ions travel to the anode, there giving up their charges and combining with metal from the anode. Thus the copper sulfate is re-formed at the anode as fast as it is broken up at the cathode, while the energy required for decomposition of $CuSO_4$ at the cathode is made up by the equivalent generation of energy through formation of $CuSO_4$ at the anode. Thus the voltage requirement is small, being chiefly that needed to overcome the small resistances.

The cathode deposit is 99.95 to 99.98 per cent copper. The entire cathodes are melted and cast into shapes for the market.

The impurities in the anode are of two classes: those which combine with the SO_4^{--} ions and dissolve in the electrolyte, and those which are insoluble and fall to the bottom of the tank in the form of *slimes*. The principal ones in the former class are nickel and arsenic; the principal ones in the latter class are lead, selenium, tellurium, and the precious metals gold and silver. Antimony and arsenic also go partly into solution and partly into the slimes; but in the subsequent treatment of the slimes the arsenic is redissolved and comes back to the tank house in solution. The slimes containing the gold, silver, and other valuable impurities are withdrawn from the bottoms of the tanks and treated for recovery of these metals.

The pure copper cathodes from the tank house are for the most part melted in large reverberatory furnaces and cast into suitable shapes for the market. The furnaces (called usually *wirebar furnaces*) and the melting process are very similar to the anode furnaces and the anode-making process. The same steps are gone through as in the anode furnace, this being necessary because oxygen and sulfur are taken up by the copper during melting. Because of the lower content of impurities than in anodes, poling must be carried to a lower oxygen percentage (about 0.03 per cent), in order to make good castings of maximum density. The copper as cast with the correct oxygen content is termed "tough-pitch" copper (see page 249). The table on page 250 gives a typical analysis of wirebar or tough-pitch copper. The name wirebar furnace is used because the greater part of the copper is cast into bars ready for rolling and drawing into wire.

Some copper cathodes are sold without melting, and some are made into oxygen-free or deoxidized copper. Some plants use electric arc or induction furnaces for melting the cathodes. The operation then is essentially a continuous one, unmelted cathodes being fed in as the molten copper runs out. Air being excluded and there being no absorption of sulfur, poling is not required.

The work of the copper refinery stops with the cathode-melting process, the shaping and adapting of metal to use being carried out by the so-called fabricator of copper.

Lake Copper. The furnace-refined Michigan copper is cast directly into shapes for the market, such silver as it contains remaining in it. This brand of copper is sold under the name of *lake copper* as distinguished from electrolytic copper. Except for the silver content of about 0.03

per cent, it is generally equal to electrolytic copper in purity and is used for the same purposes. Some of it, however, is high in arsenic, and if this is not removed in refining, it may be sold as "arsenical lake copper," containing 0.04 per cent or more arsenic. Before the electrolytic process had been developed to its present degree of perfection, lake copper was better than electrolytic; it was then more reliable and is still preferred by some consumers, particularly for making certain alloys.

Hydrometallurgy of Copper. The advantages of leaching methods in general as well as the typical outline of the process have been set forth in Chap. 3. It will therefore be necessary here to discuss only some of the special features of application to copper ores. The conditions most favorable to the wet methods of copper extraction are as follows:

1. When large-scale operations can be carried on.
2. For low-grade ores with a suitable type of gangue.
3. For ores low in gold and silver.
4. For localities where fuel, fluxes, or furnace materials are unusually costly.
5. For large deposits of ores peculiarly easy to leach, such as the copper-bearing pyrites of Rio Tinto, Spain, and the hydrous copper sulfate ore (brochantite) of Chile.

The details of the wet processes vary greatly at the various plants, being dependent on the type of ore, so that no single description of practice would fit any two plants. In the fundamental factor of choice of solvent there is some variation, but sulfuric acid is used most. It is a cheap solvent and can be regenerated when the copper is recovered from the solution by electrodeposition, as shown by the equation

$$CuSO_4 + H_2O \rightarrow Cu + H_2SO_4 + O$$

But it will not dissolve Cu_2S, so that with this solvent sulfide ores must first be roasted, and any copper remaining unoxidized is lost. It will not dissolve native or unoxidized copper and extracts but little silver and no gold. Sulfuric acid cannot be used when the gangue would be much attacked by it, as in the case of carbonates and some iron minerals.

Recovery of Copper from Sulfate Solutions. Two methods are widely used to obtain the copper from sulfate solutions. The older method is precipitation of the copper on scrap iron. This is a chemical replacement of the copper by the iron due to the higher position of iron in the electropotential series of metals:

$$CuSO_4 + Fe \rightarrow FeSO_4 + Cu$$

Such a process is called *cementation*, and the copper obtained in this way is called cement copper. It comes down on the surface of the iron as a loose crystalline plating, which when scraped off contains considerable iron and other impurities. This cement copper must be melted down and refined.

The other method of obtaining the copper is by electrodeposition. This is in most respects the same as the electrolytic refining already described, but the copper instead of coming from impure metal used as anodes comes from the solution which is used as electrolyte and is continuously renewed so as to keep up the supply of copper. The anodes must be of an insoluble material. Pure copper is deposited on the cathodes, which are simply remelted and cast into shapes for the market in the same way as are the cathodes obtained in electrolytic refining. The electrolyte, after deposition of part of its copper and concomitant regeneration of sulfuric acid, is returned to the leaching tanks as the solvent, making a cyclic process.

Nickel. About 85 per cent of the world's production of nickel is obtained from Ontario, Canada. Most of the Canadian mines are owned by the International Nickel Company, which has large metallurgical plants in Canada, the United States, and Great Britain. The Canadian ore contains sulfide minerals of iron, nickel, and copper in a siliceous gangue, the nickel content averaging under 2 per cent and the copper roughly half of the nickel.

The early stages of the extractive metallurgy follow closely the metallurgy of copper, while the latter stages are designed to separate these two metals, refine them, and recover the by-product metals gold, silver, platinum-group metals, cobalt, selenium, and tellurium. A feature of the ore is its comparative richness in platinum and palladium. Since extension of electrolytic refining to most of the nickel some years ago, Canada has become, with Russia, one of the two leading countries in production of platinum.

The ore is first concentrated by flotation, then smelted to matte in large reverberatory furnaces, and the matte converted in Peirce-Smith converters. The matte is composed principally of the sulfides of nickel, copper, and iron. The converting operation is stopped at the point where the FeS has been virtually removed. The partly converted matte carries about 75 per cent nickel plus copper, the ratio between the two being that which existed in the concentrates, with the balance mostly sulfur.

In order to separate the copper and nickel sulfides, the molten matte is allowed to solidify very slowly, from one day to two weeks being allowed for cooling from the molten state to about 150°C (300°F). Slow cooling between the range of 700 and 510°C (1290 and 950°F) is particularly important. This results in the formation of an intimate mixture of separate fine crystals of copper sulfide and nickel sulfide, together with some crystals of a metallic nickel-copper alloy. The entire mixture is finely ground and treated by a flotation process, in which there is used a special organic flotation reagent that causes the copper sulfide to float and the nickel sulfide and the nickel-copper alloy to be depressed. The alloy is magnetic and is removed by magnetic separation. The nickel sulfide concentrate is roast-sintered and then usually reduced to impure nickel from which anodes are cast for electrolytic refining. The copper sulfide concentrate requires regrinding and refloating to make its nickel content sufficiently low, after which it is converted to blister copper.

The well-known Orford or "tops-and-bottoms" process was superseded by the matte-flotation process in 1949, and consequently will not be described here. The new method permits a greater recovery of nickel and copper as well as recovery of cobalt and the precious metals.

Another older process, the Mond process, is used at a smaller plant in Wales. In this interesting method, nickel is acted on by producer gas at a temperature of 60°C (140°F) to form gaseous nickel carbonyl [$Ni(CO)_4$]. When heated to 180°C (356°F), this decomposes, yielding metallic nickel in the form of shot of high purity. The precious metals are recovered from the residue. A process based on the same principle is sometimes used to make iron of high purity for special purposes ("carbonyl iron").

Nickel for the steel industry is also produced in the form of nickel oxide sinter. A large plant for making this product was built recently by the International Nickel Company at Copper Cliff, Ontario.

Electrolytic Refining. The anodes made at the end of the matte process are used for electrolytic refining in a manner similar to copper refining. Since they contain a little copper, a modification must be introduced to prevent deposition of the copper with the cathode nickel. This consists of separating the electrolyte (impure nickel sulfate containing boric acid) in anode and cathode compartments by means of a canvas diaphragm. Electrolyte from the anode compartment is withdrawn continuously and circulated through finely divided metallic nickel. The copper is thus deposited by cementation, and the purified electrolyte is returned to the cathode compartment.

Electrolytic nickel cathodes contain 99.95 per cent nickel plus cobalt, the cobalt content now being only about 0.1 per cent. The principal impurities are iron and copper. In melting the cathodes to make ingot or shot nickel, additional impurities are taken up. These consist chiefly of about 0.05 per cent each of carbon and silicon and about 0.005 per cent sulfur. For nickel ingots a little manganese is added to prevent hot-shortness, and the metal is degassed with magnesium, titanium, or boron.

Monel. Monel is an alloy made directly from the ore rather than by melting the metal constituents together. Sintered oxide made from converter matte which has not been treated for separation of the copper and nickel in it is fused in a reverberatory furnace and reduced to metal with charcoal. The composition is often adjusted by adding a little nickel or copper. Monel contains about 67 per cent nickel, 30 per cent copper, with the balance chiefly iron and manganese.

Lead. The next three metals to be discussed are produced chiefly by reducing smelting, but in this case smelting direct to metal; any small amount of matte, formed because of some sulfur in the furnace charge, is subsidiary to the metal product.

Most of our lead is derived from one mineral, the simple sulfide, galena (PbS). This is associated in ores differently in different localities. Most of the ores are of the "argentiferous" type, containing important amounts not only of silver, but also of gold and copper, which are recovered as by-products. In most ores also the lead sulfide is associated with zinc sulfide, and either of the two may predominate. When relatively large amounts of zinc and copper sulfides are present, they may be separated from the galena by selective flotation. United States lead ores average about 5 per cent lead. Before smelting they are concentrated, usually by flotation, the concentrates carrying 40 to 70 per cent lead.

Lead ore is most commonly smelted in blast furnaces, but important amounts of the nonargentiferous ores are smelted in the ore hearth, a type of furnace and process which is peculiar to the metallurgy of lead. Very little lead is obtained by leaching, because lead compounds are insoluble in the low-cost solvents. There is a small application of leaching in strong brine (NaCl solution).

Lead Blast-furnace Smelting. This is most often the best process, because it allows recovery of the silver and gold, and because it can handle ores that are low in lead and high in impurities. The concentrates are first roasted to remove most of the sulfur, changing PbS to a mixture of PbO and $PbSO_4$. Since the sulfur is not completely removed in roasting, a small amount of matte is formed. The matte has the valuable function of taking up most of the copper; any copper not entering the matte goes into the lead metal, from which it is removed later. The amount of matte formed, and consequently the distribution of the copper, can be controlled by the amount of sulfur left in roasting.

The lead blast furnace differs greatly from the iron blast furnace. It is rectangular instead of cylindrical in shape, and is not so high. The rectangular shape, of long and narrow section, is necessary in order to permit the relatively low-pressure blast to penetrate to the center of the furnace from the tuyères. The lead collects inside the furnace and passes out through a siphon tap. Slag and matte are tapped together from a taphole and run into settlers. The slag overflows from the settler while the matte collects in the bottom.

The ore is charged into the blast furnace usually in the form of Dwight-Lloyd sinter, together with coke and flux. The flux includes both iron ore and limestone, making a slag that is essentially a silicate of iron and lime. The blast is not preheated.

Ore-hearth Smelting. The ore hearth is a small, partly open furnace, in some respects intermediate between a blast furnace and a reverberatory. Only a small amount of coke and a little blast are used. Flux is not used, and the temperature does not rise high enough for fusion of all the charge. Molten lead forms readily, however, because of its low melting point. Some of this is reduced by C or CO, but the main action is oxidation of PbS to PbO and $PbSO_4$, followed by interaction between these and more of the PbS:

$$2PbO + PbS \rightarrow 3Pb + SO_2$$
$$PbSO_4 + PbS \rightarrow 2Pb + 2SO_2$$

This is the "roast-reaction" principle. No separate roasting of the ore is required. High-grade lead is produced directly and usually marketed without subsequent refining.

Compared with the blast furnace, ore-hearth smelting is simple and cheap, but it is limited to very rich concentrates, carrying not more than 4 or 5 per cent silica. The method is used only for nonargentiferous ores because there would be large losses of silver by volatilization, whereas in the blast furnace this can be prevented by keeping the top of the furnace at a low temperature. A good deal of lead is left in the residues from the ore hearth, so that it is necessary to resmelt these in a blast furnace.

Softening. The lead bullion obtained from the blast furnace must be refined and the silver and gold recovered from it. Before desilverization, the other impurities, which would interfere with the desilverization process, must be removed. This step is called *softening*.

The chief impurities in lead bullion are silver, copper, antimony, arsenic, tin, bismuth, sulfur, and zinc. The usual softening process consists of melting the lead bullion in a reverberatory furnace holding up to 350 tons of lead and subjecting it to oxidation. Such oxidation will not remove copper, bismuth, or silver. The copper is removed by adding a little sulfur, which causes the copper to come to the top as copper sulfide. Then arsenic, tin, and antimony are oxidized and skimmed off, mixed with a good deal of lead oxide that is unavoidably formed. The oxidation is accomplished by the air passing over the molten bath, usually aided by additions of litharge (PbO).

Another method of softening, carried on in the desilverizing kettles instead of a separate furnace, employs caustic soda (NaOH) and niter ($NaNO_3$) to take up arsenic, antimony, and tin in the form of sodium salts, which are skimmed off molten mixed with excess caustic. Sometimes arsenic alone is removed by caustic soda prior to furnace softening.

Desilverization. The softened lead bullion, still containing the gold, silver, and bismuth, is now ready for desilverizing, which is commonly done by the Parkes process. The lead bullion is held in kettles, and zinc is added to the melt. The zinc alloys with the silver and gold and some lead, rising to the top in a scum called the zinc crust, which is removed as it forms. After about 18 hr the bath is practically free from silver, but the remaining lead has dissolved about 0.6 per cent of zinc. The zinc is usually taken out with chlorine gas, making zinc chloride as a by-product. More recently a "vacuum dezincing" method has been successfully used, in which the zinc is removed by vaporizing in a vacuum chamber over the kettle. The Parkes process does not remove bismuth, but the product is of high grade, provided the original bullion was sufficiently low in bismuth. Sometimes bismuth is subsequently removed from the lead by adding metallic calcium and magnesium; these form compounds with the bismuth, which rise to the top and are skimmed off.

The zinc crust removed from the desilverizing kettle is treated for recovery of the silver and gold, which are subsequently parted and refined.

Refining and desilverizing of lead may also be done electrolytically instead of by the furnace processes described above. The process is identical in principle with electrolytic copper refining by the multiple system. The electrolyte is an unusual one, an aqueous solution of lead fluosilicate ($PbSiF_6$). Gold, silver, and bismuth remain undissolved at the anode, forming a slime which is collected and treated for the recovery of those metals. Most of our bismuth is produced as a by-product of lead refining by this process.

Tin. There are no tin ore deposits of any importance in the United States. Of the annual world's production about two-thirds comes from southeast Asia, where the two leading producers are Malaya and Indonesia. Bolivia is also a large producer, and in 1942 a tin smelter of larger capacity than any other in the world was built at Texas City, Tex., to treat Bolivian ore. This plant can supply about half of the normal United States requirements if it continues to receive sufficient ore.

Ore and Ore Treatment. There is only one mineral of great importance as a source of tin, namely, the oxide cassiterite (SnO_2). Like gold ore, it occurs in two types of deposits, alluvial or placer deposits and vein or lode deposits. The first are more common and typically contain as little as 1 lb of tin per ton of ore. The latter contain usually 2 to 4 per cent tin.

Since cassiterite is an easily reducible oxide, concentration followed by simple reducing smelting with carbon would seem to be indicated; but a number of difficulties are encountered. The oxide ore is not readily concentrated by flotation. Cassiterite is a very heavy mineral, but the ores commonly contain other heavy minerals, including sulfides, as impurities, and these tend to remain with the SnO_2 in gravity concentration. Roasting and leaching are commonly employed, not as a means of extracting tin, but as steps in the concentration process. Concentrates containing about 70 per cent tin are produced, except from the more impure Bolivian ore.

Smelting is usually carried out in reverberatory furnaces, occasionally in blast furnaces. In the former, coal is added to the charge as a reducing agent, with limestone as a flux. Since tin oxide may act as either an acid or a base in forming compounds, it is difficult to obtain a slag with a low percentage of tin. Accordingly a two-stage smelting is commonly adopted. In the first smelting no effort is made to produce a slag low in tin, and this slag contains 10 to 25 per cent tin. This is resmelted, the second slag having 1 or 2 per cent tin.

The crude tin obtained by smelting contains iron and often arsenic, sulfur, tungsten, and bismuth. It is refined first by liquation, which may be accomplished by placing the bars on a sloping hearth and melting them slowly. The tin that melts first and flows off is fairly pure, and its refining may be completed by oxidation of the impurities from a molten bath.

Detinning. Perhaps a quarter of the requirements of tin in the United States are supplied from secondary or scrap material, but most of this is in the form of alloys or compounds. Some pig tin is obtained by detinning of scrap tin plate, using the cuttings from the manufacture of cans and other clean scrap. During 1943 and 1944 considerable effort was expended in collecting and detinning old tin-plate cans, but only about 3,000 tons of tin was actually obtained therefrom. The bulkiness of old cans makes it uneconomical to collect them in time of peace, and their contamination with rust and waste material is also undesirable.

Two principal methods of detinning are in use. In one, the tin is dissolved with caustic soda, and pure tin is deposited by electrolysis of the resulting sodium stannate solution. In the other, chlorine gas is used to combine with the tin, forming $SnCl_4$, a liquid at ordinary temperature. The detinned scrap is shipped to a steel plant.

Cobalt. Cobalt is primarily a by-product metal, but the processes used in separating it are varied and complex. Smelting, roasting, wet methods, and electrolysis are involved in one or more of the procedures in use.

The sources of cobalt are limited. At present no other metal is in such short supply relative to the demand for it. It is commonly associated with nickel in nature, but until recently has not ordinarily been separated in the metallurgy of nickel. Now the greater part of this cobalt is recovered, but since the cobalt content of nickel ores is only of the order of 0.5 per cent of the nickel content, recovery of all the associated cobalt would amount to only about 1,000 tons annually.

The largest source of cobalt at present is a cobaltiferous sulfide copper ore mined and smelted in Belgian Congo. Some is also obtained from French Morocco, and a new source has recently been discovered in Idaho. When the Belgian Congo ore is smelted for copper, a slag high in cobalt is produced. This is resmelted in an electric furnace with reduction by carbon, making a copper-cobalt-iron alloy. One production method involves solution of the alloy in sulfuric acid, purification of the solution, and precipitation of the cobalt as hydroxide. In a later modification cobalt is deposited by electrolysis from a sulfate solution, similar to electrodeposition of nickel.

On heating, the hydroxide is changed to Co_3O_4, which is either sold in that form or reduced to metallic cobalt with charcoal. Reduction may be without fusion, forming small round slugs called "rondelles"; or the metal may be fused and poured into water to form shot.

Zinc. The next group of metals to be discussed, embracing zinc, cadmium, mercury, antimony, and arsenic, comprises those in which vaporization is employed as a principal means of separating the metal from its ore. In the case of the first three, the metal itself is vaporized; with the last two, the oxide is vaporized. The vapor in each case is recovered by condensing it.

Because of the relatively low boiling point of zinc, and particularly because it vaporizes at a temperature lower than the reduction temperature of zinc oxide, the extraction of zinc from its ores has been to a major extent a process of vaporization. This was the universal method of extraction until the First World War, but the hydrometallurgical process developed then has steadily grown in use until now about 38 per cent of our zinc is produced by the leaching method and 62 per cent by the distillation process. Zinc is deposited by electrolysis from the solutions obtained in leaching, and hence zinc produced by the hydrometallurgical method is termed "electrolytic zinc."

A number of different zinc minerals are used as commercial sources of the metal in different parts of the world, but only two are of widespread occurrence. These are the sulfide ore called sphalerite or zinc blende (ZnS) and a carbonate ore usually called calamine. Of these the sulfide is by far the more important. The average zinc content of the ores as mined is about 5 per cent; before metallurgical treatment they are concentrated to a grade of usually 40 to 50 per cent. Sphalerite is usually associated with galena. Zinc ores are often of the complex type, and selective flotation is even more important as a source of zinc than it is of lead.

Roasting Zinc Ore. Zinc that is to be extracted by distillation must not be present as sulfide, while ore that is to be leached must have the metal in a form that is soluble in dilute sulfuric acid. For distillation the roasting should be as nearly complete as possible, since any sulfur remaining will result in loss of zinc through ZnS being left in the residue. The roasting temperature is relatively high.

Roasting prior to leaching is carried out in multiple-hearth furnaces, and the temperature is carefully controlled at a lower limit so as to retain a small part of the zinc as $ZnSO_4$. When the leaching solutions are electrolyzed for deposition of zinc, the SO_4 ions form H_2SO_4, which is used over again for leaching. Formation of a small amount of $ZnSO_4$ in roasting supplies enough additional H_2SO_4 to make up for losses in the process.

Zinc Smelting. The pyrometallurgical method of extracting zinc is commonly referred to as zinc smelting, but since the charge is not fused, this term is in reality a misnomer. The more proper designation is zinc distillation. Two types of process are in use, the older batch process employing horizontal retorts and the newer continuous process using vertical retorts. The former is still most commonly used, and will be described first.

The crushed and roasted or oxidized ore is mixed with carbon and heated in retorts made of fire clay, reducing the oxide to metallic zinc. The temperature inside the retort gradually increases, reaching at least 1150°C (2100°F). It must not, however, become high enough to fuse the charge. The metal is vaporized as it is reduced and passes out of the retort along with CO. These gases, containing about 45 per cent zinc vapor, pass from the retort directly into the condenser, which is made of fire clay and is attached to the end of the retort. Here the temperature is much lower, but is above the melting point of zinc. The zinc vapor, accordingly, condenses to liquid metal and collects in the bottom of the condenser, whence it is drawn out at intervals. The uncondensable gases pass on through, and the CO burns as it comes out into the air.

The zinc condenses first in fine droplets, and these may become coated with ZnO, formed because the reduction of zinc by CO is a reversible reaction and some CO_2 is always present:

$$ZnO + CO \rightleftarrows Zn + CO_2$$

Particles of zinc coated with ZnO is this manner, amounting often to 15 per cent or more of the total zinc reduced, do not coalesce but float on the liquid zinc, forming the product called *blue powder*. This is recharged into the retorts, so that it does not constitute a loss of material, but is a circulating load. It is essential to have a considerable excess of carbon in the charge so as to reduce most of the CO_2 back to CO and minimize the formation of blue powder:

$$CO_2 + C \rightarrow 2CO$$

The summation of the two reactions above is expressed in the one reaction

$$ZnO + C \rightarrow Zn + CO$$

The necessary carbon is obtained by mixing fine coal with the charge, using an amount equal to 40 to 50 per cent of the weight of the ore.

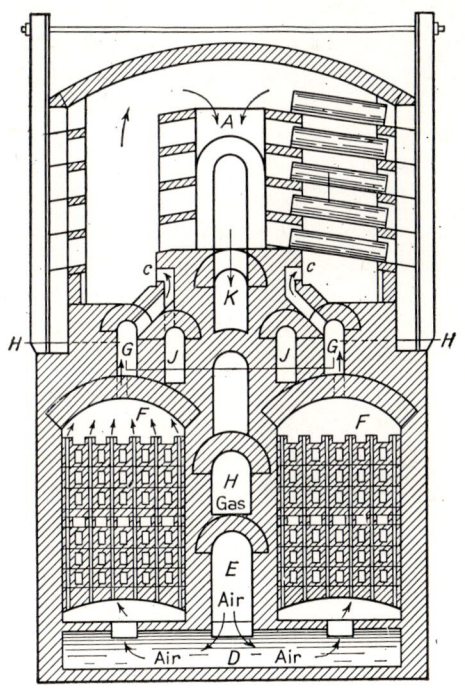

Fig. 188. Diagram of horizontal-retort zinc furnace.

Heat is supplied by burning gas around the retort. Either natural gas or producer gas may be used. The producer gas is made from coal, and the amount of this *heating coal* added to the *reduction coal* makes a total coal consumption of 1½ to 2 tons per ton of zinc produced. The thermal efficiency of the process is very low. About 10 per cent of the zinc in the ore escapes reduction or distillation and is thus lost in the residue. There is no slagging action, and the ore charge must be such as to avoid the formation of fusible silicates, which cause corrosion of the retorts and interfere with their being cleaned of the residue at the end of a run. The usual retorts last only 30 or 40 days, and are a large item in the labor and expense. They are made of specially selected clay, molded by hydraulic press, and baked with extreme care. In some cases silicon carbide can be mixed with fire clay, giving longer life, greater strength, and greater thermal conductivity. Each retort yields about 45 to 75 lb of zinc in 24 hr. As usually operated, an entire run from charging to discharge of residue occupies 24 hr, but under the conditions at some plants a 48-hr cycle has been found more economical.

Horizontal zinc retorts have the shape of long cylinders, usually elliptical but sometimes circular in cross section. Typical dimensions are 5 ft in length by 8 to 10 in. inside diameter. They are erected in blocks having about five rows of retorts one above the other, and in two sections back to back, so that a pair of blocks may be fired from the center and charged and discharged at both sides (see Fig. 188).

Continuous Distillation in Vertical Retorts. It is evident that the small size of the zinc retort and the intermittent nature of its operation in small batches are serious disadvantages. Efforts to get around them were unsuccessful until the development of a vertical-retort process by the New Jersey Zinc Company. In this process the retorts, made of the same kind of material as the small retorts, are very much larger and are erected vertically so that the charge is put in at the top at frequent intervals and the residue is discharged continuously at the bottom into a water seal. The retort, heated as before by burning gas around the outside, is heated to a height of about 25 ft. The sectional area is usually 1 by 6 ft; the retort must be narrow to permit the penetration of sufficient heat to the center (see Fig. 189). With the old type of charge, the heat could not penetrate even this distance; the mixture of ore and coal is therefore mixed with a binder and baked into briquettes, giving a more efficient heat transfer and a charge that does not pack in the retort.

The condenser is a horizontal sump connected to the retort near the top, as shown in Fig. 190, which provides for rapid cooling of the

FIG. 189. Vertical retort for continuous zinc distillation. This view shows a retort partly installed in the furnace setting, with the long walls fitting into slots provided with glands to allow for expansion and contraction without permitting escape of zinc vapor. (*Courtesy of New Jersey Zinc Company.*)

gases before they enter the condenser proper, in which relatively slow cooling condenses the zinc vapor to liquid zinc with little formation of blue powder. The large size permits the tapping of over a ton of zinc in 24 hr, and the life of a retort may be 3 years or more. Still larger condensers are now used, and several retorts may discharge into the same condenser. A device providing fine droplets of liquid zinc by "splashing" in the chamber provides nuclei for efficient condensation. Much better thermal efficiency is obtained than in the intermittent method, and in this process it is also possible to utilize as fuel the CO issuing from the condensers, which in the old process is wasted. The purity of the zinc produced is also higher.

The St. Joseph Lead Company uses an electric shaft furnace for distillation, producing either zinc metal or zinc oxide. Current passes through the charge itself, heating it by resistance.

Refining. The zinc obtained from the horizontal retorts is not uniform in composition, and is accordingly placed in mixers, whence it is cast into slabs. It may be partially purified of lead and iron by simply holding the liquid metal near its melting point (*liquation*), when these two metals tend to collect in the bottom layers of the melt. The purity depends on the purity and composition of the concentrates charged. Usually no special refining process is employed, but sometimes a further liquation in reverberatory furnaces is practiced.

FIG. 190. Condenser for vertical retort. (*Courtesy of New Jersey Zinc Company.*)

For a high degree of refining the zinc may be redistilled. The growing demand for zinc of special high grade points to increased importance of refining by redistillation. A process and an apparatus have been developed by the New Jersey Zinc Company making use of the principle of rectification, a series of fractional distillations. By this process zinc of lower grade can be raised to 99.99 per cent quality, with recovery of cadmium as well as lead and other metals as by-products.

Hydrometallurgy and Electrodeposition of Zinc. In this process the roasted zinc ore is leached with dilute sulfuric acid, yielding a solution of zinc sulfate. The zinc sulfate solution is subjected to electrolysis to deposit the zinc from it, but before electrodeposition the solution must be carefully purified, the whole success of the process hinging on proper purification. This fact is due to the high position of zinc in the electropotential series of metals; not only will the metals below zinc—copper, iron, nickel, cobalt, arsenic, antimony, etc.—deposit with the zinc if present in the solution, but their deposition will set up electrolytic couples that cause re-solution of the zinc by the sulfuric acid present in the electrolyte and result in low current efficiency, spongy zinc deposits, impure zinc, and other troubles. The presence of antimony in the electrolyte to the amount of only one part per million is sufficient to prevent entirely the plating out of the zinc. Pure zinc, on the other hand, is only slowly soluble in sulfuric acid, and may readily be deposited from a purified sulfuric acid solution at an average current efficiency of 90 per cent.

Purification is accomplished by precipitating and filtering off the impurities in two steps. In the first the solution is allowed to become neutral, lime being added if necessary. When neutral, iron precipitates as $Fe(OH)_3$, carrying arsenic and antimony down with it; alumina and silica also precipitate. After filtering, the remaining solution is agitated with zinc dust, which causes precipitation of copper and cadmium by a cementation reaction.

The purified solution is run into the electrolytic cells containing insoluble anodes (which are of lead or lead alloy) and the zinc plated out on an aluminum cathode in a degree of purity of 99.90 to 99.99 per cent zinc. As the zinc is deposited, sulfuric acid accumulates in the electrolyte:

$$ZnSO_4 + H_2O \rightarrow Zn + H_2SO_4 + O$$

After being depleted of a large part of its zinc, the solution is withdrawn and used again as a leaching agent to replenish its zinc content.

A principal reason for the success of this process is its ability to produce zinc of the highest grade from a relatively impure or complex ore.

Waelz Process. A different type of process has become of great importance in the metallurgy of zinc since the First World War. The ore and coal mixture is heated in a large rotary kiln, similar to a cement kiln. The charge is fed continuously at the upper end, works slowly down through the kiln, and the residue is discharged at the lower end. In the kiln, zinc is reduced and vaporized as in a retort, but the vapor is immediately reoxidized as it leaves the gangue, forming ZnO which is carried out of the kiln suspended in the gases. It is recovered by filtering the gases through bags. The ZnO is impure and is mixed with dust from the charge. Accordingly the process does not produce zinc directly, but is a low-cost method of separating zinc from low-grade ores or from the residues of retort distillation. The impure ZnO may then be charged into the regular retorts for production of metallic zinc, or may be treated in a zinc oxide furnace for production of pure zinc oxide.

Electric Smelting. Smelting zinc concentrates in an electric-arc furnace has been practiced for many years under special conditions prevailing in Norway and Sweden. A new process of this type is now under development by the New Jersey Zinc Company, called the Sterling process, which is considered to hold great promise for production of zinc and by-product metals from ores of usual types. It is a true smelting process, the gangue being slagged, nonvolatile metals such as iron being collected as liquid metal, and zinc being vaporized and condensed. When used on high-grade zinc concentrates, lead, cadmium, and some silver are recovered in the zinc metal, while copper, gold, and the rest of the silver collect in a pig-iron product formed by reduction of the iron. An arc furnace of special design is used, and the zinc is not slagged because it is reduced before the gangue is fused. The zinc vapor is condensed in condensers of the splash type mentioned above.

Cadmium. Most zinc ores contain cadmium, and virtually all the world's supply of this metal is recovered as a by-product of the zinc industry. There is no ore of cadmium alone, this being one of the few metals obtained solely as a by-product. The amount of cadmium contained in the ores is variable, but a common ratio is of the order of 1 part cadmium to 100 parts zinc.

Cadmium is recovered in the treatment of zinc ore in both the pyrometallurgical and the electrolytic zinc production methods. There is considerable variation in the processes used at different plants, but two may be cited as probably the most important. One of these is treatment of the precipitate of cadmium made with zinc dust in purification of the zinc leaching solution prior to electrolysis, referred to in the section on Zinc. This precipitate, which contains a good deal of zinc and some other impurities, is oxidized, redissolved in sulfuric acid, the solution partly purified by further precipitation if necessary, and then electrolyzed with insoluble anodes. Cadmium of high purity is deposited on aluminum cathodes.

In the other leading method, especially important in treatment of zinc ore in the Missouri-Oklahoma-Kansas district, cadmium is recovered in the fume from roasting and sintering furnaces used in preparing the zinc ore for distillation. The roasting practice is adjusted to yield a fume as high as possible in cadmium. This is treated with sulfuric acid, and cadmium is precipitated from the solution with zinc dust. The cadmium precipitate may be refined by distillation or by electrolysis.

Other Metals Obtained by Vaporization Processes. Other metals whose ores are treated by vaporization methods include mercury, antimony, and arsenic. Antimony is also produced by smelting in blast furnaces, and the sulfide, Sb_2S_3, is often separated from the gangue by liquation. Because of the lesser importance of these metals in engineering applications, details of their production will not be discussed here.

Vaporization is also used to a minor extent in the production of magnesium from its ores (see page 409).

Aluminum. The next group of metals comprises those produced by the electrolysis of a fused salt bath. While several of the chemically strong metals are produced in this way, the only ones of sufficient engineering importance to be discussed here are aluminum, magnesium, and beryllium. The reasons for the application of this method have been noted on page 59.

All the world's aluminum is produced by electrolysis of a fused bath of sodium aluminum fluoride, in which is dissolved about 2 to 5 per cent of purified alumina (Al_2O_3).

The source of most of the alumina from which aluminum is electrolytically reduced is the mineral bauxite, which occurs in nature as an impure hydrated alumina. The principal impurities are silica, iron oxide, and titanium oxide. Until recently, only the higher grades of bauxite were used for aluminum production, namely, those containing 50 to 65 per cent Al_2O_3, with SiO_2 not exceeding 8 per cent. The iron oxide content is widely variable, and since it is easily removed, may be as high as 25 per cent. The TiO_2 content is also not a serious limitation, but is usually 1 to 4 per cent.

Purification of Bauxite. The production of aluminum is primarily one of reducing Al_2O_3 to aluminum. But this is not readily accomplished, on account of the high position of aluminum in the electropotential series of metals. The bauxite must be purified before reduction in the electrolytic cell, otherwise iron, silicon, and titanium, all of which are chemically weaker than aluminum, would be reduced in preference to the desired metal. It would not be feasible to make an impure aluminum and then refine it afterward, as is done with most other metals, because if it was attempted to oxidize the impurities out of aluminum, the aluminum itself would oxidize, owing to its high affinity for oxygen. Furthermore, it is expensive to refine crude aluminum electrolytically since aluminum cannot be electrodeposited from an aqueous solution; the metal is so strong chemically that when an attempt is made to plate it out electrolytically in the presence of water it combines with the water, forming $Al(OH)_3$. It can be refined using a molten electrolyte, but this increases the cost.

The Bayer Process. Several methods are applicable for preparation of pure alumina, but for high-grade bauxite the one most commonly used is the Bayer process. This involves a long and expensive chemical treatment. The bauxite is first crushed, calcined in rotary kilns to eliminate the water of hydration, and finely ground. To dissolve the Al_2O_3, the finely ground mineral is digested with strong caustic soda (NaOH) for several hours at about 160°C (320°F) and 4 or 5 atm pressure. A solution of sodium aluminate ($NaAlO_2$) is formed, iron oxide remaining insoluble and giving the name "red mud" to the residue. The residue also contains a compound of silica, alumina, and soda, so that every per cent of silica present causes a serious loss of both alumina and soda. After the solution has been filtered, some crystalline $Al(OH)_3$ is added to start precipitation. Pure $Al(OH)_3$ then begins to precipitate from it and continues for perhaps 60 hr while the solution is agitated. The soda is set free for further use, and the precipitate is calcined to pure Al_2O_3 in rotary kilns.

The Lime-soda-sinter Process. Difficulty in the separation of silica is a severe limitation on the Bayer process for treatment of lower-grade bauxite, or of any source of alumina containing more than 8 per cent SiO_2. High-grade bauxite, while sufficiently plentiful for production of aluminum on the scale which prevailed before the Second World War, is not an abundant material; deposits in the United States are very limited. The tremendous expansion in aluminum production during the war, combined with difficulty in importing bauxite from foreign sources, made it necessary to develop methods for using other materials. The most important of these in the United States are the lower-grade bauxites and the red mud accumulated from former use of the Bayer process. For these, the lime-soda-sinter process has achieved the greatest success. It is being used for bauxites containing up to 13 or 15 per cent SiO_2, either alone or in combination with the Bayer process. In this process the bauxite is calcined with admixtures of limestone and soda ash, and the sinter is leached with hot water to extract the $NaAlO_2$. Some of the silica is eliminated as insoluble calcium silicate, and pure $Al(OH)_3$ is precipitated from the aluminate solution.

Other Processes for Pure Alumina. The Bayer, lime-soda-sinter, and combination processes are alkaline processes. Acid processes include use of sulfuric acid, ammonium sulfate, sulfurous acid, and hydrochloric acid. Electric-furnace processes have also been successfully used. One of these produces pure alumina by reducing the impurities and recovering them as a ferroalloy. Another produces a high-alumina slag, from which Al_2O_3 is leached with Na_2CO_3 and NaOH. Another forms Al_2S_3. Some of the above types of process were designed for application to a particular kind of material.

Since all clays are fundamentally silicates of alumina, it is technically possible to produce aluminum from clay, the supply of which is inexhaustible. There has been some production from high-grade clay, but in most localities and under ordinary conditions the cost of such treatment is too high to make it commercially successful at present.

Aluminum Reduction. The principle of using a fused bath of cryolite (Na_3AlF_6) to dissolve Al_2O_3 for production of aluminum by electrolysis was discovered independently by Charles M. Hall in the United States and P. L. T. Héroult in France in the same year, 1886. Until a few years ago the cryolite was obtained entirely from Greenland, where the only commercial deposits in the world exist, the mineral occurring in a sufficiently pure state so that it requires no chemical purification before use. Now a large part of the sodium aluminum fluoride used for aluminum production is made artifically from the mineral fluorspar (CaF_2).

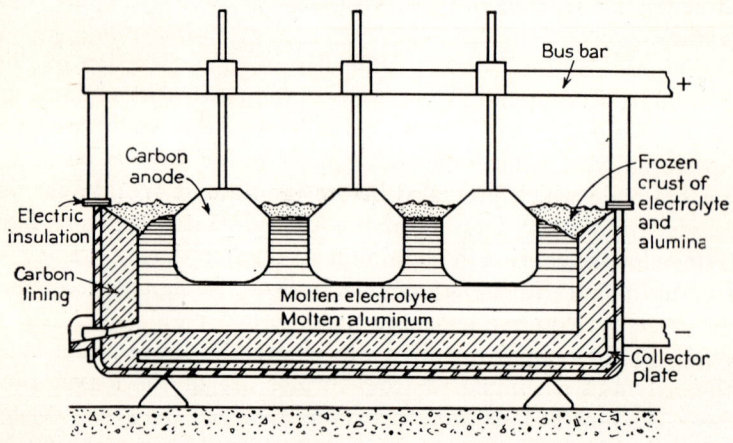

FIG. 191. Section of modern electrolytic cell for production of aluminum, Hall-Heroult process.

The amount required is not large, since the electrolysis decomposes only the Al_2O_3 and not the fluoride. The high melting point of Al_2O_3, 2050°C (3720°F), precludes the possibility of using fused Al_2O_3 alone. The cryolite bath melts at about 900°C (1650°F).

The electrolytic cells (Fig. 191 and 192) are made of steel plate, with a carbon lining to act as cathode. The melting point of aluminum is 660°C (1220°F), and being slightly heavier than the electrolyte, it collects in a pool in the bottom of the tank, whence it is tapped out at intervals. Each cell may receive about 30,000 amp, yielding about 420 lb of aluminum in 24 hr. Many cells are smaller, but some recently built take as much as 40,000 amp.

The anodes are carbon blocks, which dip into the electrolyte from above, reaching nearly to the surface of the molten metal. As the Al_2O_3 is reduced, the oxygen thus set free combines with the carbon of the electrodes, forming CO and CO_2. Thus there is a large electrode consumption, making one of the chief items of cost. Every pound of aluminum produced requires the consumption of about 2 lb of bauxite, 0.75 lb of electrodes, and 0.08 lb of cryolite.

Refining. None of the principal uses of aluminum requires highly pure metal. Consequently most of it is marketed as the direct product of the electrolytic cell, except for remelting to free it from included electrolyte. The purity is usually not over 99.7 per cent and is often below 99.5, the chief impurities being iron and silicon.

A small amount of aluminum is refined to purities of 99.9 up to 99.99 per cent. This is accomplished by the Hoopes process, which uses a

Fig. 192. A row of electrolytic cells in an aluminum reduction works. (*Courtesy of Aluminum Company of America.*)

fused electrolyte similar to the Hall-Héroult process. However, some barium fluoride is added to the electrolyte to make it heavier than pure aluminum. The aluminum to be refined is alloyed with copper, making it heavier than the electrolyte. Consequently the cell in operation has three molten layers: the anode of aluminum-copper alloy at the bottom, the electrolyte next, and pure aluminum as cathode at the top.

Magnesium. The principal method of producing magnesium is by electrolysis of a fused salt bath containing magnesium chloride in solution with sodium or potassium chloride. Processes for reduction of magnesium from the oxide at temperatures above the vaporization point, obtaining the metal by condensation of the vapor, were developed shortly before and during the Second World War. Vaporization plants having a capacity for yearly production of over 80,000 tons were built in the United States. These reached their maximum output in 1944, when they produced about 32,000 tons of magnesium, 19 per cent of the United States production in that year. After the war they ceased operation, and although these processes produce high-purity metal, and are suitable for smaller-scale operation, it is doubtful whether they can compete with the electrolytic process under ordinary conditions unless their operating costs can be substantially reduced.

Sources. Prior to 1939 nearly all the United States magnesium was produced by the Dow Chemical Company from brine containing some $MgCl_2$, pumped from deep wells in Michigan. The raw materials used in other countries were chiefly magnesite ($MgCO_3$) and dolomite ($MgCO_3.CaCO_3$), from which $MgCl_2$ is produced by reaction with chlorine. Just before the war, processes for extracting $MgCl_2$ from ocean water were developed in the United States and in England. Plants have been built on the Gulf of Mexico by the Dow Chemical Company, the principal one at Freeport, Tex. Nearly all the present United States production is from this source. Magnesite and dolomite continue to be the principal foreign sources; these were also used on a large scale in the United States during the war, and several kinds of brine obtained as by-products of the chemical industry were also used.

Sea water contains on the average about 0.13 per cent magnesium as $MgCl_2$. In the Dow process, lime obtained by calcining oyster shells that are dredged from the ocean bottom is used to precipitate the magnesium as $Mg(OH)_2$ from sea water in large settling tanks:

$$MgCl_2 + Ca(OH)_2 \rightarrow Mg(OH)_2 + CaCl_2$$

The precipitate is filtered off and treated with hydrochloric acid to produce $MgCl_2$:

$$Mg(OH)_2 + 2HCl \rightarrow MgCl_2 + H_2O$$

The HCl is made from natural gas and chlorine.

The Electrolytic Process. One of the problems encountered is dehydration of the magnesium chloride, which ordinarily exists as $MgCl_2.6H_2O$. If this were used directly in the electrolyte, electrolysis of water and accumulation of insoluble compounds would result. The molecules of water are reduced from 6 to about 1.25 by methods of air drying and heating. A completely anhydrous salt can be made by drying this product in a current of gaseous HCl. Some plants use the anhydrous material for feeding to the electrolytic cells, while others use the partially dehydrated material or a mixture of the two, since this will be dehydrated in the cell if it is fed continuously in small amounts into a proper fused chloride bath operating at a temperature of about 700°C (1290°F). In the United States the main component of the electrolyte is NaCl, together with considerable amounts of $CaCl_2$ present as impurity. $MgCl_2$ is dissolved in this bath, the amount present being much less than the NaCl. In other countries KCl is often used as the solvent. NaCl and KCl have the functions of reducing the melting point and increasing the conductivity of the bath as compared with one of pure $MgCl_2$.

Design of magnesium cells varies considerably. The Dow cells are rectangular steel pots, with graphite anodes entering through a cover plate at the top. The liberated chlorine, containing some HCl and CO_2, is piped out of the cell under suction. The metal liberated at the cathode at the bottom of the cell is lighter than the electrolyte; it rises to the top and collects under an inverted trough which leads it to wells from which it is ladled two or three times a day. These cells are of large capacity, taking 30,000 to 70,000 amp at a current efficiency of 75 to 80 per cent; the lower current and efficiency values give an output of 1,080 lb per day per cell. The Dow cells are provided with external heating, but this is not essential to the process. The metal has a purity of over 99.9 per cent, so that the refining is not necessary.

Vaporizing Processes. These, called the direct reduction processes, are of two kinds. In the more important one, silicon in the form of 75 per cent ferrosilicon is the reducing agent. The principal form of the ferrosilicon process is the Pidgeon process. Reduction is carried out in heat-resistant alloy steel retorts under high vacuum at a temperature of 1150°C (2100°F). The metal is reduced as vapor, and condenses in bright crystals of high purity on a water-cooled condenser head.

The other direct reduction process is the carbothermic or Hansgirg process. Carbon is the reducing agent, and reduction is accomplished in an arc furnace at 2000°C (3630°F). The reaction reverses at 1800°C (3270°F), so that much of the magnesium is reoxidized. In order to get a suitable yield it is necessary to "shock cool" the gas mixture by passing it into cold hydrogen or, better, natural gas. The finely divided magnesium condensate must be carefully handled to prevent its taking fire; it is redistilled in a vacuum and the vapor condensed to solid magnesium.

These processes, especially the ferrosilicon, were extremely useful during the war because they enabled a very rapid expansion of production, without requiring scarce equipment for producing direct current or copper for bus bars. Because of scarcity of copper, silver bus bars had to be used in some of the electrolytic plants.

Beryllium. Production of beryllium is chiefly in the form of a master beryllium-copper alloy containing 3.75 to 4.50 per cent beryllium. This alloy is made by direct reduction of beryllium oxide or fluoride in the presence of molten copper, instead of producing metallic beryllium first. The master alloy is used to make commercial beryllium copper containing 1.60 to 2.25 per cent beryllium.

The only commercial ore of beryllium is beryl, a beryllium aluminum silicate ($3BeO \cdot Al_2O_3 \cdot 6SiO_2$). Several methods of treating the ore have been used. The processes now favored involve heating with a fluoride, the reaction producing sodium beryllium fluoride. From this, beryllium hydroxide is precipitated with caustic soda:

$$Na_2BeF_4 + 2NaOH \rightarrow Be(OH)_2 + 4NaF$$

The hydroxide may be heated to form BeO, or, more commonly, is converted to BeF_2. A molten fluoride bath has been used for direct electrolytic production of the master alloy by carrying on the electrolysis over a molten copper cathode, which dissolves the beryllium as it is liberated. The method now used most in this country is reduction by means of carbon in the presence of molten copper in an electric-arc furnace.

Metallic beryllium also can be produced by electrolysis of fused salt baths, one process using a chloride and one a fluoride electrolyte. Thermal reduction with magnesium is now employed for making metallic beryllium of high purity.

Tungsten. A group of metals including tungsten, molybdenum, and tantalum is often produced by extracting the oxide of the metal from the ore, purifying it, and then reducing the oxide to a metallic powder. This method is used because of the extremely high melting points of these metals.

Tungsten, which is also called wolfram, is derived chiefly from the minerals wolframite [$(Fe,Mn)WO_4$] and scheelite ($CaWO_4$). The ores containing these minerals are concentrated by gravity or other methods, sometimes supplemented by magnetic separation, to concentrates containing 60 or 65 per cent tungstic oxide (WO_3). The largest tungsten ore deposits are in China, though several other countries, including the United States, have tungsten resources.

The first step in producing metallic tungsten from the concentrates is to extract nearly pure WO_3 by means of a chemical treatment. This often consists of sintering with sodium carbonate (Na_2CO_3), forming sodium tungstate (Na_2WO_4), which is dissolved out with water. Or KOH may be used to digest WO_3, forming K_2WO_4, which is also soluble in water. Addition of an acid to the solution then precipitates tungstic acid (H_2WO_4) (hydrated WO_3) as a yellow powder which is filtered off. This is reduced to metal either with carbon or hydrogen. The former yields tungsten powder about 98 per cent pure, suitable for use in steel.

For very pure tungsten, such as that required for electric-light filaments, the WO_3 is reduced with hydrogen. The operation is carried out at 700 to 900°C (1290 to 1650°F). To convert the resulting tungsten powder to dense metal it is neither necessary nor practicable to fuse the powder, since the melting point of tungsten is 3390°C (6130°F). The powder is molded into a small rectangular rod or ingot and then sintered at a temperature of 1100°C (2010°F) in an atmosphere of hydrogen, producing a porous slug that can be handled without breaking. This is

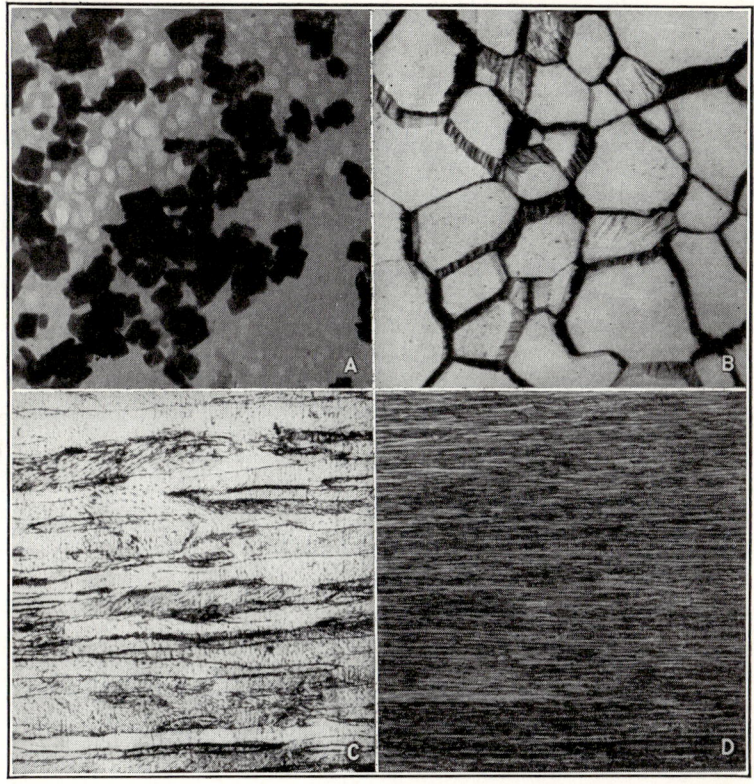

FIG. 193. (a) Electron micrograph of precipitated tungstic acid (H_2WO_4). The platelets range in size from 0.03 to 0.20 micron. Original magnification 10,200 ×, enlarged to 25,500 ×. (b) Structure of a tungsten ingot after consolidation by resistance heating. Original magnification 200 ×, enlarged to 500 ×. Intentionally overetched to show the cleavage planes. (c) Structure of longitudinal section of a swaged tungsten bar. Original magnification 100 ×, enlarged to 250 ×. (d) Structure of drawn tungsten wire, longitudinal section. Original magnification 200 ×, enlarged to 250 ×. (*Courtesy of Westinghouse Electric Corporation, Lamp Division. Photomicrographs by G. R. Moritz.*)

clamped between two electrodes in hydrogen and a high current passed through. It is thus heated by resistance to about 3000°C (5430°F) for 10 or 15 min. A welding action between the tungsten particles results in a large increase in density and forms a brittle rod.

The next operation is one of mechanical working that renders the metal ductile through changing its structure from that of equiaxed grains to fibers, as shown in the micrographs of Fig. 193. This may be done by rolling at high speed, but is usually done by swaging. The operation of swaging is one of rapid hammering with blows normal to the surface, rounding and elongating the ingot. The swaging machine contains two blocks of high-speed steel that strike the ingot several thousand times per minute. The ingot is reheated and swaged alternately until reduced to a diameter of 0.03 in., starting at a temperature of about 1300°C (2370°F) and reheating to a lower and lower temperature as the size is reduced. When reduced to 0.03 in. and the structure has become fibrous, the metal is ductile even when cold. The wire-drawing operation is facilitated, however, by performing it hot; diamond dies are used for the smaller sizes of wire. The smallest tungsten wire drawn has a diameter of 0.000455 in.; diameters less than half this can be attained by etching with a fused mixture of sodium nitrate and nitrite.

If the wire is made of pure tungsten alone, it does not stand up well in use for lamp filaments. Additions to prevent sag and give resistance to vibration have been noted on page 319.

The steel industry incorporates tungsten in steel either by using 98 per cent tungsten powder or by using ferrotungsten. The ferroalloy contains about 80 per cent tungsten. It is made by reduction with carbon in an electric-arc furnace. Its melting point is about 1850°C (3360°F), and although it fuses in the furnace, it is commonly made in small batches which are allowed to solidify before removal.

Molybdenum. Like tungsten, molybdenum is first obtained from the ore as the oxide, MoO_3. This may be used as such, or may be reduced to ferromolybdenum in electric furnaces or, for purposes requiring relatively pure metal, may be reduced to metallic form by hydrogen without fusion. However, the metallurgy of molybdenum differs from that of tungsten in a number of respects.

The only important molybdenum mineral is the sulfide, molybdenite (MoS_2). The United States ores, which account for 90 per cent of the world's production, contain less than 0.4 per cent molybdenum as mined. The ore is concentrated to a molybdenum content of 55 to 60 per cent and then roasted in multiple-hearth furnaces. Much of the roasted concentrate is used directly in that form by the steel industry. An equally large part is made into briquettes with pitch as a binder. A somewhat smaller portion is mixed with lime, the mixture being termed "calcium molybdate." These three forms in which the oxide is used account for about two-thirds of the total consumption of molybdenum.

The greater part of the remaining use of molybdenum is in the form of ferromolybdenum, carrying 50 to 60 per cent molybdenum. The form in which molybdenum is used in iron and steel making is partly a matter of individual preference, partly of the type of process, and partly of the amount of molybdenum to be added. The oxide forms are cheaper than the ferroalloy and are usually preferred for amounts up to 1 per cent. Ferromolybdenum is made both by reduction with carbon in the electric furnace and by the thermit process (see page 106), using aluminum powder.

The melting point of molybdenum metal is 2620°C (4750°F); consequently it is often made by reduction to powder without fusion. Either carbon or hydrogen may be the reducing agent. Sometimes also the thermit process is applied. Consolidation of molybdenum powder into dense metal, and subsequent fabrication into wire and sheet, follows the same principles as in the metallurgy of tungsten. A method involving melting the powder in a vacuum with an electric arc and then casting an ingot for fabrication has been developed recently.

Titanium. The principal titanium ore is ilmenite ($FeO.TiO_2$). This is found in a number of localities; a deposit said to contain 125,000,000 tons averaging 32 per cent TiO_2 was recently discovered in Quebec and will soon be in large-scale production. Large bodies of titaniferous iron ore have been worked for some time in the Adirondack region of New York. A much smaller source is the mineral rutile (TiO_2).

The principal production method for the metal at present is the modified Kroll process. The ore is treated with chlorine to make pure $TiCl_4$. Instead of using the ore directly, it may be smelted in an electric furnace to make a slag containing over 70 per cent TiO_2, which is then treated. The $TiCl_4$ is heated in a reaction chamber with molten magnesium at about 700°C (1290°F). Titanium is reduced in solid particles or in a spongy form, with accompanying formation of $MgCl_2$. The product is melted in an electric arc or induction furnace in an atmosphere of helium or argon. The $MgCl_2$ together with unreacted magnesium are vaporized and eliminated at the high furnace temperature. The fused titanium may be cast in continuous ingots or in separate ingots, or the solid sponge may be ground to powder and consolidated by pressing and sintering.

In a process developed by Van Arkel, de Boer, and Fast, crude titanium reacts with iodine to form TiI_4. When this compound is heated above 1100°C (2010°F), it decomposes, depositing pure titanium on a heated surface, with release of the iodine for reuse. The metal builds up slowly in a thin layer, and the method is best adapted as a refining process for producing high-purity metal in small quantities. It is not at present a commercial production process. The same principle of thermal decomposition of a gaseous compound to deposit a metal coating may be used for zirconium, silicon, and other metals.

Other processes for titanium are being developed, including one at a Canadian government-built pilot plant at Haley, Ontario. Details of processes are changing as experimentation and experience continue.

Gold and Silver. The extractive metallurgy of gold and silver is chiefly in the domain of hydrometallurgy. The two metals usually occur together in nature, although in some of the leading producing regions of each the other is absent or present in a very minor amount. Gold and silver form a continuous series of solid solutions with each other. They have similar chemical properties, and accordingly the principal extraction processes recover both metals together from ores in which both are present.

The principal type of gold ore is the native ore, in which the gold occurs finely disseminated in the free or metallic state, frequently in particles so small as to be invisible when embedded in the gangue. Silver also occurs as native silver, or dissolved in native gold, but the most important occurrence of silver is in the form of the sulfide, Ag_2S. This is usually associated with the sulfides of copper or lead. Most copper and lead ores contain both silver and gold. In the United States more than half of the silver production and about a tenth of the gold production is accounted for by these ores. Since in addition gold and silver ores are often added to the charges of copper or lead smelting furnaces, even larger proportions (about 90 per cent of the total silver) are obtained as by-products in the smelting and refining of copper and lead. This is not true, however, in the Union of South Africa, which is the world's largest gold-producing country, and numerous other localities.

Both gold and silver are dissolved rapidly by mercury, forming "amalgam." This fact has been made use of for centuries as a principal method of extracting the metals from their ores. The other principal solvent for leaching gold and silver ores is a very dilute solution of sodium cyanide (NaCN). In the amalgamation process the metals are recovered from the amalgam by heating it to a temperature high enough to vaporize the mercury, leaving the metals in an impure state, from which they are separated ("parted") and refined. In the cyanide process the metals are precipitated from the solution, zinc dust being the usual precipitating agent; the precipitate is then subjected to parting and refining treatment.

The principal methods employed for gold and silver recovery may be summarized in outline as follows:

A. Smelting: the ore is added to the charge of a copper or lead smelting furnace.
B. Wet methods:
  1. Washing: a gravity separation of particles of free gold and silver, carried on at the same time as the mining of the metal-bearing sands and gravels, and usually assisted by addition of mercury for amalgamation.
  2. Milling: the ore is crushed or ground and the metals are dissolved by
     a. Mercury (amalgamation).
     b. A dilute solution of NaCN (cyanidation).

Both metals are produced in a high degree of purity. Electrolytic refining is often employed, and gold is also refined by oxidizing the impurities with chlorine, converting them to chlorides. Details of the extraction and refining methods will not be given here because of the limited importance of these metals as engineering materials. But it should be noted that the engineering uses of silver are increasing, and the over-all importance of gold, chiefly as a monetary standard, is such that the total annual value of the world's gold production has in some years exceeded that of any other nonferrous metal.

Ferroalloys. Certain metals, including manganese, silicon, chromium, and vanadium, are produced and used largely in the form of ferroalloys. A *ferroalloy* is defined as a crude alloy of iron with one or more other elements, used as a reagent in the manufacture of iron and steel. The phrase "as a reagent" in this definition embraces use as deoxidizers for steel and as agents for the incorporation of alloying elements in alloy steels. Ferroalloys are not to be confused with alloy steels. Even plain carbon steel cannot be produced without ferroalloys as deoxidizers; consequently these essential materials are used in great quantities.

Ferroalloys used as deoxidizers must be those of the chemically strong elements. Consequently high temperatures are required to reduce them from their ores, and these are most easily attained in electric furnaces. Most ferroalloys are made in electric-arc furnaces, though ferrophosphorus and the lower grades of ferrosilicon and ferromanganese are made in blast furnaces. In either case the process is one of reduction by carbon. For some purposes, as in supplying the chromium for some stainless steels, it is necessary to have the ferroalloy very low in carbon. This may be accomplished by using silicon instead of carbon as the reducing agent in the furnace.

The iron content of ferroalloys is derived either from iron oxide, which may be present in the ore or may be added as a component of the charge, or from scrap iron and steel.

Manganese. Ferromanganese is the ferroalloy used in the largest tonnages. The standard grade contains approximately 80 per cent manganese, 12 to 14 per cent iron, 6 to 8 per cent carbon, and smaller amounts of other elements. A lower grade called "spiegeleisen" contains about 20 per cent manganese. In recent years pure manganese metal has been made by a leaching process followed by electrolysis, similar to production of electrolytic zinc. Electrolytic manganese, which has a purity of about 99.97 per cent, is more expensive than the ferroalloy. Its largest use is for incorporation of manganese in certain nonferrous alloys, especially those of copper. Its use is increasing.

Silicon. Silicon metal can readily be produced in unlimited quantities. Unfortunately it is mechanically weak and extremely brittle. It is used to a small extent as a deoxidizer and for making certain alloys. Ferrosilicon, on the other hand, is a material of great importance to the steel industry, both as a deoxidizer and for making silicon steels and cast irons. It is made in several grades, chiefly those of 50, 75, and 90 per cent silicon.

Chromium. As a component of stainless steels and other important alloy steels, this metal has become indispensable. It is also a main constituent of some of the nonferrous heat-resisting alloys, and the pure metal is known to everyone in chromium plating. Ferrochromium for the steel industry contains about 70 per cent chromium; it is made in either a low-carbon or a high-carbon grade, depending on the type of steel for which it is to be used. For chromium plating, pure chromium is deposited by electrolysis from a solution of chromic acid (CrO_3).

Bibliography

Comprehensive

ANON.: "World's Non-Ferrous Smelters and Refineries," 3d ed., Quin Press, Ltd., London, 1948.

BRAY, J. L.: "Non-ferrous Production Metallurgy," 2d ed., John Wiley & Sons, Inc., New York, 1947.

EVANS, U. R.: "Metals and Metallic Compounds," 4 vols., Edward Arnold & Co., London; Longmans, Green & Co., Inc., New York, 1923.

FRIEND, J. N. (editor): "A Textbook of Inorganic Chemistry," 16 vols., Charles Griffin & Co., Ltd., London, 1914–1931.

HAYWARD, C. R.: "An Outline of Metallurgical Practice," 3d ed., D. Van Nostrand Company, Inc., New York, 1952.

LIDDELL, D. M. (editor): "Handbook of Non-ferrous Metallurgy," 2d ed., Vol. II, "Recovery of the Metals," McGraw-Hill Book Company, Inc., New York, 1945.

MELLOR, J. W.: "A Comprehensive Treatise on Inorganic and Theoretical Chemistry," 16 vols., Longmans, Green & Co., Inc., New York, 1922–1937.

Individual Metals

ALICO, J.: "Introduction to Magnesium and Its Alloys," Ziff-Davis Publishing Company, Chicago, 1945.

AMERICAN INSTITUTE OF MINING AND METALLURGICAL ENGINEERS: "Copper Metallurgy," *Transactions*, Vol. 106, 1933.

———: "Metallurgy of Lead and Zinc," *Transactions*, Vol. 121, 1936.

ANDERSON, R. J.: "Secondary Aluminum," The Sherwood Press, Inc., Cleveland, Ohio, 1931.

BARKSDALE, J.: "Titanium: Its Occurrence, Chemistry, and Technology," The Ronald Press Company, New York, 1949.

BROWN, H.: "Aluminum and Its Applications," Pitman Publishing Corp., New York, 1948.

BUDGEN, N. F.: "Cadmium: Its Metallurgy, Properties, and Uses," Charles Griffin & Co., Ltd., London, 1924.

DEMENT, J. A., and H. C. DAKE: "Rarer Metals in Science and Industry," Chemical Publishing Company, Inc., Brooklyn, 1946.

DORR, J. V. N., and F. L. BOSQUI: "Cyanidation and Concentration of Gold and Silver Ores," 2d ed., McGraw-Hill Book Company, Inc., New York, 1950.

DRUCE, J. G. F.: "Rhenium," Cambridge University Press, London, 1948.

DUSCHAK, L. H., and C. N. SCHUETTE: The Metallurgy of Quicksilver, *U.S. Bureau of Mines Bull.* 222, 1925.

EDWARDS, J. D., F. C. FRARY, and ZAY JEFFRIES: "The Aluminum Industry," Vol. I, "Aluminum and Its Production," McGraw-Hill Book Company, Inc., New York, 1930.

HOFMAN, H. O.: "Metallurgy of Lead," McGraw-Hill Book Company, Inc., New York, 1918.

———: "Metallurgy of Zinc and Cadmium," McGraw-Hill Book Company, Inc., New York, 1925.

———, and C. R. HAYWARD: "Metallurgy of Copper," 2d ed., McGraw-Hill Book Company, Inc., New York, 1925.

HOKE, C. M.: "Refining Precious Metal Wastes," Metallurgical Publishing Company, New York, 1940.

LI, K. C., and C. Y. WANG: "Tungsten: Its History, Geology, Ore-dressing, Metallurgy, Chemistry, Analysis, Applications, and Economics," 2d ed., Reinhold Publishing Corporation, New York, 1947.

MANTELL, C. L.: "Calcium Metallurgy and Technology," Reinhold Publishing Corporation, New York, 1945.

———: "Tin: Its Mining, Production, Technology, and Applications," 2d ed., Reinhold Publishing Corporation, New York, 1949.

NEWTON, J., and C. L. WILSON: "Metallurgy of Copper," John Wiley & Sons, Inc., New York, 1942.

PANNELL, E. V.: "Magnesium: Its Production and Use," Pitman Publishing Corp., New York, 1944.

ROSE, T. K., and W. A. C. NEWMAN: "Metallurgy of Gold," 7th ed., Charles Griffin & Co., Ltd., London, 1937.

SLOMAN, H. A., and C. B. SAWYER: "The Beryllium Industries of Germany and Italy," U.S. Department of Commerce, Washington, 1948.

SMITH, E. A.: "Platinum Metals," Sir Isaac Pitman & Sons, Ltd., London, 1925.

SMITHELLS, C. J.: "Tungsten: Metallurgy, Properties, and Applications," 2d ed., Chapman & Hall, Ltd., London, 1936.

WANG, C. Y.: "Antimony," 2d ed., Charles Griffin & Co., Ltd., London, 1919.

YOST, D. M., H. RUSSELL, JR., and C. S. GARNER: "The Rare-Earth Metals and Their Compounds," John Wiley & Sons, Inc., New York, 1947.

YOUNG, R. S.: "Cobalt," Reinhold Publishing Corporation, New York, 1948.

CHAPTER 15

FURNACES, REFRACTORIES, AND FUELS

FURNACES

Metallurgical furnaces may be classified according to function as follows:

1. Furnaces used in extractive metallurgy, *i.e.*, for roasting, smelting, and refining processes.

2. Furnaces used for melting, either for combining metals to form alloys or preparatory to making castings as in foundry work.

3. Furnaces used in physical and mechanical metallurgy, either (*a*) for heat-treatment, or (*b*) for heating ingots, billets, and other shapes prior to hot-working operations.

The furnaces may also be classified according to source of heat into (*a*) fuel-fired furnaces and (*b*) electric furnaces.

Fuel-fired Furnaces Used in Extractive Metallurgy. The design of these furnaces is dependent on the relation between the fuel and the charge, giving rise to three types:

1. Furnaces in which the fuel is in contact with the charge.

2. Furnaces in which the fuel is separated from the charge, but the products of combustion of the fuel are in contact with the charge.

3. Furnaces in which the charge is not in contact either with the fuel or with the products of combustion.

FIG. 194. Shaft furnace. Fuel and charge fed together at the top. This is a view of an iron blast furnace of the Carnegie-Illinois Steel Corporation. (*Courtesy of U.S. Steel Corporation.*)

The first of the above types is often constructed in the form of a *shaft furnace*, the characteristic of which is a hearth of small area at the bottom of a shaft, the charge being fed in at the top and progressing down through the furnace, yielding the finished product at the bottom. Blast furnaces for smelting ores of iron, copper, and lead belong to this

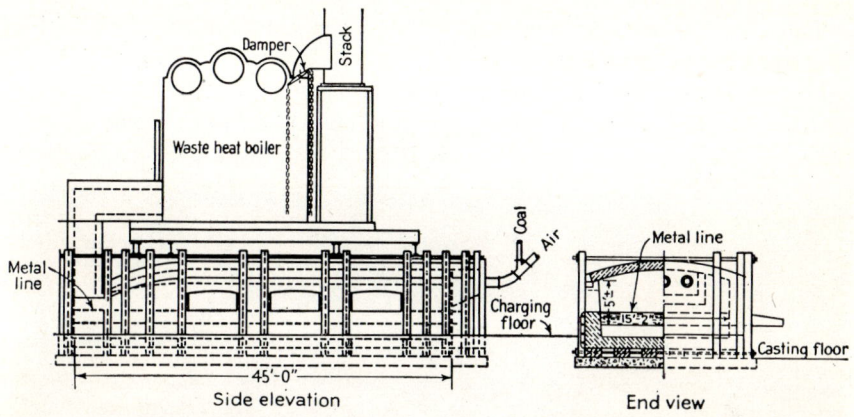

Fig. 195. Reverberatory furnace, copper refining. Fuel (here pulverized coal) burned at the right; flame sweeps over the charge and gases leave furnace at the left.

class, and also many roasting furnaces. The intimate contact of charge and fuel results in the maximum thermal efficiency, which may reach 60 or 70 per cent in this type of furnace.

The second type above is most commonly, though by no means always, constructed in the form of a *reverberatory furnace*. The characteristics of the reverberatory type are a relatively shallow hearth of large area, and a low arched roof from which the heat contained in the hot products of combustion of the fuel is reflected or "reverberated" down onto the charge. The reverberatory furnace requires a fuel that burns with a long flame, carrying the heat well over the hearth; the gases passing out of the furnace retain a very large amount of heat, and the thermal efficiency is accordingly low, being commonly 10 to 20 per cent.

The third type includes muffle furnaces, crucible furnaces, and retort furnaces. Its thermal efficiency is the lowest of all, since the heat received by the charge must pass through the walls containing the charge or separating it from the hot gases. In most cases these walls are built of refractory clay or brick, which is a poor conductor of heat; more-

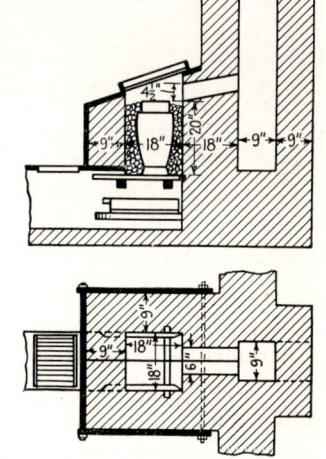

Fig. 196. Crucible pot furnace. Fuel surrounding crucible.

over, they must be fairly thick in order to give sufficient strength. Furnaces of this type are used only when it is necessary to keep the charge or products from being contaminated or adversely affected by the furnace gases. The efficiency is often as low as 5 to 10 per cent.

The above three main types of furnaces are exemplified in Figs. 194, 195, and 196, respectively.

Electric Furnaces. Electric or electrothermic furnaces are those in which electric energy is converted into heat. Except in electrolytic furnaces, such as used in the production of aluminum and magnesium,

FIG. 197. Continuous roller-hearth heating furnace for annealing, gas fired. (*Courtesy of W. S. Rockwell Company.*)

and which are best regarded as electrolytic cells operated at high temperatures rather than as furnaces, the current has no other function than to supply heat. Electric furnaces are used for smelting iron ores and producing ferroalloys; for melting iron for cast-iron and malleable-iron foundries; for melting and refining steel; for melting copper, brass, and other metals and alloys both in production processes and in foundry work; for heating metals and alloys for hardening, annealing, tempering, and other heat-treating operations.

The comparative merits of electric and fuel-fired furnaces depend on the type of application. Electrical energy is generally more costly, but higher temperatures can be attained by electric heating. In refining molten metals, combustion gases may contaminate the charge with oxygen or sulfur, but this need not occur when heating metals in muffle furnaces, since nonoxidizing atmospheres may then readily be provided in gas and oil-fired furnaces as well as in electric furnaces.

FURNACES, REFRACTORIES, AND FUELS

A part of the higher cost of electric energy is compensated for by the higher thermal efficiency at which it may be applied. Electric-furnace processes often have efficiencies of 50 to 75 per cent, which may be many times that of an alternate fuel-fired furnace.

Generally the quality of metals and alloys produced electrically is superior to the quality of those made in combustion furnaces. For example, electric steel may be lower in oxygen, sulfur, and oxidized solid inclusions than open-hearth or bessemer steel; brass melted in some types of electric furnaces may be more uniform in composition and structure,

Fig. 198. Detroit rocking furnace (indirect arc), tapping 1,000-lb heat of alloy cast iron. (*Courtesy of Kuhlman Electric Company.*)

because of better stirring and control. It should be borne in mind, however, that electric production is not *per se* an assurance of higher purity or quality.

Conversion of Electric Energy into Heat. Electricity may be converted into heat through the medium of an arc, or by means of resistance. The heat of the arc is transferred by direct contact and radiation, while the heat due to resistance is generated within the heated body, from which it may or may not be transferred to another body. Arc heating may be either indirect, *i.e.*, by radiation only, or direct; these methods are illustrated in Figs. 198 and 176, respectively. In the indirect-arc furnace the arc passes from one electrode to the other and does not touch the bath. In the direct-arc furnace the arc passes from electrode to bath, and the current is conducted through the bath for a short distance. The maximum temperature of the arc between carbon electrodes is about 3700°C (6700°F), but this maximum is attained only in a small area directly between the electrodes. The arc radiates intense heat to the furnace linings, which suffer accordingly. Nevertheless the arc is a very convenient means of heating the contents of furnaces and is much used in metallurgical work. It has the advantage of affording a method of bringing the current into the furnace without either melting the connections or contaminating the metal by contact with the electrodes.

The direct-arc system of heating applies the heat right at the surface of the bath, but does not distribute it uniformly over the area. The electrodes usually dip into the slag, but the slag does not "wet" the slippery carbon surface, and a myriad of tiny arcs pass from electrode to slag or metal.

In the resistance method of converting electricity into heat either the metallic body itself is heated by electricity, or else another body is heated and then this energy radiated or conducted to the metallic substance. The former method is more common for melting, but the latter is commonly used in many types of industrial and laboratory heating furnaces. For example, a muffle is wound with a resistance wire—usually of nickel-chromium alloy—to which a source of electricity is directly connected. The current heats the wire, which, in turn, heats the metal within the muffle. Furnaces of this type are often made in large sizes for heating steel for annealing or hardening or tempering. Sometimes a carbonaceous material in the form of small particles is used as the "resistor," *i.e.*, the resistance element. Refractory rods containing silicon carbide and silicon are also used as resistors. The amount of electric energy which is converted into heat by resistance is the product of the square of the amperes multiplied by the resistance. Therefore, the higher the resistance of the resistor, the greater the heat generated by a given current, and the higher the voltage required to pass the current through the resistor.

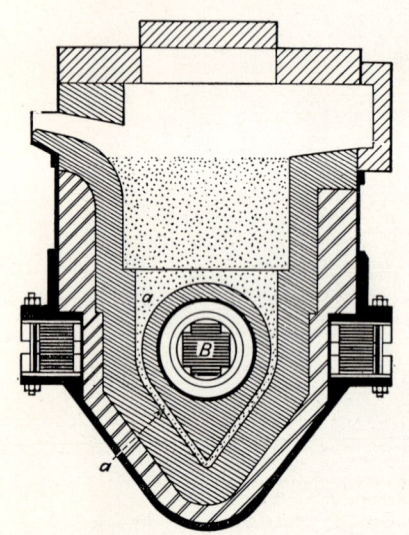

Fig. 199. Cross section of vertical-ring type induction furnace (Ajax-Wyatt).

Metallic charges in a furnace may be heated by resistance without making a direct electrical connection to the metal by means of the induction furnace, one type of which is illustrated in Fig. 199. This figure illustrates a furnace very commonly used for melting brass; the same principle is applied to melting steel and other metals. The sectional view shows the molten metal in the form of a triangle a, a, surrounding part of the lining through which passes the iron core of a magnet B. The iron core is magnetized by the primary current, which is carried by a copper tubing wound around it and connected to a convenient source of alternating current. Water circulates within the copper tubing to keep it cool. The magnetic field surrounding the core induces a secondary

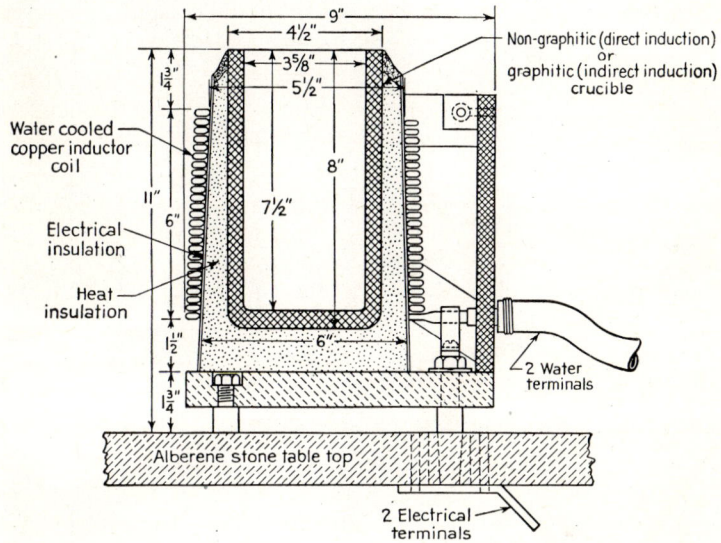

Fig. 200. Cross section of small-top conical type of Ajax-Northrup high-frequency induction furnace, portable skeleton coil. (*Courtesy of Ajax Electrothermic Corporation.*)

current in the circuit a, a. The secondary current is of the order of 10,000 amp and 4 to 6 volts, depending on the size of furnace. This high current produces a "motor" effect, which creates a circulation of the metal, causing it to flow out of the triangle a, a and to stir the whole bath and maintain an even temperature and composition.

Another type of induction furnace, the high-frequency, is shown in Figs. 200 and 201. The former is typical of melting-type induction furnaces, whereas the latter illustrates the use of induction heating for heat-treating, brazing, etc. In this furnace no core is used; instead, the induced current is caused to flow directly in the charge in the form of eddy currents, a primary current of very high frequency, several thousand to several hundred thousand cycles per second, being employed to bring about this result. Extremely rapid heating is achieved. By using a conducting crucible, such as graphite, a nonconducting charge may be heated because the current is induced in the crucible itself. This type of furnace is especially adapted to rather small crucible charges and is being increasingly used for high-quality steel, nonferrous alloys, and precious metals. A later application of this type of heating, now become of great importance, is for surface hardening of steel parts (see page 181). This is made possible because with high-frequency current the heating effect is concentrated near the surface. The depth of penetration of the induced current is inversely proportional to the square root of the

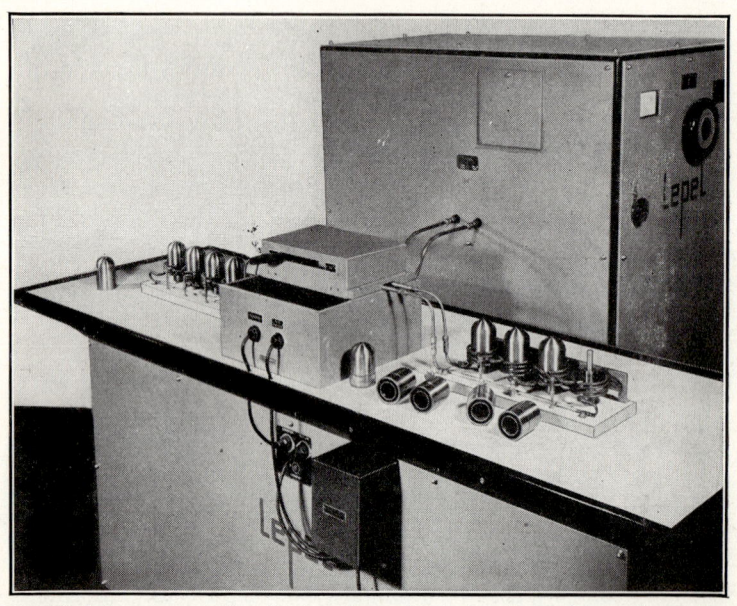

FIG. 201. High-frequency induction heating. Eight heating coils are shown in use for brazing steel to steel parts with a silver brazing alloy. Current is supplied from the enclosed high-frequency converter at the rear. Time, 85 sec with 15-kw converter. The brazing outfit can readily be detached and other coils connected to the same converter, such as coils for surface hardening (with provision for automatic quenching) or for melting in a crucible. (*Courtesy of Lepel High Frequency Laboratories, Inc.*)

frequency. Other applications are for annealing and for brazing (see Fig. 201).

Melting Furnaces. Furnaces used for melting metals and alloys, as with those used for extractive processes, may be either fuel-fired or electric. Here, however, the electric furnaces have a relatively greater importance.

The *cupola* is a modified type of blast furnace used for melting cast iron in foundries. It uses coke as fuel, and the metal charge is chiefly pig iron, often with some scrap and ferroalloy.

Small crucible furnaces are frequently employed for melting nonferrous metals. They are usually of the tilting type to facilitate pouring, and may be fired with oil or gas. Somewhat larger pot furnaces made of cast iron or steel are used for melting aluminum, lead, and other low-melting metals.

Fuel-fired reverberatory furnaces are also used for melting copper cathodes, for making aluminum alloys, for melting nickel and zinc, and in other cases where a considerable quantity of metal is to be melted.

Electric furnaces are used for melting steel scrap to make steel castings, for melting copper cathodes, for making and casting brass and other nonferrous alloys, for making nickel alloys, for melting precious metals, etc. These usually employ arc or induction heating, occasionally resistance heating for salt baths and low-melting metals.

Heating Furnaces. Electric heating of metals offers some advantages over other means, particularly from the standpoint of cleanliness and simplicity of installation and control. As a general rule electric resistance heating is more costly than the use of fuels such as city gas up to a temperature of 875 to 1000°C (1600 to 1800°F), but above that temperature electric heating may be somewhat cheaper because of the large amount of sensible heat carried away in the products of combustion of a gas-fired furnace. Electric heating is cleaner and requires no provision for exhausting the products of combustion, but temperature control is no more accurate than in modern fuel-fired furnaces, and the time required to heat a given piece of metal is often longer in an electric resistance furnace than in an open fuel-fired furnace where the hot gases of combustion can envelop and sweep over the part being heated.

The group of furnaces known as "heating" or "reheating" furnaces covers a very wide field in the treatment of both ferrous and nonferrous metals. In this general classification are included billet, slab, bar-mill, sheet-bar, strip-mill, rod-mill, wire-mill, and many other varieties of specially designed furnaces. Every gradation in size is found from small rivet-heating furnaces to large continuous automatic equipment more than 100 ft long. Any source of heat may be used—electricity, gas, coal, oil, tar, powdered coal, and even combinations of these. For large high-temperature furnaces, regenerators or recuperators (see page 430) are often provided, and under these conditions gas heating is usually cheaper than electric heating.

Atmosphere Control. To prevent scaling, decarburization, dezincification, and discoloration through oxidation during heating, increased use is being made of controlled atmospheres in either electrically heated or fuel-fired furnaces. In such furnaces the chamber containing the charge, or a specially constructed heat-resistant alloy retort or muffle, is filled with a nonoxidizing atmosphere consisting either of partly burned fuel gas, nitrogen, hydrogen, or a mixture of nitrogen and hydrogen obtained from the dissociation of ammonia. Hydrogen, either alone or in the nitrogen-hydrogen mixture, is explosive when improperly handled, and great care must be exercised in use. Controlled-atmosphere furnaces are most often of the continuous-muffle type where the charge is conveyed through an alloy muffle, or the furnace chamber itself may contain the nonoxidizing atmosphere. However, they are often also of the bell type, in which a cylinder or bell containing the heating units or fuel burners is placed over the retort containing the charge with a liquid seal at the bottom. The time of treatment in such furnaces may be 40 hr or more.

Refining by Electric Heating. Refining also is often done in electric furnaces. Since there are no gases resulting from the combustion of fuel in the furnace, and air may be excluded, the atmosphere surrounding the charge may be controlled and the charge held for some time without oxidation or absorption of impurities; thus the action of some particular refining agent can be made effective and a better product obtained. The production of electric steel is the most important example of this type of process.

REFRACTORIES AND HEAT LOSSES IN INDUSTRIAL FURNACES

The parts of a furnace that are subjected to very high temperatures must be constructed of a material that will not melt, nor even soften extensively, at the temperature within the furnace; or else they must be cooled in some manner to maintain them at a lower temperature. Both of these devices are widely employed in the construction of metallurgical furnaces.

The sides of lead blast furnaces enclosing the smelting zone are made of hollow steel "jackets" through which water is continually passing. Such a device causes the inside of the furnace walls to become coated with a layer of frozen slag or unmelted charge, which is kept cool by contact with the outer wall. Iron blast furnaces are run at such a high temperature that this type of construction is not practicable. In the hottest parts, however, the brick walls are partially water-cooled by inserting hollow plates containing circulating water. Such plates also are frequently employed in the bridge walls of reverberatory furnaces. Water-cooling plates of this kind, however, are only an aid in preserving the walls, and the main reliance must be on the material of which the walls are built. In fact, many furnaces use no water cooling at all, but are built, or rather lined, with brick composed of a material of very high melting point. Such a material is known technically as a *refractory*.

Refractories. Refractory materials are considerably costlier than ordinary clay or brick, and consequently they are used only for the furnace parts which become extremely hot. Usually the outside of a furnace may be built of cheaper brick, or of steel plates, giving the necessary strength, and then an inside layer of refractory brick is put in. In some furnaces refractory clay may be rammed into certain parts, or loose refractory material may be thrown onto certain portions of the hearth. Where refractory bricks are used, they must be put together with refractory mortar.

From the principles stated in the discussion of slags and fluxes, it is evident that refractories for the most part consist of certain oxides in a fairly pure state, *i.e.*, not mixed or combined with any considerable amount of other oxides, since the result of such admixture would be a lowering of the melting temperature. It also follows that refractories, like fluxes, fall into three classes—acid, basic, and neutral.

Because of the chemical reactivity between acids and bases, it is a vital principle in the employment of refractories that a furnace in which a basic slag is to be produced be lined with a basic refractory, and for an acid slag an acid refractory must be used. Contact between slags and refractories of opposite chemical character at high temperature results in rapid corrosion of the furnace walls.

Table 38 lists and classifies the most commonly used refractories and gives their approximate melting and softening points. The lower values

TABLE 38. PRINCIPAL COMMERCIAL REFRACTORIES

Refractory	Softening point, °C	Melting point, °C
Acid:		
Silica (SiO_2)	1400–1700	1625–1750
Fire clay (chiefly $SiO_2 + Al_2O_3$)	1500–1600	1500–1750
Basic:		
Magnesite (MgO)	1300–2000	2160–2800
Dolomite (CaO + MgO)	Variable: Inferior to magnesite	
Bauxite or alumina (Al_2O_3)	1300–1950	2000
Zirconia (ZrO_2)	1800–1900	2550–2600
Neutral:		
Chromite ($FeO.Cr_2O_3$)	2000	2180
Graphite (C) or amorphous carbon	....	3900 (vaporizes)
Silicon carbide (carborundum) (SiC)	1400–2200	2220 (decomposes)

for the ranges listed apply chiefly to bonded materials, the higher values to the pure granular substance.

Neutral refractories may be used with either acid or basic charges. Silica brick is the best material for the roofs of reverberatory furnaces. When the hearth of a furnace is to be made of basic brick and the roof of acid, it is often advantageous to use a layer of neutral brick (usually chrome) to separate the junction in the side walls.

The discussion of refractories has been given on the basis of their use for furnaces, but they have other applications of importance. One of these is in making crucibles. Crucibles used for melting metals are usually "graphite" crucibles; these are made of a mixture of fire clay and flake graphite. Another large use of refractory clay is in making retorts, such as are used for treatment of zinc ore. Still another use is in the construction of "checkers" in regenerative furnaces, as described on pages 366 and 430.

Properties and Requirements of Refractories. Most refractories have a very high resistance to the passage of heat. This is of advantage in furnace walls, but a disadvantage in crucibles and retorts. Another characteristic of most refractories is a tendency to crack, especially in cooling. The presence of moisture increases the tendency to crack, and furnaces, crucibles, etc., must usually be slowly and carefully dried before heating to a high temperature. Change of volume is often a troublesome feature in the behavior of refractory materials. When merely a matter of ordinary expansion or contraction with change of temperature, this action can be allowed for, but often it is due to a permanent change of a chemical nature, such as expulsion of combined water or CO_2. Before bonding, refractory materials should be calcined (fired) as fully as possible, preferably by electrical fusion when costs permit, and after bonding should be baked at a temperature higher than the maximum to which they will be subjected in use.

It may be useful to list requirements to be considered in the selection of refractories, as follows:

1. Cost.
2. Melting point and softening point.
3. Chemical character—resistance to corrosion.
4. Weight and compressive strength.
5. Strength at high temperatures.
6. Binding power.
7. Hardness and resistance to abrasion.
8. Resistance to cracking—ability to withstand sudden changes of temperature.
9. Expansion and shrinkage.
10. Thermal conductivity.
11. Porosity to slag and metal; permeability to gases.

Refractory brick are supplied by the manufacturers in numerous standardized sizes and shapes. Ordinary price quotations are for a "standard size" or a "standard brick," which means a straight brick of dimensions $2\frac{1}{2}$ by $4\frac{1}{2}$ by 9 in. Other sizes and shapes, such as arch brick, wedge brick, splits, etc., are listed in special catalogues and price lists. A *course* of brick is a $2\frac{1}{2}$-in. layer.

Brick of fire clay, which is the commonest material for furnace construction, is termed *firebrick*. F. T. Havard gives the number of bricks used in the construction of a 60-ton basic open-hearth steel furnace as 700,000, of which 30,000 would be magnesite and chrome bricks, 270,000 silica bricks, 200,000 firebricks, and 200,000 common red bricks.

The higher the temperature at which a furnace is run, the higher must be the quality of the refractory used. In many electric-furnace and other high-temperature processes, obtaining a suitable refractory is a difficult matter. The improvement of refractories is one of the biggest problems of future metallurgical progress.

Refractories for Heating and Heat-treating Furnaces. Service conditions in heating furnaces such as are used to heat steel for rolling, forging, or welding are rather severe and similar in many ways to conditions in melting furnaces. Severity of the conditions is determined principally by the temperature, the amount and fluidity of iron or other metal oxide, the rapidity and frequency of temperature fluctuations, and the amount of abrasion from the charge. Possibly the most important variable is temperature. Hearth, roof, and side walls present different refractory problems and often are made from different types of brick.

The refractories going into a furnace hearth must resist the slagging action of iron oxide and the abrasion of the charge, although skid rails are frequently provided to protect the hearth brick. Heavy fire-clay, high-alumina, and burned-magnesite brick are commonly used, and where conditions are particularly severe, plastic chrome ore will repay its greater cost with longer service.

Roofs and side walls deteriorate principally by spalling. In high-temperature furnaces the side-wall brick may also spall or deform from actual softening. Intermittent service and wide fluctuation of temperatures accelerate spalling. Generally speaking, where heavy brick are used, fire-clay brick are satisfactory for roofs and walls. Occasionally service demands are such that superduty fire clay, or even alumina or sillimanite brick, are required. Regardless of location and type, all heating-furnace brick should be laid with thin joints of a mortar of a quality and softening temperature at least as high as the brick itself.

Furnaces for heat-treatment present much less severe problems. In general they operate at moderate temperatures. Until about fifteen years ago such furnaces were also built with fire-clay brick. More recently it has been found that insulating firebrick give satisfactory service and at the same time reduce heat-storage capacity and tremendously reduce heating time. Although made from the same basic refractory ingredients, insulating firebrick show a structure similar to sponge rubber and have up to three times the insulating value of the older solid bricks. Thus it is now not uncommon to build furnaces for temperatures as high as 1100°C (2010°F) with insulating firebrick walls only 10 in. thick. Heavy firebrick construction would formerly have required wall thicknesses up to 18 in., and even at this thickness greater heat losses would be experienced. Insulating brick are not nearly so strong as the solid types, and where the brick must support unusually heavy loads, dense fire-clay, alumina, or silicon carbide brick must be used.

Heat Losses in Furnaces. The ways in which heat may be lost in a furnace operation may be listed as follows:

1. Losses in combustion:
    a. Fuel going into the ashes without being burned.
    b. Burning of carbon to CO instead of to CO_2.
2. Heat carried out in the hot flue gases.
3. Heat carried out in other waste products of the furnace, and in cooling water.
4. Heat transferred to surroundings.
    a. By conduction to the ground and to parts of the furnace itself.
    b. By convection to the air.
    c. By radiation to surroundings.

With proper care, losses in combustion are not large.

Heat lost in the waste flue gases is often a very large item. In a furnace of the reverberatory type it may amount to 60 per cent of the heat received from the fuel. The higher the temperature at which this furnace is run, the greater this loss becomes, since the gases leave at a temperature close to the operating temperature of the furnace. In a shaft furnace, on the other hand, most of the heat in the gases is given up to the descending charge in the shaft as the gases ascend through it, and consequently the amount of heat leaving the furnace in this form is small. Reverberatory furnaces, including open-hearth steel furnaces, are in many plants equipped with waste-heat boilers, the hot gases passing through the boiler and giving up a large part of their heat to make steam, instead of carrying it directly out the stack. In this way the loss may be reduced to 10 per cent or less.

Another way in which heat in the waste gases is sometimes salvaged—and this method is always used in open-hearth steel furnaces in addition to the use of waste-heat boilers—is to pass the hot gases through *regenerators*. These consist of chambers containing a checkerwork of refractory brick, so that the *checkers* or regenerators absorb heat from the gases. The heat thus absorbed is, in turn, given up to incoming fuel gas, or air that is to be used in burning the fuel, and so returned to the furnace instead of being allowed to escape. Thus the heat is said to be regenerated, and a furnace employing this principle is called a *regenerative furnace*. The method of operation is illustrated in Fig. 173. The hot gases first pass through the regenerators at, say, the right side of the furnace, continuing to do so until this brickwork has absorbed so much heat that it is practically at the temperature of the outgoing gases. Then by reversing a valve the hot gases are caused to pass out at the opposite side of the furnace, and the incoming fuel gas, or air, or both, is caused to flow through the just-heated regenerators, absorbing heat from them until they have cooled down again. Thus the operation continues in cycles, with one side heating while the other is cooling; reversals are usually made every 15 to 30 min.

The heat contained in waste gases is also frequently saved by a continuous method without the use of reversing valves. In this method the hot gases pass through a flue surrounding the pipes through which the fuel gas or air is entering the furnace; the heat passes through the pipes and so there is a continuous transfer of heat from hot flue gases to cooler entering gas or air. This method is usually called *recuperation;* it is employed in furnaces where the temperatures required are much lower than in the open-hearth steel furnace. It is less efficient than the other method, but gives steady conditions and avoids mechanical difficulties. The principle is illustrated in Fig. 202.

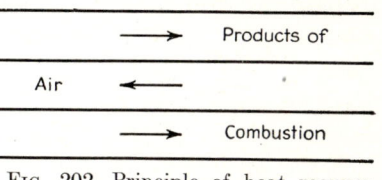

Fig. 202. Principle of heat recuperation.

In addition to recovering a large amount of heat that would otherwise be lost, regenerative furnaces have another advantage that is often of equal and even greater importance. This is in producing a higher operating temperature in the furnace. This they accomplish by preheating the fuel gas or air before it enters into combustion, so that the combustion yields a much higher temperature than if it were produced with cold air and gas.

The amount of heat lost in other waste products from the furnace and in cooling water is a comparatively small item.

Heat lost by radiation, conduction, and convection varies greatly with the type of furnace, but is nearly always large and frequently is the largest source of loss. It can be minimized by building the furnace walls of material of low thermal conductivity, or by making them thick; also by keeping the furnace tightly closed as much as possible. Electric furnaces are frequently built with a layer of Sil-O-Cel incorporated in the walls, and electric muffles are often surrounded by loosely packed magnesia. Radiation can be cut down by painting the outside of a furnace with aluminum paint or some other material of low emissivity, but often this is not practicable. Convection loss can be minimized by having the furnace under shelter and protected from wind or air drafts.

FUELS

A *fuel* is a substance that is burned for the purpose of generation of heat or production of power. The metallurgical industry is an enormous user of fuels. Choice of the best type of fuel for a particular process and means for the most efficient combustion of it are matters of great technical and economic importance to the metallurgist. The fuel of widest use is coal, of which about one and a half billion tons is consumed in the world each year, supplying the greater part of the power used in industrial plants, on railroads and steamships, etc., as well as being the leading fuel for direct combustion in industrial furnaces and for domestic heating. The leading metallurgical fuel as regards amount consumed, though not with respect to variety of applications, is coke, since it is most suitable for the largest fuel-consuming furnace—the iron blast furnace. But since coke is made directly from coal, the latter may be regarded as the leading metallurgical fuel from the standpoint of the raw material. Oil is of great importance for metallurgical as well as other purposes; and gas, both natural and manufactured, is also used in large and increasing amounts in metallurgical furnaces.

Fuels may be listed and classified according to their structure as follows:

Dense solid fuels—coal.

Semiporous solid fuels—wood, peat.

Porous solid fuels—coke, charcoal.

Liquid fuels—oil, tar. [Coal is also used in pulverized form (see page 440), in which form it behaves like a liquid fuel.]

Gaseous fuels—natural gas, manufactured gases.

Another useful classification of fuels is based on whether they occur in nature or are manufactured. All the important artificial fuels are prepared from some natural fuel; in the accompanying list the artificial fuels are shown opposite the natural fuels from which they are derived.

Natural fuels	*Artificial fuels*
Coal	Coke, tar, artificial gas, synthetic gasoline
Wood	Charcoal
Petroleum (crude oil)	Fuel oil, gasoline, kerosene, etc.
Natural gas	Natural-gas gasoline
Peat	

In addition, important amounts of other liquid fuels are derived from coal, and some gas is made from oil. Finely divided coal is sometimes pressed into briquettes, usually with some tar or pitch as a binder.

The chief combustible element in all fuels is carbon. In addition, most fuels contain a considerable amount of hydrogen, either as free hydrogen or combined as hydrocarbons. These are the only combustible elements of importance as heat producers. Other combustible elements may be present in small amounts, notably sulfur; but though sulfur contributes heat in burning, its presence is often very undesirable.

A comparison of the relative importance of the different natural fuels and of water power in the United States may be obtained from data compiled annually by the U.S. Bureau of Mines. For comparison it is necessary to express the amount of each fuel in terms of the amount of energy derived from each in the aggregate. These amounts are as follows for the year 1949, the figures representing trillions of Btu; the figures for water power are the energy equivalent of the power produced calculated from the prevailing central power station equivalent, which for that year was 1.30 lb of coal per kilowatt-hour:

From	Trillion Btu
Bituminous coal and lignite	11,397
Anthracite	1,084
Petroleum	11,572
Natural gas	6,181
Water power, at prevailing energy equivalent	1,552
Total	31,786

Fortunately, deposits of coal and lignite, both in the United States and in the world as a whole, are enormous—sufficient to last for centuries to come. Supplies of petroleum and natural gas, on the other hand, are so limited as to cause concern for the comparatively near future.

Coal. A number of different classifications of coal into grades, based on the amounts of different constituents present, have been proposed and used by various authors. The carbon content of coal is partly fixed, *i.e.*, it does not pass off with simple heating, and partly volatile, all of the latter being chemically combined with hydrogen; the higher the content of volatile matter, the lower the content of fixed carbon.

According to the classification of Kent,[1] anthracite, or "hard coal," has 90 to 97 per cent of its carbon content in the form of fixed carbon. It is mined in commercial amounts in but few places; the only one in the United States is the state of Pennsylvania. The importance of anthracite as a fuel is exaggerated in the minds of people residing in the eastern part of the United States and Canada, for it is little used in most other parts of the world.

Most of the coal used is of the bituminous type, or soft coal, in which 50 to 70 per cent of the carbon is fixed. The content of ash, moisture, sulfur, etc., in coal varies greatly in different deposits, and these factors together with its heating value (calorific power) determine its value as a fuel. Commercially, the location or accessibility of a coal deposit in relation to the demand for it is perhaps the greatest factor in its value.

[1] "Mechanical Engineers' Handbook," 12th ed., John Wiley & Sons, Inc., New York, 1950.

The following is typical of the composition of bituminous coal of ordinary grades (dry analysis):

Per cent

Carbon	62
Hydrogen	5
Oxygen	15
Sulfur	2
Nitrogen	1
Ash	15
Calorific power	5,970 Cal per kg (10,740 Btu per lb)

Lignite, or "brown coal," is inferior to bituminous coal as a fuel. Less than 50 per cent of its carbon content is fixed carbon. It is much used in Europe, but little in the United States, although there are large reserves of it here.

Coke. About 17 per cent of the soft coal mined in the United States is converted into coke. The operation consists of heating the coal to a high temperature (1200 to 1400°C or 2190 to 2550°F) without allowing air to burn it, with the result that nearly all the volatile matter of the coal is thus expelled, while the passage of the gas leaves behind the fixed carbon and ash in the form of a porous cellular material of great strength. It is this cell structure and strength which give the coke its valuable properties as a fuel for blast furnaces and the iron cupola. The porosity permits the fuel to be readily penetrated by air, resulting in rapid combustion; but more important than this, the strength of the coke enables it to support above it in the shaft furnace the weight of a heavy column of charge, whereas bituminous coal in a similar position would crumble and pack into a solid mass. Thus the coke maintains an open charge permitting ready penetration of the blast and ascension of the gases, while soft coal would permit smelting to continue only very slowly, if at all. Not all bituminous coals are capable of being converted into coke; coking and noncoking coals cannot be distinguished by chemical analysis, but the coking qualities are easily determined by a laboratory trial.

Two principal methods are used in making coke. In the older beehive process the volatile matter that is driven out of the coal is allowed to go to waste, while in the by-product process the volatile matter is piped off and furnishes many valuable by-products. In the United States only about 5 per cent or less of the total coke is now made by the beehive process. When demand for coke is great, the less economical beehive ovens are put into service, and during the Second World War the proportion supplied by them reached 11 per cent.

Iron blast furnaces use about three-quarters of all the coke produced in the United States. A by-product coke plant is commonly operated in conjunction with the blast-furnace plant.

By-product Coke Process. The coke ovens are narrow rectangular chambers, or *retorts*, which are charged with coal to within a few inches of the top. The retorts are kept tightly closed during the coking operation except for a pipe at the top, which conducts the volatile matter away as it is evolved. No air whatever is admitted, and there is no burning within the retort. The necessary heat is supplied by returning a portion (about one-third) of the evolved gas and burning it around the retort. The retorts are so built that each has a combustion chamber surrounding it (see Fig. 203), and thus the coking proceeds from each side toward the center. The operation is complete in about 16 to 20 hr. The retorts are built in long rows side by side, alternating with combustion chambers. They are charged through holes at the top, and the finished coke is discharged by opening the entire end of the retort and pushing the coke out with a mechanical pusher.

The volatile matter is sent through a series of condensers which cause tar, ammonia, and various oils to condense out in succession, so that each is recovered separately. The coal tar may be burned as a fuel, or it may be further treated to produce the many valuable coal-tar products. The cleaned gas remaining after treatment is a rich fuel gas, a portion of it being used for firing the coke ovens as described above, and the excess being sold to municipal gas companies for domestic gas or used in the steelworks for firing open-hearth and other furnaces. As the large steel plants make their own coke for their blast furnaces, the coke-oven gas is a welcome fuel in the plant. Table 39 shows the products recovered and their average amounts per ton of coal, the figures being averages for United States plants in 1948, as reported by the U.S. Bureau of Mines.

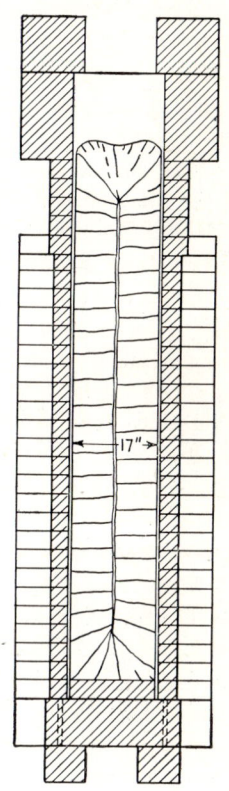

Fig. 203. Cross section of by-product coke retort, showing structure of coke and refractory brick walls.

Oil. Oil as an industrial fuel has some very decided advantages over coal, but in most localities is more expensive. The chief points of advantage are the following:

1. Firing may be started or stopped instantly, and the heat raised or lowered more rapidly and kept more uniform.

2. Oil is easily transported, firing is easier, and less labor is required in handling.

3. There are no ashes to handle or to contaminate the charge in the furnace.

4. A high temperature may be attained more easily.

5. Less air is required for complete combustion, and higher thermal efficiency results.

Oil is much used in furnaces of the reverberatory type. It burns with a long flame that sweeps through the furnace readily.

Crude oil (petroleum) is chiefly composed of hydrocarbons, and averages about 82 to 86 per cent carbon, with the balance nearly all hydrogen. Most petroleum belongs either to the paraffin group, represented by the general formula C_nH_{2n+2}, or to the naphthene group, represented by the

TABLE 39. AVERAGE YIELD OF COKE AND BY-PRODUCTS IN BY-PRODUCT COKE OVENS IN THE UNITED STATES IN 1948, PER 2,000 LB OF COAL CHARGED

Product	Quantity	Value
Coke, pounds	1,404	$8.73
Gas, cubic feet:		
Burned in coke ovens	3,810	
Wasted	170	
Surplus sold or used	6,250	
Total gas	10,230	1.29
Tar sold or used, gallons	7.6	0.43
Ammonium sulfate and other ammonia calculated as sulfate, pounds	19.1	0.36
Light oil (including crude light oil, benzol, toluol, solvent naphtha, etc.), gallons	2.6	0.48

general formula C_nH_{2n} or $(C_nH_{2n-6} + H_6)$. A more commonly used classification is that of paraffin-base and asphaltic-base crude oil, depending on which substance is yielded on refining. However, most crude oils are mixed base, *i.e.*, containing both of these substances. The color varies from light straw to nearly black, and the specific gravity from about 0.77 to 1.00. Usually, the lighter the color, the lighter the weight. The viscosity also varies greatly, as well as the amounts of the lighter oils that may be obtained by distillation. On the average, petroleum weighs about 7.5 lb per gal. It is sold by the barrel of 42 gal. The calorific power of crude oil averages about 19,000 Btu per lb, against only 9,000 to 14,000 Btu per lb for bituminous coal. But in addition to its higher cost, oil is more troublesome than coal to store.

When crude oil is heated without access of air (that is, distilled), it breaks up into various oils which vaporize at different temperatures, the lighter oils being the more volatile and therefore coming off first. The chief of these light oils obtained in this way are, in order, petroleum ether, gasoline, benzine, and naphtha. Then follow kerosene, lubricating oils, and paraffin, and petroleum coke, the last being similar to ordinary coke but of greater carbon content and higher purity. Distillation is usually not carried beyond the point of kerosene liberation, or it may be stopped before that point is reached, and the remaining oil then constitutes what is called *fuel oil*. It is this oil rather than crude oil that is most often used as an industrial fuel, the light oils being first extracted for motor fuel. The technology of petroleum refining is, however, by no means as simple

Fig. 204. Battery of by-product coke ovens, Jones & Laughlin Steel Corporation. (*Courtesy of Koppers Company, Inc.*)

as this brief statement may make it appear, and great progress is being made in obtaining increased yields of gasoline or motor fuel from petroleum. By the "cracking" process the maximum yield of gasoline from a given weight of crude oil has been increased steadily from about 35 to over 60 per cent, an outstanding example of chemical research.

For oil to be burned effectively, it must be atomized, *i.e.*, broken up into fine droplets; otherwise the air for combustion cannot come into contact with the oil to a sufficient degree. Accordingly, oil burners are always employed. The burner requires a jet of compressed air or steam which impinges on and mixes with the entering stream of oil, thus atomizing the oil and spraying it out from the burner with a considerable velocity that aids greatly in lengthening and spreading the flame.

Gas. Gas as a fuel has all the advantages in use possessed by oil, some to an even greater degree. But it is more difficult to store and cannot be transported except by piping. Its cost, too, is greater than that of oil, except that natural gas is cheaper in some localities.

Natural Gas. Natural gas has been called the ideal fuel, but its use is limited by the cost of transporting it far from the locality in which it occurs. Great strides have been made in recent years, however, in pipeline construction, and as a result the volume of natural gas used in the United States has grown at an accelerated rate. The amount used as fuel in 1948 was nearly 5,000 billion cubic feet. It is an important fuel in the zinc industry; about half of the zinc plants in the United States use natural gas, and the other half use producer gas. Some is used in iron and steel plants, and some at copper smelters. From Texas, natural gas is piped to the entire Middle West, and recently the Big Inch and Little Inch pipe lines have brought it to the eastern seaboard, while other lines will carry it to Southern California. These long-distance pipe lines have been made possible only by improved manufacture of seamless and welded steel pipe capable of withstanding the high pressures involved. The cost of the gas at the source is very low, only 6.5 cents per thousand cubic feet in 1948, but at the point of consumption the average value was 24 cents per thousand cubic feet.

Natural gas consists largely of methane (CH_4); it may contain also as much as 30 per cent hydrogen, several per cent of higher hydrocarbons, and small amounts of other gases. About 90 per cent of it is treated at the source for extraction of natural-gas gasoline, a valuable by-product being thus obtained and the piping qualities of the gas improved. About 10 per cent of the production of natural gas is used in the manufacture of carbon black, and nearly 20 per cent is used for domestic purposes.

Natural gas is slower burning than coke-oven gas or producer gas, but has a much higher heating value. It is often mixed with manufactured gas to provide a calorific power of 650 to 1,100 Btu per cu ft, whereas standards for manufactured gas vary from about 510 to 575 Btu in different localities. Because of its slow-burning qualities, natural gas is adaptable to furnace use requiring a long or luminous flame. Where short-flame velocity burners are used, this characteristic is a disadvantage. Gas burners made for natural gas cannot be used for manufactured gas unless specially built for interchangeability. Combustion chambers in furnaces and in controlled-atmosphere generators must be different for natural and manufactured gas.

In most localities domestic use of natural gas takes precedence over industrial use, and supplies to plants may be suddenly reduced or cut off during winter months. This has given rise to a new type of fuel often called "liquefied petroleum" gas, consisting of mixtures of propane and butane which are easily liquefied at moderate pressure and are stored in that condition in large stand-by tanks for supplementary or emergency use. By expanding to only a few pounds pressure and premixing with air, propane and butane are brought to the furnace burners at the same heating value in Btu per cubic foot as the natural gas they supplant.

The cost of a fuel per unit of heating value is not always the determining factor in its use. Some natural gases are nearly free from sulfur, and one large metal plant was built in West Virginia because of the availability of gas which would not contain harmful amounts of sulfur.

Coke-oven Gas and City Gas. Coke-oven gas is an excellent fuel; it has already been discussed. City gas is made in retorts in a manner similar to coking, but here it is the gas and not the coke that is the primary product; also it is commonly enriched by distillation of some oil in addition to the coal; otherwise the percentage of hydrocarbons present in the gas would not be great enough to provide the high calorific power required.

Producer Gas. A type of manufactured gas much used in metallurgical work is producer gas. This gas is usually made from soft coal by means of controlled partial combustion through limitation of the air supply. In addition steam is often used along with the air, so that the reactions which account for the combustible components of the gas are as follows:

$$C + \text{air} \rightarrow CO + N_2$$
$$C + H_2O \rightarrow CO + H_2 \text{ (above a temperature of 800°C)}$$

Since a minimum temperature must be maintained in the producer, the amount of steam which can be added is limited. The reaction of carbon with water vapor absorbs heat; enough steam can be used to absorb only the excess of heat generated by the combustion with air.

Producer gas contains a large proportion of inert gases such as nitrogen from the air used in combustion, CO_2 derived from some unavoidable complete combustion, and water vapor from undecomposed steam and the moisture in the fuel. Such a gas has a much lower calorific power than coke-oven gas; nevertheless, by preheating according to the regenerative system (see page 430), it yields a temperature high enough for open-hearth steel furnaces. Although at one time most open-hearth furnaces were fired with producer gas, its use has declined greatly in recent years.

The gas producer has a grate on which the fuel is burned and steam and air are blown in from below. The essential feature of the combustion is the carrying of a deep bed of fuel above the grate, the fuel being fed in from the top of the producer. This deep bed of fuel results in the formation of CO, since carbon burned to CO_2 at the grate is reduced back to CO by the excess fuel above. Most of the volatile matter of the coal will be liberated before reaching the incandescent zone, and this volatile matter joins the rest of the gas to enrich it considerably. If the steam and air are blown into the producer alternately instead of together, a richer gas is produced on one cycle. The steam cycle yields a gas known as *water gas* in which hydrogen replaces the inert nitrogen liberated when air is used.

It is evident that the gasifying of coal into producer gas, instead of using the coal itself in the furnace, is merely an indirect method of burning coal as a fuel. It results in the loss of up to 15 per cent of the original heating value of the coal, but the many advantages of gas firing over coal firing often more than offset this loss. Indeed, the efficiency with which gas may be applied as a fuel may be so much greater than the efficiency with coal that the heat loss in generating the gas may be much more than made up. Gas producers were built in large numbers during the era when beehive coke ovens predominated, but with the present great preponderance of by-product coke ovens which save all the gas formerly lost, the importance of producer gas has diminished. Coke-oven gas mixed with blast-furnace gas is now much used in steel plants.

Pulverized Coal. If coal is burned in powdered form, many of the advantages of oil or gas firing are obtained, and with a fuel of lower cost. Low grades of coal can be effectively burned in this manner. The finely ground coal is injected into the firebox or furnace chamber with compressed air from a burner, which must be directed into an open space sufficiently large for free development of the flame; otherwise the coal is not fully burned. More complete combustion can be attained than if the same coal were burned in lump form, and the amount of air required for combustion is little in excess of the theoretical quantity (see page 430). Consequently a greater proportion of the calorific power of the coal is actually developed in the furnace, and a higher temperature is attained. A disadvantage is that some of the ash of the coal, which may be large in amount if low-grade coal is used, is deposited, falling on the furnace charge and tending to insulate or contaminate it, or accumulating in the flues and passages.

Pulverized coal cannot be stored more than 48 hr, since it may ignite through spontaneous combustion. Pulverization and feeding of the coal to the burners must be properly carried out, and care must be taken to avoid explosion of a coal-dust–air mixture. This method of firing coal is much used for kilns, reverberatory furnaces, and boiler installations. Upward of 30,000,000 tons of coal is now burned annually in the United States in finely ground form.

Bibliography

Furnaces and Refractories

Austin, J. B.: "The Flow of Heat in Metals," American Society for Metals, Cleveland, Ohio, 1942.

Curtis, F. W.: "High-frequency Induction Heating," 2d ed., McGraw-Hill Book Company, Inc., New York, 1950.

Etherington, H.: "Modern Furnace Technology," 2d ed., Tait Book Company, Melbourne, Australia, 1944.

Harbison-Walker Refractories Company: "Modern Refractory Practice," 3d ed., Pittsburgh, 1949.

Lincoln, E. S.: "Industrial Electric Heating and Electrical Furnaces," William Collins Sons & Company, Canada, Ltd., Toronto, 1946.

McAdams, W. H.: "Heat Transmission," 2d ed., McGraw-Hill Book Company, Inc., New York, 1942.

Norton, F. H.: "Refractories," 3d ed., McGraw-Hill Book Company, Inc., New York, 1949.

Osborn, H. B., Jr., P. H. Brace, W. G. Johnson, J. W. Cable, and T. E. Eagan: "Induction Heating," American Society for Metals, Cleveland, Ohio, 1946.

Paschkis, V.: "Industrial Electric Furnaces and Appliances," 2 vols., Interscience Publishers, Inc., New York, 1945.

Robiette, A. G.: "Electric Melting Practice," Charles Griffin & Co., Ltd., London, 1935.

Searle, A. B.: "Refractory Materials: Their Manufacture and Uses," 3d ed., Charles Griffin & Co., Ltd., London, 1940.

Stansel, N. R.: "Industrial Electric Heating," John Wiley & Sons, Inc., New York, 1933.

———: "Induction Heating," McGraw-Hill Book Company, Inc., New York, 1949.

Stoever, H. J.: "Applied Heat Transmission," McGraw-Hill Book Company, Inc., New York, 1941.

Trinks, W.: "Industrial Furnaces," 2 vols., 2d ed., John Wiley & Sons, Inc., New York, 1942.

Fuels and Combustion

American Gas Association: "Fuel Flue Gases," New York, 1941.

Bone, W. A., and G. W. Himus: "Coal, Its Constitution and Uses" (with chapter on fuel economy and heat transmission by R. J. Sarjant), Longmans, Green & Co., Inc., New York, 1936.

Carr, A. R., and C. W. Selheimer: "Fuels and Their Utilization," Pitman Publishing Corp., New York, 1940.

De Lorenzi, O. (editor): "Combustion Engineering," Combustion Engineering Company, New York, 1947.

Griswold, J.: "Fuels, Combustion, and Furnaces," McGraw-Hill Book Company, Inc., New York, 1946.

Gruse, W. A., and D. R. Stevens: "The Chemical Technology of Petroleum," 2d ed., McGraw-Hill Book Company, Inc., New York, 1942.

Haslam, R. T., and R. P. Russell: "Fuels and Their Combustion," McGraw-Hill Book Company, Inc., New York, 1926.

Himus, G. W.: "Elements of Fuel Technology," Leonard Hill, Ltd., London, 1947.

Jones, P. J.: "Petroleum Production," Reinhold Publishing Corporation, New York, 1948.

Korevaar, A.: "Combustion in the Gas Producer and the Blast Furnace," Lockwood & Son, London, 1924.

Moore, E. S.: "Coal," 2d ed., John Wiley & Sons, New York, 1940.

Nash, A. W., and D. A. Howes: "Principles of Motor Fuel Production and Application," 2 vols., John Wiley & Sons, New York, 1935.

Sexton, A. H.: "Fuel and Refractory Materials," 2d ed., Chemical Publishing Company, Inc., Brooklyn, 1940.

Smith, M. L., and K. W. Stinson: "Fuels and Combustion," McGraw-Hill Book Company, Inc., New York, 1952.

Steiner, K.: "Fuels and Fuel Burners," McGraw-Hill Book Company, Inc., New York, 1946.

CHAPTER 16

MEASUREMENT OF TEMPERATURE IN INDUSTRIAL OPERATIONS

Most heat-treating operations must be carried out at well-defined and closely controlled temperatures, which means first of all accurately measured temperatures. Hand in hand with the modern development of heat-treatment has gone development of means of measuring high temperature; and of scarcely less importance is the measurement of temperature in many metallurgical processes, such as roasting, smelting, refining, casting, and rolling. While in many cases these latter processes after reaching the routine stage proceed without any particular care as to temperature, the scientific study and improvement of them demand a close knowledge of the temperatures under which they are operated at their various stages and under varying conditions. Temperature measurement is an important factor, too, in the study of fuel economy, disposal of waste furnace gases, steam boiler-plant operation, heat transfer and heat losses, etc.

Temperatures, particularly in enclosed places, such as inside furnaces, can be judged by color after red heat has been attained, and in some cases estimated within the required limits. Such estimation, of course, had to be relied on entirely before the development of precise measuring techniques. It is remarkable to what extent many experienced furnacemen can tell temperatures with the unaided eye, that is, within certain ranges between a red and a white heat. This relation between temperatures and color is given in the accompanying table, known as Howe's color scale:

Color	Temperature °C	Temperature °F
Lowest visible red	475	885
Dull red	550–625	1020–1155
Full cherry red	700	1290
Light red	850	1560
Orange	900	1650
Full yellow	950–1000	1740–1830
Light yellow	1050	1920
White	1150 up	2100 up

One trouble with such a scale is that different observers' opinions of color vary widely, and a further difficulty is that anyone's judgment of such colors depends on the lightness or darkness of the surroundings.

Before the various devices for measuring temperatures are discussed, it will be well to recall the exact meaning of temperature. Temperature is not heat, it is the degree or intensity of heat and is measured in degrees. Heat itself, that is, quantity of heat, is measured in calories or British thermal units (Btu). Temperature, then, is not a quantity, but an intensity factor, and it is measured by its effects.

A device designed to measure temperatures is called a *thermometer;* according to customary usage this term is applied to instruments suitable for the lower temperature ranges. One used to measure high temperatures is called a *pyrometer.* There is at present no sharp distinction between the two terms.

TABLE 40. MODERN TEMPERATURE-MEASURING DEVICES

Device	Approximate practical temperature range °C	Approximate practical temperature range °F	Temperature effect on which based
Mercury thermometer, glass..	−39 to 525	−39 to 975	Expansion
Mercury thermometer, fused silica..................	−39 to 800	−39 to 1470	Expansion
Gas expansion thermometer (nitrogen)................	−130 to 540	−200 to 1000	Expansion
Metal expansion thermometer	0 to 500	32 to 930	Expansion
Resistance thermometer......	−180 to 660[1]	−290 to 1220	Change of electrical resistance
Thermoelectric pyrometer, Le Châtelier, noble metal......	0 to 1540[1]	32 to 2800	Generation of thermo-electricity
Thermoelectric pyrometer, base metal	−180 to 1150[1]	−290 to 2100	Generation of thermo-electricity
Seger cones................	600 to 2000	1110 to 3630	Fusion
Tempilstiks................	45 to 1090	113 to 2000	Fusion
Radiation pyrometer.........	400 up	750 up	Radiation of heat
Optical pyrometer...........	750 to 3500	1380 to 6330	Radiation of light

[1] The platinum resistance and thermoelectric pyrometers may be used to measure temperatures somewhat higher for intermittent readings; the upper figure here given is the maximum for prolonged use. Some base-metal couples can be used to 1315°C (2400°F) for intermittent readings.

Many kinds of devices for measuring temperature, based on various thermal effects, have been tried or used. Table 40 gives those which are used industrially at the present time, together with the temperature limits within which each is used, and the temperature effect which each utilizes.

There are two classes of temperature-measuring devices: (1) those which are placed at the point whose temperature is to be measured and thus become heated themselves to the temperature in question, and (2) those which operate at a distance and record the effect of the heat waves or light waves radiated from the hot body. Obviously, only the second class can be used to measure extremely high temperatures, while the first class is, in general, more accurate for the temperatures at which it can be employed.

In Table 40 the last two pyrometers belong to the second class and all the others to the first.

In the following pages the different types of temperature-measuring devices are taken up approximately in the order of their importance in metallurgical work.

Thermoelectric Pyrometers. This type of pyrometer was first brought out by Henri Le Châtelier in 1886, and provided the first simple and accurate method of measuring temperatures above the range of the mercury-in-glass thermometer. With the development of the rugged low-cost base-metal thermocouples and the means of automatically making continuous records of the temperature, this type of pyrometer has become the leader in industrial furnace work, and is doubtless used in greater number than all the other types of high-temperature instruments combined.

The thermoelectric pyrometer consists of three parts: (1) a junction of two different metals or alloys formed by fusing together the ends of two wires, (2) a protection tube in which the junction is enclosed, and (3) a potentiometer or millivoltmeter for measuring the emf produced when the junction is heated.

The junction and the two wires forming it are called a *thermocouple*. The principle on which its use is based may be stated as follows: When two different metals or alloys are joined in two places so as to form a closed circuit, a potential difference is set up between the two junctions that is proportional to the difference in temperature between the junctions. The two junctions are called the measuring junction and the reference junction. Since the thermoelectric pyrometer is most often used for measuring high temperatures, the measuring junction is usually the "hot junction" and the reference junction the "cold junction." The two junctions are thus commonly called the hot and cold junctions, but in case low temperatures are being measured, the measuring junction would be the colder. A thermocouple element thus consists of two wires of dissimilar materials which must be electrically insulated from each other except at the two junctions, the thermoelectric properties of the materials being such that, with the reference junction at a known temperature, the temperature of the measuring junction can be determined by measuring the emf developed.

In practice the two wires are actually joined to each other at only one place, namely, the measuring, or hot, junction; the other junction is made through the measuring instrument. The reference, or cold, junction is thus located at the instrument and is transferred to its terminals by means of thermocouple wires or suitable extension wires. The relations of the parts will be made clear by reference to Fig. 205.

It is important to remember that the emf corresponds not to the actual temperature of the hot junction, but to the *difference* in temperature between the hot and cold junctions. Most instruments are designed to compensate automatically for the cold-junction temperature, so that the

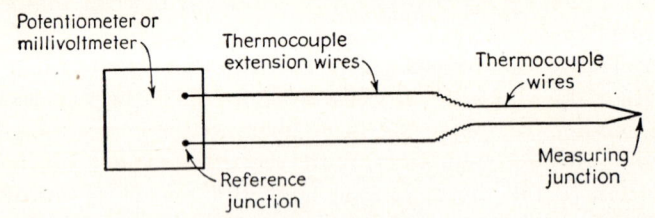

FIG. 205. Parts of thermoelectric pyrometer (protection tube not shown).

hot-junction temperature may be read or recorded directly. In the laboratory, the measuring instrument often indicates only in millivolts; the reading is then referred to a calibration table to obtain the corresponding temperature.

In the original Le Châtelier pyrometer one of the wires was platinum and the other an alloy of 90 per cent platinum with 10 per cent of either rhodium or iridium. Present-day thermocouples of this type are always made with rhodium as the alloying element, the percentage of rhodium in the alloy wire being usually 10 per cent, sometimes 13 per cent. The noble-metal type is of greater permanence and therefore of somewhat greater reliability as well as of higher range than the base-metal type. In this type every 100°C rise in temperature of the junction produces an emf of about 1 millivolt.

A number of combinations are used as base-metal couples, but only three are of wide commercial application at the present time. These are given in Table 41, together with their upper temperature limits for constant use and for periodic use and the approximate millivoltage per 100°C rise.

It will be seen that the base-metal couples have an advantage over the noble-metal in producing a higher emf for a given temperature. They are also much cheaper and, being made of heavier wires, are less liable to breakage. But being subject to oxidation and other possibilities of change in composition, they require more care and more frequent checking. Noble-metal couples, too, are subject to contamination, especially by carbon, hydrogen, or metal vapors, if not properly protected.

In thermocouples the two component wires are insulated from each other to prevent short-circuiting of the current. The wires are encased in protection tubes to protect them from the gases, liquids, or other substances which would change their composition by corroding or alloying with them. Various materials are used for these tubes; for moderate-

TABLE 41. THERMOCOUPLES AND THEIR TEMPERATURE RANGES

Couple	Upper limit For prolonged use °C	Upper limit For prolonged use °F	Upper limit For intermittent use °C	Upper limit For intermittent use °F	Approximate millivolts per 100°C[1]
Copper–constantan..........	370	700	540	1000	5.0
Iron–constantan............	760	1400	980	1800	5.5
Chromel–alumel............	1150	2100	1315	2400	4.0
Platinum–platinum-rhodium..	1540	2800	1650	3000	1.0

[1] These values vary somewhat with the temperature; the calibration curve is not a straight line.

temperature work iron, copper, and nickel-chromium alloys are common; for high temperatures, porcelain or fused silica; and for extremely high temperatures, silicon carbide over porcelain. The tubes should be as thin-walled as is consistent with sufficient strength and lack of porosity, in order that the heat may pass through them readily and quickly bring the junction to the temperature it is desired to measure. There is always some lag in the temperature indication of an enclosed junction. In the laboratory under suitable conditions the protection tube may be dispensed with, but this cannot often be done in the plant.

Millivoltmeters and potentiometers are commonly used to indicate the emf. If a millivoltmeter is used, its resistance must be high in proportion to the resistance of the thermocouple and lead wires; otherwise changes in the circuit resistance would affect its readings appreciably. Potentiometers are more accurate and are more widely used.

Both millivoltmeters and potentiometers may be obtained in the form of an indicating instrument or a recording instrument. The latter has a rotating chart or roll of graduated paper which is turned by a synchronous motor, and the instrument pointer is provided with a pen point or other means of drawing a curve, so as to make a permanent record of the temperature. The rotating charts may be either in continuous strip form or in circular form. Multiple-point recorders can be obtained which draw the curves of two or more thermocouples on the same chart.

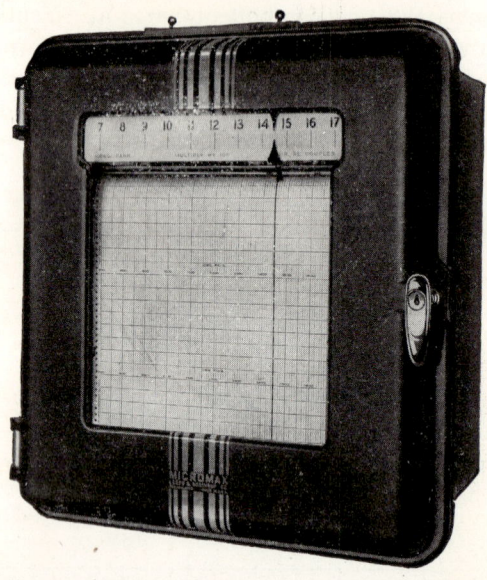

Fig. 206. A recording potentiometer and temperature controller, with case closed. (*Courtesy of Leeds & Northrup Company.*)

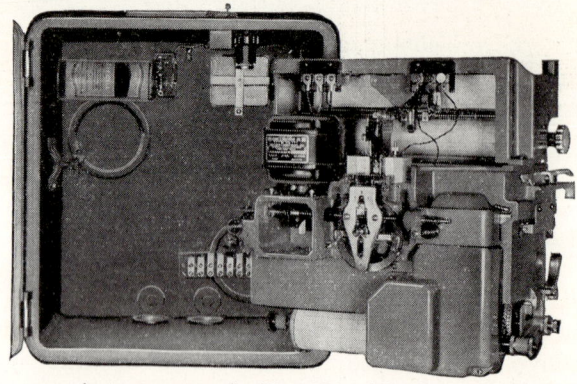

Fig. 207. The same instrument as in Fig. 206 with the mechanism swung out for inspection or adjustment.

Either the indicating or the recording potentiometer is often combined with a device for automatic temperature control, whereby the pyrometer serves to regulate within desired limits the temperature of the furnace to which it is attached. The recorder-controller is especially useful in heat-treating furnaces, but has many other applications.

MEASUREMENT OF TEMPERATURE IN INDUSTRIAL OPERATIONS   449

The potentiometer for temperature indicating, recording, or recorder controlling requires a balancing device. This usually consists of a galvanometer which controls a balancing mechanism through a small electric motor, operating at small time intervals. Recently electronically balanced potentiometers have been developed and are finding increasing use. These employ a vacuum-tube system instead of a galvanometer; they balance continuously and with extreme rapidity by means of a small reversing motor actuated by the current from an amplifier. The instruments are rugged, highly sensitive, and scarcely affected by vibration.

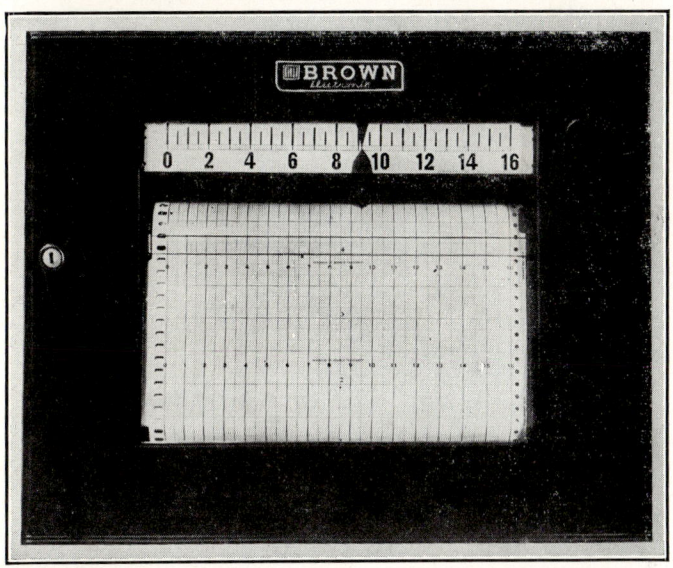

Fig. 208. Electronically balanced strip chart controller with external index-setting knob. (*Courtesy of Minneapolis-Honeywell Regulator Company, Brown Instruments Division.*)

Plant installations are used with thermocouples for furnaces, with radiation pyrometers to control rolling temperatures, etc. Laboratory models for even greater speeds will record such rapid temperature gradients as those of steel during quenching or in welding. The Electronik and the Speedomax instruments are examples.

The indicating or recording instrument may show the emf in millivolts, in which case a calibration curve or table must be used to obtain the temperature corresponding to the emf; or the instrument may be graduated to show the temperature directly. This latter arrangement is nearly always used in the works and frequently in the laboratory. Direct-reading instruments are commonly employed with all the other types of pyrometers as well as with the thermoelectric. The disadvantage is that if the calibration changes, the direct temperature readings are no longer correct. For accurate scientific work, instruments with calibration curves should be used, while in operating work, thermo-

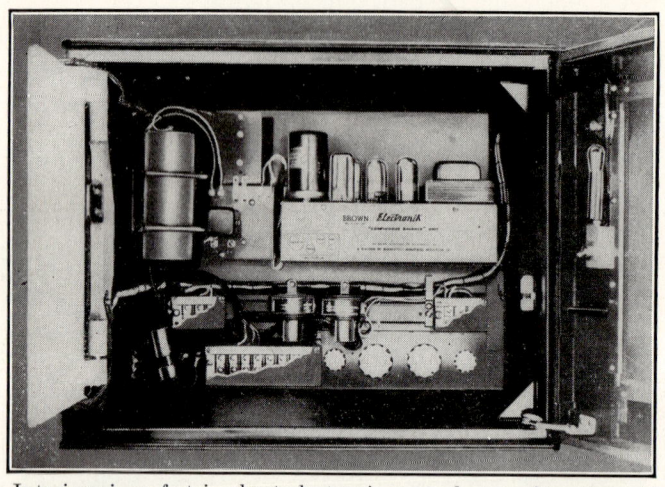

Fig. 209. Interior view of strip-chart electronic control potentiometer. (*Courtesy of Minneapolis-Honeywell Regulator Company, Brown Instruments Division.*)

couples should be checked frequently by recalibration and should be replaced when they are no longer capable of indicating the correct temperature.

Space will not permit a discussion of calibration of thermocouples, but it may be noted that the simplest method is by direct comparison with a standard pyrometer of undoubted accuracy. A method usually more accurate is by making use of standard fixed and accurately reproducible temperatures, *e.g.*, the melting points of pure palladium, gold, copper, silver, antimony, tin, ice, etc., and the boiling points of sulfur, naphthalene, and water (see Fig. 210). Details of methods have been given by W. F. Roeser and H. T. Wensel.[1]

Fig. 210. Typical calibration curve of a platinum and platinum-rhodium (10 per cent rhodium) thermocouple.

Optical Pyrometers. This type of pyrometer is much used in measuring temperatures of molten steel and other high-melting metals, electric

[1] *Research, Nat. Bur. Standards, Research Paper* 768, p. 247, 1935.

furnaces, and other temperatures over 1500°C (2730°F). It is also used a great deal for lower temperatures down to 760°C (1400°F) where it is not convenient to bring the pyrometer in contact with the heat whose intensity is to be measured. While it has good accuracy, it is usually less accurate in the lower temperature ranges than the thermoelectric pyrometer, and its use is often less simple.

Fig. 211. Optical pyrometer in use for measuring the temperature of a stream of molten metal. At the bottom is shown the disappearing filament. In the left-hand view the filament is too cold and appears dark, in the right-hand view it glows too brightly, and in the middle view it is at the same intensity as the image of the hot metal, showing that the pyrometer is then adjusted for correct temperature reading. (*Courtesy of Leeds & Northrup Company.*)

The first optical pyrometer was that of Mesuré and Nouel, brought out about 1889. This and similar types which followed later were in a measure merely a means of assisting the eye in estimation, the instrument containing a prism through which a light ray from the hot body passed, and which could be turned through an indicated angle in such a way as to vary the color or the intensity of the light; when a standard color was reached, or when the intensity matched a standard which appeared in the instrument, the angle which had been turned through indicated the temperature.

The modern optical pyrometer is usually of the disappearing-filament type (Fig. 211). The user, as in all types of optical pyrometers, sights the telescope of the instrument on the hot body. In the field there appears a red background, the intensity or brightness of which depends on the temperature of the object sighted, and also an electric-light filament, which will glow with an intensity different from that of the background, depending on the amount of current passing through it. The intensity of the lamp may be varied by varying the current with a rheostat contained in the instrument, and when the two intensities are of equal brightness the filament will no longer be visible (see Fig. 211). The milliamperes passing will then be a measure of the temperature. For measurement of the current a potentiometer may be employed. In another type the lamp is maintained at a fixed intensity, and the intensity (color) is varied by means of a rotating translucent glass wedge, the angle of turn being used as a measure of the temperature.

Since the optical pyrometer employs light radiation as a measure of temperature, anything that interferes either with the radiation from the hot body or with the free passage of the light rays to the pyrometer will affect the accuracy of the measurement. Smoke or metallic vapor will cause errors, and this often causes great difficulty in obtaining accurate readings at very high temperatures. A useful way of avoiding this trouble in some cases is to insert a tube, closed at the bottom, into the furnace, and then sight through the tube onto the bottom. Again, the amount of light radiated from a hot body depends on the color and nature of the surface, and corrections due to this fact must sometimes be applied. If, however, the body is enclosed, as when inside a furnace, the radiation may be independent of the character of the surface. This question is discussed below under Radiation Pyrometers.

Radiation Pyrometers. This type measures the amount of energy radiated from the hot body and uses that as a measure of the temperature of the body. The radiated waves (both heat and light) are received on a mirror or lens system at the back of a tube or telescope and are reflected to a group of thermocouples (thermopile). The thermopile itself is heated only a few degrees, but its temperature rise is proportional to the temperature of the source of heat, and the millivoltmeter or potentiometer to which it is connected is graduated to indicate the temperature of the original source instead of the temperature of the thermopile itself. A special focusing arrangement makes the reading independent of the distance from the instrument to the hot body, within certain limits.

This method of temperature measurement obviously is based on the ability of the hot body to radiate energy at a rate dependent only on its temperature. But that relation does not hold under all conditions, as the nature of the surface may also be a factor. It will hold always for a body that absorbs all heat radiated *to* it, without reflecting or transmitting any of it. Heat will also radiate *from* such a body at the maximum rate; and since it has been found that lampblack and other dull black surfaces approximate this condition, such a body has been termed a *black body*. A black body is one that emits by radiation at the maximum rate; it is said to have an emissivity of 1. When the body whose temperature is being measured is in the open, a radiation pyrometer indicates directly the true temperature only if the body is a black body. But if the hot body is enclosed, as when within the walls of a furnace, and is in thermal equilibrium, it is then receiving and emitting energy by radiation at the same rate; otherwise it would not remain in equilibrium. Consequently, an enclosed body always acts like a black body, regardless of the nature of its surface, and the radiation pyrometer will indicate directly the true temperatures of materials inside of furnaces when focused upon them. The instrument may also be provided with an adjustment to compensate for the emissivity factor, for use when the hot body is not enclosed but the emissivity of the surface is known.

Radiation-pyrometer readings are also affected by smoke, etc., the accuracy of optical and radiation pyrometers being affected by the same factors. Corrections to be applied to optical pyrometer indications when used under other than black-body conditions are, in general, much smaller than for radiation pyrometers and can sometimes be neglected when the corresponding radiation corrections could not be. Theoretically, the corrections for both optical and radiation pyrometers can be calculated when the emissivity and certain other factors are known.

One type of radiation pyrometer, the Rayotube, is designed for use either with a hand-operated indicator or for permanent installation by connecting the lead wires from the thermopile to a Micromax or Speedomax potentiometer recorder or recorder-controller. The radiation pyrometer can be used at temperatures too low for the optical pyrometer and is especially useful for measuring temperatures of moving pieces of metal, since no contact is required, or in places where a thermocouple would be subject to damage or need too frequent recalibration.

Mercury Thermometers. This type is so well known that it requires no description. In its usual form it cannot be used at temperatures approaching the boiling point of mercury, which is 357°C (675°F). But by using nitrogen under pressure, instead of a vacuum, above the mercury column, this type may be used up to the point where the glass softens appreciably, that is, at a low red heat. Such thermometers are often used in boiler-room work. They have the advantage of being simple and unvarying, but the high-range instruments lack precision.

Resistance Thermometer. This type is the most accurate of all temperature-measuring devices for temperatures up to 660°C (1220°F).

It depends on the fact that the electrical resistance of a metal increases proportionately to the temperature. The pyrometer has three parts corresponding to the three parts of the thermoelectric type, but, instead of a thermocouple, the protection tube encloses a small coil of wire wound on an insulating spool, as shown at the bottom, Fig. 212. The indicating or recording instrument is essentially a Wheatstone bridge, which measures the resistance of the coil when it has been inserted in the source of heat whose temperature is to be measured. A dry cell supplies current to the coil. The resistance of the lead wires running to the coil is exactly counterbalanced by a third wire called the "compensating lead." Thus only the resistance of the coil itself is a factor. The coil is usually made of platinum, since platinum will not change permanently with repeated heating and cooling, provided that it is not heated beyond 660°C (1220°F) for long periods. Sometimes nickel-alloy coils are used for temperatures up to 500°C (930°F) and copper coils for lower temperatures.

Resistance thermometers are excellent for measuring temperatures below zero. Specially designed instruments can measure temperatures accurately within 0.0001°C over a considerable range. This is about 10 to 100 times the accuracy of the best mercury-expansion thermometer of similar range. The industrial resistance thermometer, shown in Fig. 213, is accurate to within 1°C up to 660°C (1220°F).

Another merit of the resistance type is that it can employ a coil of any size, so that if the coil is made to traverse the entire cross section of a pipe, for example, the instrument will read the average temperature over the whole cross section, whereas other types of pyrometers indicate the temperature at a single spot only.

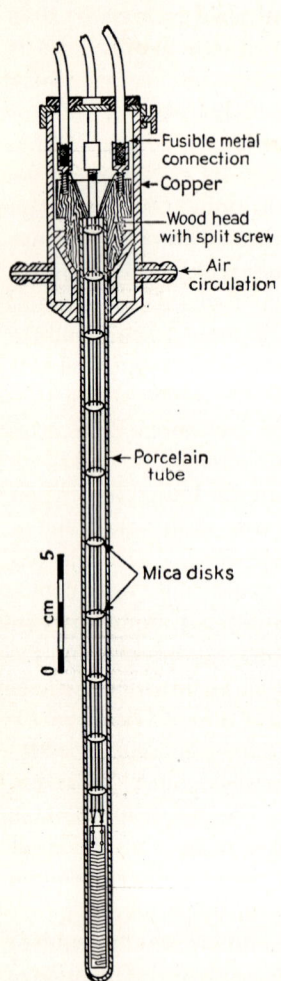

FIG. 212. Sectional view of a laboratory-type resistance pyrometer.

High-temperature Expansion Thermometer. One design of this type operates through the difference in expansion between graphite rods and a steel stem enclosing the rods, the difference in expansion being indicated in degrees on a dial. Often strips of two different metals are employed in much the same way. Thermometers on oven doors of domestic ranges are commonly of this type.

Under this heading may be mentioned also the gas-pressure high-temperature thermometer. This type has a small amount of nitrogen enclosed in a copper bulb. When heated, the nitrogen tends to expand, and the pressure so generated is transmitted through a capillary tube to a pressure gage, usually a recording gage graduated to indicate the temperature directly. This type was much used before the perfection of the base-metal thermocouple.

Seger Cones and Tempilstiks. Seger cones are little three-sided pyramids of standard clayey mixtures, each of a definite composition which begins to soften at a specified known temperature. The cone is

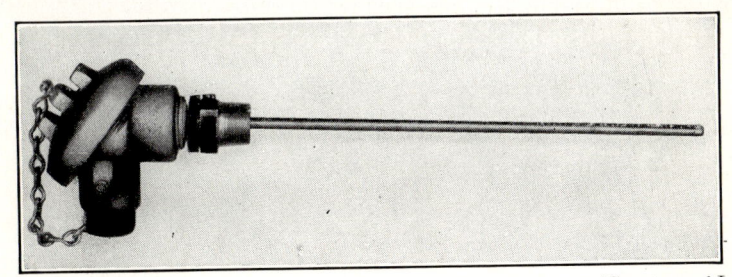

Fig. 213. Thermohm type of industrial resistance thermometer. (*Courtesy of Leeds & Northrup Company.*)

placed in the furnace, and if the point of the cone fuses, the temperature is known to be at or above the designated cone temperature. These cones are useful in determining when a rising temperature has reached a desired point. They are seldom used in metallurgy, but are much used in the pottery, enamel, and refractory industries, being suitable for very high temperatures. They are made up by mixing Al_2O_3 and SiO_2 with various other oxides, such as CaO, Fe_2O_3, Na_2O, K_2O, B_2O_3, and PbO. The standard series of Seger cones ranges from a temperature of 600 to 2000°C (1112 to 3632°F).

The same principle is used with substances of lower melting points. Thus "Tempilstiks," made in the form of crayons and convenient for application to hot surfaces of which the temperature is desired, are available in the range of 45 to 1090°C (113 to 2000°F). They are said to have an accuracy within 1 per cent. A pellet form, "Tempil Pellets," has a range up to 1370°C (2500°F).

Bibliography

Anon.: "Temperature: Its Measurement and Control in Science and Industry," (Symposium), Reinhold Publishing Corporation, New York, 1940.

GRIFFITHS, E.: "Methods of Measuring Temperature," 3d ed., Charles Griffin & Co., Ltd., London, 1947.

SOSMAN, R. B.: "The Pyrometry of Solids and Surfaces," American Society for Metals, Cleveland, Ohio, 1940.

WEBER, R. L.: "Temperature Measurement and Control," The Blakiston Company, Philadelphia, 1941.

WOOD, W. P., and J. M. CORK: "Pyrometry," 2d ed., McGraw-Hill Book Company, Inc., New York, 1941.

SOME AVAILABLE MOTION PICTURES

A modern trend in education is the visual presentation of operations to go hand-in-hand with written or verbal explanations. This may well involve the use of motion pictures as well as other visual aids. Films are gladly loaned by those manufacturers who have them, and many will also supply lecturers who will show and explain the films. While this is in the nature of advertising, the advertising feature is subordinated, and manufacturers are eager to contribute to education. Scores of films are available besides those listed herein, and the manufacturers mentioned are also revising old films and producing new ones frequently. Some motion-picture films of metallurgical operations are also available for rent. All films are listed hereafter under headings arranged according to chapters; however, many pictures belong under more than one classification and the entire list should therefore be consulted.

All the films are understood to be sound films except where noted as silent.

GENERAL

GENERAL ELECTRIC COMPANY, 1 River Road, Schenectady 5, N.Y.: "Metal Magic." 16 and 35 mm. Modern metals and how they are made; the crystalline structure of metal; alloys and the parts they play in modern airplanes, trains, and the like.

AMERICAN SOCIETY FOR METALS, 7301 Euclid Ave., Cleveland: "Metal Crystals." 16 mm. 3 reels, 900 ft, silent. An educational film showing crystalline and non-crystalline substances, atom arrangement, space lattices, the solidification of metals, formation of dendrites, grain boundaries, microscopic and polishing technique, etching, temperatures of solidification, and formation of equilibrium diagrams.

GENERAL MOTORS CORPORATION, Department of Public Relations, 1775 Broadway, New York 19: "Progress through Engineering." 16 mm. 18 min. Shows the relationship of modern civilization to the engineering profession; how wide the latter is, touching the fields of transportation, sound transmission, sanitation, etc.

METALS AS MATERIALS OF CONSTRUCTION

BAKELITE CORPORATION, 300 Madison Ave., New York 17: "Selecting the Right Thermosetting Molding Materials." 16 mm. The wide variety of thermosetting molding materials and how to determine the best for a given use.

"Product Design and Molding Technique for Thermosetting Plastics." 16 mm. Mold making and design. Details of construction and action.

CLIMAX MOLYBDENUM COMPANY, 500 Fifth Ave., New York 18: "Alloy Steels—A Story of Their Development." 16 and 35 mm. 20 min. History. Huntsman, Mushet, early alloy steels. High-speed steel. Modern plants and equipment for heat-treating and fabrication.

GENERAL MOTORS CORPORATION, Department of Public Relations, 1775 Broadway, New York 19: "On to Jupiter." 16 mm. 20 min. Through powder metallurgy for example, and through the development of the two-cycle diesel engine, new steel processes, etc., we are advancing to a life that can be more abundant.

INSTITUTE OF VISUAL TRAINING, 40 E. 49th St., New York: "Payloads Pay Off." 16 and 35 mm. 3 reels, 26 min. Material handling, filmed with the cooperation of General Electric Company.

JAM HANDY ORGANIZATION, 2821 E. Grand Blvd., Detroit 11: "Basic Shop Safety." To help promote safety education and to be integrated with shop safety programs.

MODERN PLASTICS MAGAZINE, 122 E. 42d St., New York: "Modern Plastics Preferred." 16 mm. Color. 20 min. Development of the plastics industry.

NATIONAL CARBON COMPANY, INC., 30 E. 42d St., New York: "Carbon—Black Treasure." 16 mm. Characteristics and development of fabricated carbon and its uses. Electric steel manufacture with carbon electrodes.

ROTHACKER, D. D., 729 Seventh Ave., New York 19: "Nickel Tales." 16 mm. 9 min. Made in cooperation with the International Nickel Company. The world's greatest nickel deposit and the use of nickel in transportation, communication, industry, and the home.

"Nickel and Nickel Alloys." 16 mm. 32 min. Made in cooperation with the International Nickel Company. Crushing, grinding, weighing, deoxidizing. Operation of high-frequency electric furnace, arc furnace, open-hearth furnace. Reheating, forging, rolling, machining, chipping, etc.

SIZING AND SHAPING METALLIC BODIES

ALLEGHENY-LUDLUM STEEL CORPORATION, Brackenridge, Pa.: "Exploring with the Microtimer." 16 mm. 30 min. Stainless-steel machining operations filmed in ultraslow motion.

ALUMINUM COMPANY OF AMERICA, 801 Gulf Building, Pittsburgh, Pa.: "Aluminum Fabricating Processes." 16 and 35 mm. 20 min.

"How to Form Aluminum." 16 and 35 mm. (1) General Sheet Metal Practice." 20 min. (2) "Blanking and Piercing." 15 min. (3) "Drawing, Stretching, and Stamping." 22 min. (4) "Tube and Shape Bending." 13 min. (5) "Spinning." 16 min.

"How to Machine Aluminum." 16 and 35 mm. 32 min.

"How to Rivet Aluminum." 16 and 35 mm. 26 min.

LUKENS STEEL COMPANY, Coatesville, Pa.: "World's Largest Plate Mill." 16 mm. 30 min. From open-hearth steelmaking through rolling.

"Head Work." 16 mm. 27 min. Spinning and pressing of ferrous and nonferrous heads, including a steel head clad with silver.

"Steel Shapes for Industry." 16 mm. 20 min. Flame cutting, bending, shearing, pressing, blanking and other processes.

"The Manufacture of Lukens Clad Steels." 16 mm. Silent. 23 min. Assembly and making of nickel-, Inconel- and monel-clad steels.

NATIONAL TUBE COMPANY, P. O. Box 236, Pittsburgh 30: "Walls without Welds." 16 mm. Color. 28 min. Manufacture of seamless steel pipe and steel tubes.

WELDING AND JOINING

ALLEGHENY-LUDLUM STEEL CORPORATION, Brackenridge, Pa.: "Arc Welding Stainless Steel." 16 mm. Color. 20 min.

ALUMINUM COMPANY OF AMERICA, 801 Gulf Building, Pittsburgh, Pa.: "How to Braze Aluminum." 16 and 35 mm. 7 min.

"How to Weld Aluminum." 16 and 35 mm. (1) "Torch Welding." 17 min. (2) "Arc Welding." 10 min. (3) "Resistance Welding." 12 min.

CHICAGO FILM LABORATORY, 1322 Belmont Ave., Chicago: "New Horizons in Welding." 30 min. Welding as a production tool.

GENERAL ELECTRIC COMPANY, 1 River Road, Schenectady, N.Y.: All 16 mm. "The Inside of Arc Welding." 6 parts, each 10 min. "The Inside of Atomic-Hydrogen Arc Welding." 2 parts, each 10 min. "This Is Resistance Welding." Color. 25 min. Spot, seam, and projection welding.

LUKENS STEEL COMPANY, Coatesville, Pa.: "Lukenweld." 16 mm. 20 min. America's first commercial weldery. High lights in construction from steel plate to finished weldment of a modern diesel engine frame. Also other weldments.

U.S. BUREAU OF MINES, EXPERIMENT STATION, 4800 Forbes St., Pittsburgh 13: "Modern Metalworking with the Oxyacetylene Flame." 16 or 35 mm. 2 reels. Made in cooperation with the Union Carbide & Carbon Company.

JAM HANDY ORGANIZATION, 2821 E. Grand Blvd., Detroit 11: "Soldering." A discussional-type slide film, comprising 92 teaching pictures: uses, definition, methods, applications, and safety precautions.

"Oxyacetylene Welding." Discussional-type slide films, containing 742 pictures: steel, aluminum, cutting, brazing, silver soldering.

LINCOLN ELECTRIC COMPANY, 12818 Coit Road, Cleveland 1: This company has many motion-picture films illustrating arc welding. 16 mm.

"Magic Wand of Industry." 3 reels. 26 min. Color.

(Also released by the U.S. Bureau of Mines at Pittsburgh, Pa.) The company should be contacted for other films.

LINDE AIR PRODUCTS COMPANY, 30 E. 42d St., New York: Sixteen different films available on oxyacetylene welding. 16 mm.

MARQUETTE MANUFACTURING COMPANY, INC., Minneapolis 14: "Marquette Story." 16 mm. Color. 33 min. Marquette "instant arc" welders.

METAL & THERMIT CORPORATION, 120 Broadway, New York 5: "Mass Production of Massive Parts." 16 mm. Color. Thermit welding.

LEPEL HIGH FREQUENCY LABORATORIES, INC., 39 W. 60th St., New York: "High Frequency Soldering." 16 mm. 18 min. Operation and theory.

METALLURGICAL INSPECTION AND TESTING

Almost all films on steel manufacture or fabrication devote some space to inspection and testing.

BETHLEHEM STEEL COMPANY, Bethlehem, Pa.: The film "Streamlined Steel" shows tests and inspections made at different steps of steel production. Likewise "Alloy Steel" and "Highlights of Steelmaking," Part II. See under Producing and Refining Iron and Steel.

JONES & LAUGHLIN STEEL CORPORATION, Pittsburgh: "Pilot Mill and Physical Testing." 45 min. Color. Shown only when a representative of the Corporation accompanies the films.

UNITED STATES STEEL CORPORATION, 436 Seventh Ave., Pittsburgh 30: "Steel—Man's Servant" and "The Making and Shaping of Steel" both have views devoted to inspection and testing.

THE HEAT-TREATMENT OF STEEL AND OF NONFERROUS ALLOYS

ALLIS-CHALMERS MANUFACTURING COMPANY, Milwaukee: "Metal Magic." 16 mm. Color. 12 min. Demonstrates modern induction heating.

American Society for Metals, 7301 Euclid Ave., Cleveland: "Metal Crystals." 16 mm. Especially adapted to explain the structure of metals and the building of an equilibrium diagram.

Westinghouse Electric Corporation, Pittsburgh 30: "Radio Frequency Heating." 16 mm. Either color or black and white. 40 min. Part I, Theory of Induction Heating, showing applications to soldering, brazing, annealing, and hardening. Part II, Theory of Dielectric Heating, dealing with preheating of plastic preforms, bonding of laminates and plywood, textile drying, curing and drying of rubber, and other applications.

Properties and Uses of Iron and Steel

American Institute of Steel Construction, Inc., 200 Madison Ave, New York: "The Backbone of Progress," 16 and 35 mm, sound. 16 mm, silent only. 30 min. How steel has built the world of today, and why it is better as a building material.

"Empires of Steel." 16 mm. 3 reels. 40 min. Fabrication and erection of the steel in the Empire State Building in New York City.

"Bridging Marble Canyon." 16 mm. 10 min. How a steel arch bridge was constructed across Marble Canyon, miles away from the railway.

Bethlehem Steel Company, Bethlehem, Pa.: "Building the Golden Gate Bridge." 16 mm. 45 min. The longest suspension span in the world (1948).

John A. Roebling's Sons Co., Trenton, N.J.: "Span Supreme," 35 mm. 4 reels. 60 min. Erection of the George Washington Bridge across the Hudson River.

"Bridging a Century." 16 mm. 4 reels. 45 min. The Golden Gate Bridge (San Francisco), the longest suspension span in the world (1948). Also views of the Brooklyn Bridge and an account of wiremaking.

Meehanite Metal Corporation, New Rochelle, N.Y.: "Meehanite Means Better Castings." 16 mm. 29 min. Characteristics and applications of Meehanite castings.

United States Steel Corporation, 436 Seventh Ave., Pittsburgh 30: "Building for the Nation." 16 mm. Color. 35 min. Making and fabricating steel sections into structural units, and erecting them.

Properties and Uses of Nonferrous Metals

Aluminum Company of America, 801 Gulf Building, Pittsburgh: "Aluminum Fabricating Processes." 16 and 35 mm. 20 min.

"This Is Aluminum." 16 and 35 mm. 35 min.

"How to Form Aluminum." 16 and 35 mm. (1) "General Sheet Metal Practice." 20 min. (2) "Blanking and Piercing." 15 min. (3) "Drawing, Stretching, and Stamping." 22 min. (4) "Tube and Shape Bending." 13 min. (5) "Spinning." 16 min.

"How to Machine Aluminum." 16 and 35 mm. 32 min.

"How to Rivet Aluminum." 16 and 35 mm. 26 min.

"How to Braze Aluminum." 16 and 35 mm. 7 min.

"How to Weld Aluminum." 16 and 35 mm. (1) "Torch Welding." 17 min. (2) "Arc Welding." 10 min. (3) "Resistance Welding." 12 min.

(The above may be obtained also from U.S. Bureau of Mines, Experiment Station, 4800 Forbes St., Pittsburgh 13.)

Ampco Metal Company, Inc., 1745 S. 38th St., Milwaukee 4: "Golden Horizons." 16 mm. Color. History, development, manufacture, and applications of aluminum bronze and other copper-base alloys.

BETHLEHEM STEEL COMPANY, Bethlehem, Pa.: "Steel Plus." 16 mm. 45 min. Manufacture of tin plate; both hot-dip and electrotinning processes.

DOW CHEMICAL COMPANY, Midland, Mich.: "Magnesium." Forming, machining, riveting, welding, and surface treatment.

HILLS-MCCANNA COMPANY, 3025 N. Western Ave., Chicago 18: "Magnesium—the Miracle Metal." Alloys, fabrication, properties, and uses.

NEW JERSEY ZINC COMPANY, 160 Front St., New York, N.Y.: "Die Casting." 16 mm. Color. 30 min. Methods, equipment, and applications of die casting. In addition to zinc-base, there are included aluminum-base, magnesium-base, and brass die castings.

REYNOLDS METALS COMPANY, 2000 S. Ninth St., Louisville 1, Ky.: "Pigs and Progress." 16 mm. Color. Mining of bauxite, conversion to pure alumina, electrolytic reduction, mill fabrication, applications of aluminum and its alloys.

U.S. BUREAU OF MINES, EXPERIMENT STATION, 4800 Forbes St., Pittsburgh 13: "Fabrication of Copper." 16 and 35 mm. Silent. 3 reels. Rolling, wire and cable manufacture, making pipe and tubing, extrusion, forging, etc. (Phelps Dodge Copper Products Corporation).

CORROSION AND ITS PREVENTION

ALLEGHENY-LUDLUM STEEL CORPORATION, Brackenridge, Pa.: "Corrosion." 16 mm. Color. 10 min. Mechanism of corrosive attack and development of stainless steels.

INTERNATIONAL NICKEL CO., INC., 67 Wall St., New York 5: "Corrosion in Action." 16 mm. Color. Part 1, 20 min. Part 2, 26 min. Part 3, 17 min. Theory of corrosion, passivity, electrolytes, corrosion resistant alloys, corrosion potentials, protective films, etc.

LUKENS STEEL COMPANY, Coatesville, Pa.: "Solving Corrosion Problems." 16 mm. Color. 13 min. General problems of corrosion in processing industries, combatting corrosion, and use of nickel-clad, Inconel-clad, and monel-clad steels.

PRODUCING AND REFINING IRON AND STEEL

Almost all the steel companies have motion pictures of their operations. Many of these are in color, showing the brilliant reds and yellows of high temperatures. Many companies are glad to furnish speakers with the pictures, who will explain the operations. Some outstanding pictures which are readily available are listed below:

BETHLEHEM STEEL COMPANY, Bethlehem, Pa.: "Streamlined Steel." 16 mm. 45 min. From ore to finished product; especially hot-rolled and cold-rolled sheets and coiled strip.

"Sinews of Steel." 16 mm. 45 min. From ore to finished wire rope.

"Alloy Steels—A Picture of Controlled Production." 16 and 35 mm. 45 min. From open hearth to loading alloy-steel bars, including inspections and tests.

"Highlights in Steelmaking." 16 mm. 2 reels, 45 min. each. First reel is from ore to rolling of ingots; the second covers rolling, chipping, heat-treating, testing, etc.

"This is Steel." 16 mm. 28 min. From ore through steel manufacturing processes; includes some testing and inspection.

UNITED STATES STEEL CORPORATION, 436 Seventh Ave., Pittsburgh 30: "Steel—Man's Servant," From ore to finished product.

"The Making and Shaping of Steel." 7 reels, 16 and 35 mm. From ore to finished product. Each reel is complete in itself. The first two reels describe the basic operations. More recent than "Man's Servant."

ALLEGHENY-LUDLUM STEEL CORPORATION, Brackenridge, Pa.: "Steel for the Ages." 16 mm. Color. 30 min. Production of high-alloy steels.
"Stainless Steel." 16 mm. 30 min. Especially adapted for students.

AMERICAN INSTITUTE OF STEEL CONSTRUCTION, INC., 200 Madison Ave., New York: "Steel." 16 mm. 2 reels, 20 min total. Produced by the American Iron and Steel Institute to illustrate the making of steel from the raw material to the rolled product.

A. M. BYERS COMPANY, Pittsburgh: "Eternally Yours." 16 and 35 mm. History and development of processes; also the Aston process for making wrought iron. Properties, corrosion resistance, life, fabrication, and uses.

JONES & LAUGHLIN STEEL CORPORATION, Pittsburgh: This corporation has a number of motion-picture films in black and white and in color; only shown when a representative accompanies.

BRAY PICTURES CORPORATION, 729 Seventh Ave., New York: "The Manufacture of Pig Iron." 16 mm. Silent. ½ reel.
"Bessemer and Open Hearth Steel." 16 mm. Silent. ½ reel.

COLUMBIA TOOL STEEL COMPANY, Chicago Heights, Ill. Colored film showing remarkably well the heat colors of the various operations. 16 mm. Would prefer not to place this in the hands of others, but will send the film with representative to locations in Ohio, Michigan, Wisconsin, Indiana, Illinois, or Missouri.

REPUBLIC STEEL CORPORATION, Cleveland: "Enduro" (a stainless steel). 16 mm. 40 min. It is the custom of the Republic Steel Corporation to send equipment and a representative with the film. From ore to finished product.
"Woven Wire Fence." 16 mm. 45 min.

UDDEHOLM COMPANY OF AMERICA, INC., 155 E. 44th St., New York: "Uddeholm, One of the World's Truly Remarkable Industries—Where Iron Ore Becomes Watch Springs and Forest Becomes Silk." 16 mm. 30 min. Depicting Swedish iron and steelmaking with interesting side lights on Sweden.

VULCAN CRUCIBLE STEEL COMPANY, Aliquippa, Pa.: "The Making of Fine Tool Steel." 16 mm. Silent, but in full color. 50 min. Sent only with a representative of the company. Shortened edition, 16 mm. Silent. 30 min. Sent without company representative if desired.

MALLEABLE IRON FOUNDERS' SOCIETY, Union Commerce Building, Cleveland: "This Moving World; the Story of Malleable Iron, How It is Made, Tested, and Used." Color.

U.S. BUREAU OF MINES, Experiment Station, 4800 Forbes St., Pittsburgh 13: "The Drama of Steel." 16 mm. 34 min. Manufacture and uses. History of producing steel and iron castings. Ore mining, loading, coke manufacture, blast furnace, open-hearth steel manufacture, rolling, annealing, tempering, coating, fabricating, and uses. Made in cooperation with Inland Steel Company.

PRODUCING AND REFINING NONFERROUS METALS

ALUMINUM COMPANY OF AMERICA, 801 Gulf Building, Pittsburgh: "Unfinished Rainbows." 16 and 35 mm. Color. 37 min. History, development, and applications of aluminum.
"Dateline Tomorrow." 16 and 35 mm. 19 min. Development and applications of aluminum.
"Curiosity Shop." 16 and 35 mm. 30 min.

AMERICAN BRASS COMPANY, Waterbury, Conn.: "Open-pit Copper Mining in Chile." 16 mm. Color. 16 min. Mining, crushing, leaching, electrodeposition, and casting at Chuquicamata (Chile Exploration Company).

"Operations of the Cananea Consolidated Copper Company." 16 mm. Color. Mining and metallurgy of copper at Cananea, Mexico.

ANACONDA COPPER MINING COMPANY, 25 Broadway, New York 4: "Copper Mining, Smelting, and Refining." 16 mm. Color. 35 min. Operations at the company's plants in Montana.

U.S. BUREAU OF MINES, EXPERIMENT STATION, 4800 Forbes St., Pittsburgh 13: "Aluminum—Mine to Metal." 16 mm, sound. 16 and 35 mm, silent. 28 min. Mining and purification of bauxite, electrolytic reduction, fabrication, uses, testing (Aluminum Company of America).

"Aluminum—Fabricating Processes." 16 mm; sound. 16 and 35 mm; silent. 19 min. Rolling, cable manufacture, extrusion, forging, casting, die casting, welding, testing, etc.

"A Story of Copper." 16 mm. 34 min. Mining, concentration, smelting, refining (Phelps Dodge Corporation).

"Copper Leaching and Concentration." 16 and 35 mm. Silent. 1 reel (Phelps Dodge Corporation).

"Copper Refining." 16 and 35 mm. Silent. 1 reel. Electrolytic refining, cathode melting and casting (Phelps Dodge Corporation).

"Copper Smelting." 16 and 35 mm. Silent. 1 reel. Roasting and reverberatory smelting (Phelps Dodge Corporation).

"Lead Milling, Smelting, and Refining." 16 mm. 34 min (St. Joseph Lead Company).

"Magnesium—Metal from the Sea." 16 mm. 23 min. Properties, applications, and production processes (Dow Chemical Company).

"Tin from Bolivia." 16 mm. 20 min. Uses, mining, concentration, smelting, refining (Patino Mines and Enterprises Consolidated, Inc.).

"Story of Nickel." 16 mm. 35 min. Mining, milling, smelting, and refining of nickel (International Nickel Company).

"Nickel Tales." 16 mm. 9 min.

"Nickel Milling and Smelting." 16 mm. 18 min. International Nickel Company operations.

"Nickel Refining." 16 mm. 9 min. International Nickel Company operations.

"Nickel and Nickel Alloys." 16 mm. 32 min. Melting in electric and open-hearth furnaces, rolling and other working operations, surface finishing, etc. (These are obtainable also from D. D. Rothacker, 729 Seventh Ave., New York 19.)

WOLVERINE TUBE DIVISION, CALUMET & HECLA CONSOLIDATED COPPER COMPANY: "Copper Tubing." 16 mm. Color. 30 min. Operations from mine to the finished tubing.

INDEX

A

Abrasion tests, 130
Accelerated aging, 192
Acoustic tests, 145
Admiralty metal, 263
Aging, aluminum alloys, 294
  steel, 209, 213
  strain, 213
  theory, 192
Alclad, 284
Allotropic forms of iron, 164, 167
Alloy cast iron, 223
Alloy steels, AISI classification, 230
  alloying elements, effects, 230
  boron in, 232
  chromium, 234, 238
  cobalt, 316
  constructional, properties (table), 235
  copper, 233
  creep curves, 32
  elastic modulus, 215
  hardenability, 232
  hardness, 196, 202
  heat-treatment, 236
  high-speed, 236
  history, 229
  magnetic, 238
  manganese, 234
  molybdenum, 321
  nickel, 233
  nickel-chromium, 233
  prices, 229
  properties, 228
    table, 10, 11, 235
  purposes of alloying, 228
  strength-weight factors, 330
  stress-strain diagram, 14
  tempering, 232
  tensile strength, 196
  tungsten, 318
  vanadium, 236
Alloys, aluminum, 287, 291
  aluminum-copper, 293
  beryllium copper, 266
  bibliography, 169
  cobalt, 315
  constitution, 25
  copper, 254
  cupronickel, 267

Alloys, definition, 8, 150
  eutectic, 155
  eutectoid, 159
  freezing, 152, 155
  fusible, 162
  gold, 324
  heat-resisting, 336
  iron-carbon, 164–169, 171–195
  lead, 278
  lead-tin, 162
  magnesium, 303
  mechanical properties (table), 10
  molybdenum, 321
  nickel, 312, 392
  nonferrous, 191, 261
  primary crystals, 160
  properties, 8, 151, 161
    variation of, 161, 162
  silver, 324
  size of crystals, 160
  solid-solution, 152
  structure, 151
  tin, 309
  tin-lead, 162
  types, 152
  zinc, 271
Alnico, 24, 313
Alumilite process, 285
Alumina-silica diagram, 55
Aluminum, alclad, 284
  anodizing, 285, 350
  bauxite purification, 404
  Bayer process, 404
  calorizing, 355
  casting, 285
  cold welding, 97
  corrosion resistance, 283
  ductility, 285
  electrical conductivity, 283
  endurance limit, 20
  Hall-Héroult process, 406
  hardness, 285
  lime-soda sinter process, 405
  machinability ratings, 91
  marketed forms, 296
  microstructure, 298
  production and value, 42
  production processes, 404
  properties, 281–285
    table, 24

Aluminum, refining, 407
  rolling, 286
  specific gravity, 281
  specifications, 297
  in steel deoxidation, 197, 368
  strength, 281
  strength-weight factors, 330, 331
  thermal properties, 283
  uses, 296
  welding and soldering, 286
  wire drawing, 286
  working temperatures, 74
Aluminum alloys, 287
  age hardening, 192, 294
  composition (table), 291
  heat-treatment, 292
  microstructure, 297, 298
  properties (table), 10, 295
Aluminum bronze, 265
Aluminum castings, 285
Aluminum-copper constitution diagram, 293
Aluminum-silicon alloys, 290
Amalgamation, gold and silver, 414
American Iron and Steel Institute (AISI) classification of steels, 230
Analysis, chemical, 122
  spectrographic, 122
Annealing, nonferrous metals, 193
  steel, 188
Anodizing, 285, 350
Antimonial lead, 276
Antimony, in bearing alloys, 163
  crystal growth, 28
  mechanical treatment, 74
  production processes, 404
  properties (table), 10, 24
Antimony-lead diagram, 54
Arc furnaces, 421
Arc welding, 103, 110
Atomic-energy development, use of metals, 337
Atomic hydrogen arc welding, 104
Austempering, 175
Austenite, 167, 170
Austenitic grain size, 136, 206, 368
Automobile manufacture, use of metals, 331

B

Babbitt, Issac, 309
Babbitt (metal), 309
Bain, E. C., 175, 180, 231
Bainite, 179, 180
Baur, J., 229
Bauxite purification, 404

Bayer process, alumina, 404
Bearing metals, 163
Bend test of fusion weld, 111
Beryllium, in atomic-energy development, 338
  in magnesium, 301
  production processes, 409
  properties, 321
Beryllium copper, 266, 322
Bessemer process, 364, 369, 370
Bethanizing, 271
Bibliography, alloys, 169
  corrosion, 356
  fuels and combustion, 441
  furnaces and refractories, 441
  heat-treatment, 194
  inspection and testing, 148
  iron and steel, 241, 380
  metals, as materials of construction, 37
  nonferrous, 325, 416
  production metallurgy, 63
  sizing and shaping, 95
  temperature measurement, 455
  welding, 117
Bismuth, mechanical treatment, 74
  properties (table), 10, 24
Black-body conditions, 453
Blast furnaces, construction, 426
  gases, 363
  iron, 358
  lead, 393
  temperature regulation, 363
  top-pressure, 360
Blowholes, 374
Blue heat in steel, 210, 211
Blue powder, 398
Boiling points, 22
  table, 24
Bolton, J. W., 218
Bornstein, H., 218
Boron in steel, 232
Brass, alpha, 256–258
  beta, 256–258
  cartridge, 263
  cartridge-case manufacture, 80
  classifications, 256
  cold drawing, 80, 83
  color, 247, 256
  composition, 255
  corrosion, 262
  dezincification, 262, 346
  endurance limit, 20
  fabrication, 258
  grain size, 137, 259, 261
  leaded, 263
  machinability ratings, 91
  nickel in, 263

INDEX

Brass, properties (table), 10
  season cracking, 262
  stress-strain diagram, 14
  uses, 260
  varieties, 263
  working temperatures, 74
  zinc content, effect of, 256, 258
Brazing, 98, 113
Bridges, use of metals in, 333
Brinell hardness, 21, 22
Brinell-hardness tester, 127
Brittle failure, 29, 33
Brittle range, steel, 210, 211
Brittleness, 18
Bronze, aluminum, 265
  bearing alloys, 163
  manganese, 263
  mechanical treatment, 74
  phosphor, 265
  properties (table), 10
  silicon, 265
  varieties, 264
Bullens, D. K., 231
Butt welding, 101
By-product coking, 435

C

Cadmium, production processes, 403
  properties (table), 24
  in zinc, 274
Calcining, 49
Calorizing, 355
Carbides in alloy steels, 232
Carboloy, 316, 319
Carbon, effect of, on hardness of steel, 199
  on iron (table), 198
Carbon content of steels (table), 200
Carbonitriding, 182
Carburization, 140, 182
Cartridge brass, 263
Cartridge-case manufacture, 80
Casehardening, 182–184
Cast iron, alloy, 223
  chilled, 218, 221
  compositions, 219, 222
  corrosion, 353
  corrosion-resistant, 221
  damping, 223
  ductile, 224, 225
  elastic modulus, 215
  graphite in, 218, 222, 224–226
  gray, 218, 220, 226
  heat-treatment, 224
  high-strength, 221
  machinability, 91
  malleable, 226

Cast iron, Meehanite, 223
  Ni-resist, 221
  pearlitic, 222, 227
  phosphorus in, 220
  properties, 168, 218–223
    control, 220
    table, 11
  stress-strain diagram, 14
  uses, 363
  white, 219
Casting, 65–73
  aluminum, 285
  centrifugal, 67
  continuous (*see* Continuous casting)
  copper, 248, 251, 387
  die, 70, 272
Cathodic protection, 351
Caustic embrittlement, 348
Cells, unit, 25, 26, 28
Cementation, 57
Cementite, 164, 168
Centrifugal casting, 67
Charpy test, 16
Chemical analysis, 122
Chemical elements, 8, 40
Chemical metallurgy, 1
Chemical strength, 45
Chemistry, iron smelting, 360, 361
  open-hearth process, 365
  steel manufacture, 365
Chilled cast iron, 218, 221
Chipman, J., 337n.
Chromium, in nickel alloys, 314
  properties (table), 24
  in steel, 233
  uses, 416
Chromium-nickel steels, 238
Chromium plating, 352, 416
Chromium steels, 234, 238
Civilization, dependence on metals, 3
Clarke, F. W., 41
Coal, 433
  pulverized, 440
Cobalt, production processes, 396
  properties, 10, 24, 315
  working temperatures, 74
Cobalt alloys, 315
Coercive force, 24
Cohesion and strength, 29
Coke, by-product process, 435
  characteristics, 434
Cold drawing, 83
  effects on metals (table), 83
Cold rolling, 82
Cold welding, 97
Cold work, effect on copper, 246
Cold working, 79–88

Color of metals, 25
Composition, aluminum alloys (table), 291
  brass, 255
  copper alloys (table), 255
  earth's crust, 41
  iron castings, 219, 222
  magnesium alloys (table), 303
  magnet steels (table), 240
  slags (table), 56
  stainless steels (table), 239
  steel, 164, 197
Concentration of ores, 44
Conductivity, aluminum, 283
  copper, 244
  electrical, 23
    iron and steel, 217
    metals (table), 24
    variation of, in alloys, 161, 162
  IACS, 245
  mass, 245
  silver, 323
  thermal, 23
Cone test, 132, 180
Constantan, 314
Constitution of metals and alloys, 25
Constitution diagram (see Equilibrium diagram)
Continuous casting, 72
  copper, 248
  steel, 378
Contraction, thermal, 25
Controlled atmospheres in furnaces, 425
Converting, 51, 384
Copper, in aluminum alloys, 293
  analysis, wirebars, 250
  anode furnace, 386
  casting, 248, 251, 387
    continuous, 248
  cementation, 390
  color, 246
  converting, 384
  corrosion, 246
  deoxidized, 251
  ductility, 247
  effect of cold work, 246
  electrical conductivity, 244
  electroposition from leaching solutions, 391
  electrolytic refining, 388
  endurance limit, 20
  fabrication, 251
  flowsheet of extraction and refining, 383
  furnace refining, 386
  hardness, 248
  hydrometallurgy, 390

Copper, impurities in, 249
  lake copper, 389
  machinability, 253
  malleability, 247
  marketed forms, 248
  ores, 383
  oxygen in, 250, 251
  oxygen-free, 250, 251
  phosphorized, 251
  production and value, 42
  production methods, 383
  properties (table), 10, 24
  rolling, 252
  smelting, 384
    slag composition, 56
  specifications, 253
  in steel, 205, 233
  tellurium, 253
  tensile properties, 247
  tinned wire, 306
  tough-pitch, 249, 250
  toughness, 248
  uses, 253
  wire drawing, 252
  working temperatures, 74
  in zinc alloys, 273
Copper alloys, 254–267
  machinability ratings, 91
Copper-nickel alloys, 267, 313
Copper-zinc constitution diagram, 257
Corrosion, agents, 340
  bibliography, 356
  brass, 262
  cathodic protection, 351
  coatings, comparison, 352
  electrochemical, 341
  equations, 356
  erosion-corrosion, 346, 347
  films, 341, 355
  forms of, 345
  galvanic protection, 352
  high-temperature, 354
  inhibitors, 345
  intergranular, 348
  passivity, 345
  pitting, 345
  potential differences, 341
  prevention, 345, 349
  rates, 355
  reactions, types of, 343
  stress-, 348
  surface treatments for, 350, 351
  testing, 354
  theory, 341, 355
Corrosion fatigue, 19, 215
Corrosion-fatigue strength, metals (table), 20

INDEX

Corrosion resistance, aluminum, 283
  cast iron, 221
  causes of, 344
  copper, 246
  iron and steel, comparative, 353
  lead, 276
  magnesium, 302
  nickel, 311
  tin, 306
  titanium, 323
  zinc, 269
Creep, in metals, 31
  in steel, 212
Creep limit, 31
Critical points in steel, 168, 170
Crucible steel, 364, 373
Crystals, metal, 27
Cupronickel, 267
Curie point, 23, 167, 315
Cutting metals, 114
Cyanidation of gold and silver, 414

D

Damascus, swords of, 3
Damping of cast iron, 223
Davenport, E. S., 175
Decarburization, 140
Deep-etch test, 132, 134
Defects, in rolling or forging, 75
  in steel, 134, 197, 374
Deformation, 30, 33
Dendritic structure, 27, 210
Density and porosity, 25
Detinning, 396
Dezincification, 262, 346
Die casting, 70, 272
Directional properties of iron and steel, 218
Distillation, 53
  zinc, 398
Divisions of metallurgy, 1
Drawing, steel treatment, 184–188
Drop forging, 76
Ductile and brittle fracture, 17
Ductile cast iron, 224, 225
  properties (table), 11
Ductile metals, flow, 30
Ductility, aluminum, 285
  copper, 247
  definition, 15
  measurement, 15
  slow-bend, 211
  tests, 130
  welds, 108
Duralumin, composition, 291
  endurance limit, 20
  working temperatures, 74

E

Earth's crust, composition, 41
Effects, comparative, of cold working, 79
  of rolling and forging, 76
Efficiency of welds, 99, 101, 110
Elastic limit, 13
Elastic modulus, 12, 29
  iron and steel, 215
  magnesium, 299
  metals and alloys (table), 10
Elasticity, 12, 34
Electric furnaces, 372, 420–426
Electric smelting, 62
  zinc, 403
Electric steel, 364, 371, 373
Electric welding, 100–103, 110
Electrical conductivity (*see* Conductivity)
Electrical tests of metals, 146
Electrodeposition from leaching solutions, copper, 391
  zinc, 401
Electroforming, 62
Electrogalvanizing, 270
Electrolysis, 58
  fused salts, 59, 406, 408
Electrolytic precipitation, 61
Electrolytic refining, 60
  copper, 388
  lead, 395
  nickel, 392
Electrometallurgy, 58
Electron micrographs, 304, 411
Electroplating, 61, 352
Electropotential series of metals (table), 46
Electrothermic processes, 62
Electrotinning, 308
Elements, chemical, 40
Elongation, aluminum alloys, 295
  iron and steel products (table), 11
  metals and alloys (table), 10
  steel, 210
Endurance limit, aluminum alloys, 295
  iron and steel products (table), 11
  metals (table), 20
  and alloys (table), 10
  steel, 215
Epstein, S., 214
Equilibrium diagram, aluminum-copper, 293
  antimony-lead, 54
  construction of, 156, 157
  copper-zinc, 257
  iron-carbon, 165, 171
  lead-tin, 163

Equilibrium diagram, silica-alumina, 55
　types, 154, 157, 158
Erosion-corrosion, 346, 347
Eutectic, 155
Eutectoid, 159
Evans, U. R., 340
Expansion, thermal, 25
Expansion thermometers, 444, 454
Extension-under-load method for yield strength, 14
Extensometer, 126
Extrusion, 79, 288

F

Failure, brittle, 33
　fatigue, 18
　temperature effect, 33
　types of, 29
Faraday's laws, 59
Fatigue, corrosion, 19
Fatigue failure, 18
Fatigue limit (see Endurance limit)
Fatigue strength, corrosion-, metals (table), 20
　steel, 215
Fatigue stresses, 19, 333
Ferrite, 164
Ferroalloys, production processes, 415
Ferrochromium, 416
Ferromanganese, 415
Ferrosilicon, 415
Finishing temperatures, hot working, 78
Flame hardening, 181
Flame machining, 117
Flame softening, 190
Flash welding, 101
Flotation, 44
Flow, plastic, 30
Flue dust and fume, 51
Fluorescent penetrant test, 143
Fluxes, 55
Fluxing, 54
Fontana, M. G., 345
Forging, 68, 69, 75, 76, 287
Foundry operations, 65-70
Fractography, 139
Fracture, brittle, 17
　ductile, 17
　tensile, 126
　wrought iron, 127
Frederickson, A. F., 337
Freezing of metals, 27
Freezing-point curves, 152, 153, 156
Fuels, bibliography, 441
　classification, 432

Fuels, coal, 433
　coke, 434
　natural gas, 433, 438
　oil, 435
　producer gas, 439
　pulverized coal, 440
　relative importance, 433
Furnaces, bibliography, 441
　classification, 418
　controlled-atmosphere, 425
　electric (see Electric furnaces)
　fuel-fired, 418
　heat losses, 430
　heating, 425
　induction, 422-424
　melting, 424
　open-hearth, 366
　regenerative, 366, 430
　retort, zinc, 399
　reverberatory, copper, 384, 385, 386, 419
Fused salts, electrolysis, 406, 408
Fusibility, 22
Fusible alloys, 162
Fusion welding, 102, 107

G

Galvanic protection in corrosion, 352
Galvanized iron, 270, 352
Galvanizing, 269, 275
Gangue, 43
Gas, coke-oven, 436, 438
　as fuel, 438
　natural, 433, 438
　producer, 439
Gas welding, 99, 108, 112
Gases, furnace, 51
　in steel, 205
Gensamer, M., 214
Gold, production and value, 42
　production processes, 414
　properties, 323
　uses, 323
Gold alloys, 324
Grain size, austenitic, 136, 206, 368
　brass, 137, 259, 261
　magnesium, 300
　steel, 138, 205
Grain-size chart, nonferrous alloys, 261
　steel, 208
Grant, N. J., 337
Graphite in cast iron, 218, 222, 224-226
Gravity separation, 44
Gray cast iron, 218, 220, 226
Grossman, M. A., 178, 229

INDEX

H

Hall-Héroult process, 406
Hammer welding, 98
Hansgirg process, magnesium, 409
Hard lead, 276
Hard surfacing, 114
Hardenability, cone test, 132
  curves, 178, 179
  effect of alloying elements on, 232
  nature of, 176
  testing, 177
Hardening, casehardening, 182–184
  differential, 180
  flame, 181
  induction, 181
  precipitation, 192, 209, 266, 293
  secondary, 187
  surface, 181
Hardness, aluminum, 285
  aluminum alloys, 295
  Brinell, 21, 22
  conversion table, 21
  copper, 248
  heat-treating for, 190
  iron and steel products (table), 11
  nature of, 20, 35
  relation to strength, 195, 196
  steel, 202, 216
  variation of, in alloys, 161, 162
Hardness numbers, conversion table, 21
Hardness tests, 126–129
Hastelloy, 315
Heat conductivities (table), 24
Heat conductivity of metals, 23
Heat losses in furnaces, 430
Heat-resisting alloys, 336
Heat-treatment, alloy steels, 236
  aluminum alloys, 292
  beryllium copper, 266
  bibliography, 194
  cast iron, 224
  furnaces, 425, 426
  nonferrous alloys, 191
  precipitation hardening, 192
  steel 170–191
Heats of formation, oxides (table), 48
Heussler's alloy, 24
High-frequency induction heating, 423
High-speed steel, 236
High-strength cast iron, 221
High-temperature corrosion, 354
High-temperature metals and alloys, 334
High-temperature properties of steel, 210, 211
High-temperature strength, 18, 32
Hipernik, 313

History of metallurgy, 2
Hot vs. cold work, 87
Howe, H. M., 236
Howe's color scale, 443
Hudson, J. C., 340
Hydrometallurgy, 56
  copper, 390
  gold and silver, 414
  zinc, 401
Hypo- and hypereutectoid steel, 170, 173
Hysteresis, 24
Hysteresis curves, 217

I

Illium, 315
Impact extrusion, 307
Impact strength, 16
  iron and steel products (table), 11
  steel, 214
Impact test specimens, standard, 130
Impact tests, 129, 211
Impurities, in copper, 249
  in metals, 52
  in steel, 197, 203
  in zinc, 273
Inclusions in steel, 204, 374
Inconel, 314
Induction hardening, 181
Induction heating, 422–424
Inert gas welding, 105
Ingot iron, 195
Ingots, steel, 374
Inhibitors, 345
Inspection, casehardened parts, 184
  metallurgical, 119–122, 141–147
Intergranular corrosion, 348
International Annealed Copper Standard (IACS), 245
Invar, 313
Investment casting, 71
Iodide process, titanium, 413
Iron, allotropic forms, 164, 167
  blast furnace, 358
  cast (see Cast iron)
  commercial forms, 357
  corrosion, 343
  effects of carbon (table), 198
  galvanized, 270
  ingot, 195
  malleable (see Malleable iron)
  pig (see Pig iron)
  production and value, 42
  properties (table), 10, 11, 24
  smelting, 56, 358
  and steel, bibliography, 241, 380
    corrosion, comparative, 353

Iron, and steel, directional properties, 218
  elastic modulus, 215
  electrical conductivity, 217
  hysteresis curves, 217
  manufacture, processes, 364, 378
  phosphating, 351
  working temperatures, 74
  wrought (*see* Wrought iron)
Iron-carbon alloys, 164–169, 171–195
Isothermal transformation curves, 174, 175, 191
Izod test, 16

J

Jominy test, 179

K

Kanter, J. J., 212
Kennametal, 319
Knerr, H. C., 330
Kroll process, titanium, 413

L

Leaching, 57
Lead, blast furnace, 393
  in copper and brass, 263
  corrosion resistance, 276
  desilverization, 395
  fusibility, 277
  marketed grades, 279
  ore hearth, 394
  production and value, 42
  production processes, 393
  properties, 10, 24, 276
  smelting, 393
    slag composition, 56
  softening, 394
  specifications, 279
  storage batteries, 277
  uses, 275, 277, 279
  working temperatures, 74
Lead alloys, 278
Lead-antimony diagram, 54
Lead burning, 108
Lead poisoning, 277
Lead-tin alloys, 162
Le Châtelier, H., 445
Liquation, 53, 401
Liquid shaping, 65, 67
Liquidus, 153
Literature, metallurgical, 5

M

McAdam, D. J., Jr., 20
McDonald, H. J., 348
McQuaid-Ehn test, 136, 206

Machinability, 88
  copper, 253
  ratings (table), 91
  relation to properties and structure, 90
  steel, 216
Machine design, use of metals, 332
Machining, 88
  flame, 117
  spark, 92
Magnesium, corrosion, 302
  electrolytic process, 408
  fabrication, 300
  grain refinement, 300
  inflammability, 301
  oxidation, 301
  production processes, 407
  properties, 10, 24, 298
  sea-water process, 408
  sources, 408
  surface treatment, 302
  uses, 305
  vaporizing processes, 409
  welding, 301
  working temperatures, 74
Magnesium alloys, compositions and uses (table), 303
  machinability, 91
  properties (table), 10
Magnet steels (table), 240
Magnetic-field testing, 144
Magnetic-particle inspection, 142
Magnetic permeability of steel, 216, 238
Magnetic steels, 238
Magnetism, 23
  in nickel, 311
Malleability, 17
Malleable iron, 226
  elastic modulus, 215
  machinability, 91
  properties (table), 11
Manganese, ferroalloys, 415
  in open-hearth process, 367
  properties, 24
  in steel, 197, 202
  in steel production, 373
Manganese bronze, 10, 263
Manganese steels, 234
Manufactures, metallurgical, 1
Martempering, 175
Martensite, 171, 172
Mass conductivity, 245
Matte, 50
Matte flotation, nickel, 392
Mechanical metallurgy, 1
Mechanical processes, types, 65
Mechanical properties, determination, 124

INDEX

Mechanical properties, iron and steel products (table), 11
   metals and alloys (table), 10
Mechanical treatment, temperatures (table), 74
Mechanical work, effect on properties, 212
Meehanite, 223
Melting point, 22
Melting points of metals (table), 24
Mercury, properties, 24
Mercury thermometers, 444, 453
Metal crystals, 27, 28
Metal-joining processes (table), 99
Metal powders, methods of making, 94
Metallizing, 114, 271
Metalloids, 8
Metallurgy, chemical, 1
   definition, 1
   divisions, 1, 45
   electrometallurgy, 58
   history, 2
   hydrometallurgy, 56
   mechanical, 1
   periodicals, 6
   physical, 1
   powder, 92
   problems, use of, 5
   pyrometallurgy, 48
   value of products, 1
   welding, 109
Metals, application, examples, 328
   in atomic-energy development, 337
   in automobile manufacture, 331
   bearing, 163
   chemical analysis, 122
   and civilization, 3
   commercially used, 9
   constitution, 25
   corrosion-resistant, 344
   creep in, 31
   cutting, 114
   definition, 8
   effect of temperature, 35
   electropotential series (table), 46
   freezing, 151
   heat-resisting applications, 334
   high-temperature service, 334
   history, 2
   inspection, 119–122, 141–147
   machinability ratings (table), 91
   in machine design, 332
   magnetic, 23
   as materials of construction, 8
   mechanical properties (table), 10
   oxides, heats of formation (table), 48
   prices (table), 42, 329

Metals, properties, classes, 8
   physical, 22
      table, 24
   in roalroad rolling stock, 332
   recrystallization temperatures (table), 81
   shaping, 64–96
   sources, 40
   specifications, 120
   in static structures, 333
   strength, 9
   strength-weight factors (table), 330
   testing, 119–149
   value, total (table), 42
   and wealth, 4
   welding, 97–118
   working temperatures, 74, 77
   world production (table), 42
Metcalf test, 133
Mineral preparation, 44
Minerals, 42
Microhardness tests, 126, 129
Microscopic examination, 133, 136
Modulus, of elasticity (*see* Elastic modulus)
   of rigidity, steel, 215
Molybdenum, production processes, 412
   properties, 320
      table, 10, 24
   workability, 74
Molybdenum steels, 321
Mond process, nickel, 392
Monel, cold-drawing effect, 83
   endurance limit, 20
   production process, 392
   properties, 10, 313
   working temperatures, 74
Motion pictures, list of, 457
Muntz metal, 263

N

National Emergency (N.E.) steels, 230, 320
Natural gas, 433, 438
Nickel, in brass, 263
   cold drawing, effect of, 83
   electrolytic refining, 392
   marketed forms, 310
   matte flotation, 391
   Mond process, 392
   production and value, 42
   production processes, 391
   properties, 10, 24, 311
   in steel, 205, 233
   uses, 310, 311
   working temperatures, 74

Nickel alloys, 312, 392
Nickel-copper alloys, 267, 313, 314
Nickel-iron alloys, 312
Nickel plating, 311
Nickel silver, 263
Ni-resist, 221
Ni-span C, 314
Nitriding, 183
Nitrogen in steel, 197
Nondestructive tests, 141
Nonferrous alloys, grain-size chart, 261
   heat-treatment, 191
Nonferrous metals, annealing, 193
   bibliography, 325, 416
   fatigue, 18
   production methods, 382
   properties and uses, 243–327
Normalizing, 189
Notch sensitivity, 17
Notch toughness, 17
Notched-bar tests, 129, 211

O

Offset method for yield strength, 13
Oil, advantages as fuel, 436
   classification, 436
   combustion, 437
Open-hearth process, 365
Optical pyrometers, 444, 450
Ore dressing, 44
Ore hearth, lead, 394
Ores, 43
   grade, average (table), 42
   treatment, 45
Overaging, 193
Oxides, heats of formation, 48
Oxygen, in copper, 250, 251
   in open-hearth process, 368
   in steel, 197

P

Passivity, 345
Patenting, 189
Patterns, 65
Payson, P., 188
Pearlite, 166, 172
Percussion welding, 101
Periodicals, metallurgical, 6
Permalloy, 24, 313
Permanent-magnet steel, 217
Permanent magnets, 241
Permanent-mold casting, 67
Permeability, 216, 238
P-F test, 131, 180
Pewter, 309

Phase diagram (see Equilibrium diagram)
Phosphating, 350, 351
Phosphor bronze, 265
Phosphorus, in cast iron, 220
   in steel, 197, 203
Physical metallurgy, 1
Physical properties of metals and alloys, 22
Pidgeon process, magnesium, 409
Pig iron, gray, 362
   production process, 357
   quality, 362
   white, 363
Pinhole detection, 147
Pipe formation in steel, 375
Plastic flow, 30
Plastics, 35
   strength-weight factors, 330
Plutonium, 337, 338
Poole, H. W., 147
Porosity, 25
Postheating, welds, 109
Potentiometers, pyrometric, 447
Powder metallurgy, 92
Precipitation hardening, 192, 209
   aluminum-copper alloys, 293
   beryllium copper, 266
Pressing, 77
   metal powders, 93
Pressure welding, 100
Prestressing, 87
Prices, alloy steels, 229
   metals (table), 42
   by weight and volume (table), 329
Primary crystals, 160
Primary and storage cells, 62
Problems, metallurgical, use of, 5
Process annealing, 189
Producer gas, 439
Properties, adjusting, means of, 64
   alloy steels, 228
      table, 235
   aluminum, 281–285
   aluminum alloys (table), 295
   beryllium, 321
   cast iron, chilled, 221
      control of, 220
   effect of mechanical work, 212
   gold, 323
   high-temperature, 210, 211
   iron and steel, 195–242
   iron-carbon alloys, 168
   lead, 276
   magnesium, 298
   metals and alloys, 8, 9
   molybdenum, 320
   nickel, 311

INDEX

Properties, nonferrous metals, 243
  physical, 22
  silver, 323
  steel, 214
  tin, 305
  titanium, 322
  tungsten, 317
  wrought iron, 241, 379
  zinc, 268
Proportional elastic limit, 13
Pulverized coal, 440
Pyrometallurgy, 48
Pyrometers, bibliography, 455
  black-body conditions, 453
  optical, 444, 450
  radiation, 444, 452
  recorders and controllers, 448
  resistance, 444, 453
  temperature ranges (tables), 444, 447
  thermocouples, 445, 447, 450
  thermoelectric, 445, 446
  types (table), 444

Q

Quality control, statistical, 147
Quenching media, 175
Quenching methods, steel, 176

R

Radiation pyrometers, 444, 452
Radiography, 141
Railroad rolling stock, use of metals, 332
Reactions, corrosion, 343
  iron blast furnace, 360
Recrystallization temperatures (table), 81
Recuperation, heat, 431
Reduction, of area, iron and steel products (table), 11
  metals and alloys (table), 10
  of metals without fusion, 53
Refining, 52
  aluminum, 407
  copper, 386–389
  electrolytic, 60
  zinc, 401
Refractories, bibliography, 441
  characteristics, 426
  commercial (table), 427
  for heating furnaces, 429
  properties and requirements, 428
Regenerative furnaces, 366, 430
Reinartz, L. R., 367
Residual stresses, 208
Residuals in steel, 165, 205

Resilience, 17, 216
Resistance heating, 422
Resistance thermometer, 444, 453
Resistance welding, 100
Resistivity, copper, 245
Reverberatory furnaces, 384–386, 419
Rigidity, modulus of, steel, 215
Rimming steel, 377
Roasting, 49, 398
Rockwell hardness, 21, 22
Rockwell-hardness tester, 127
Roeser, W. F., 450
Rolling, 70, 75
  aluminum, 286
  cold, 82
  copper, 252
  zinc, 268
Rupture stress, 32

S

"S" curves, 173, 175
Sand molds, 66
Scaling, 35
Schoop process, 271
Scott, K. L., 241
Seam welding, 102
Season cracking, 262
Secondary hardening, 187
Seger cones, 455
Semiliquid compression, 73
Shaping of metals, 64–96
Shaping processes, 65
Shell molding, 72
Shepherd, B. F., 131, 180
Sherardizing, 271
Shore scleroscope hardness, 21, 22, 128
Shot peening, 86
Silica-alumina diagram, 55
Silicon, ferroalloys, 415
  in iron smelting, 361
  in steel, 197, 203, 216
  in steel deoxidation, 368
Silicon bronze, 265
Silmanal, 24
Silver, production and value, 42
  production processes, 414
  properties, 24, 323
  uses, 324
Silver alloys, 324
Silver brazing alloys, 113
Simmons, W. F., 337
Sintering, 49
Slag, compositions (table), 56
  functions, 54
  smelting, 51, 56
Slip, 18, 30, 34, 139

Slipbands, 30
Slow-bend tests, 211
Slushing compounds, 350
Smelting, 49–51
  copper, 384
  electric, 62
  iron, 358
  lead, 393
  tin, 396
  zinc, 398
Softness in metals, 35
Solder, 162, 309
Soldering, 112
Soldering temperatures, 98
Solid solutions, 152
Solidus, 153
Space lattices, 25, 26
Spark machining, 92
Spark test, 123
Specific gravities (table), 24
Specifications, aluminum, 297
  copper, 253
  lead, 297
  standard, 120
  zinc, 274
Spectrographic analysis, 122
Sperry electrical tests, 146
Spheroidizing, 189
Spinning, 79, 288
Spot welding, 101, 102
Stainless steel, carburization, 140
  cold drawing, 85
    effect of, 83
  compositions (table), 239
  creep limits, 33
  18 and 8, 233
  elastic modulus, 215
  endurance limit, 20
  heat-resisting, 336
  history, 237
  machinability, 91
  properties (table), 10, 11
  stress to rupture, 33
  types, 237, 239
Statistical quality control, 147
Steel, acid open-hearth, quality, 364, 379
  aging, 209, 213
  alloy (*see* Alloy steels)
  annealing, 188
  austempering, 175
  austenite, 170
  austenitic grain size, 136, 206, 368
  basic open-hearth, quality, 364, 379
  bessemer, quality, 364, 380
  bessemer process, 364, 369, 370
  blue heat, 210, 211
  brittle range, 210, 211

Steel, carburization, 140
  carburizing, 182
  casehardening, 182–184
  castings, 378
  chromium, effects in, 234, 238
  classification, AISI, 230
  cold drawing, effects of, 83
  composition, 164, 197
  continuous casting, 378
  cooling after freezing, 165, 166
  copper in, 205
  corrosion, 353
  corrosion fatigue, 215
  cracks, internal, 375
  creep data, 212
  critical points, 168, 170
  crucible, 364, 373
  cutting, 116
  decarburization, 140
  defects, 134, 197, 374
  directional properties, 218
  drawing, 184–188
  duplex process, 371
  elastic modulus, 215
  electric process, 364, 371–373
  electrical conductivity, 217
  elements added, 202
  elongation, 210
  endurance limit, 20, 215
  fatigue, 215
  gaseous impurities, 205
  grain size, 138, 205
    chart, 208
  hardenability, 176
  hardness, 195, 196, 216
    effect of carbon on, 199
    maximum, 202
  heat-resisting, 336
  heat-treatment, 170–191
  high-speed, 236
  high-temperature properties, 210, 211
  hypo- and hypereutectoid, 170, 173
  hysteresis curves, 217
  impact strength, 214
  impact tests, 211
  impurities, 197, 203
  inclusions, 204, 374
  ingot making, 374
  killed, 377
  machinability, 216
  machinability ratings, 91
  magnet (table), 240
  magnetic, 238
  magnetic permeability, 216
  manganese in, 202, 234
  manufacture, résumé, 120
  martempering, 175

Steel, martensite, 171, 172
  mechanical work, effect of, 212
  N.E., 230, 320
  nickel in, 205
  nitriding, 183
  normalizing, 189
  notch toughness, 17
  open-hearth, quality, 364, 367
  open-hearth process, acid, 368
    basic, 365
    controls, 368
    slag compositions, 56
  pearlite, 166, 172
  permanent-magnet, 217
  phosphorus in, 203
  pipe formation, 375
  production processes, 364
  properties, 195, 214
    table, 10, 11
    variation of, 197
  quality, relative, 364, 379
  quenching, 175, 176
  recarburization, 373
  residuals in, 165, 205
  resilience, 216
  rigidity, modulus of, 215
  rimming, 377
  "S" curves, 173, 175
  silicon in, 203, 216
  slow-bend tests, 211
  spheroidizing, 189
  stainless (see Stainless steel)
  strength, heat-treating for, 190
  stress-strain diagrams, 14, 82, 213, 214
  stresses, residual, 208
  sulfur in, 203
  tempering, 184–188
  tensile strength, 195, 196, 198, 210, 211
  tool, 236
  torsion, 215
  transformation curves, 174, 175, 191
  uses, 198, 328
    table, 200
  vanadium in, 236
  working temperatures, 74
Stellite, 316
  mechanical treatment, 74
Step-down test, 131
Sterling process, zinc, 403
Storage batteries, 277
Strain, 12
Strain aging, 213
Strain hardening, 31
Strength, metals, 9, 29
  relation to hardness, 195, 196
  variation of, in alloys, 161, 162
Strength-weight factors (table), 330

Stress, fatigue, 19
  residual, 209
  to rupture, 32
  and strain, 12
  unit, 12
Stress-corrosion, 262, 348
Stress raisers, 18
Stress-rupture curves, 335, 336
Stress-strain curves, steel, 213, 214
Stress-strain diagrams, 14, 82
Structure of welds, 109
Sublimation, 53
Submerged melt welding, 105
Sulfur, in iron smelting, 361
  in steel, 197, 203
Sulfur prints, 133, 136
Supersonic tests, 145
Surface hardening, 181
Surface treatments for corrosion, 350, 351

T

Tarnishing, 344
Taylor, M. E., 337
Tellurium in copper, 253
Temper brittleness, 187
Temperature, brazing, 98
  effect of, on metals, 35
    on properties of steel, 210, 211
    on strength of wrought iron, 211
  finishing, hot working, 78
  Howe's color scale, 443
  measurement of, 443
  mechanical treatment (table), 74
  ranges, pyrometers, 444, 447
  recrystallization (table), 81
  sintering, powder-metallurgy, 93
  soldering, 98
  welding, 98
Temperature control, pyrometric, 448
  rolling, 79
Tempering, 184–188
  alloy steels, 232
Tempilstiks, 455
Tensile strength, 15
  aluminum alloys, 295
  copper, 247
  iron and steel products (table), 11
  metals and alloys (table), 10
  steel, 210, 211
  wrought iron, 211
Tensile test specimens, standard, 125
Tensile testing, 124
Terne plate, 278, 308
Tests, abrasion, 130
  acoustic, 145
  bibliography, 148

Tests, Brinell hardness, 22, 127
  Charpy impact, 16
  chemical analysis, 122
  cone, 132, 180
  corrosion, 354
  corrosion-fatigue, 20
  deep-etch, 132, 134
  ductility, 130
  electrical, 146
  fatigue, 20
  fluorescent penetrant, 143
  fractography, 139
  hardenability, 132, 177
  hardness, 22, 126
  impact, 16, 129
  Izod, 16
  Jominy, 179
  light, high-intensity, 147
  McQuaid-Ehn, 136, 206
  magnetic-field, 144
  magnetic-particle, 142
  Metcalf, 133
  microhardness, 126, 129
  microscopic examination, 133, 136
  nondestructive, 141
  optical examination, 132
  P-F, 131, 180
  Pinhole detection, 147
  radiography, 141
  Rockwell hardness, 22, 127
  Shore scleroscope, 22, 128
  slow-bend, 211
  spark, 123
  Sperry, 146
  step-down, 131
  sulfur prints, 133, 136
  supersonic, 145
  tensile, 124
  torsion, 215
  toughness, 129
  Vickers hardness, 22, 128
  welding, 111
Thermal conductivity, 23
Thermocouples, 445, 447, 450
Thermoelectric pyrometers, 445, 446
Thermometers, expansion, 444, 454
  mercury, 444, 453
  resistance, 444, 453
Tin, allotropy, 307
  in bronze, 264
  corrosion resistance, 306
  detinning, 396
  fusibility, 306
  production and value, 42
  production processes, 395
  properties, 10, 24, 305
  shaping, 307

Tin, uses, 307
  working temperatures, 74
Tin alloys, 309
Tin-lead alloys, 162
Tin plate, 308, 352
Titanium, production processes, 413
  properties, 10, 24, 322
Tool steels, 236
Top-pressure blast furnace, 360
Torsion test, steel, 215
Toughness, 16, 34
  copper, 248
  heat-treating for, 190
  tests, 129
Transactions of metallurgical societies, 7
Transcrystalline failure, 29
Transformation curves, steel, 174, 175, 191
Tube drawing, 83, 84
Tungsten, filaments, 318
  mechanical working, 411
  production processes, 410
  properties, 10, 24, 317
  uses, 318
  working temperatures, 74
Tungsten carbide, 316, 319
Tungsten steels, 318
Types of alloys, 152

U

Uhlig, H. H., 351
Ultimate strength, 9, 10, 15
  iron and steel products (table), 11
Unit cells, 25, 26, 28
Unit stress, 12
Universal impact machine, 129
Universal mill, 70
Universal tensile machine, 124
Uranium, 337, 338
Uses, aluminum, 296
  beryllium, 321
  brass, 260
  chromium, 416
  cobalt, 317
  copper, 253
  gold, 323
  iron and steel, 195–242
    table, 200
  lead, 275, 277, 279
  magnesium, 305
  molybdenum, 320
  nickel, 310, 311
  silver, 324
  steel, 328
  tin, 307
  tungsten, 318
  zinc, 273, 274

INDEX

V

Vanadium, properties, 24
Vanadium steel, 236
Vertical-retort process, zinc, 400
Vicalloy, 316
Vickers hardness, 21, 22, 128
Vitallium, 316, 336
Volatility, 23

W

Waber, J. T., 348
Waelz process, zinc, 402
Watts, O. P., 343
Welding, 97–118
  aluminum, 97, 286
  arc, 103, 110
  atomic hydrogen, 104
  bibliography, 117
  butt, 101
  carbon-arc, 103, 110
  comparison of methods, 110
  economy, 111
  effects on metal, 98
  electric, 100–103, 110
  fields of different processes, 112
  flash, 101
  fusion, 102, 107
  gas, 99, 108, 112
    inert, 105
  hammer, 98
  magnesium, 301
  metal-arc, 103, 110
  metallurgy of, 109
  percussion, 101
  postheating and preheating, 109
  pressure, 100
  processes, 99
    fields, 112
  resistance, 100
  seam, 102
  spot, 102, 103
  submerged melt, 105
  surface applications, 114
  temperatures, 98
  thermit, 106
Welds, butt, 101
  ductility, 108
  efficiency, 99, 101, 110
  fusion, 103
  resistance, 100
  strength, 108
  structure, 109
  testing, 111
Wensel, H. T., 450
Westerman, A. B., 337

White cast iron, 219
Wire drawing, 84, 86, 286
Wolfram (*see* Tungsten)
Working temperatures of metals, 74, 77
World production of metals (table), 42
Wrought iron, corrosion, 353
  early, 3
  elastic modulus, 215
  fracture, 127
  nature of, 195, 357
  properties, 241, 379
    table, 11
  tensile strength, effect of temperature, 211
  uses, 200

Y

Yield point, 13
Yield strength, 13
  aluminum alloys, 295
  determination of, 14, 15
  extension-under-load for, 14
  iron and steel products (table), 11
  metals and alloys (table), 10
Young's modulus, 13, 215

Z

Zapffe, C. A., 139
Zinc, blue powder, 398
  in brass, 256, 258
  cadmium in, 274
  condensation, 398
  corrosion resistance, 269
  die castings, 272, 275
  electric smelting, 403
  electrodeposition from leaching solutions, 401
  hydrometallurgy, 401
  impurities in, 273
  production and value, 42
  production processes, 397
  properties, 10, 24, 268
  refining, 401
  roasting, 398
  rolled, 268, 272
  smelting, 398
  specifications, 274
  Sterling process, 403
  uses, 273, 274
  vertical-retort process, 400
  Waelz process, 402
  working temperatures, 74
Zinc alloys, 271
Zinc coating, 269
Zinc oxide, 273
Zirconium in atomic-energy development, 338